CW00408447

The Butterflies and Moths of Bedfordshire

Camberwell Beauty

Dedicated to the memory of
Roy Anthony Collings
1943-1987
His love of the natural world,
his friendship and good humour
is a treasured memory

Also dedicated to all those who have contributed
in so many ways to make this book possible

The Butterflies and Moths of Bedfordshire

V.W. Arnold

C.R.B. Baker

D.V. Manning

I.P. Woiwod

Meadow Brown

The Bedfordshire Natural History Society

© 1997 The Bedfordshire Natural History Society
c/o Bedford Museum, Castle Street, Bedford MK40 3XD

A CIP record for this book is available from British Library
ISBN 0 950 6521 5 6

First published 1997 by the Bedfordshire Natural History Society
(Registered Charity No. 268659)

All rights reserved. No part of this book may be reproduced, stored in a retrieval system, or transmitted in any form or by any means, optical, electrical, mechanical, photocopying or otherwise without permission of the publisher.

Printed in the United Kingdom by Graphic Techniques (Milton Keynes) Ltd.

Cover Photographs: Small Copper (front), *Pyrausta aurata* (spine) and Red Underwing (back).

Credits

We are grateful to the following individuals and institutions for providing illustrations and for giving us permission to reproduce copyright © material:

Maps: Ordnance Survey – the sketch maps on pages 18, 19, 24, 38, 42, 43, 44, 45, 48, 50, 51, 53 and 64 and the Bedfordshire boundary used in the species distribution maps are based on Ordnance Survey maps with permission of Ordnance Survey, © Crown Copyright (85495M).

Drawings: B.B.West – drawings on pages 21 and 37 and all line drawings of butterflies and macro-moths; D.V.Manning – all line drawings of micro-moths.

Black-and-white photographs: V.W.Arnold (pilot J.Flynn) – figures 21, 23, 25; C.R.B.Baker – figures 16, 20, 26; R.C.Revels – figures 1, 12, 28, 34, 35, 36, 37, 41; Luton Museum Service and Luton News – figure 13; Hunting Aerofilms Ltd – figures 30, 33; Cambridge University Collection of Air Photographs, copyright reserved – figure 18; Ministry of Defence – figures 17, 22, 24, 29, 31, 32, © Crown Copyright/MOD, reproduced with the permission of the Controller of HMSO; W.A.Smith – figure 19; J.Wheeler – figure 7; Bedford Hospital NHS Trust – figure 8; Curators of Oxford University Museum – figure 6; Chiltern Photo – figure 15; I.P.Woiwod – figure 42.

Colour photographs: V.W.Arnold – plate 33; C.R.B.Baker – plates 13, 15, 16, 18, 19, 21, 35, 38, 42, 43, 44, 46, 47, 48, 49, 50, 51, 57, 59, 60, 61, 62, 77, 80, 81, 82, 83, 96, 97, 98, 101, 102, 103; R.C.Revels – plates 2, 3, 4, 5, 6, 7, 9, 10, 11, 12, 17, 22, 23, 24, 25, 26, 27, 28, 30, 31, 32, 34, 39, 40, 41, 45, 52, 54, 56, 58, 63, 64, 65, 66, 67, 68, 69, 70, 71, 72, 73, 74, 75, 78, 79, 84, 85, 86, 87, 88, 89, 90, 91, 92, 93, 94, 95, 100 and cover; A.R.Outen – plates 14, 20, 36, 37, 53, 55, 76, 99; T.Tween – plate 1; D. Tyler – plates 8, 29; Rothamsted Experimental Station – plate 104.

Contents

Foreword

The Butterflies and Moths of Bedfordshire is a book designed for the modern naturalist. Large collections, crammed full of duplicates, belong to the past. Today's lepidopterist may need a small collection of voucher specimens of species that are difficult to identify, but his main interests are life histories, distribution and conservation. He gets more satisfaction from filling gaps in distribution maps than from adding to a collection, and he is eager to learn why species occur where they do, and if they have vanished from their former haunts, the reason for their departure. Man is not always to blame. In 1836, long before the days of insecticides and inimical agricultural practices, Edward Doubleday wrote:

> "The number of insects is increased or diminished by causes which seem to defy all our attempts at discovering them. Species vanish from spots where they have abounded, and we know not why; no change perceptible to us has taken place in any of the peculiarities of the spot, but its old inhabitants are gone. The hand of man cannot have exterminated them".

On the other hand, man does alter the face of the environment and thereby influences distribution. This book records and analyses changes that have taken place in a number of localities noted for their Lepidoptera. First we need to know what species they supported in bygone days, so that comparisons can be made with their current fauna. The authors have achieved this by scholarly research into the activities of the County's former lepidopterists, from the end of the eighteenth century onwards. Wherever possible, their collections have been traced and studied, their diaries and correspondence scanned. The authors disparagingly describe the information gleaned as slight, but the reader cannot fail to be impressed. Similarly painstaking research has been bestowed on the habitats that are found in Bedfordshire and the changes they have experienced with the passage of time. The text is supported by an admirable range of photographs. Where an old print depicts a noted locality, the authors have photographed the site from the same viewpoint so that comparisons may be drawn. Early aerial photos have been utilised and one of the authors has himself taken to the air to secure modern counterparts.

This historical approach is continued in the systematic list of species. The only other comprehensive account of the Lepidoptera of Bedfordshire is the chapter by C.G.Barrett in *The Victoria History of the County of Bedford*, published in 1904. In the present work the entry for each species is, where applicable, divided into three sections, Pre VCH, VCH and Post VCH, enabling comparisons to be drawn which are often interesting, especially for the butterflies and larger moths.

Conservation is never far from the authors' minds. It is necessary to know which species are at risk and the methods employed to secure this information are admirably expounded in the chapter entitled *Monitoring Population Changes*. Measures that are being taken to promote conservation in selected habitats and nature reserves are given in the chapter on *Habitats*.

The art work is an important feature of the book. In addition to the photographs already mentioned, there are neat sketches of many of the butterflies and moths chosen to represent their families, shown not as set specimens but in their natural resting posture, as befits a work more concerned with living than dead insects. Bernard West is the artist for the butterflies and larger moths, David Manning for the smaller moths.

Bedfordshire is lucky to have a team of experts to share in the authorship. Vic Arnold's interest in moths has been sustained for almost half a century. He has been County recorder for the larger moths for nearly 20 years and has given practical expression to his concern for conservation by membership of early working parties engaged in the improvement of habitats. Charles Baker's interest in Lepidoptera also goes back to his boyhood. He was formerly an entomologist at the Central Science Laboratory of the Ministry of Agriculture, Fisheries and

Food, specialising in pests arriving from overseas. He combines the expertise of the professional entomologist with the zest of the amateur. Since retirement he has become the County recorder for butterflies and is a voluntary warden for the local Wildlife Trust. He has taken the leading part in historical research which is such an important feature of this book. David Manning is a self-taught microlepidopterist and has now become an acknowledged expert in the identification of difficult species by dissecting the genitalia. He was a relatively late convert to entomology, and on his return to Bedfordshire from abroad directed his attention to the microlepidoptera because no one else could identify them and they had been woefully neglected in consequence. He has added so many species to the County list that the editorial team decided that it would be monotonous to place his initials after all his records. The massive scale of his research can be demonstrated from three of the larger groups. The Victoria County History recorded two species in the Nepticulidae, six in the Lithocolletinae and eight in the Coleophoridae; the number of records now stands at 64, 37 and 57 respectively. For the chapter on *Monitoring Population Changes* the County has been able to call on the services of possibly the best qualified author in Britain. Ian Woiwod has worked at Rothamsted Experimental Station in Hertfordshire for nearly 30 years. Currently Head of the Populations, Biodiversity and Environmental Interactions Group, he has special responsibility for the national light-trap network of the Rothamsted Insect Survey. He now lives in Bedfordshire at Cockayne Hatley, site of the Rothamsted trap which has done so much to enhance our knowledge of the County's moths.

Here is a book which will give you up-to-date information about the lepidopterous fauna of Bedfordshire. It also gives a fascinating account of the County's changing scene, which will be of interest to lepidopterists and non-lepidopterists alike. I heartily recommend it to readers in both categories.

A. M. Emmet MBE, TD, MA, FLS, HON FRES
Saffron Walden

Editor of *The Moths and Butterflies of Great Britain and Ireland*

Introduction

Bedfordshire appears to have been a county to travel through, rather than to visit. Several major trunk roads, including the M1 and A1, and three main railway lines cross the county as they radiate northwards from London. Millions of people travel through Bedfordshire each year on these routes, as well as through Luton International Airport, but how many actually notice the county they are in ? At one time, travellers on the M1 could not fail to notice the smell of the old brickworks at Brogborough, or on the A1 the overpowering smell of brussels sprouts in the autumn and winter. People with a culinary interest may have heard of the 'Bedfordshire Clanger'. For others this is the county of John Bunyan, author of *The Pilgrim's Progress*. Bedfordshire is a small county, approximately 55 km in length by 30 km in width. Despite its small size, it is a county with a variety of habitats from chalk hills to ancient woodlands. It does not always spring to mind when one thinks of natural history sites, but it is remarkably rich in wildlife.

Figure 1 A Bedfordshire Scene – the Chiltern Scarp at Sharpenhoe Clappers in 1996.

We have tried to draw together in this book knowledge of the butterflies and moths of Bedfordshire since the publication in 1904 of *The Victoria History of the County of Bedford* and also as many of the earlier records as could be found. Bedfordshire has a place in entomological history as the county where the Chequered Skipper was first found in Britain and also from the early naming of the Small Blue as the Bedford Blue. However it was never a mecca for collectors in the way that sites such as the New Forest and Royston have been. Indeed the few local collectors, whose collections or records we have been able to trace, often travelled outside the County to amass series of specimens from the famous sites. Unfortunately this applies particularly to the butterfly species, such as the fritillaries, which have declined or become extinct since the late 1940s. This has been a great problem in trying to piece together information on the status of species in the County during the first half of this century.

Sources

At one time the earliest reference to Bedfordshire butterflies was thought to be in the unusual heraldry on the tomb of Sir John Sewell (1350) in Houghton Regis church, described in Meynell (1950) as a chevron between three butterflies. However, the insects depicted there appear to be bees, not butterflies. Although the natural history of Bedfordshire is mentioned in some 18th century works, the first serious entomologist that we have been able to trace was the Reverend Dr Charles Abbot (1761-1817). One of Abbot's notebooks, a few specimens and some other manuscripts have been located and contribute greatly to knowledge of the Lepidoptera during that period. Only a few papers were published between 1800 and *The Victoria History of the County of Bedford* (VCH) in 1904. Charles Barrett died in 1904 and he may have been terminally ill when he wrote the Lepidoptera section of the VCH. In the circumstances it is a remarkable compilation, but more detail might have been added had he been in better health. From 1875 until 1878 there was a short-lived Bedfordshire Natural History Society. This was followed in 1888 by the Bedford Natural History Society which survived until about 1953 under various names. Unfortunately the minutes of meetings were sparse and rarely provide any useful records, nor did the Society publish many papers on Lepidoptera.

The present Bedfordshire Natural History Society was formed in 1946 and since that date a succession of individuals have acted as 'recorders' for the Lepidoptera. The first recorder was B.B.West who held the post until 1971. He was followed until 1977 by W.J.Champkin, after which the task was split between A.J.Martin (butterflies) and V.W. Arnold (moths). D.V.Manning took over the recording of the microlepidoptera in 1985 and C.R.B.Baker the butterflies in 1993. The recorders' annual reports have been published in the Society's journal, *The Bedfordshire Naturalist*, and are listed in the bibliography and reference section but not cited individually in the text.

A great deal of effort is currently being put into understanding and if possible reversing the serious declines which a number of species have suffered throughout Britain in recent years. There are also concerns about the possible effects of climate change. We therefore thought it important to assemble as much historical information as possible for future use in conservation work. In addition to searching the literature for published information, we have searched a number of old collections for records but we were saddened by the extent to which data have been lost over the years. The great collections of W.G.Nash and W.S.Brocklehurst were dispersed and several others have vanished without trace. The collecting of Lepidoptera for the sake of collecting is widely rejected these days. Certainly many of the excesses of the past are to be deplored. This may be one reason why old collections seem to be seriously under-valued, but they are treasure-houses of information both in their data labels and possibly as sources of material for future study using the techniques of molecular biology. When searching collections, attention was focused on species now rare or extinct in the County and records from this source of commoner species may not be complete.

A considerable amount of information on the status of butterflies and moths in the County before the start of the Society has been obtained by discussion with those who knew the County at that time. The attribution 'pers. comm.' has mostly been omitted from the text to improve the readability but almost all the discussions took place in 1994 and 1995. All relevant letters and other documents will be deposited in Bedford Museum.

Layout of the Systematic Chapters

Under each species, the information is divided into five sections. These are 'Pre VCH', 'VCH', 'Post VCH', 'Flight' and 'Larval Foodplants'. Any of the first three sections may be omitted if no information is available. Likewise the last two sections are usually omitted from entries describing long-extinct species or erroneous records. Although the classification of the Lepidoptera is revised in Emmet (1996), this came too late for inclusion here. The species' order follows Emmet (1991) and the logbook numbers are included for convenience though these are likely to be superseded when a revised logbook incorporating the new classification is published. Where a species has been found only once, the finder's name is given. However, since most of the micro-moths have been recorded by D.V. Manning, his name is omitted. Because the status of some species is uncertain, numbers of British species given in the family and subfamily headings are sometimes vague. We have tried to include the earliest known record in the County where this was readily accessible.

Distribution Records and Maps

In Bedfordshire the concept of mapping the distribution of animals and plants in a 2 km square (tetrad) grid was advocated by J.G.Dony (1972) and pioneered by him in his plant atlas for the County (Dony, 1976).

Recording of the distribution of butterflies on a tetrad basis was started by W.J.Champkin and expanded greatly when A.J.Martin took over as recorder in 1977. Since then, records have been obtained from all the 378 tetrads in the County, apart from four astride the county boundary. Two categories of species are almost certainly substantially under- recorded. The hairstreaks are difficult to observe and colonies probably remain undetected in many parts of the County. Secondly the Essex Skipper and Brown Argus are not easy for the less experienced observer to distinguish from the Small Skipper and brown form of the female Common Blue respectively, and may therefore have been missed. The number of tetrads in which each species has been seen is given in the text.

For some species, such as the larger fritillaries or the Swallowtail, there is the possibility that records of single specimens may relate to unreported releases of individuals bred in captivity. Such records can often be recognised because they tend to be significantly earlier than the normal flight period for the species. Where an unusual record appears to be of a truly wild individual it has been included on the map but qualified in the accompanying text. It has also proved difficult to establish whether some butterfly species were truly native to the localities where they occurred. Butterflies have been artificially introduced into

● = New records 1990 - 1996

◉ = 1977 - 1989, still present 1990-1996

○ = 1977 - 1989

✳ = 1900 - 1976

\+ = VCH or before but not later

Key to Butterfly Maps

● = 1960 - 1996

✳ = 1900 - 1959

\+ = VCH or before but not later

Key to Moth Maps

various sites during this century, possibly even earlier. Some of these introductions are documented, others are hearsay. They relate both to species currently present in the County and to some now extinct and are discussed under the sections on individual species.

The butterflies have been intensively recorded since 1977. The maps may include, in the post-1977 category, a few records collected earlier but this cannot be checked as the original records from the 1970s are no longer available. A few records for 1996 up to the time of going to press have been added to the maps. Records collected in the last 7 years (1990-96 inclusive) are distinguished on the species maps by a different symbol from those collected earlier. However, apparent changes in distribution since the 1977-89 period must be viewed with caution as the effort put into surveying was not constant from year to year. Where the records suggest that a real change in distribution may have occurred, this is commented on in the text.

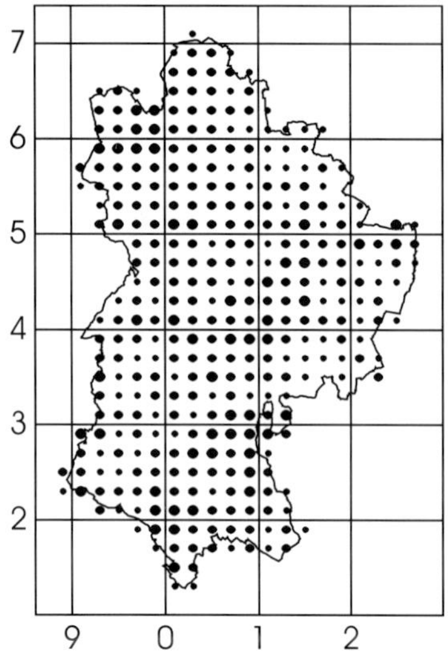

Figure 2 Number of butterfly species recorded in each tetrad from 1990 to 1996 inclusive. Largest dots – more than 21 species recorded. Most of these are in tetrads covering chalk downland sites and the better-known woods.

The maps of moths are plotted on a 10 km grid because fewer people have collected records than for butterflies. Most of the moth records come from light-traps but it has not been possible to run traps regularly in all the tetrads in the County. Indeed, even if the records had been available it would not have been practicable to print tetrad maps for all species in a book of reasonable size. Many of the records come from traps run nightly as part of the Rothamsted Insect Survey (RIS), described by I.P.Woiwod in his chapter on monitoring population changes, and are noted as such in the text. The majority of the records of moths relate to the period 1970-1996 but some records from the 1960s are included. Sites on which traps of all types have been run and moths recorded in other ways are plotted in Figure 3. The number of species of macro- and micro-moths found in each 10 km square is shown in Figures 4 and 5. For some scarce and local species the number of sites mentioned in the text may not be the same as the number of dots on the map. This is usually because some records, particularly in earlier years, were reported only as 10 km square or tetrad numbers. There are also some sites, such as Bedford, Chicksands Wood and Sharnbrook, which cover more than one grid square. The distribution maps have been produced using the DMAP computer package developed by A.J.Morton. Old records, such as those from the VCH or before, have been placed in the most likely square. Thus records from "Bedford" or "Bedford District" have been placed in TL05 and those from "Luton" in TL02.

We have taken the current boundary of the administrative county of Bedfordshire as the basis for recording. The area broadly coincides with Watsonian Vice-county 30 but there are discrepancies at a number of points. Most of these are listed in Dony (1953). Some of the records from Caddington, Kensworth and Studham Common are from areas included in VC 20, and most of those from Aspley Heath are from VC 24. Grid squares with only a small part of their area in Bedfordshire have been surveyed less diligently than the remainder.

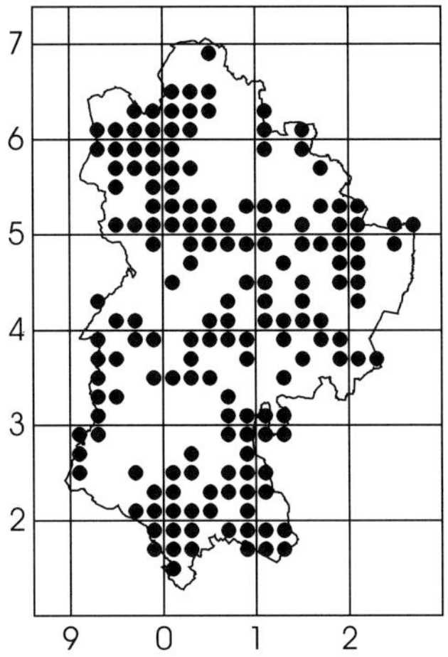

Figure 3 Sites where moths have been surveyed by light-trapping, sweeping and other methods, mapped by tetrad.

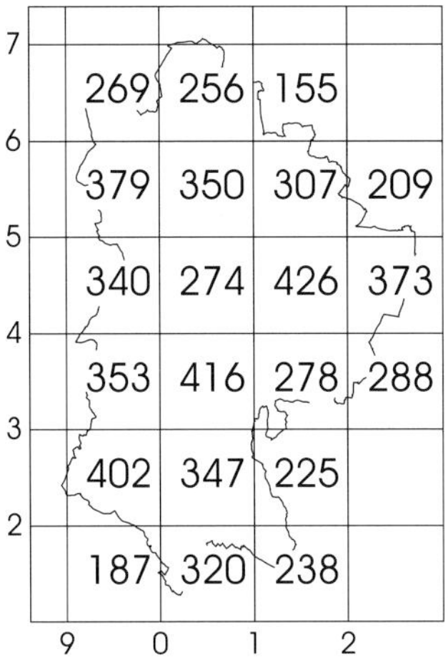

Figure 4 Macro-moth species recorded in each 10 km square.

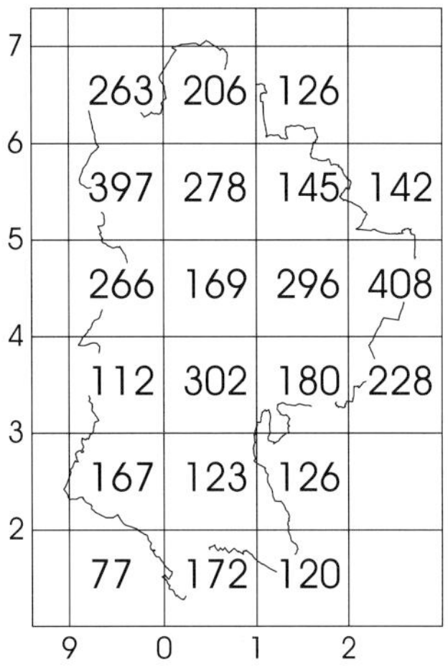

Figure 5 Micro-moth species recorded in each 10 km square.

We are only too aware that our knowledge, particularly of distribution, is incomplete. This especially so for the micro-moths, where the coverage is more biassed towards the areas surrounding the recorders' homes, than for the larger species. Even in this small county there are many locations which have not yet been surveyed. There is also a great need for more detailed and quantitative surveying within sites to monitor the success or failure of management techniques. However, we hope that this publication will be useful both as a measure, where the coverage is adequate, against which future changes in the distribution of individual species can be assessed, and also as a stimulus to others to fill in the gaps in the records. Information received will be published in *The Bedfordshire Naturalist*.

Nomenclature

To improve the readability for the general naturalist, we have used English names wherever possible in the chapters on habitats and monitoring without the associated scientific names. The latter can be found in the systematic sections. For clarity, scientific names quoted from old manuscripts have usually been italicised, although this would not have been the convention in the originals. A few more recent synonyms of scientific names have been included, mostly for species for which there is no English name in common use.

The scientific nomenclature used throughout for the Lepidoptera follows that used in Emmet (1991) or more recent usage. English names, where appropriate, are derived from the same source and from Seymour (1989). Scientific names for plants follow Stace (1991) with English names from Dony *et al.* (1986). The name 'sallows' is retained for *Salix caprea* and *S. cinerea* as this is widely used by lepidopterists.

Illustrations

Unless the magnification is given, all line and colour illustrations of individual butterflies and moths are approximately life-size.

Flight Times

Adult flight times have been culled from the literature, but local observations since 1970 are included whenever possible. Flight times for butterflies still present in the County have been extracted mainly from records of transect walks, a list of which is given on page 63. Flight times for moths have been derived largely from the Bedfordshire records of the Rothamsted Insect Survey supplemented by individual observations in the County. Where the records allow, the weeks of 'peak' flight activity are noted in addition to the beginning and end of the main flight period. In most years the occasional individual will be on the wing before or after the main flight and exceptionally at some quite abnormal time of year. These records have mostly been omitted. All flight times recorded in Bedfordshire are marked with an asterisk (*). The week numbers cited are the standard week numbers used in the Rothamsted Insect Survey. The weeks of the year are numbered consecutively from 1 to 52 omitting 29 February and 31 December. These numbers approximate to those printed in pocket diaries.

Standard week numbers used to describe flight periods of butterflies and moths.
(When working out the standard weeks, 29 February and 31 December are omitted.)

Week No.	Dates			Week No.	Dates		
1	1 January	-	7 January	27	2 July	-	8 July
2	8 January	-	14 January	28	9 July	-	15 July
3	15 January	-	21 January	29	16 July	-	22 July
4	22 January	-	28 January	30	23 July	-	29 July
5	29 January	-	4 February	31	30 July	-	5 August
6	5 February	-	11 February	32	6 August	-	12 August
7	12 February	-	18 February	33	13 August	-	19 August
8	19 February	-	25 February	34	20 August	-	26 August
9	26 February	-	4 March	35	27 August	-	2 September
10	5 March	-	11 March	36	3 September	-	9 September
11	12 March	-	18 March	37	10 September	-	16 September
12	19 March	-	25 March	38	17 September	-	23 September
13	26 March	-	1 April	39	24 September	-	30 September
14	2 April	-	8 April	40	1 October	-	7 October
15	9 April	-	15 April	41	8 October	-	14 October
16	16 April	-	22 April	42	15 October	-	21 October
17	23 April	-	29 April	43	22 October	-	28 October
18	30 April	-	6 May	44	29 October	-	4 November
19	7 May	-	13 May	45	5 November	-	11 November
20	14 May	-	20 May	46	12 November	-	18 November
21	21 May	-	27 May	47	19 November	-	25 November
22	28 May	-	3 June	48	26 November	-	2 December
23	4 June	-	10 June	49	3 December	-	9 December
24	11 June	-	17 June	50	10 December	-	16 December
25	18 June	-	24 June	51	17 December	-	23 December
26	25 June	-	1 July	52	24 December	-	30 December

Larval Foodplants

Foodplants are also included for the convenience of the reader. They have been obtained principally from Skinner (1984) and Emmet (1991). Again, observations pertaining to Bedfordshire are marked with an asterisk (*) and refer to the finding of eggs or larvae on the plant. This does not necessarily mean that in all cases the plant is suitable for the whole development of the larva. The information has been contributed mainly by J.B.Barnwell, D.V.Manning, R.C.Revels and A.M.Riley. Citations are not given individually in the text.

Identification and Biology

This book is not intended to be an aid to the identification of Bedfordshire Lepidoptera, nor to provide information on the biology of each species. There are already excellent identification guides available for the butterflies, the larger macro-moths and to some families of the micro-moths. A selection of these is listed below. The short notes under family and subfamily headings are intended only to highlight a few features of each group. Families and subfamilies are usually distinguished from one another by esoteric characters, such as differences in wing venation, which are beyond the scope of this book. In general we have tried not to repeat information readily available elsewhere, apart from that on flight times and larval foodplants as mentioned above.

Books on Identification and Biology:

Butterflies

Thomas, J.A. (1992) *Butterflies of the British Isles.* Hamlyn Guide.
Whalley, P. (1981) *The Mitchell Beazley Pocket Guide to Butterflies.*
Higgins, L.G. & Riley, N.D. (1970 & later revisions) *A Field Guide to the Butterflies of Britain and Europe.* Collins.
Thomas, J.E. & Lewington, R. (1991) *The Butterflies of Britain and Ireland.* Dorling Kindersley.
Brooks, M.M. & Knight, C. (1982) *A Complete Guide to British Butterflies.* Jonathan Cape.
Howarth, T.G. (1973) *South's British Butterflies.* Warne.

Butterflies and Moths:

Emmet, A.M. & Heath, J. (1976-1996) *The Moths and Butterflies of Great Britain and Ireland.* Harley Books. (7 volumes published. More to follow.)
Carter, D. & Hargreaves, B. (1986) *A Field Guide to the Caterpillars of Butterflies and Moths.* Collins.
Meyrick, E. ([1928], reprint 1970) *A Revised Handbook of British Lepidoptera.* Watkins and Doncaster. Reprint E.W.Classey.

Macro-moths:

Skinner, B. (1984) *Colour Identification Guide to Moths of the British Isles.* Viking.
Brooks, M.M. (1991) *A Complete Guide to British Moths.* Jonathan Cape.
South, R. (1907-08 and subsequent editions and impressions) *The Moths of the British Isles.* Vols 1 and 2. Warne.

Micro-moths:

Emmet, A.M. (1988) *A Field Guide to the Smaller British Lepidoptera.* British Entomological and Natural History Society.
Bradley, J.D., Tremewan, W.G., Smith, A. (1973-79) *British Tortricoid Moths.* Vols 1 and 2. Ray Society.
Goater, B. (1986) *British Pyralid Moths.* Harley Books.

Acknowledgements

A great many people have contributed in one way and another to the production of this book and we can only apologise if we have failed to acknowledge anyone's help.

We are especially grateful to the Lindeth Charitable Trust, the Robert Kiln Charitable Trust, the Peter Smith Charitable Trust for Nature, Luton Borough Council, Unilever Research Ltd, and the Beds and Northants Branch of Butterfly Conservation and to others who wished to remain anonymous for their generous financial support.

We are deeply indebted to Maitland Emmet for consenting to write the foreword and for spending many hours checking nomenclature and other editorial points. Rosemary Brind, Adrian Riley, Valerie Aitkenhead, John Comont, Bernard Nau, John Niles, Richard Revels, Greg Herbert and Graham Bellamy also read all or parts of the book and provided helpful comments and advice. All these people have contributed greatly to reducing errors and any remaining mistakes and omissions are ours alone.

A further debt is owed to Jim Barnwell, Robert Craske, Sidney Humphrey, John Payne, Peter Taylor, Bernard Verdcourt and Bernard West for providing information unobtainable from other sources.

We are also grateful to: Alan Martin for providing much information and early drafts of the butterfly chapter and both him and Alan Outen for their work in starting off this project; Richard Revels for acting as photographic editor; Mary Sheridan for typing sections of the book; Howard Mendel, Mike Williams and especially Tony Smith for advice on text handling and publication problems; Pat Baker for checking plant names; Alan Outen and Richard Revels for loaning photographs for preparation of line drawings; Ivan Dunn for help with scanning illustrations and other computing problems; Stephen Halton for preparing most of the original drawings for the sketch maps in the *Habitats* chapter; Jonathan Palmer for the base map for figure 27 and all those listed under 'Credits' for providing drawings and photographs.

We thank E.Pollard, J.N.Greatorex-Davies, P.Harding and the Biological Records Centre for provision of unpublished data from the Institute of Terrestrial Ecology's Butterfly Monitoring Scheme used in Figures 39 and 40 and Table 4.

Our thanks are due the following who have provided help with library searches and access to collections and associated information: J.Ruffle of the Royal Entomological Society Library; J.Harvey and L.Mitchell of the Entomology Library of the Natural History Museum; S.W.Humphrey (Humphrey-Kershaw collection); H.A.Smith (G.Ping collection); B.B.West (B.B.West collection); D.J.Carter of the Natural History Museum, London (Entomology Department collections); G.R.Chancellor and M.Hillier of Peterborough Museum (E.Craske collection); E.G.Hancock of Glasgow Art Gallery and Museum (P.N.Crow collection); C.Palmer of the Hampshire County Museums Service (G.F.B.Prior collection); G.C.McGavin and I.Lansbury of Oxford University Museum (Dale Collection) and S.Brecknell of the Hope Library (Dale archives); R.A.Brind of Bedford Museum (Rylands collection); P.S.Hyman of Luton Museum (Tebbs collection); B.Sawford of North Herts Museum Services; D.Curry of St Albans Museum (Hopkins-Alexander and Graveley-Edwards collections); K.Hebditch of Dorset County Museum; J.Campbell of Oxford County Museum (G.Prior collection); K.M.Hawkins of Buckinghamshire County Museum; G.Legg of the Booth Museum, Brighton (Kershaw diaries); W.Parry of the Welwyn-Hatfield Museum Service (R.S.Ferry collection), K.Walker of the Museum of Victoria, Melbourne, Australia (Curtis diaries), J.Bowdrey of Colchester Museum Services (Temple collection), J.Hatton of Liverpool Museum (Turner and Robinson collections), W.J.D.Eberlie of Ontario, Canada, J.Tebbs, T.J.Barfield of English Nature and to the many other people who responded to postal enquiries.

and to all the following who have provided records to the Society over the years:
J.,A.&J.Adams, N.Agar, D.J.L.Agassiz, A.Aldhous, D.Aldred, D.M.Allen, M.F.Allen, P.Almond, B.&Y.Anderson, D.&K.Anderson, G.A.M.Arnold, D.Askew, P.M.Baker, D.Ball, C.Barford, T.Barker, J.B.Barnwell, R.I.Bashford, R.Bates, G.Bellamy, H.A.Bellringer, M.Bierton, P.Binks, E.S.Binns, S.Blathwayt, T.Bliss, J.M.Boon, C.R.Boon, S.R.Bowden, J.Bowler, R.Bowerbank, E.G.& B.M.Bowskill, M.Boyd, E.S.Bradford, R.Bradshaw, S.Brennan, R.F.Bretherton, L.Brightman, R.A.Brind, D.W.Brockwell, D.C.G.Brown, L.Brown, M.G.&A.Brown, R.Brown, N.H.Browne, D.Brunt, Mrs Bryan, A.Bucknall, R.S.K.Buisson, N.Burns, I.Burrows, C.W.Burton, G.Burton, G.J.Buss, J.W.Buss, L.Carman, J.Carroll, G.Castle, A.&R.Catchpole, V.Chadwick, S.Cham, V.H.Chambers, E.Chambers, W.J.Champkin, C.Carpenter, D.Chandler, A.H.Chapman, T.D.Charlton, J.E.Childs, A.W.Clarke, G.Clarke, P.&P.Clarke, P.J.Clements, M.J.Clifton, B.M.Clutten, L.Collings, R.Collings, G.Collins, P.C.Colyer, J.Comont, A.Cutts, A.G.Davies, F.B.M.Davies, G.Dawes, I.K.Dawson, N.Dawson, R.Dazley, G.Dennis, J.Dick, B.Dickerson, M.Dobson, A.Donnelly, J.G.&C.Dony, A.Doody, W.R.Drayton, R.A.&I.Dunn, J.N.Dymond, R.Edwards, J.C.Ellingham, D.W.Elliot, A.M.Emmet, M.Evans, M.Fail, H.Felce, L.Field, S.Finney, A.T.&C.J.Ferguson, A.Fleckney, J.Flynn, A.Ford, P.Fossey, P.Franghiadi, R.Frith, H.A.N.Game, A.Gammell, B.O.C.Gardiner, B.George, W.J.Gerrard, C.Gibbons, P.Glenister, D.Goddard, J.Gould, D.&M.Green, J.Green, P.Green, Mrs Greenhall, Mr & Mrs Greenhill, T.Greenwell, L.Greenwood, J.M.S.Hague, N.G.M.Hague, S.F.Halton, M.Hammond, B.D.&M.Harding, R.Harris, S.Harris, Mr & Mrs J.G.Headon, R.J.Henry, G.Herbert, C.Higgs, T.S.Hollingworth, C.Holmes, P.&G.Hooper, P.Hopper, A.Horder, C.P.Horton, J.Howe, Mr Hughes, A.Hurst, H.E.Hutson, P.S.Hyman, T.Ilott, B.M.Inns, P.Irving, M.J.Izzard, N.James, L.Janes, N.F.Janes, J.Jarrett, L.R.Jarrett, B.Jarvis, J.Jarvis, D.M.Jeffreys, J.B.B.&V.K.Johnstone, H.Jones, A.W.&V.Keech, M.Kemp, J.Kemp-Gee, I.&S.Kimsey, D.J.King, E.King, P.J.Kitchener, T.F.Knight, J.P.Knowles, J.R.Langmaid, B.R.Laurence, Hon.H.de B.Lawson Johnston, K.Lee, Mr and Mrs R.Lee, T.Liggett, H.Loxdale, I.Ludman, M.McCarrick, R.,A.&P.Madgett, E.J.Makinen, S.M.Manning, A.J.Martin, D.Mason, J.Mayhead, D.Mellor, N.Miers, E.Milne, E.Moffitt, J.A.Moore, T.Moxey, D.Mucklestone, A.J.Muir-Howie, H.Muir-Howie, R.Munday, J.Murray, B.S.Nau, E.G.Neal, R.M.Newland, E.Newman, B.Nightingale, J.R.A.Niles, T.Norriss, R.Nye, D.Odell, J.O'Sullivan, D.Otter, A.R.Outen, M.Paine, M.J.Palmer, A.Parker, F.Parlett, R.Parsonage, L.&D.Parsons, K.Parsons, P.&R.Passley, J.H.Payne, V.Peck, T.N.D.Peet, E.C.Pelham-Clinton, A.Peterkin, M.J.Pettit, G.H.Pickerell, P.C.Pilcher, G.Pilkington, G.Ping, S.Pittman, G.Player, M.Pocock, R.Port, R.Porter, W.Powell, A.Proud, A.Puttock, A.Pyke, A.Randall, E.B.Rands, D.G.Rands, P.J.Reay, J.Reid, R.C.Revels, C.W.Ridge, A.M.Riley, D.K.Riley, B.Roe, G.Roe, P.Roseveare, M.B. Rowland, M.Rowler, A.J.Rundle, M.D.Russell, J.Schneider, M.Seaman, P.Sefick, C.Selby, E.Sharman, V.Sharman, K.M.Sharpe, J.T.R.Sharrock, L.Sharrock, M.Sheridan, S.Sheridan, E.J.Sensicall, D.Silver, H.Simpson, S.Simpson, P.Smart, Dr & Mrs D.C.Smith, H.A.Smith, K.G.V.Smith, S.Sollars, B.R.Squires, D.Stapleton, P.Steele, R.B.Stephenson, C.Tack, J.Temple, R.Theobald, E.Thomas, T.J.Thomas, C.Tomalin, A.Tomczynski, J.Toomer, C.M.Towner, M.C.Townsend, P.Trodd, T.Tween, C.Tucker, D.Tyler, R.W.J.Uffen, C.Vaughan, B.Verdcourt, B.D.Vissian, R.V.A.Wagstaff, J.&A.Walford, A.D.Walker, S.Wanting, C.Ward, M.Wardle, A.&G.Warne, A.Warren, M.Watson, C.Watts, H.M.Webb, K.F.Webb, K.&M.Weeden, B.B.West, K.E.West, D.Whitfield, R.Whittemore, D.Wickings, M.C.Williams, V.Williams, R.Wilson, H.Winter, R.Woodall, A.Woodgate, D.Woodhead, K.Woods, G.Woodward, R.J.Woolnough, L.Wright, R.Wyatt, I.Wynne, E.P.Young, Mr & Mrs Young, and to all those who contributed to the Chalk Grassland and Woodland Butterfly Surveys and to other members of the Beds and Northants Branch of Butterfly Conservation who helped with the transect walks.

Vic Arnold **Charles Baker** **David Manning** **Ian Woiwod**
October 1996

Some Bedfordshire Lepidopterists

C.R.B.Baker

Our knowledge of the people who in the past have taken an interest in the Lepidoptera of Bedfordshire, is really very slight. Such information as has been uncovered so far is summarised in this chapter in the hope that it will encourage others to come forward with more.

It seems improbable that nobody in the County noticed the butterflies before Charles Abbot and Thomas Orlebar Marsh came on the scene around 1800 but, if they did, no record of their activities has been found. Although these two reverend gentlemen left notebooks, which have survived along with a few of Abbot's specimens, almost the only records of their successors through the 19th century are occasional notes in the entomological journals. A few names appear in published lists of entomologists but without any other information. It is not until the turn of the century with the publication of the VCH and the restart of the Bedford Natural History Society that more names appear but even of these little information has surfaced. We have indeed been fortunate in having the help of Robert Craske who lived in Bedford between 1918 and 1927. He knew W.G.Nash who was the leading lepidopterist of that period in the County and was much quoted in the VCH and in other contemporary works on Lepidoptera. Recollections of the generation of lepidopterists active in the County in the 1930s, '40s and '50s, such as S.H.Kershaw, R.E.R.Sanderson and K.E.West, have been provided by Jim Barnwell, Sidney Humphrey and Bernard West.

It has been said disparagingly of the early lepidopterists that they were merely collectors but, whatever their motivation, without their interest we would know almost nothing of the history of the butterflies and moths of the County. It also has to be remembered that they lacked modern monitoring tools, such as the mercury-vapour moth-trap. They therefore spent more time in the field and in rearing the immature stages so acquiring an in-depth knowledge of the group which few could equal today.

The Reverend Charles Abbot, DD, FLS. (1761-1817) was the first person in Bedfordshire known to have taken an interest in Lepidoptera. He was usher or under-master at Bedford Grammar School, Vicar of Oakley Reynes and of Goldington and a curate at two Bedford churches. He was elected a Fellow of the Linnean Society in 1793 (five years after its foundation) and in 1798 published the first flora of the County, *Flora Bedfordiensis*. This was only the third printed county flora and is an important work. Dony (1949) gave a biographical account of Charles Abbot and reviewed his contribution to botany. Although Dony described Abbot's interest in entomology, more information has been collected recently and merits comment in some detail here.

Abbot conducted an extensive correspondence with contemporary naturalists. Many of his letters to Sir James Smith, founder of the Linnean Society and author of *Flora Britannica*, and to J.Sowerby, author of *English Botany*, have survived. Most are on botanical matters but there are occasional references to insects.

According to his contemporary, the Reverend T.Orlebar Marsh (MS2), Abbot's collection of insects, in two large framed and glazed mahogany cases, was bought for four guineas by Mr Bucklow of the Swan Inn, Bedford. Whether this was after Abbot's death or earlier is not clear; the phrase "at his sales" was used. Bucklow then sold it in 1817 for ten guineas to J.C.Dale (see below). There are a few specimens in the Dale collection attributed to

Abbot, but the list in Dale's collection catalogue (MS2) indicates that there were originally many more. As Dale was only 25 in 1817 it is possible that Abbot's collection formed a substantial addition to his own. He would have replaced Abbot's specimens with better ones as he acquired them retaining only the more interesting examples.

J.C.Dale also seems to have bought several of Abbot's entomological books. The only entomological notebook seen so far, *Lepidoptera Anglica cum Libellulis* (Abbot, MS1) is with the Dale papers in the Hope Library, Oxford University Museum. This little volume (Figure 6) is about 10 cm square. The handwriting of most of the notes conforms to that in various letters written by Charles Abbot but there are a few entries in a rather smaller and finer script. One of the latter is annotated "Mrs Abbot's writing ?". Other annotations in pencil are probably by J.C.Dale. The first dated entry is 1797, the year before Abbot first recorded the Chequered Skipper in Britain in Clapham Park Wood.

Figure 6 Charles Abbot's notebook *Lepidoptera Anglica cum Libellulis.*

Fortunately this notebook remained with the Dale archives but another was sold with the Dale library in London in 1906. The sale catalogue described it as *Entomologia Selecta*, a volume of notes in MS of over 300 pages referring to the Lepidoptera of the [Bedford] district. This was sold as one lot with a copy of Abbot's *Flora Bedfordiensis.* The title is in keeping with volumes of his herbarium which he named *Flora Selecta*. Another MS, *Linnaei Insecta Anglica Lepidoptera*, described as "being an account of the English Lepidoptera according to Linnaeus, with descriptions of their food plants, localities, etc., also further MS notes on localities by J.C.Dale, the later owner" was listed in Wheldon and Wesley's catalogue of 1928 as "together with a copy of *Flora Bedfordiensis*, 1798, bound in 2 vols, 8vo, calf". It is not clear whether this is the same MS appearing for sale twice under different descriptions or whether they are two different MS. These documents have not yet been traced despite extensive enquiries in the UK and in the USA, though earlier authors, such as South (1906), appear to have had access to more information on Abbot's records than is currently available. J.C.Dale's notes contain many references to Abbot's records, particularly of butterflies, but almost all of these can be traced back to *Lepidoptera Anglica cum Libellulis*. This notebook covers only the years 1797 to 1800 and one can only wonder what the other manuscript(s) might have contained and why J.C.Dale did not refer to them more often.

In the sale of W.G.Nash's collection in 1936 there was mention of a book, *A Short Life History of Insects* (1798), apparently by Charles Abbot. However, there is in a private collection a copy of *A Short History of Insects* which is attributed to Eleanor Fenn but has no author printed in it. This copy has Charles Abbot's bookplate in it, so it is almost certainly the same copy. The writer of the Nash sale catalogue presumably thought that Charles Abbot was the author.

Since Abbot's records of Lepidoptera are effectively the first for Bedfordshire, it is important to establish whether they can be trusted. Dony (1949) wrote "It is difficult to estimate his worth as a naturalist. He was an optimist and always travelled hopefully. His enthusiasm led him to see the unusual when it was not there." However good his standing as a botanist, his notebook indicates that in 1797 he was relatively inexperienced as an entomologist. The bulk of the section on Lepidoptera is taken up with short descriptions of each species of butterfly, just what an enthusiastic novice might assemble as a field guide in the days before pocket-sized guides were available. This part of the notebook cannot readily be dated and may well have been written before the actual records of captures and sightings were added. To what extent he took an interest in Lepidoptera while he was compiling his flora is not clear but his inexperience at this stage is confirmed by a phrase in the manuscript reporting to the Linnean Society his finding of the Chequered Skipper. He describes missing a Swallowtail and excuses it as "being his first season" as an Aurelian, *i.e.* a lepidopterist, in 1797.

P.B.M.Allan in his book *Talking of Moths* (1943) writes extensively about the unscrupulous dealers in Lepidoptera whose activities have caused so much confusion over 19th century records. Discussing a dealer named Plastead he wrote "His chief dupes appear to have been John Curtis, James Stephens of the *Illustrations*, and the great Dr Abbott."⋆ Whether Allan used the adjective "great" sarcastically we cannot know but from the writings seen so far, Abbot hardly merited such an accolade as an entomologist alongside Curtis and Stephens. He also wrote "Dr. Abbott, another of Plastead's patrons seems to have been intent chiefly upon introducing North American species into Bedfordshire. He caught *Hesperia bucephalus*, a large Yankee skipper, in Clapham Park Wood and then proceeded to take *Pyrgus oileus*." "Did the Reverend Dr. Abbott take any other rarities ? Believe me he did. He took *lathonia*, *podalirius*, *daplidice*, *niobe* and many other exotics, all in Bedfordshire. But he seems to have missed *Thecla spini* which is strange as it was a popular insect in English collections at that time. Perhaps it was too popular for the reverend doctor who preferred rarities which other collectors did not possess." It is most unfortunate that Allan did not list the source of this information.

L.H.Newman (1954) has described one technique used to fool collectors. In essence, the dealer would tell collectors that he had seen a rare insect and for a consideration would guide one to a suitable place where he released the rarity for the collector to catch. However, Clapham Park and White Wood seem peculiar places to choose as venues for such fraud. The other point to be borne in mind is that good textbooks were few at that time and species of Lepidoptera new to Britain were being found every year. So it is perhaps not surprising that a relative novice lepidopterist might have been duped even if he was competent in other areas of natural history.

Haworth (1803) in the introduction to his *Lepidoptera Britannica* wrote "Since the body of this work was printed, my friend the Rev. Dr. Abbott of Bedford has informed me that he took in May last, near Clapham Park Wood in Bedfordshire, a specimen of *Papilio Podalirius* in the winged state: and that he also took in June last in White Wood near Gamlingay, Cambridgeshire the *Papilio Daplidice* (in a faded state) and likewise *Papilio Lathonia*. These are three extremely interesting species and there is not a British specimen extant, except the above." He goes on to comment that "*Lathonia* was not very rare in Gamlingay Wood, Cambridgeshire in the days of Petiver." The three specimens, Queen of Spain Fritillary (*lathonia*), Scarce Swallowtail (*podalirius*) and Bath White (*daplidice*) remain in the Dale collection.

⋆ Abbot's name was frequently mis-spelled by others.

Certainly the capture of three rare species within a short period in 1803 gives rise to doubts. There is no evidence that the weather in May and June of that year was exceptionally favourable for migrants though Manley (1974) listed estimated temperatures, not wind directions. Wilkinson (1982) gave guarded acceptance to these records but mentioned that Abbot took other rare species. The exotic skippers are mentioned in the lists which J.C.Dale made of the specimens in Abbot's collection. Specimens said to have been "taken near Bedford ... several years ago" were also included in a collection which Abbot sent to Haworth for naming. Their receipt is recorded in the minute book of the Aurelian Society for 12 September 1804. No statements in Abbot's handwriting claiming that the exotic skippers were actually caught in the wild in Bedfordshire have yet been seen, though it is possible they were included in the missing manuscript(s) and P.B.M.Allan saw references to them and the "many other exotics" there.

In one of his notebooks (MS3), *The Entomological Calendars of the late Revd Charles Abbot, D.D. F.L. & A.S. and of James Charles Dale, M.A. F.L.S.*, J.C.Dale copied out many of the entries in Abbot's notebook in diary form and then continued with his own. There are also several annotations in what appears to be another hand including on the title page "Mr Walcott of Southampton knew Dr Abbot & says his veracity was undoubted". Further on: "Mr Walcott formerly of Winckton Hants now of Bristol knew Dr Abbot intimately & that he was only 2nd Master in Bedford School & when 1st was vacant another person was put over him which had such an effect on him he died of a broken heart it was supposed." "Mr Dawson was one of his pupils (perhaps well flogged ?) & said he had cracked his skull & had a piece of silver plate let in & fancied odd things. Schoolboys do not always speak well of their masters !!!". (Could this have been J.F.Dawson? – see below)

Whether or not one accepts any of Abbot's list of rarities as genuine, there seems little reason to doubt most of his other records of native British Lepidoptera. Fortunately, the specimens in his collection were listed by J.C.Dale, so we have the identifications independently confirmed. Also the two most important finds which Abbot made, Chequered Skipper and Large Blue, were subsequently re-recorded in Bedfordshire by Dale and others.

Charles Golding Barrett (1836-1904) was a noted entomologist and wrote major works on Lepidoptera. In his last years he compiled the Lepidoptera section of *The Victoria History of the County of Bedford*. (Obituary: Anon, 1905)

William Bond-Smith (1865-1949) is acknowledged in the VCH as providing "a useful list of the larger species found at Potton". He ran a grocery business in Potton and was a County Councillor. According to his obituary "His great hobby was entomology; he possessed a valuable collection of butterflies and moths which were either bred or caught by him." The fate of his collection is not known. He contributed notes to the *Entomologist's Record* in 1891 and 1896. (Obituary: Braybrooks, 1949)

Sydney R.Bowden (1904-1991) lived in Hertfordshire and observed butterflies around Knocking Hoe and Pegsdon Hills for some 40 years from around 1917. He published several annual reports on butterflies in the Journal of the Letchworth Natural History Society, notes on Adonis Blue and other species and a series of papers on the races of the Green-veined White butterfly. His collection of specimens from these studies was deposited in the Natural History Museum.

Walter Studholme Brocklehurst JP (1873-1953) was Chairman of Bedford Divisional Bench and founder of Bedford Special Constabulary. He lived at Grove House, Bromham Road, Bedford and collected with Gifford Nash. His very substantial collection, which included some 30 drawers of micro-moths was sold in 1938. No specimens have been seen but some, found with Gifford Nash's specimens, labelled "Bedford District" with no collector's name, might have been his. His obituary records him as a former chairman of the Bedfordshire Natural History Society but this was an error. It should have read Bedford Natural History and Archaeological Society of which he was Honorary Vice-President between 1934 and 1953. (Obituary: Anon, 1953b)

James Charles Dale FLS (1792-1872) lived at Glanvilles Wootton in Dorset, a wealthy country squire and at one time High Sheriff of Dorset. He went to Sidney Sussex College, Cambridge where he obtained his BA in 1815 and MA in 1818. On his way from Dorset to Cambridge in 1817 he probably stopped at the Swan Inn in Bedford, saw Abbot's collection there and bought it from Mr W.Bucklow, together with Abbot's notebooks. According to his papers he also visited Bedford in 1818, 1819, 1820, 1826 and 1833 and collected in Clapham Park Wood, along the River Ouse near Bedford, at the Large Blue sites around Bromham and also in White Wood, Gamlingay.

J.C.Dale became a fellow of the Linnean Society in 1818 and was highly respected as an entomologist. He amassed a huge collection encompassing most insect orders. He seems to have been an inveterate cataloguer and a prodigious correspondent. There are some 50 notebooks and annotated lists in the Dale archives. He often copied the same information into different lists so it is not surprising that occasional errors crept in. He corresponded with most of the leading entomologists of his day and the archives contain over 5000 letters which he received. Among these are several letters from Bucklow, both from Bedford and after the latter's move to London. His papers and collection are in the University Museum at Oxford. The latter was rearranged by his son, C.W.Dale, who did not achieve his father's status as an entomologist. (Obituary: Anon, 1872. See also Brown, 1988)

Darrell M.Jefferys (1918-1979) came to Bedford in 1948 and worked as a doctor there. He was keen on breeding the larger Lepidoptera and collaborated with Bernard West in many moth-trapping sessions.

Sidney Hardinge Kershaw Col., DSO (1881-1964). After a distinguished army career, Col. Kershaw retired to Alderman's Place, Aspley Heath in 1932. He was a keen naturalist and an enthusiastic lepidopterist. Through the generosity of his daughter, Mrs J.Wheeler, his notebooks have been placed in the Booth Museum in Brighton. The notebooks record 55 visits to Pegsdon Hills between 1932 and 1960 and 99 visits to Totternhoe Knolls 1943-60, as well as visits to Sharpenhoe and other sites in Bedfordshire and elsewhere. He visited King's Wood, Heath and Reach, on no less than 40 occasions between 1951 and 1958 and witnessed the last surge in numbers of the fritillaries there. He wrote several reports on the wood for the Nature Conservancy. For some 25 years he ran a moth trap on the roof of the boiler house at Alderman's Place and recorded some 345 species there. The large collection which he amassed contains many specimens from Bedfordshire and is well labelled. Together with the notebooks, it forms an important record of the Lepidoptera of the County from the 1930s to the late 1950s. (Obituary: Allan, 1964)

Figure 7 Col. S.H.Kershaw

The Reverend Thomas Orlebar Marsh FLS (1749-1831) was Vicar of Stevington. He made extensive notes on natural history and strange occurrences in Bedfordshire (MS1) which contain a few references to Lepidoptera. He also collected biographical notes on notable people in the County (MS2) which included Charles Abbot.

Walter Gifford Nash (1862-1935) was senior surgeon at Bedford Hospital and made a major contribution to the hospital's development. His portrait (Figure 8) is in the South Wing there. It is said that after he had finished operating in the evening he would open the windows of the operating theatre and collect the moths attracted to the bright lights! He collected with W.S. Brocklehurst and supplied information to Barrett (acknowledged in VCH), Foster and Tutt. He was President of the Bedford Natural History Society in 1895, 1904, 1909 and 1919. He contributed at least 19 lectures and the Society met at his house in De Parys Avenue between July 1895 and October 1897. His extensive collection was sold in 1936. The sale catalogue described it as in some 91 drawers. A few specimens were seen in the P.N.Crow and Oxford County Museum collections. The source of the latter was said to have been the duplicate drawers in the collections of the British Entomological and Natural History Society. (Obituary: Anon, 1935)

Figure 8 Walter Gifford Nash

Harry Nicholls collected with Gifford Nash. The minutes of the Bedford Natural History Society in 1915 describe a talk by Nicholls and refer to his substantial collection but no trace of the latter has been found.

Ray Palmer (1896-1975) took a keen interest in many aspects of natural history. His diaries, which contain several references to Lepidoptera, are in Bedford Museum.

Ralph Paul Kirkland Rylands (1883-1926) came from Cheshire and worked in the coal and iron business. His family were among the founder members of the Warrington Natural History Society. He appears to have lived in Bedford between 1907 and 1911. His collection from that period is in Bedford Museum.

R.E.R.Sanderson (?-1946) lived in Luton and practised as a GP there. He was clearly interested in the butterflies of the chalk downs and often visited the Chalkhill Blue sites on Therfield Heath. He was said to have introduced the Adonis Blue to various places along the downs. His collection was left to the Natural History Museum but some specimens are in Luton Museum.

J.A.Saunders. Barrett wrote in the VCH: "At Luton excellent work done by Mr J.A. Saunders, now unhappily deceased, and to documents left by him, and obligingly lent by his father Mr. Jas. Saunders, A.S.S., to Mr. A.E. Gibbs, I am indebted for an extensive list of species both of Macro- and Micro-Lepidoptera supplied for that district." (See also Dony, 1948)

Emily Shore (1819-1839) lived at Potton and Everton but died at the early age of 19. She kept a remarkable diary which was later published (Anon, 1891). The diary contains a few records of butterflies and moths.

Horace Aubrey Nelson Tebbs, MBE (1905-87) was a solicitor in Bedford who started collecting butterflies and, to a lesser extent, moths as a schoolboy in the 1920s, inspired by Horace Finlinson. He continued collecting until 1945 and was especially interested in breeding butterflies. He attended meetings of entomological societies in London and made the acquaintance of other lepidopterists including F.W.Frowhawk. A selection from his collection is in Luton Museum.

W.Temple lived at 80 Ampthill Road, Bedford and gave a talk on 'Moths' to the Bedford Natural History Society on 12 January 1912. Part of his collection is in Colchester Museum but the remainder has not been located. From the dates on labels on some of his specimens, he evidently collected with Ralph Rylands at sites such as Hanger Wood.

K.F.Webb (1940-1984) lived in Luton and contributed several notes on moths in Bedfordshire to the *Entomologist's Record*.

Kenneth Egbert West (1897-1985) was a founder member of the Bedfordshire Natural History Society. He was born in Campton and could recall being taken to see the "larger brother" of the Small Tortoiseshell in Chicksands Wood and seeing the clouds of blue butterflies on Pegsdon Hills. He saw the return of the Comma and White Admiral to Bedfordshire and his enthusiasm inspired his son, Bernard West, who became the first county recorder for Lepidoptera.

The following either appear to have observed or collected only sporadically in Bedfordshire or little information on them has been obtained:

Alan Bell – "formerly of Welwyn". His collection and some notes are in the Welwyn-Hatfield Museum, without dates but thought to be 1910-1930.

John Christopher Beadnell (Jack) Craske (1902-1958) visited Bedfordshire, particularly Dunstable Downs, during the 1930s and between 1948 and 1953 with his brother Robert Craske. (Obituaries: A.E.C. (1959), Worms (1959))

Peter Noel Crow (? - 1987) lived in Harpenden for a time in the late 1950s and collected in the south of Bedfordshire. (Obituary: Baker and Morgan, 1989)

W.Darrington exhibited butterflies and moths to the Bedford Natural History Society on 9 October 1929.

The Reverend John Fredric Dawson (1802-1870) "of the Woodlands, Clapham, near Bedford" was described by Graham (1878) as an "accomplished coleopterist" who also wrote a paper "some years ago" on "*Cinxia*" (the Glanville Fritillary) in *The Zoologist*.

W.Farrow of Woburn is included in a list of British Entomologists published in the *Entomologist's Annual* for 1859. What branch of entomology he was interested in is not known.

Ralph Stanton (Roger) Ferry (?- 1983) lived in Welwyn and collected in the Pegsdon and Barton Hills area. His collection (1938-1977) and diaries are in the Welwyn-Hatfield Museum.

Horace W.Finlinson collected with E.R.Williams around 1894 and encouraged H.A.N.Tebbs in his interest in Lepidoptera.

Dr Arthur Herbert Foster (? - 1946) was Lepidoptera recorder for the Hertfordshire Natural History Society. He collected in the Pegsdon Hills area. (See Sawford, 1987)

J.C.F. (later Sir John) Fryer KBE, FRS (1886-1947) was director of the Ministry of Agriculture, Fisheries and Food's Plant Pathology Laboratory in Harpenden. His collection is at Rothamsted Experimental Station.

Arthur Ernest Gibbs (1859-1917) produced the first county list of Lepidoptera for Hertfordshire in 1902 and contributed many papers to the Transactions of the Hertfordshire Natural History Society. He is acknowledged as making a major contribution to the VCH for Bedfordshire. (Obituary: Rowland-Brown, 1917)

A.L.Goodson (collected 1930-1951) worked at Tring Museum. His collection is in the City Museum, St Albans.

W.B.Graham wrote a paper in 1878 on Bedfordshire entomology. He lived in Sharnbrook and was a Superintendent of Police.

George Graveley-Edwards (1896 -1973) actor and playwright, was born in Charleston, S. Carolina and came to England as a baby. In Bedfordshire he collected mainly on Totternhoe Knolls, Dunstable Downs and Barton Hills. His collection is in the City Museum, St Albans. (Obituary: Anon, 1973a)

W.Greenwell-Lax wrote a paper in 1878 and lived at 101 Tavistock St, Bedford.

The Reverend O.W.Harries is acknowledged in the VCH as providing lists of the larger Lepidoptera from Bedford.

A.Hasted – notes from 1890 are in Bedford Museum.

E.A.S.Hatton (known from a paper in1898) lived at Ullsthorpe, St Michael's Road, Bedford.

G.Hawes lived in the Woburn Sands area and collected with J.B.Barnwell and S.H.Kershaw.

H.A.Hill – known only from a record in 1889.

G.H.E.Hopkins (1899-1973) – his collection is in the City Museum, St Albans.

Josiah King of Biggleswade is included in a list of British Entomologists published in the *Entomologist's Annual* for 1858. What branch of entomology he was interested in is not known.

Alfred Lucas – lived in Luton but is known only from his 1855 paper on diurnal Lepidoptera around Luton.

G.B.Oliver (1876-1966) lived in Luton for a time and was known for his ability in rearing Lepidoptera. Specimens from his collection are in the Buckinghamshire County Museum at Halton. (Obituary: Anon, 1966)

G.H.B.Oliver. Specimens from his collection are in the Buckinghamshire County Museum at Halton.

G.F.B.Prior lived in St Albans and collected on Dunstable Downs and Totternhoe in the 1940s and early 1950s. His collection is with Hampshire Museum Services at Winchester.

J.Sharpin is acknowledged as contributing information on "the smaller groups" for the VCH.

D.H.S.Steuart is known only from two papers in 1891, one describing a month's collecting at Bedford. His address was given as Prestwich, Lancashire.

Herbert Studman is acknowledged in the VCH as contributing a list of a few species at Woburn. He died on 28 May 1916, aged 52, and for 25 years was headmaster of Woburn Boys School.

J.C.Thynne of Haynes Park is included in a list of British Entomologists published in the *Entomologist's Annual* for 1857. What branch of entomology he was interested in is not known.

G.E.Tite worked at Tring Museum. His collection (1926 -1955) is in the City Museum, St Albans.

A.West is mentioned in the minutes of the Bedford Natural History Society around 1917 as interested in butterflies and exhibited butterflies and moths to the Society on 9 October 1929.

E.R.Williams collected in the Bedford area around 1894-5. B.R.Mitchell has his copy of Morris (1895) with marginal annotations.

Habitats for Butterflies and Moths in Bedfordshire

C.R.B.Baker and V.W.Arnold

In this chapter we will look at some of the habitats in Bedfordshire, examine the situation there today and review what is known of past changes. We will also consider, wherever possible, how these changes might have affected the numbers of butterflies and moths, and finally outline conservation needs. The geology and geography of Bedfordshire have been described in several publications. Nau *et al.* in *Bedfordshire Wildlife* (1987) give a comprehensive survey from the general natural history viewpoint and a brief description can be found in Dazley and Trodd (1994). Reviews like these give a good picture of the Bedfordshire countryside as we see it today but we all know it has undergone great changes during this century, especially during the last 50 years. We see evidence of such change in motorways, factories, new housing estates (*e.g.* Figure 9), quarries, and huge arable fields being sprayed with pesticides. But what was the countryside like to start with?

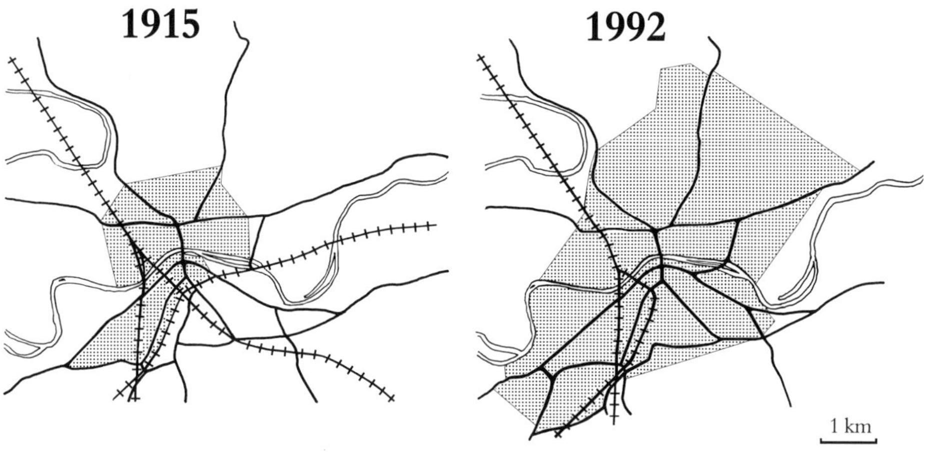

Figure 9 Change in Bedfordshire – the growth of Bedford between 1915 and 1992. Similar urban expansion has occurred in most towns and villages throughout the County resulting in loss of habitat, especially for butterflies. The abandoned railway lines form valuable corridor habitats along which species can move.

It is easy to imagine an idyllic landscape, butterflies flitting across flower-filled meadows bounded by well-kept hedges, road verges bright with flowers, woodland rides wide and sunny, coppice well-managed and everywhere rough corners where butterflies and moths could thrive. However pleasing this image may be, we could find little evidence in pictures or in written descriptions for such a 'baseline' picture of the Bedfordshire countryside. In reality, the 'baseline' would be different depending on which date was chosen. There was probably no time in the last 200 years when the countryside was static for a long period. We may feel that agricultural change is a recent phenomenon, but the enclosures from the

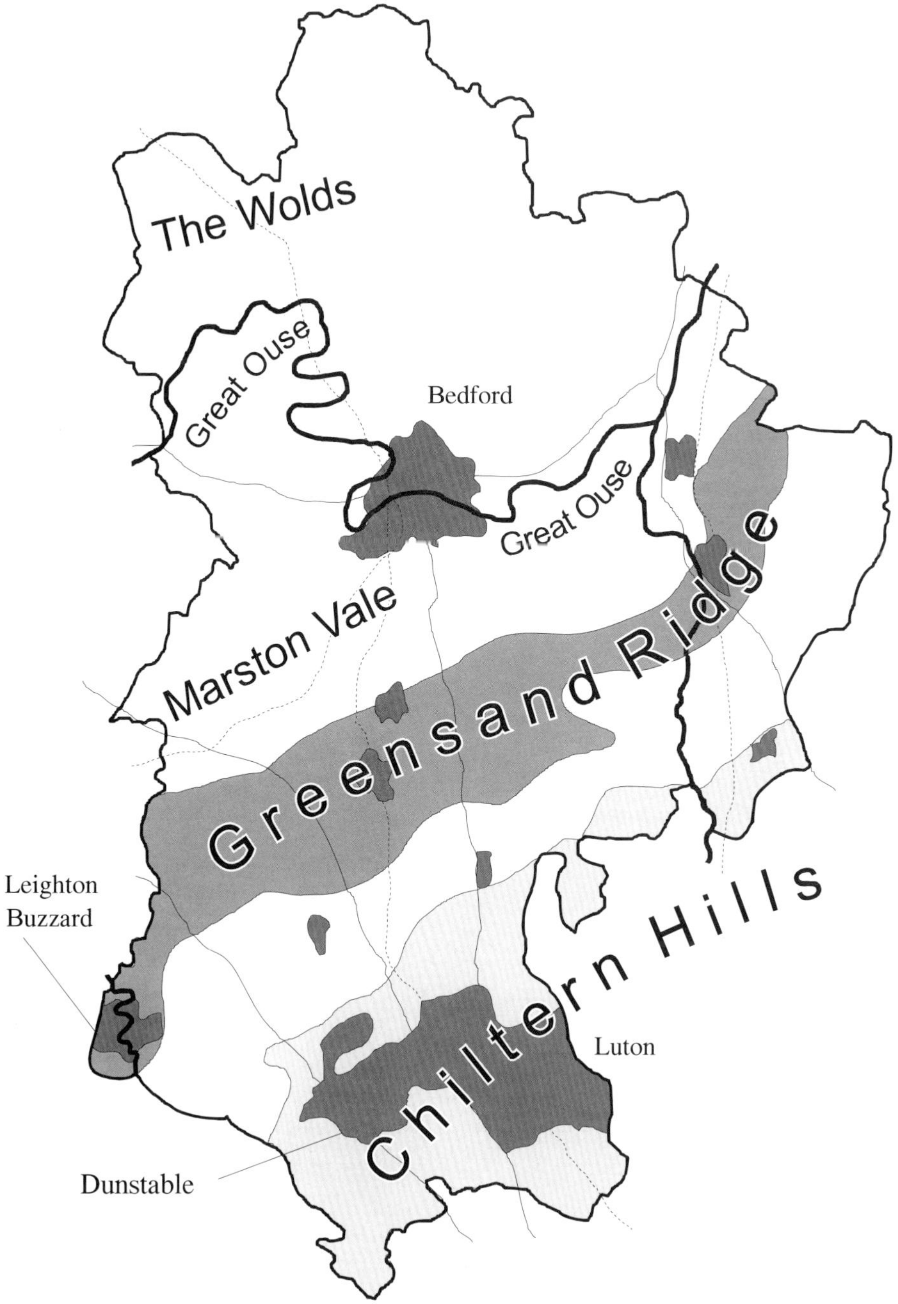

Figure 10 The main topographical features of Bedfordshire occur as bands running south-west to north-east across the County. The sequence from south to north is: Chiltern Hills, the Flit valley, the Greensand Ridge, the Marston Vale and Ouse valley and the Northern Wolds. (Darkest shading – main urban areas)

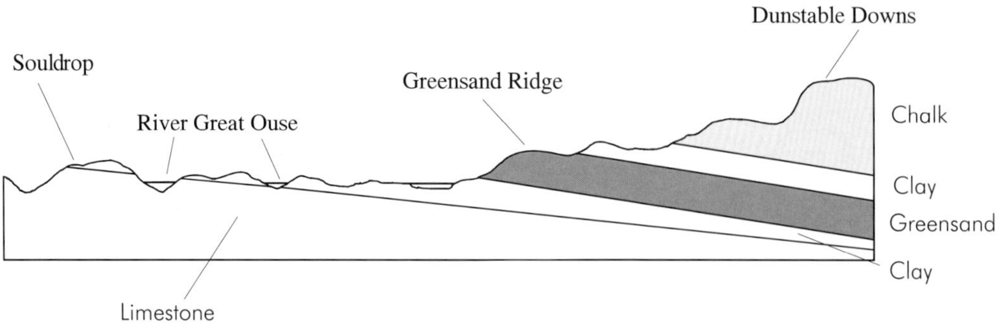

Figure 11 North-south section through Bedfordshire from Dunstable Downs to Souldrop, showing the topography and some of the underlying geology. The vertical scale is exaggerated.

mid-1800s would have produced a dramatic change. Certainly there has been more than one fluctuation in the ratio of arable to pasture land. Only for the last 40 to 50 years do we have a useful collection of photographs of habitats. Even then features of particular interest to the entomologist may not be recorded. From about 1940 back to 1900, photographs of the countryside become progressively more scarce and before 1900 there are very few indeed. The early photographers seem to have concentrated on towns and villages, and rarely pointed their lenses at wholly rural scenes. A number of pictures of the chalk downs survive but we could find few pictures that show for example the state of woods in Bedfordshire before 1920. Maps show the extent of woodland and the location of field boundaries, but we do not know in detail how the hedges were maintained or to what extent habitat suitable for different species of Lepidoptera would have been continuous or fragmented. Today, although butterflies and moths can be found throughout the County, the main concentrations of species survive in islands of semi-natural habitat surrounded by comparatively sterile urban and agricultural areas.

Large Tortoiseshell - extinct in Bedfordshire

Records for butterflies are patchy during the 19th century and the first three-quarters of the 20th century but they are sufficient to give some indication of changes, particularly local extinctions. Sixty-two species of butterfly have been recorded in the County. Of these, five are migrant species that do not regularly overwinter in the County, *i.e.* Clouded Yellow, Pale Clouded Yellow, Red Admiral, Painted Lady and Camberwell Beauty. The records for eleven species are either doubtful or the butterflies are likely to have been released, *i.e.* Scarce Swallowtail, Swallowtail, Berger's Clouded Yellow, Long-tailed Blue, Mazarine Blue, Silver-studded Blue, Large Copper, Glanville Fritillary, Bath White, Queen of Spain Fritillary and Monarch.

The chalk downs. A view from Barton Hills towards Sharpenhoe Clappers with Chalkhill Blues, a butterfly typical of chalk grassland.

Four breeding species, *i.e.* Chequered Skipper, Black-veined White, Large Blue and Heath Fritillary, were extinct in Bedfordshire before the publication of the Victoria County History in 1904. Since then a further 10 species have been lost. These are: Silver-spotted Skipper, Adonis Blue, Large Tortoiseshell, Small Pearl-bordered Fritillary, Pearl-bordered Fritillary, High Brown Fritillary, Marsh Fritillary, Grayling, Purple Emperor and Silver-washed Fritillary. There have been several casual sightings of the last two species but there is no evidence that they have bred in the County for many years. The Brown Hairstreak should probably be added to this list but it is so elusive that it may remain undetected somewhere in the County. Thirty-one species regularly overwinter and breed in Bedfordshire.

Early records for moths are sparse but of the 355 species of macro-moth recorded in the VCH or earlier, 11 species have not been found since. These include Mullein Wave, Frosted Yellow, Dark Tussock, Small Chocolate-tip, Red-necked Footman, Red Sword-grass and The Anomalous. Since the VCH, 182 new species of macro-moths have been added to the county list. The figures for micro-moths are 284 species listed in the VCH, 34 not found since and 485 added subsequently. Counts are somewhat confused by changes in scientific names but these figures broadly indicate that a smaller proportion of moth species may have become extinct in the County than of butterflies. The reason for this is not known and the scarcity of detailed records makes it difficult to comment on the effect of changes in land management on populations of moths.

Grassland Habitats

Chalk Downland

The eastern end of the Chiltern Hills (Figures 10 and 11) rises to a height of 242 m on Dunstable Downs and is a distinctive feature of the County. The present county boundary lies within a few hundred metres of the White Lion cut into the chalk on the scarp in Whipsnade Wild Animal Park on the east side of the Gade Valley gap. From there the chalk downs extend north-east past the Dunstable gap, through which the Romans took Watling Street, past the Lea gap at Luton to Pegsdon Hills in the east and thence into Hertfordshire.

Figure 12 Sundon quarry 1990.

However, it is not a simple line of hills with the steep scarp facing north-west. The curves, re-entrants and other small-scale topographical features produce areas with almost every aspect and slope. These features, combined with variations in soil type, create a host of habitats with different microclimates and different flora and fauna.

The natural topography has also been reshaped by quarries and cuttings for road and rail, providing yet more habitats. The chalk area around Dunstable and Luton contains many examples of such modification of the landscape. There are large chalk quarries at Kensworth, Totternhoe, Sewell, Houghton Regis, Sundon (Figure 12) and Barton, several of which are over 50 ha in extent, as well as the old railway cutting at Sewell and the A5 cutting north of Dunstable. After such workings were completed or abandoned, plant succession began on the bare chalk. Kidney vetch is an early coloniser and populations of the Small Blue have benefited accordingly. So also has Duke of Burgundy for which the later stages of succession have provided shelter and foodplant. Some of these quarries have been much used by motorcyclists and drivers of four-wheel-drive vehicles, activities usually viewed with dismay by conservationists. However in some situations wear by these vehicles may play an important part in keeping succession at bay.

Figure 13 Sheep flock on Dunstable Downs about 1937. Note the lack of scrub and fencing.

During the early part of this century much of this grassland was grazed by sheep (Figure 13), probably in fairly mobile flocks tended by shepherds who moved the flocks to the downland during the day and folded them at night, usually on enclosed pasture or arable fields. The intensity of grazing would have varied. Together with rabbits and some cattle, the sheep would have produced areas of the close-cropped flower-rich turf which favours the typical butterflies of chalk grassland, such as Adonis Blue, Chalkhill Blue, Silver-spotted Skipper and Dark Green Fritillary. The Bedfordshire downs were not as famous for butterflies as Royston and sites elsewhere on the Chilterns, particularly Kop Hill. Nevertheless, several thousands of Chalkhill Blues could be seen in a day on Dunstable Downs in the 1930s. Even today, where the habitat is suitable, a wide range of butterflies and moths can still be found. The butterflies include Duke of Burgundy, Chalkhill Blue, Small Blue, Green Hairstreak, Marbled White, Brown Argus and Dingy and Grizzled Skippers. Among the many species of macro-moths on the downs are the Cistus Forester, Wood Tiger, Chimney Sweeper, Narrow-bordered Five-spot Burnet, Six-spot Burnet, Emperor Moth, Fox Moth, Small Elephant Hawk-moth, Dusky Sallow, Reddish Light Arches and Light Feathered Rustic. Characteristic micro-moths include *Stigmella poterii*, *Nemophora cupriacella*, *N. metallica*, *Coleophora niveicostella* and *Pyrausta nigrata*.

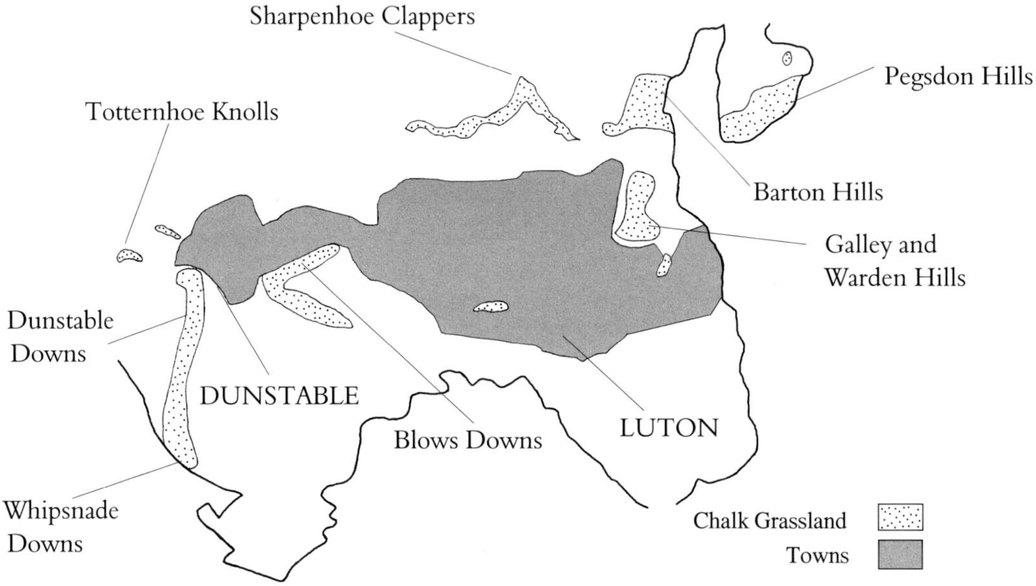

Figure 14 Diagram showing the current extent of fragmentation of the chalk grassland by urban and arable areas. The areas shown above as grassland are in turn sub-divided by scrub.

In the early 1900s the grassland along the escarpment would have been almost continuous but Figure 14 shows the extent to which chalk grassland has become fragmented. The gaps are filled by building development, agricultural land and scrub. These form barriers which many species will rarely cross and the downland colonies of species, such as Chalkhill Blue, Small Blue and Cistus Forester, are liable to become isolated (see page 59 for some of the consequences of this isolation). At the base of the scarp slope, the conurbation of Dunstable and Luton makes a formidable barrier although parks and urban wildlife reserves may act as 'stepping stones' for some species. Elsewhere both above and below the scarp, much of the land is now arable. The Land Utilisation Survey (Anon, 1929-31) indicates that pasture was then more extensive and would have provided greater continuity of habitat. With few exceptions, all the fields remaining under grass have been 'improved' by resowing and/or treatment with herbicides and fertilisers. As a result they have an impoverished broad-leaved flora. Even areas of common land have deteriorated. For example, Whipsnade Green and

Chimney Sweeper

Heath were grazed until the early 1960s by free-ranging cattle and sheep. The older inhabitants of Whipsnade remember the Green there as bright with flowers but there are few there today and the Heath is now largely scrub and woodland. Harman and Boyd (1990 pp 138-142) describe a similar situation in Buckinghamshire in the 1920s and 1930s.The grass-feeding skippers and 'browns' are probably sufficiently widespread to form interlinked populations and the Common Blue, Brown Argus and Small Copper are mobile species which appear to be able to colonise the floristically richer remnants. Males of the Chalkhill Blue have been seen well away from their usual localities and so may be able to move between colonies, but it is not known if the females ever do so. How quickly the Small Blue is able to colonise new stands of kidney vetch has not been studied in Bedfordshire but the chalk quarries and road cuttings may help this species to move between sites.

Totternhoe Knolls

An early photo of Totternhoe Knolls taken around 1895 (Figure 15) shows the mound of the Norman castle almost bare of scrub and trees. Sheep-grazing ceased on this site in 1931. By 1951 scrub was beginning to develop on the castle mound and on the medieval stone workings on its northern slope (Figure 17). The rabbits were killed by myxomatosis in the early 1950s. The longer grass would have made conditions unsuitable for those butterflies whose early stages need warm conditions for their development. It was unfortunate that this change in the habitat coincided with a period of cool summers which began in the mid-1950s and lasted, with occasional exceptions, until the early 1980s. The last Marsh Fritillary was seen in 1953 and the Adonis Blue had already disappeared although both had been abundant in the 1940s. Chalkhill Blue which can tolerate longer grass was still present. By 1963 (Figure 18) the hawthorn scrub was becoming dense. Woodland had developed along the steep western face, some of it from earlier plantings. Since then great efforts have been made to clear the scrub and re-introduce grazing. However this type of management, though it may be very beneficial to butterfly populations, is precarious and subject to disruption as people and circumstances change. Clearances and grazing in the 1970s resulted in an improvement in the floristic quality of the turf but grazing lapsed around 1990 and the long-grass reappeared. There was also a resurgence in scrub growth from the untreated stumps of previous clearances. Subsequently the numbers of rabbits increased and areas of short turf are again evident, but there is now a risk of excessive rabbit numbers resulting in over-grazing. The spread of tor-grass may also suppress many butterfly foodplants. Management on the site has the difficult task of balancing the needs of the rich flora and of invertebrates. Unfortunately butterfly and moth populations have not been monitored on this site. We therefore cannot comment on the effects of the recent management but Small Blue and Chalkhill Blue are still present though not in large numbers. Duke of Burgundy has been seen recently and may have spread from the adjacent quarry. Among the more

Dusky Sallow

Figure 15 Totternhoe Knolls from the west taken around 1895. Note the absence of scrub and trees.

Figure 16 Totternhoe Knolls from the west taken in 1995. The slopes are obscured by scrub though other parts, out of sight from this viewpoint, have been cleared.

Figure 17 Totternhoe Knolls from the air looking north in 1951. Scattered scrub is beginning to appear. A donis Blue and Marsh Fritillary were lost shortly afterwards.

Figure 18 Totternhoe Knolls from the air looking north in 1963. Note the extent to which the scrub has invaded in the space of 12 years.

local moths found onTotternhoe Knolls are Grass Rivulet, Chimney Sweeper, Light Feathered Rustic and the scabious-feeding longhorn, *Nemophora cupriacella*.

Dunstable and Whipsnade Downs

From the county boundary at the south-western end of Whipsnade Wild Animal Park through to the northern end of Dunstable Downs are some 130 ha almost all of which used to be open chalk downland (as in Figures 13 and 19). Following the cessation of grazing and advent of myxomatosis, Dunstable and Whipsnade Downs underwent changes similar to those on Totternhoe Knolls. An aerial photograph of the Downs taken in 1952 (Dony, 1953, plate 22 and also Hepple and Doggett, 1992, plate 17) shows well-spaced bushes scattered over the area. By the 1970s dense areas of scrub had formed (see Anon, 1980 for maps comparing areas of scrub in 1947 and 1976). These changes again resulted in the loss of Marsh Fritillary and Adonis Blue. Silver-spotted Skipper, which needs the shortest turf, had probably disappeared much earlier. Dark Green Fritillary became very scarce. Other butterfly species which prefer longer grass and the shelter provided by the scrub have benefited, especially the grass-feeding species including Small, Essex and Large Skippers, Speckled Wood, Marbled White and Ringlet. The scrub also provided perches for the Duke of Burgundy and preferred sites for egg-laying on cowslips. During 1995 and 1996, the introduction of sheep grazing coupled with a marked increase in rabbit numbers and low rainfall has greatly reduced the height of the sward over the northern end of the Downs. Whether this will have any long-term effect on the butterfly fauna remains to be seen.

Within the boundaries of the Whipsnade Wild Animal Park the chalk scarp has been grazed and largely kept clear of scrub by free-ranging wallabies and small deer. At the numbers usually present, these animals were unable to keep the grass short enough for large populations of 'blues' to develop, though the Marbled White and other common 'browns' can be present in good numbers. Only around the burrows of the prairie dogs and in the bison enclosure was the turf kept short. However, in 1996 a situation similar to that on Dunstable Downs developed with the sward being very short over much of the area. Again the effect on the butterflies of the site will be interesting to follow.

Along the remainder of the Downs efforts to clear the scrub and introduce sheep grazing have begun to make an impact. The scrub clearances on Whipsnade Downs provide a cautionary tale. Those removing the scrub at one stage were unaware of the importance of the sallow bushes there for the Lunar Hornet Moth and several bushes were destroyed unnecessarily. Numbers of the Duke of Burgundy also declined as the shelter provided by the scrub was reduced. Now specific areas are being managed for the latter species by creating glades which will be enlarged as the scrub regrows. It is vital that adequate information is available to site managers and that they are aware of the existence of such information. Several years of transect data are now available for Whipsnade Downs. Out of a total of 31 species of butterfly recorded from the site, 30 have been seen on the transect. The table on page 381 shows the annual transect counts for the last 10 years. Comparison of these with similar data from other sites should allow the effects of local management to be distinguished from those of more widespread influences, such as weather, which may affect several sites. However, species may show similar trends in numbers if sites have been managed similarly, making it difficult to distinguish local influences.

Figure 19 Dunstable Downs from the Tring road taken around 1900.

Figure 20 Dunstable Downs from about the same viewpoint as in Figure 19, taken in 1995.

The abundance of common rock-rose has supported populations of the brilliant green Cistus Forester though few have been seen in recent years. Wood Tiger also used to be present but has not been reported lately. Chimney Sweeper, whose larvae feed on pignut, remains common. The larvae of *Stigmella poterii* mine in the leaves of salad burnet. The longhorn moth, *Nemophora metallica*, can be seen on scabious flowers. Marjoram and wild thyme are host to *Pyrausta nigrata*. Other local moths recorded from Dunstable and Whipsnade Downs include Chalk Carpet, Water Carpet, Pinion-spotted Pug, Satyr Pug, Light Feathered Rustic and *Ectoedemia arcuatella*.

Ringlet – a butterfly which has benefited from scrub growth on the downs.

Dunstable Downs is an important recreational area which attracts large numbers of visitors who walk, picnic and take part in activities such as hang-gliding and parascending. The damage to the turf caused by trampling poses a major management problem for the future, in addition to the task of keeping the scrub at bay,

Figure 21 Sharpenhoe Clappers from the air in 1996. The area in the foreground to the west of the Streatley - Sharpenhoe road is the one frequented by lepidopterists during the first half of this century. At present the unimproved grassland across much of the site supports good numbers of Chalkhill Blue.

Sundon Hills and Sharpenhoe Clappers

Scrub invasion and conversion to woodland has also occurred along many of the slopes along the Sundon and Markham Hills and around Sharpenhoe Clappers (Figures 1 and 21) (see Anon, 1980 for maps comparing areas of scrub in 1947 and 1976). Again the Marsh Fritillary and Adonis Blue have been casualties. Considerable areas have been cleared by hand at the latter site and 31 species of butterfly have been recorded there during the 1990s, including good numbers of Chalkhill Blue. The use of semi-wild goats to clear scrub is being trialled in this area as a longer term method of scrub control. According to Robert Craske, the favoured haunt of earlier lepidopterists, such as W.G.Nash, was on the west side of the Streatley to Sharpenhoe road, just up the hill from Moleskin. Most, possibly all, of the older records from Sharpenhoe refer to this area, rather than to the Clappers.

Antler moth – a widespread grassland species.

The downs around Luton

The battle against invading scrub has been waged with some success on the slopes that fringe Dunstable and Luton, namely Blows Downs, Dallow Downs, Bradgers Hill, Galley Hill and Warden Hill (Plate 1) which cover over 140 ha in total (see Anon, 1980 for maps comparing areas of scrub in 1947 and 1976). In recent years the Chalk Grasslands Butterfly Survey has monitored the local distribution of butterflies on many of these sites, though not changes in their populations. Most sites contain around 26 species of butterfly. Detailed mapping by Trevor Tween and his helpers on Warden and Galley Hills has shown how localised butterfly colonies can be on downland. Strong concentrations were found in small areas which had been features of an abandoned golf course. On Bradgers Hill the survey enabled the changes in butterfly distribution following scrub clearance to be monitored.

Barton Hills

To the east of the main A6 road there are two major chalk grassland sites, Barton Hills and Pegsdon Hills. The former (Figures 22 and 23) (44 ha) has been a National Nature Reserve since 1981. As on other downland further west, this site deteriorated during the late 1940s and 1950s resulting in the extinction of Silver-spotted Skipper and Adonis Blue (see Anon, 1980 for maps comparing areas of scrub in 1947 and 1976). A considerable amount of invading scrub had to be cleared during the 1980s. Conditions must have been even more different in the early part of the last century when Grayling was recorded from Barton Hills. Thirty species of butterfly have been recorded on transect walks and the table on page 380 shows the annual transect counts for 9 years.

Silver-spotted Skipper, lost from the chalk downs in the 1950s.

Figure 22 Barton Hills from the air in 1949, looking south. Adonis Blue would still have been present at this time although the hills do not appear tightly grazed in this photograph.

Figure 23 Barton Hills from the air in 1996, looking south. A large area on the left of the picture was converted to arable in the 1950s and the tree cover in Leet Wood, on the right, is more dense. The hills have been grazed since 1988. Much effort has been put into clearing scrub, particularly in the hollows and on the further slope where the bare chalk, exposed by the activities of rabbits, shows white.

Figure 24 Pegsdon Hills from the air in 1949, looking south. Adonis Blue and Silver-spotted Skipper would have been present at this time. Barn Hole, the valley on the right, was almost clear of scrub, although areas of scrub were present in the bottom of the other valleys.

Figure 25 Pegsdon Hills from the air in 1996, looking south. The fields immediately surrounding the Hills are those purchased by the local Wildlife Trust. They are being returned to grass and will form a valuable buffer-zone around core of the reserve.

Pegsdon Hills

During the early 1940s, Adonis Blue, Marsh Fritillary and Silver-spotted Skipper were still present on Pegsdon Hills (Figure 24). Silver-spotted Skipper had been recorded there in the 19th century and the other species may well have been present there at that time. All these species were lost, as at other sites, with the reduction in grazing by sheep and rabbits. As on other downland sites there was invasion by scrub (see Anon, 1980 for maps comparing areas of scrub in 1947 and 1976). Part of this is now being cleared under the management programme of the local Wildlife Trust which bought 79 ha of the site in 1992. In addition to the dry valley the purchase included several of the adjacent fields. These had been under arable cultivation for 50 years or more but are now being restored to grassland. Although this area may take many decades to regain anything approaching the flora and fauna of ancient chalk grassland, its acquisition will allow more flexible management of the whole reserve. It will become both a valuable resource for butterflies and moths and a vital buffer-zone to protect the rest of the reserve from run-off and drift of agricultural chemicals. Some 23 butterfly species have been recorded on Pegsdon Hills during the 1990s, including Chalkhill Blue and Dingy Skipper. Dark Green Fritillary occurred in the mid-1980s but there have been no definite records in recent years. The more local moths include Fox Moth and Satyr Pug. The Lobster Moths which came to light probably fed as larvae on the beech trees along the southern edge of the site. These would also been the source of *Cydia fagiglandana* which was found there in 1986. The presence of Map-winged Swift is surprising but there is bracken in neighbouring woodlands. Cistus Forester was once common on Pegsdon Hills but does not appear to have been seen there for 50 years. A species which also feeds on common rock-rose and is still present is *Scythris crassiuscula*. Other local micro-moths include *Stigmella poterii* on salad burnet, *Nemophora metallica* on scabious and *Pyrausta nigrata* on marjoram and wild thyme.

Just to the north of Pegsdon Hills are two important fragments of chalk grassland at Chicken Hole and Knocking Hoe. The latter has been a National Nature Reserve since 1953 and, from the assemblage of unusual plants there, is thought to be truly ancient chalk grassland. Twenty species of butterfly, including Dingy and Grizzled Skippers, have been recorded recently but Silver-spotted Skipper, Adonis Blue, and Marsh Fritillary have once again been lost and Chalkhill Blue does not appear to have been seen for some years. Dark Green Fritillary was once common and Silver-washed Fritillary strayed from the adjacent woods from which it has long since disappeared. Currently the richness of these sites is threatened by an explosion in numbers of rabbits.

Grassland on the Northern Wolds

Only a few tiny fragments of unimproved grassland remain on the chalky boulder clays of the northern wolds. The underlying limestone is exposed in several places, such as the railway cutting at Sharnbrook Summit (Figure 26), several smaller railway and road cuttings and some pastures along the Ouse valley. These sites have usually been invaded by coarse grasses and scrub. Horseshoe vetch is not found there and kidney vetch is rare. Characteristic butterfly species such as the Chalkhill Blue and Small Blue are therefore absent and indeed may never have been found there.

The habitat which has been lost entirely is the close-cropped turf with ant hills and wild thyme where the Large Blue was found in the early 19th century. The most famous of these sites was Mouse's Pasture where Charles Abbot and J.C.Dale found the Large Blue between

Figure 26 Rock and soil from this railway cutting and tunnel, opened in 1884, underlies the Sharnbrook Summit Nature Reserve, a site rich in Lepidoptera.

1799 and 1819. According to Bernard West, Mouse's Pasture was on land belonging to Denis Elliot of Burdeley's Manor Farm, Stagsden. Until the late 1950s it still contained ant hills covered with thyme. In 1952 at one of its regular field meetings on the farm, the Bedfordshire Natural History Society discussed the possibility of reintroducing the Large Blue there (Anon, 1953a). The field was ploughed up when the farm changed hands in the 1960s. The Large Blue locality between Hanger Wood and Astey Wood was also destroyed but the date is not known. The Marbled White was found on The Wilderness, an area of rough pasture to the south-west of Colmworth, which existed until about 1941. It was common around the northern edge of Bedford until the late 1940s. Dark Green Fritillary was found in the Wilden area in the 1920s, also suggesting the existence of more rough grassland north of Bedford than now. This is confirmed to some extent by the 1930s Land Utilisation Survey (Anon, 1929-31) which shows a considerable proportion of the area as pasture with a few fields marked as rough grazing.

Grassland on the Greensand Ridge

The soils capping the Greensand Ridge are complex, with acid and neutral areas and locally extensive deposits of chalky boulder clay. The flora reflects this variation. However so much has been modified by agriculture that there is little obvious relationship between the soil type and the lepidopterous fauna. In the centre of Maulden Wood there is an important fragment of the grass heath which in past centuries would have been widespread in the area. It is probably the loss of rough unimproved grassland on the Ridge that has produced most changes in the butterflies. For instance the rough grass around Houghton House, north of Ampthill supported good populations of Dark Green Fritillary in the 1940s, but suitable habitat is virtually absent now.

Woodland Habitats

Woodlands ranging in size from small copses to woods of over 100 ha are scattered throughout the County but, with only 5-6% of its area under woodland, Bedfordshire is one of the least wooded counties in England (Figure 27). One-fifth of Bedfordshire woodland is ancient semi-natural woodland (1468 ha). Comparison of Thomas Jefferys' map of 1765 (2 inches to the mile) with the first edition of the 1 inch to the mile Ordnance Survey maps (about 1830) and the current 1:50,000 Ordnance Survey maps shows the boundaries of many woods remaining virtually unchanged for over two hundred years. New woods have been planted, such as Mason's Plantation in Studham in 1929 and Centenary Wood near Pulloxhill in 1989. More recently there are the new plantings at Yelnow New Wood and in the Marston Vale. Some woods have indeed been destroyed. Examples in the north of the County are the greater part of Keysoepark Wood, Harners Wood (south-east of Knotting Green) and the woods which once extended south-west from Penn Wood and Worley's Wood. On the Greensand Ridge, Oxleas Wood across the A6 from Maulden Wood has been lost and in the south, Dedmansey Wood is perhaps a quarter of its former area. However, although populations of Lepidoptera have undoubtedly been destroyed with the woodlands they inhabited and others may have been weakened and lost as the remaining woods became increasingly isolated in areas of intensive agriculture, it is changes in woodland management that have been most damaging. One change has been the cessation of the traditional practice of rotational coppicing and ride management which has resulted in woods with a dense canopy of trees and narrow shaded rides. The other is the practice of clear-felling the broad-leaved trees and replanting with conifers, all alien to the area. The woods of Bedfordshire are not unique in these changes which have occurred throughout much of England. As on the chalk downs, the coincidence of habitat change with climatic deterioration in the 1950s and 1960s has resulted in severe contractions in the ranges of several species of butterflies and moths.

The moth that perhaps makes its presence felt more than any other woodland species is the Green Oak Tortrix. Found throughout the county on almost every oak tree, it increases to immense numbers every few years. The larvae strip the oak trees bare of their first flush of leaves. The green of other deciduous trees stands out in contrast to the leafless oaks. Fortunately the oaks are adapted to this type of damage. They soon produce a second flush of leaves and suffer only a slight set-back in their growth. Similar defoliation is sometimes produced by the group of geometers collectively known as 'winter moths'. The name derives from the moths being active in the winter months. The males are fully winged but the females have only small wings and cannot fly. Their larvae are catholic in their tastes, feeding on a wide range of trees and shrubs. The numbers may be so great that the sound of their droppings falling to the ground actually becomes audible.

The wingless female of the Mottled Umber – one of the 'winter moths'. (x 1.5)

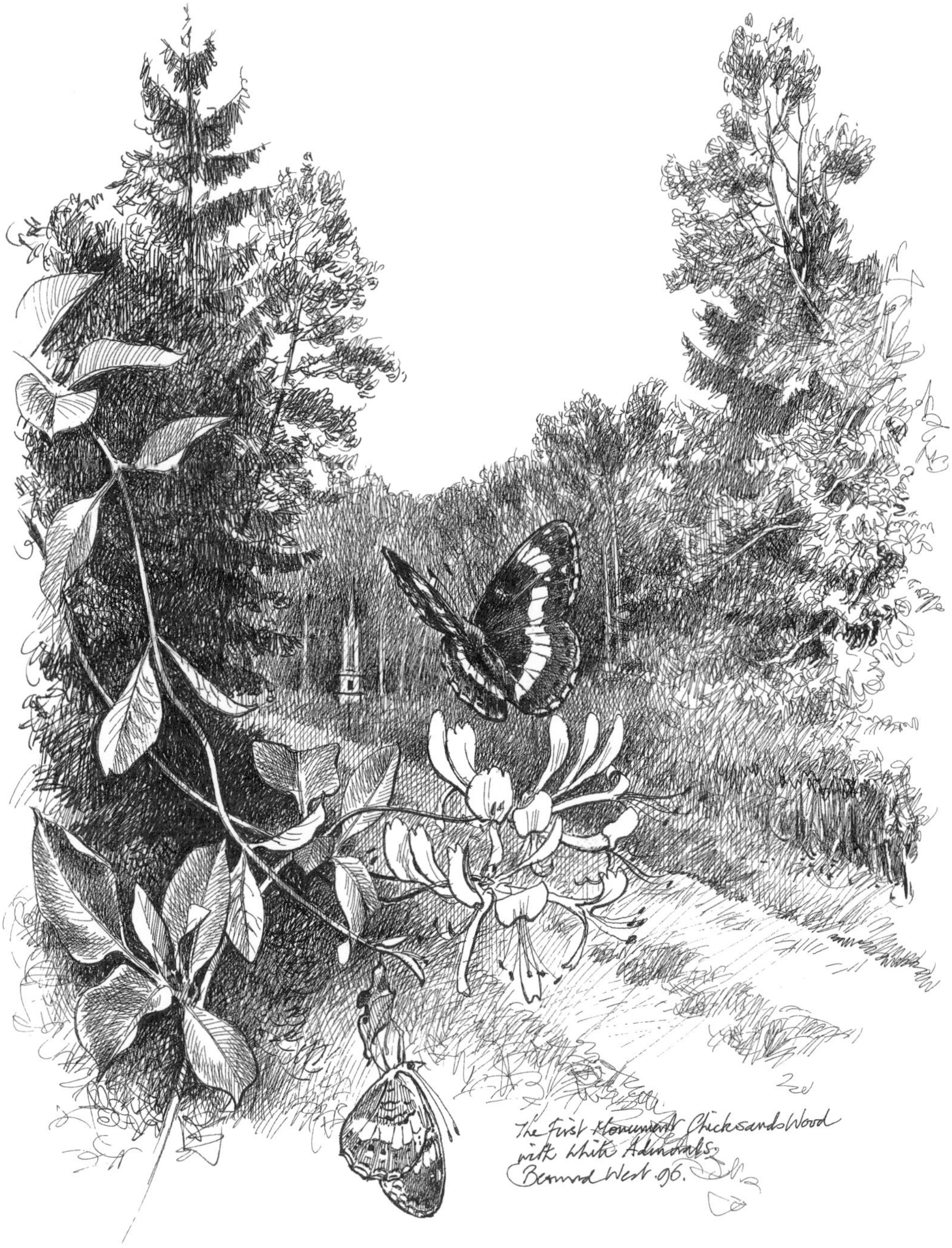

A Bedfordshire Wood. White Admirals in Chicksands Wood.

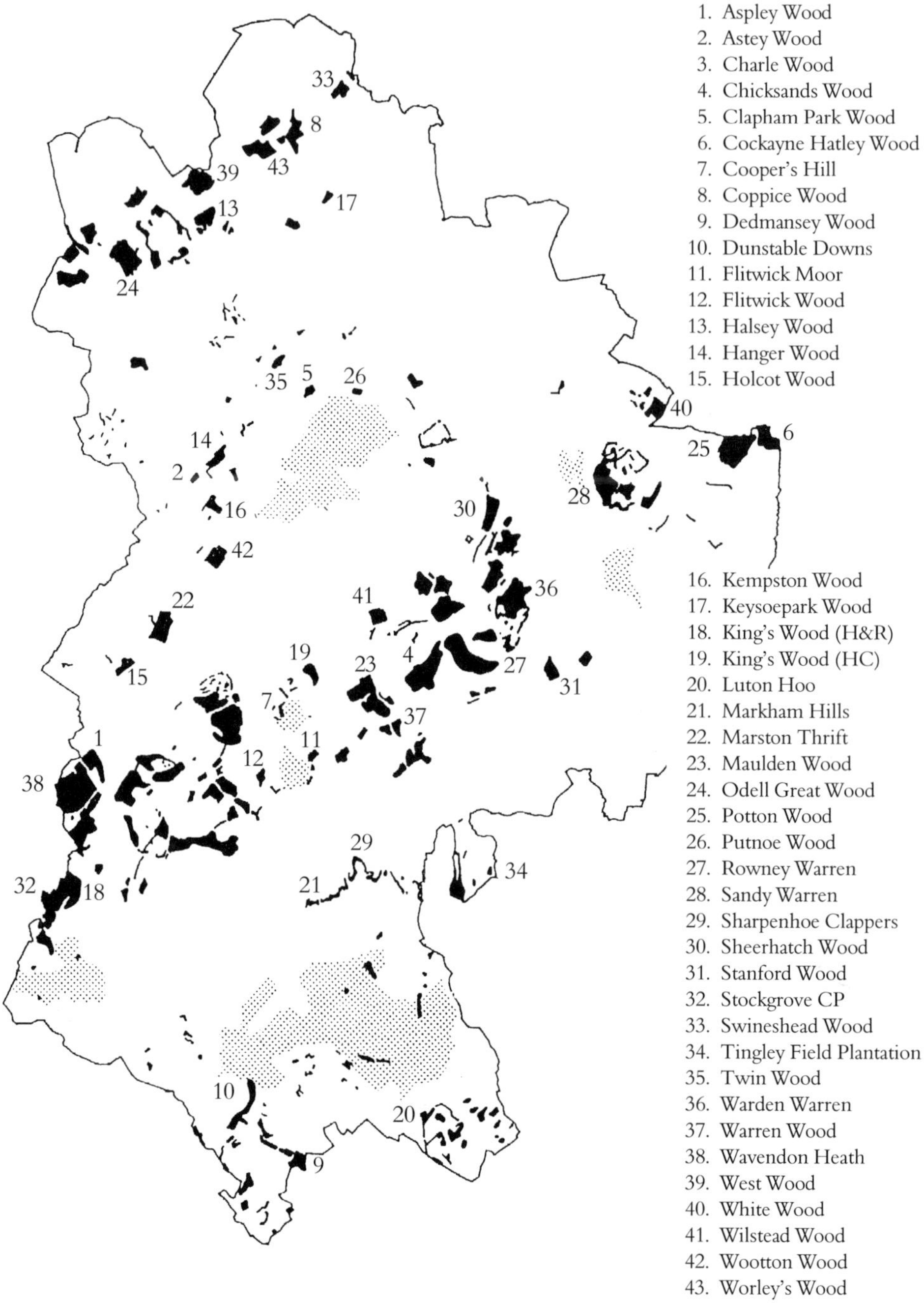

Figure 27 Bedfordshire woods and areas of downland scrub. (The shaded areas are the main towns.)

Woods on the southern clays.

There are a few woods both on the clay-with-flints cap on the chalk along the southern borders of the County and also in places on the steep scarp slopes. Although Pearl-bordered Fritillary and Silver-washed Fritillary were once found in Dedmansey Wood, these woods are not to known have supported the range of butterfly and moth species that have been found in the woods situated on the Greensand Ridge in the centre of the County and on the boulder clay in the north. However, the Dedmansey Wood complex (now about 49 ha) is only a relic of a much larger wood. Woodland in the area can be found in records dating back to 1295. The 1765 map shows the wood as including Oldhill Wood (now a housing estate) and a large area north of Buckwood Lane. On the maps of the 1930s, part of Dedmansey Wood is marked as rough pasture with scrub or trees and aerial photographs in the late 1940s show open areas, so it may well have been suitable for a wide range of species.

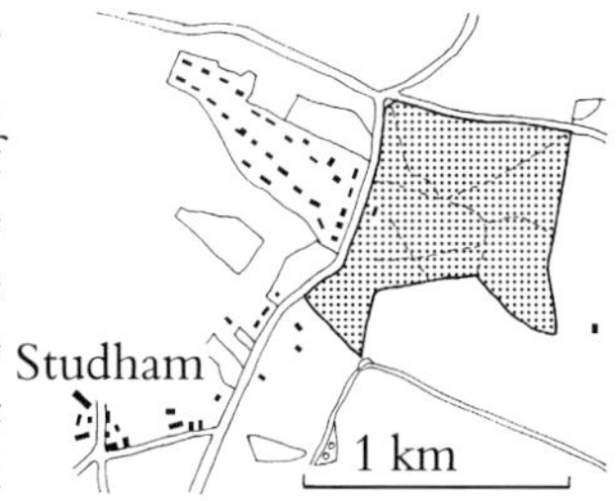

Dedmansey Wood

Woods on the Greensand Ridge

The Greensand Ridge extends diagonally across the County from Leighton Buzzard in the west to Sandy in the east, a distance of approximately 50 km. It contains some ancient broad-leaved woodlands and extensive coniferous plantations on former heathland of which only remnants survive. It is an area of great importance, especially for moths. The areas of bracken support Map-winged Swift. Orange Underwing and Yellow Horned fly round the birches. Broom is common on the sand and The Streak and Broom-tip can be found there while Pine Beauty, Pine Carpet and Pine Hawk-moth occur in the conifer plantations. True Lover's Knot and Beautiful Yellow Underwing frequent the few remnants of heather. Other characteristic species of the Greensand Ridge are Archer's Dart, Great Prominent and Rosy Footman.

There is not space here to mention all the many small woods of the region so we will concentrate on a few especially important sites.

King's Wood, Heath and Reach

At the south-west end of the Ridge near Leighton Buzzard is one of the more important woodland complexes in the County, namely Baker's Wood, Stockgrove Country Park and King's Wood, Heath and Reach. Much of this area of over 160 ha is ancient semi-natural woodland. References to King's Wood date back to 1307. The area contains a good variety of trees including oaks, birch and small-leaved lime as well as planted conifers. Before around 1950, King's Wood was noted by J.G.Dony (*in litt.*) as having "well maintained rides and rich vegetation" but in the early 1950s there was extensive felling and extraction of timber. At this time King's Wood was a prime site for

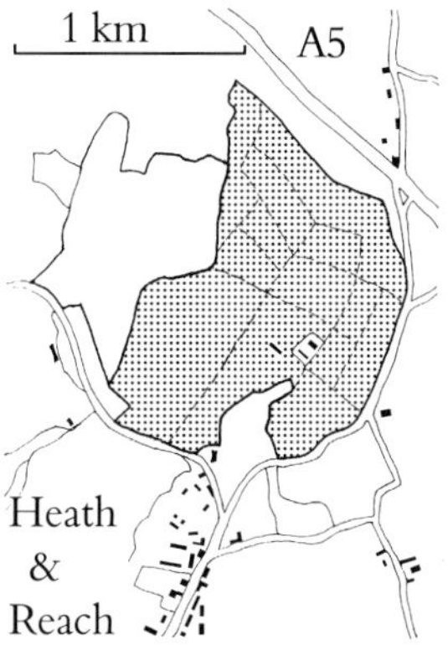

King's Wood, Heath & Reach

butterflies. S.H.Kershaw visited the wood every year from 1951 to 1958, often several times in the season and with J.B.Barnwell or S.W.Humphrey. Kershaw's notebooks, his published notes and his reports to the Nature Conservancy provide the best insight we have yet found into the changes that took place in a Bedfordshire wood during this critical period.

In his 1954 report to the Nature Conservancy and in his notebooks he listed 34 species of butterfly as currently or recently occurring in the wood. The list included all the British fritillaries except Heath and Glanville. Among the other species noted then were White Admiral, Green, Purple and White-letter Hairstreaks and Grizzled and Dingy Skippers.

Figure 28 King's Wood, Heath and Reach

There is also a reference to the past occurrence of Purple Emperor. Aerial photographs for that time show areas with a more open canopy favourable to these species and this accords with J.B.Barnwell's recollections of a much more open wood. This openness of structure may also have been a result of the felling mentioned above. Dony (1953) included a habitat study, made in 1949-50, of the plants in one of the areas dominated by birch and commented that the rides were well grazed by rabbits with herbage no more than an inch high. This close grazing is also evident in his photograph of another area of the wood with oak and bracken. Kershaw reported hares as well as rabbits in the wood. This grazing would have created ideal conditions for the fritillaries. Curiously, Dony did not record any species of violet at that survey point though he did find *Viola riviniana* as frequent at another point under an oak canopy. J.B.Barnwell recalled violets as abundant in some rides in the 1950s.

In his notebooks, Kershaw recorded seeing over 100 Pearl-bordered Fritillaries on 26 May and some 200 on 15 June 1955. He noted seeing 200 Silver-washed Fritillaries on 23 July 1956. The largest number of White Admirals noted on a single day was 50, also on 23 July 1956. High Brown, Dark Green and Small Pearl-bordered Fritillaries were in much smaller numbers. The latter was last seen in 1952. In his 1954 report he noted Marsh Fritillary "last seen 1950" and Purple Emperor "not seen for some years". It is not clear who made these observations as his notebooks suggest that he did not know of the wood until 1951. High Brown Fritillary was last noted in 1956 but he does not appear to have visited the wood in 1957 after 28 May.

J.B.Barnwell recalled that his visits to King's Wood with S.H.Kershaw started from the 'Fox and Hounds' on the A5 and that they found most butterflies in the north-eastern end of the wood. This agrees with the comment in one of Kershaw's notebooks that the path running south-west from the Dogs' Cemetery effectively formed the western boundary for Silver-washed Fritillary and White Admiral.

In his article in 1955, Kershaw described finding both ab. *nigrina* and ab. *semi-nigrina* of the White Admiral and also a remarkable aberration of the Silver-washed Fritillary, all on one day. It is clear from his notebook that the varieties of the White Admiral were not unusual and that ab. *valezina* of the Silver-washed Fritillary was also present. As indicated above, both these species were abundant at this time. However, on 2 June 1955 he noted there were no rabbits and the violets were "nearly hidden by other growing vegetation".

On 23 June 1958 Kershaw described the wood as "frightfully overgrown — rides and paths blocked by 6 ft poplars and birches (self sown)". By "poplars" we assume he meant aspens which are common in the wood. It seems then that conditions for these butterflies in King's Wood deteriorated very quickly as on his last visit to King's Wood on 24 May 1960 he could not find his favourite butterfly sites, though he did see Dingy Skipper, Orange Tip and Holly Blue. As in so many other woods, the rides became narrowed and shaded and the grass grew rank through lack of mowing and grazing by rabbits. All the fritillaries disappeared but the White Admiral survived or was able to recolonise because it prefers to lay its eggs on shaded honeysuckle. This contrasts with the Broad-bordered Bee Hawk-moth which needs honeysuckle in full sun and has not been seen in the wood for many years.

In the 1960s the wood was sold off in small lots as recreational plots. This may have prevented large-scale felling and replanting with conifers but the overall neglect, as well as localised damage and planting with exotic trees, did nothing to enhance butterfly populations. In recent years the Bedfordshire County Council and the local Wildlife Trust have bought plots as these came on the market and by 1993 they owned 39 ha, sufficient for their holdings to be designated a National Nature Reserve. A further 26.5 ha, owned by Redland Aggregates, was added to the National Nature Reserve in 1995.

A start has been made on widening rides, removal of some conifers and on the reinstatement of a coppice cycle but it is too early for any effect on butterfly and moth populations to be evident. Certainly violets could not be described as abundant in 1995. White Admiral, Purple Hairstreak and White-letter Hairstreak still survive in King's Wood and a single Purple Emperor was seen there in 1995. Wood White was seen in 1986 but has not been reported since. Butterflies of the wider rides include Large Skipper, Small Copper, Brown Argus and Common Blue. All the commoner 'browns' are present and in 1995 Marbled White was seen there again.

Spring Usher, a moth of the oak woodlands.

Pine Hawk-moth

Many species of macro-moth have been recorded in King's Wood. Among the species feeding on deciduous trees and shrubs are Lunar Hornet Moth, Large Red-belted Clearwing, Poplar Lutestring, Oak Lutestring, Birch Mocha, Maiden's Blush, Early Tooth-striped, Brindled White-spot, Lobster Moth, Great Prominent, Marbled Brown and Small Black Arches. Least Black Arches feeds on lichens. Other noteworthy species are Plain Wave, Chalk Carpet, Barred Rivulet and Satyr Pug.

Among the less common micro-moths in the wood are the oak-feeders *Ectoedemia albifasciella*, *Stigmella basiguttella* and *Ypsolopha ustella*. *Ectoedemia minimella*, *Stigmella confusella* and *Parornix betulae* are among the many species feeding on birches there. Mines of *Bucculatrix thoracella* occur on small-leaved lime.

Wavendon Heath and Aspley Wood area

North-east from King's Wood is a substantial area of woodland which lies astride the border with Buckinghamshire. On the Bedfordshire side are Lowe's Wood, Charle Wood, and Aspley Wood, covering 190 ha. These are shown on the 1765 map with slightly different boundaries and now consist of blocks of oak woodland, with varying degrees of canopy closure, and conifer plantations. Silver-washed Fritillary was once abundant here, including ab. *valezina*, and White Admiral was common but only the occasional individual of the latter is now seen. Wavendon Heath (165 ha) contains some of the oldest conifer plantations in the County. From the number of moths coming to light, the main colony of the Pine Hawk-moth in Bedfordshire appears to be in this area.

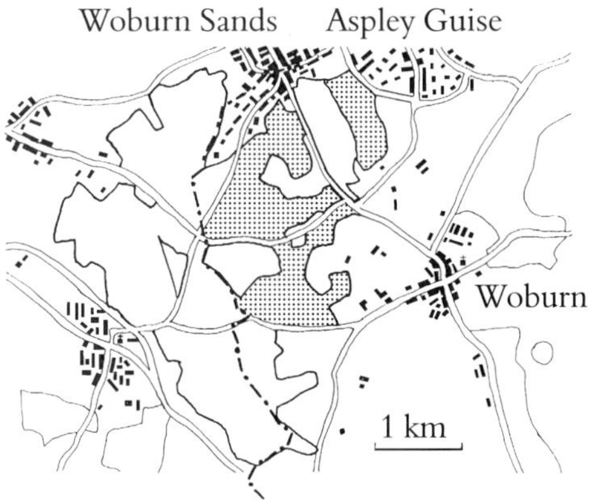

Woods around Wavendon Heath

Flitwick Moor

A few kilometres south of Ampthill in the Flit valley is Flitwick Moor (about 55 ha), a partially wooded area of quite different character, owned by the Wildlife Trust. The 'moor' is a valley mire containing the remains of extensive diggings from which peat was extracted until the 1950s for use in gas purification systems. A falling water table has caused the area to dry out and birch and oak woodland has become established. Purple Hairstreak can be seen around the oaks and White Admiral has occasionally appeared there but the moth fauna is especially important. Yellow Horned, Orange Underwing, Peacock Moth, Scarce Prominent, The Suspected, *Phylloporia bistrigella*, *Parornix betulae* and *Cochylis nana* are associated with birches. In the damp areas the May Highflyer and Dingy Shell feed on alder and the Southern Wainscot, Small Rufous, Silky Wainscot and Silver Hook feed on or in various reeds and grasses. Other local species are The Mocha, Marsh Pug, Small Seraphim, Little Thorn, Round-winged Muslin, Four-dotted Footman and The Butterbur.

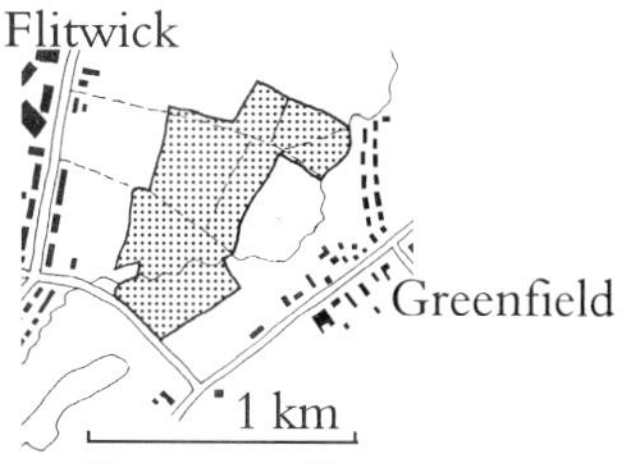

Flitwick Moor

North-east again from Flitwick Moor are four important woods covering more than 450 ha and currently managed by Forest Enterprise, wholly or in part. These are Maulden Wood, Chicksands Wood, Wilstead Wood and Rowney Warren.

Maulden Wood

The northern half of Maulden Wood on the clay soils corresponds approximately with the wood shown on the 1765 map. It contains areas of oak and ash with some conifers. The southern part of the wood, on the sands, is mostly planted with conifers, a process which started in the 1920s.

The moth fauna of Maulden Wood has been well studied, including a special winter investigation (Arnold *et al.*, 1976 & 1977). Conifer-feeding species include Pine Carpet, Spruce Carpet, Pine Hawk-moth, *Batrachedra pinicolella*, *Olethreutes bifasciana*, the Spotted Shoot Moth (*Rhyacionia pinivorana*), *Dioryctria abietella* and *Assara terebrella*. Broom is abundant on the sand and supports Grass Emerald, The Streak and Broom-tip. On the oaks there are Yellow-legged Clearwing, Oak Lutestring, Brindled White-spot, Marbled Brown, Lunar Marbled Brown, Oak Nycteoline, *Ectoedemia atrifrontella*, *Phyllonorycter lautella*, *Teleiodes luculella* and *Acrobasis consociella*.

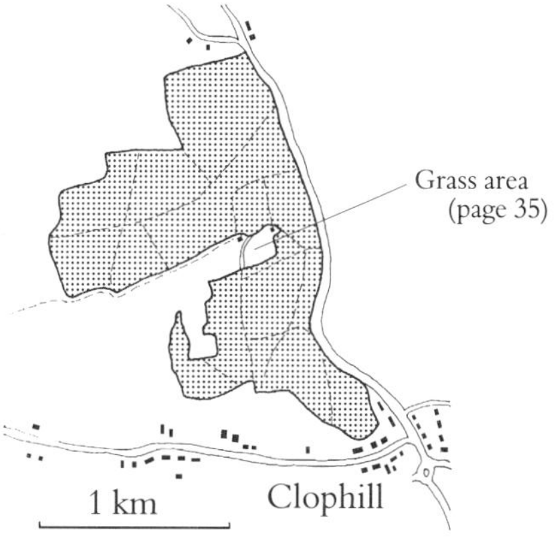

Maulden Wood

Other deciduous trees support Lunar Hornet Moth, Poplar Lutestring, Common Lutestring, Orange Underwing, Light Orange Underwing, Clay Triple-lines, Slender Pug, The Seraphim, Orange Moth, Poplar Kitten, Lobster Moth, Pale-lemon Sallow, *Ectoedemia minimella* and *Stigmella confusella*. Additional local species found there include: Map-winged Swift, Beautiful Carpet, Sharp-angled Carpet, Barred Rivulet, Rosy Footman and Marbled White-spot.

Among the butterflies, Wood White has been seen sporadically in Maulden Wood since the mid 1970s. White-letter Hairstreak was also present in the 1970s but has not been seen recently.

Chicksands Wood and Wilstead Wood

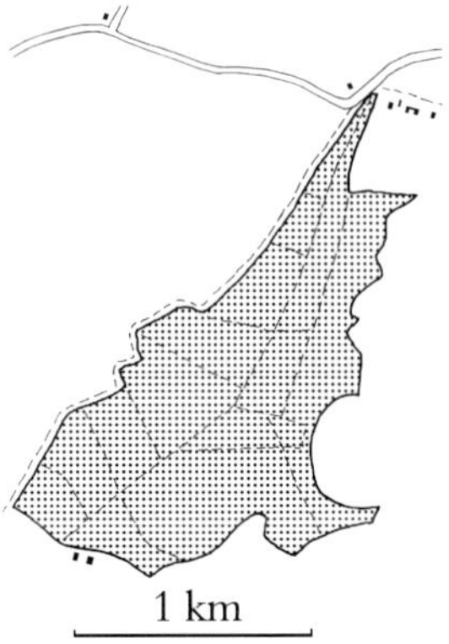

Chicksands Wood

Chicksands Wood is an ancient broad-leaved wood which was once continuous through parkland around Chicksands Priory with Campton Plantation. In the distant past the woodlands in the area must have been quite impressive. When the Norman tower of Ely Cathedral collapsed in 1322 the only accessible place where the builders could obtain the huge timbers needed for the Octagon was Chicksands Priory. Chicksands Wood was recorded as coppice woodland in the early 1930s (Anon, 1929-31). Unfortunately we know little of the butterflies and moths at that time, although the Large Tortoiseshell was to be seen there. The wood was still largely broad-leaved in 1948 but was extensively clear-felled in the 1950s and replanted with conifers. In recent years it has become the major site in the County for White-letter Hairstreak on the surviving wych elms. In 1989 the White Admiral appeared there and subsequently increased in numbers to form what is probably the largest population in the County. The wide rides support most of the commoner species and the total butterfly fauna is 30 species. The moths of Chicksands Wood have not been studied.

Although much of Wilstead Wood is on a north-facing slope, the butterfly fauna is very similar to that of Chicksands Wood but it is less well known. It was also shown as coppice in Anon (1929-31).

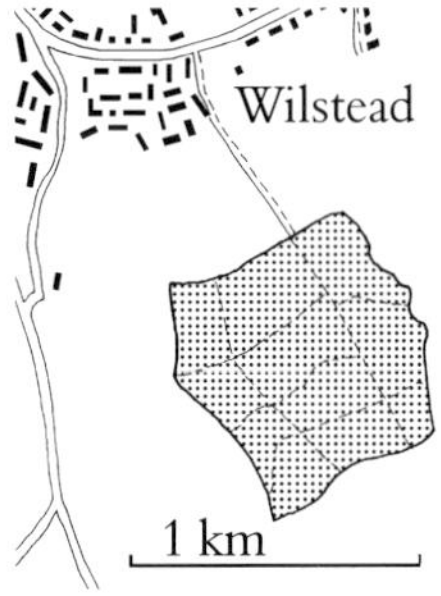

Wilstead Wood

Rowney Warren

On Thomas Jefferys' map of 1765, Rowney Warren is shown as treeless but by the mid-1800s it evidently contained a scattering of trees. Even in the mid 1950s, it still contained a substantial area of heathland and mature birch trees but was fringed by conifer plantations, some of which were planted in the early 1920s. By 1960 the birch trees had been felled and all the heathland planted with conifers. Butterfly transect walks were done in 1989-91 and 18 species recorded. Moths have been little studied recently but Foster (1934) listed the conifer-feeding Larch Pug, Tawny-barred Angle, Bordered White and Barred Red and the heather-feeding True Lover's Knot and Heath Rustic. He also listed Broad-bordered Bee Hawk-moth, Bird's Wing, Autumnal Rustic, Golden-rod Brindle, Chevron, The Engrailed, and Yellow Horned.

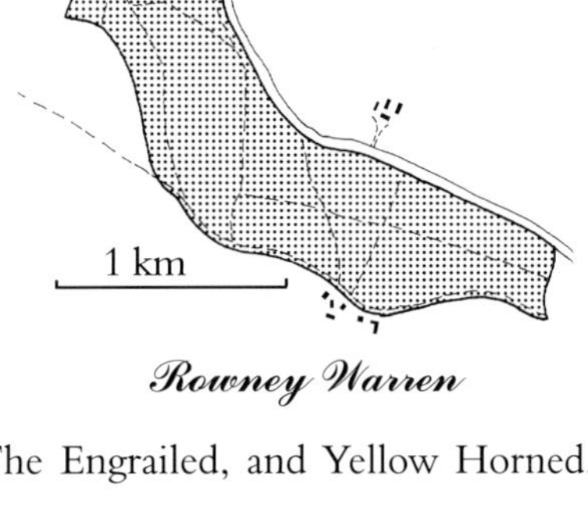

Rowney Warren

Among recent records of micro-moths that feed on conifers are *Argyresthia laevigatella*, *Cedestis gysseleniella*, *Exoteleia dodecella*, *Olethreutes bifasciana*, the Spotted Shoot Moth (*Rhyacionia pinivorana*) and *Dioryctria abietella*.

Bordered White

Sandy Warren

The Lodge at Sandy Warren is the headquarters of the Royal Society for the Protection of Birds and the surrounding woodland and heath is managed as a nature reserve. Although the 1765 map may not be reliable on this aspect, the area is not shown as wooded so it may have been largely heath at that time. Although no unusual butterflies breed there, a good number of moths has been recorded including heathland species, such as Narrow-winged Pug, True Lover's Knot, The Streak, Broom-tip, conifer-feeding species such as Pine Hawk-moth and species of deciduous woodland such as Hornet Moth, Yellow Horned, Small Brindled Beauty, Lobster Moth, Great Prominent, The Olive and Nut-tree Tussock. The lichen-feeding Rosy Footman can also be found in good numbers there.

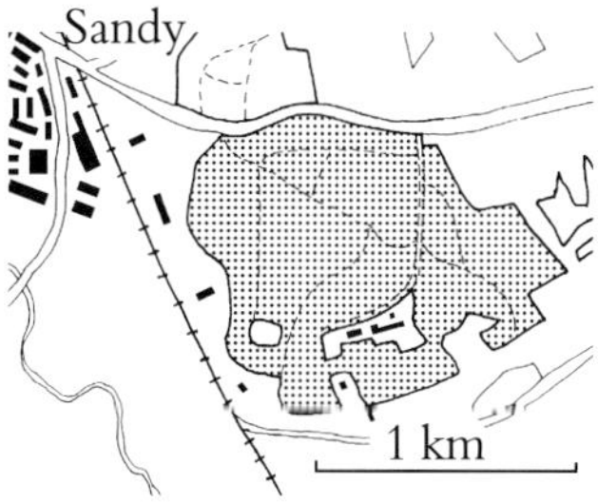

Sandy Warren

White Wood

White Wood, just inside the county boundary near Gamlingay and at the far eastern end of the Greensand Ridge, was a site for the Chequered Skipper in the early 1800s but this butterfly has long since disappeared. J.C.Dale found the Lace Border there in 1819. B.O.C.Gardiner ran a moth trap there for one night in June 1957 and recorded an impressive list of 76 species, including the Heart Moth, the only record in the County this century. The site has not been surveyed entomologically in recent years. Across most of the wood the canopy is now closed and there are few habitats for butterflies.

Woods on the eastern boulder clays

Potton Wood

Potton Wood is an ancient wood, currently managed by Forest Enterprise, lying alongside the county boundary with Cambridgeshire. It is part of a complex of ancient woodlands on the chalky boulder clay including Gamlingay, Hayley and Waresley woods in Cambridgeshire. It is discussed in detail in the next chapter because its butterfly fauna has been the subject of extensive monitoring for the last 20 years. To-date 31 species of butterflies have been recorded there. Of the moths, the Maple Prominent, Yellow-legged Clearwing, Light Orange Underwing, Green Arches and Black Arches are of note.

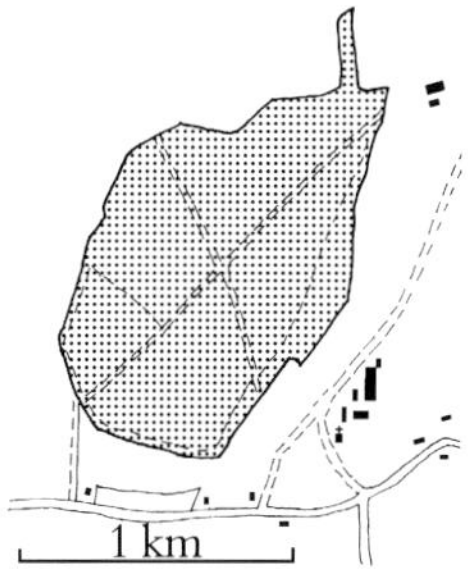

Potton Wood

Figure 29 Marston Thrift from the air in 1946. Note the scrubby area in the southern corner and open areas elsewhere in the wood.

Woods in the Marston Vale

Marston Thrift

The Marston Vale to the north of the Greensand Ridge contains one wood, Marston Thrift which is notable for the discovery there in 1984 of a colony of the Black Hairstreak. At that time this species was thought to be extinct in the County. Whether this is an ancient or recent colony is not known but the wood itself has occupied much the same area (61 ha) for at least 200 years. The wood was shown as coppice in Anon (1929-31). Aerial photographs from 1946 (Figure 29) indicate that the wood was then a more suitable habitat for Black Hairstreak than it has been in recent years (*c.f.* Figure 30). The south-west edge of the wood is bordered by a green lane fringed with blackthorn which would seem ideal hairstreak habitat were it not for the heavy deposit of dust from the adjacent landfill site.

Figure 30 Marston Thrift from the air in 1991. Most of the open areas in the previous photograph are now overgrown but the results of clearance work on the main ride are beginning to show.

The wood itself contains extensive areas of blackthorn, though much is heavily shaded at present. Detailed surveys of both the Black Hairstreak and the blackthorn in the wood are underway with the aim of formulating a management plan specifically for the protection of this butterfly. Marston Thrift contains areas of oak, birch, ash and elm with some conifer plantation. It was extensively clear-felled in the 1950s and much of the birch and ash is subsequent regrowth. The wood is managed as a nature reserve by Bedfordshire County Council and a great deal of work has been done in recent years to clear and widen rides (Plate 22). White-letter Hairstreak and White Admiral are present. Wood White was seen there in the mid-1980s and again in 1996. Local moths recorded from the Thrift include the following species which feed on deciduous trees: Scarce Prominent, Poplar Lutestring,

Frosted Green, Light Orange Underwing, The Tissue and Poplar Kitten, *Ectoedemia minimella*, *Caloptilia betulicola* and *Hypatima rhomboidella*. The tortricid *Epinotia nanana*, which feeds on spruces, has been found there.

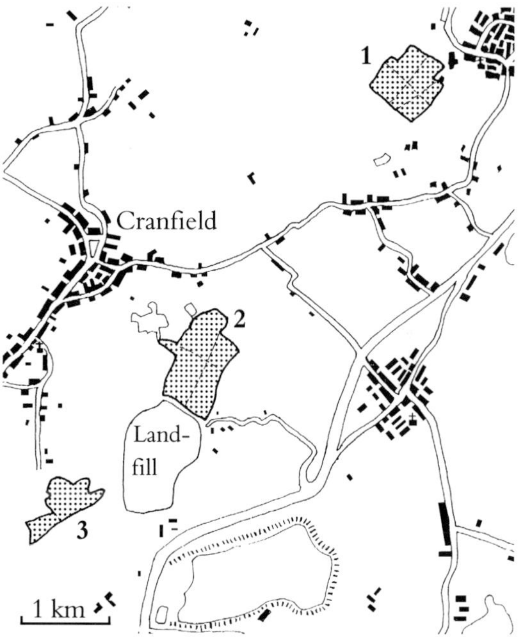

Wootton Wood (1), Marston Thrift (2) and Holcot Wood (3)

Holcot and Wootton Woods

Near Marston Thrift are Holcot Wood and Wootton Wood. They have been little explored entomologically and may contain surprises as in 1995 a single Black Hairstreak was seen in Wootton Wood. It seems unlikely that this sedentary butterfly would have crossed the 3 km of agricultural land from Marston Thrift, particularly in a year when numbers there were low, so there may be a previously unknown colony in Wootton Wood. Holcot Wood and the adjacent Brogborough Manor Farm were bought in 1992 by the Woodland Trust. Trees have now been planted in several fields to form a new wood, Reynold Wood. When these mature the area of woodland will be greatly extended. This planting is part of the Marston Vale Community Forest Project which aims to increase the area of woodland in the Vale from 3.6% to around 30% by the year 2003. If suitable species are planted and management is sympathetic, this could lead to a substantial increase in habitat for woodland species of Lepidoptera.

Woods on the northern wolds

North of the valley of the Great Ouse is the area of boulder clay which overlies the oolitic limestone in the north of the County. This is a quiet and attractive part of the County with many buildings constructed from the local limestone. The woodlands here are now fragmented but no doubt would once have been part of an extensive natural forest which included Salcey and Rockingham Forests and crossed Bedfordshire from the Turvey area towards Eaton Socon. Unlike most of the chalk downland sites and many of the woods on the Greensand Ridge, the majority of these woods are privately owned and the Lepidoptera have been surveyed in less detail. The moths of the northern woods include the Small Eggar, Blotched Emerald, Small Brindled Beauty, Marbled Brown, Lunar Marbled Brown, Purple Clay, Green Arches, The Olive and Scarce Silver-lines.

These northern woodlands were not always so quiet as they may seem today. Anyone who walks through Coppice Wood from Riseley to Melchbourne will be walking along a concrete road rather than a grassy woodland ride. The concrete roads in this area cover many miles and originate from the Second World War, when large numbers of American airmen were stationed in this area of Bedfordshire. What appear to be 'laybys' diverge from the roads at regular intervals (Figure 31). These were the dispersal areas for the munitions for the 8th Airforce bomber bases at Chelveston, Kimbolton, Little Staughton, Thurleigh and Podington. For a few years the peace of rural Bedfordshire was shattered by the roar of Flying Fortresses and Liberators (and perhaps by the music of Major Glenn Miller's Orchestra which was based for a while at Milton Ernest). Dony (1953) comments several times on these woods suffering botanically during the war but, in the absence of detailed records, what lasting damage was done to Lepidoptera populations by the felling of trees and concreting of the rides will never be known. The old dispersal bays now make good moth-trapping sites with easy access for equipment.

Figure 31 Coppice Wood, Melchbourne, from the air in 1947, showing the concrete roads and dispersal points for wartime munitions.

Clapham Park Wood

Clapham Park Wood, just north-west of Bedford, deserves special mention as the favourite haunt of the father of Bedfordshire entomology, the Rev. Charles Abbot. It was here he added the Chequered Skipper to the British list in 1798 and found an impressive list of other species in what even then was quite a small wood (now 11 ha). Perhaps these species were present in most of the other woods in the County at that time but Abbot seems to have concentrated on one site near his home, understandable in view of the difficulties of travelling any distance by horse. After Abbot's death in 1817, the eminent Victorian entomologist, J.C.Dale paid several visits to the wood, possibly influenced by Abbot's list of captures. Apart from sporadic records, such as H.W. Finlinson's sighting of Duke of Burgundy there in around 1895, the wood appears to have been neglected by succeeding entomologists. The reason is unclear and one can only speculate that the owners restricted access. Although R.M. Craske obtained access in the 1920s and B.B.West found High Brown Fritillary in Clapham Park in 1943, Dony (1953) referred to Clapham Park Wood as "inaccessible". Whatever the reason, we have no information on when Chequered Skipper, Purple Emperor and other species died out there. During the late 1970s, management of the wood was taken over by Bedfordshire County Council and a coppice cycle was reinstated but the effects of these improvements on Lepidoptera have not been monitored.

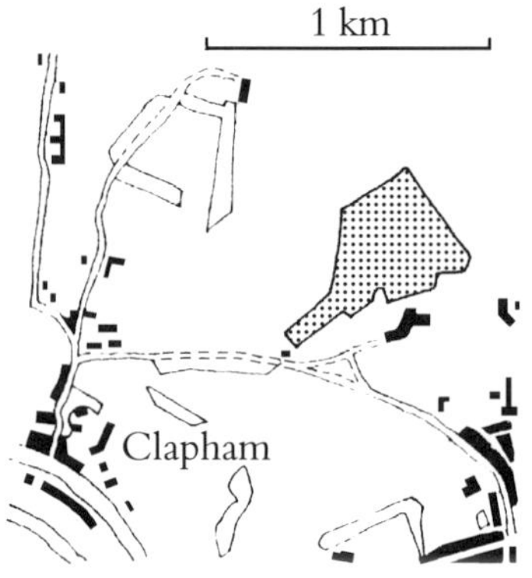

Clapham Park Wood

Odell Great Wood

At 115 ha in area, this is one of the largest units of woodland in the north of the County. The butterflies there have been observed for some 50 years by J.H.Payne who has visited the wood regularly. Odell Great Wood appears to have been almost as rich in butterfly species as King's Wood, Heath and Reach, with Pearl-bordered, Silver-washed, High Brown and Dark Green Fritillaries being present in the 1940s.

The rides radiating from the central crossing are clearly marked on the 1765 map so the wood has retained its present layout for over 200 years. It was extensively cut over probably in the 1920s (Anon, 1929-31). Comparison between aerial photographs taken in 1947 and 1991 shows the canopy closed and the rides narrowed in the latter. The White Admiral is still present in Odell Great Wood as also is Wood White. Moths found in and around the wood include Small Eggar, Poplar Lutestring and Beautiful Carpet.

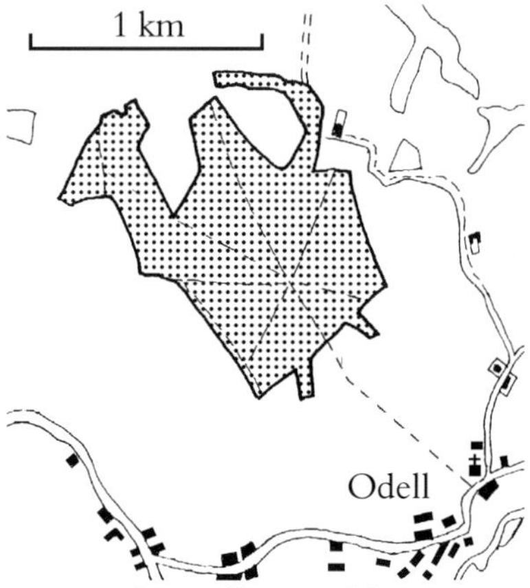

Odell Great Wood

West Wood

White Admiral has been seen in every year since 1983 in West Wood, which currently is managed by Forest Enterprise. This is the longest series of sightings of this species in any wood in the County. Wood White was also present there in the late 1970s. West Wood (82.5 ha) is an ancient oak wood which has retained most of its broad-leaf cover. Extensive areas have been coppiced in recent years and it will be interesting to note any changes in the butterfly and moth species present. Macro-moths recorded there include the tree-feeding species Poplar Lutestring, Yellow Horned, Small Brindled Beauty, Spring Usher and Oak Nycteoline as well as Barred Rivulet, Satyr Pug, Green Arches and Marbled White Spot. The micro-moths of the wood have been well studied and there is a long list of oak-feeding species including *Ectoedemia albifasciella*, *Ypsolopha alpella*, *Stenolechia gemmella*, *Teleiodes luculella*, *Strophedra nitidana* and *Cryptoblabes bistriga*.

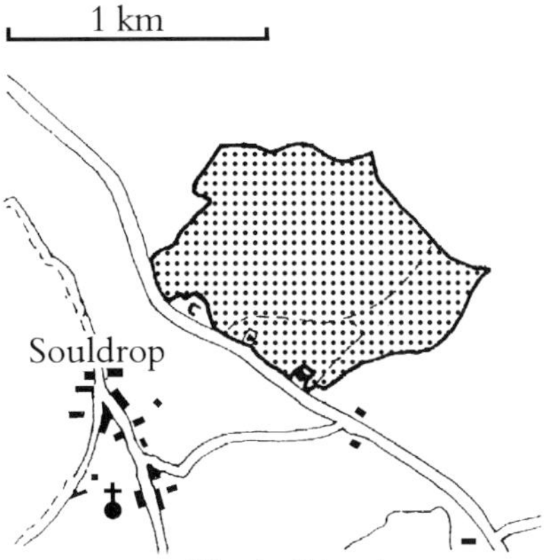

West Wood

Keysoepark Wood

Another wood where changes can be seen from aerial photographs is Keysoepark Wood which lies between Riseley and Keysoe, north-east of Bedford. In the mid-1800s this wood was more than three-times its present size (about 14 ha) but large sections were cleared for agriculture probably during the First World War. Black Hairstreak was found in Keysoepark Wood in 1944 and, until the early 1970s when it was last reported there, this wood was the only known locality in the County. Aerial photographs taken in 1945 (figure 32) show a wood with scrubby areas eminently suitable for this species. However between 1963 and 1965, 5.4 ha of the wood including some of the scrubby areas were cleared and planted with conifers. Aerial photographs from 1991 (figure 33) show clearly how the canopy of the wood had closed in the space of 46 years. This probably influenced the decline of the Black Hairstreak more than the conifer planting. Despite searches, none have been seen in recent years though a little sheltered blackthorn survives in sunny situations. It is possible that the species may still be present in numbers too small to be easily found.

Heathland Habitats

Saunders (1911) recorded heather as "common" and even in 1953 Dony could describe it as "frequent on heaths and in heathy places on the Lower Greensand and Clay-with-Flints". Today most of the areas of the Greensand Ridge which in the past were heather or grass heath have been lost to agriculture or conifer plantations, such as those on Wavendon Heath and Rowney Warren. Wavendon Heath and Aspley Wood have been quarried for fullers' earth. There is some re-colonisation by heather and other heathland plants on the restored land but, unless there is action to retain the area as heath, it will be shaded out by new conifer

Figure 32 Keysoepark Wood in 1945, a year after Black Hairstreak had been found there.

Figure 33 Keysoepark Wood from the air in 1991. Note how the canopy has closed in comparison with figure 32.

Figure 34 Cooper's Hill .

plantations. Two species whose larvae feed on bilberry, the Beautiful Snout and the tortricid *Anchylis myrtillana* have been found at Wavendon and Aspley Heaths.

The largest remnant of heather heathland in Bedfordshire is on the Wildlife Trust's reserve of Cooper's Hill at Ampthill. Maintenance there is a continuous struggle against fires and invading birch scrub and bracken. The reserve contains few butterflies but a typical heathland moth fauna, such as Archer's Dart and the heather-feeding species True Lover's Knot, Beautiful Yellow Underwing, Narrow-winged Pug, *Coleophora juncicolella*, *Aristotelia ericinella* and *Neofaculta ericetella*. Elsewhere only small remnants of heather remain, as on the RSPB reserve at the Lodge, Sandy where the heather-feeding *Coleophora pyrrhulipennella* has been found. There are plans to try to restore heathland on other sites on the Greensand Ridge from which it has been lost.

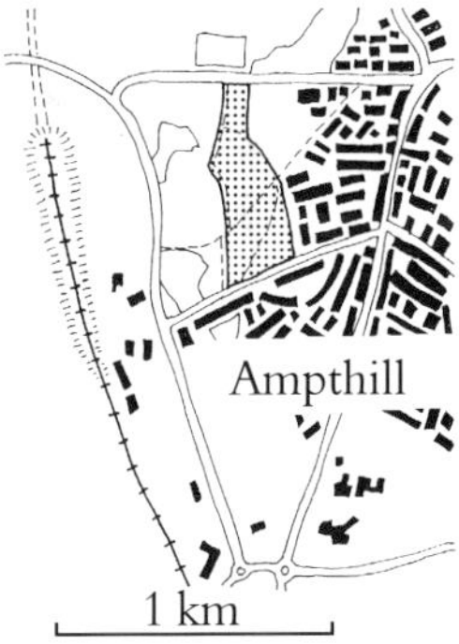

Cooper's Hill

Names such as Whipsnade Heath are the only trace left in Bedfordshire of the heathlands which once existed on the top of the chalk downs although tiny fragments can be found nearby in Hertfordshire.

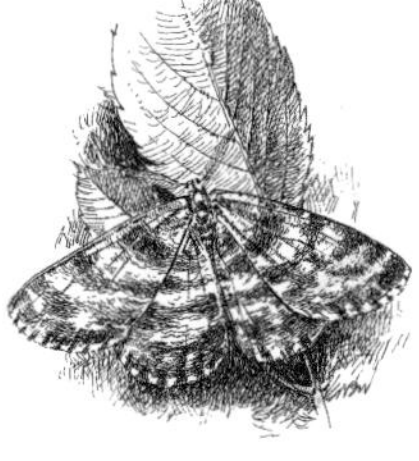

Common Heath

Bedfordshire records of the two typical butterflies of southern heathlands are enigmatic. The Grayling was recorded at Barton Hills in 1798 and at nearby Ravensburgh Castle in 1944. It was also reported from Clapham around 1915. The two more recent records are doubtful. For the Silver-studded Blue there is only a rather uncertain record by Abbot, with no locality given, and a more reliable record by J.C.Dale who found it in 1819 just outside the county border on Gamlingay Heath. (See also Page 232.)

Linear Habitats

Hedgerows, Green Lanes and Road Verges.

Searching for butterflies in the areas of the County dominated by intensive agriculture can be a rather depressing experience. Most hedgerows as well as footpaths and bridleways along field edges have probably been subjected over the years to drift from agricultural insecticides and herbicides and yield few records, although some surprising exceptions, mostly broader tracks, were found during recent surveys. With horse-drawn ploughs and the early tractor-drawn versions, a headland had to be left for turning and this allowed hedgerows to become relatively broad corridors where wildlife could live and disperse. Modern ploughs can be used to cultivate close to the base of a hedge so greatly reducing the value of the corridor. By contrast, some of the surviving green lanes with hedges on both sides can be very productive of butterflies with 10 or more species visible on a short visit. There are some excellent sites of this type in the north-east of the County around Upper and Lower Dean and Swineshead. Ashwell Green Lane (Plate 63) has been a noted site for many years (22 butterfly species). Road verges, especially the wider ones, and the small corners of rough ground where road lines have been altered are usually rather less productive but nevertheless very important as butterfly habitats. The verges of new roads appear to be colonised rapidly, especially by the grass-feeding species of butterfly and good numbers of day-flying moths are often evident. Good current examples are the verges of the Millbrook to Millbrook Station road, the Leighton Buzzard by-pass (Figure 35) and

Wall Brown, the butterfly of footpaths and bridleways.

Latticed Heath, a common moth which can be seen on road verges

In spring the Hebrew Character feeds at sallow blossoms in hedgerows

Figure 35 A road verge – the Leighton Buzzard by-pass in 1993 shortly after completion, a potentially valuable habitat for butterflies and moths.

Figure 36 A road verge near Thurleigh mown very wide, perhaps unnecessarily so. The cuttings left lying will smother many herbaceous plants.

Thurleigh Cutting. In the 1950s, R.C.Revels found 24 species of butterflies along the line of the south-bound carriageway of the A1 at Topler's Hill, near Edworth. The site was destroyed in the mid 1950s when the dual carriageway was built.

Wetlands

Only a few patches of natural wetland survive in the river valleys of Bedfordshire. The floras of Abbot (1798) and Saunders (1911) mention sites such as Ampthill Bogs and Potton Marsh which have long since been drained and converted to agriculture or used for building. Even the wetland at Flitwick Moor (see page 43) is largely artificial as seen today. The County is well-endowed with areas of water resulting from more recent workings. Examples are the gravel workings along the Ouse Valley at Felmersham Nature Reserve, Harrold-Odell Country Park and Priory Country Park at Bedford. The Ivel Valley also contains extensive flooded gravel workings around Arlesey. In the Marston Vale, clay extraction for the brickworks has produced some valuable wetland sites though unfortunately there is considerable economic pressure for them to be drained and filled with rubbish.

There are now no butterflies peculiar to wetland sites in Bedfordshire though, if the old records for Swallowtail and Large Copper are to be believed, such sites may have been richer in the past. Recently Dingy and Grizzled Skippers have been found around some of the clay pits but this is because some of their foodplants, such as creeping cinquefoil and common bird's-foot-trefoil, are early colonisers of the bare soil there. Generally the damp areas provide valuable habitats for the grass-feeding species of butterfly and the hemp-agrimony that often grows there is a much-used nectar source. There are, however, some wetland moths such as Red-tipped Clearwing feeding on willows. The Bulrush Wainscot, Large Wainscot and Southern Wainscot feed on reeds. The Butterbur and Round-winged Muslin can also be found.

Urban Areas

Flowers in town gardens and parks provide important nectar sources for butterflies but few breed regularly in the urban environment. The main exceptions are the Large and Small Whites — the 'cabbage whites' and the nettle-feeders, *i.e.* Peacock, Small Tortoiseshell, Red Admiral and to some extent Comma. The only truly urban 'blue' is the Holly Blue which in peak years has been found regularly in Bedford and Luton. The skippers and 'browns' are normally found only in small areas of countryside and wasteground that have become "trapped" within the urban sprawl. An example is Hill Rise in Bedford where 21 species of butterfly were recorded in 1993-95. The same is not true for moths, many of whose foodplants are

The Holly Blue is the only blue butterfly seen commonly in urban gardens. Its numbers fluctuate widely, due largely to parasitism by the wasp Listrodromus nycthemerus.

common in gardens. Trap catches in gardens seem to have declined during recent years. It is not clear whether this is due merely to competition between the trap as a light source and the more widespread and powerful street lighting. Alternatively it is possible that the street lighting is itself causing a decline in moth populations. The subject is complicated and has been reviewed recently by Outen (1995). Another possible cause for the decline may be increased predation by garden birds whose winter survival is aided by artificial feeding.

The larvae of Blair's Shoulder Knot feed on garden cypress plants

The Future

So far this chapter has been largely a catalogue of the devastation that has been wrought on butterfly and moth populations by intensive agriculture, urban development and changed management of woodlands. What, if anything, can be done to repair the damage and allow the butterflies and moths of Bedfordshire to flourish once again ?

This is not the place to set out detailed prescriptions for habitat management. Books by Fry and Lonsdale (1991), Kirby (1992) and Pullin (1995) provide extensive reviews and there are a number of publications on management of particular habitats, such as chalk grasslands (Butterflies Under Threat Team (BUTT), 1986), coppiced woodlands (Fuller & Warren, 1993) and woodland glades and rides (Warren & Fuller, 1993). Moreover, management plans will already have been prepared for sites managed specifically for wildlife. There are nevertheless a few generalisations that are perhaps worth making. The first priority is to encourage owners of sites to manage them in a way which is sympathetic to Lepidoptera. However, butterflies and moths are but a small part of the total fauna of a site and ways must be found to integrate the management with that for species of other groups.

Grassland

Sympathetic management means not only managing for the rarest or most interesting species but ensuring that there is the necessary diversity to allow all species characteristic of a habitat to flourish. Chalk downland may need to be kept close-cropped for blues and Silver-spotted Skipper, but with sufficient long grass to maintain good numbers of Marbled White and other 'browns' and enough scrub left to provide shelter and perch sites for Duke of Burgundy and Green Hairstreak. The requirements of various species for swards of different heights is described by the Butterflies Under Threat Team (1986). It is difficult enough for site managers to control grazing to maintain a consistent sward height from year to year, given the variations in the growth of plants and in the intensity of uncontrolled rabbit grazing. The need to maintain a mosaic of small habitats within an isolated site adds greatly to the complications. Dividing the site into compartments may be the only solution but it is expensive and may not be aesthetically acceptable in the landscape.

Most of the remaining chalk downland in Bedfordshire is currently owned or managed by public or voluntary bodies such as the County Council, Luton Borough Council, the National Trust and the Wildlife Trust. Some scrub clearance has been done by contractors and a great deal by volunteer groups. While much has been achieved since the mid 1970s, these methods may not be sustainable or cost-effective in the long-term. Grazing seems likely to be the main technique for downland maintenance as it was in the past but there is still much to be resolved in terms of the most suitable animals and their management specifications. Not the least among the problems is the integration of grazing with access by the many visitors and local people who increasingly use the downs for recreation. The grazing experiments with sheep that are currently under way on popular recreational sites, such as Whipsnade and Dunstable Downs, combined with monitoring of butterflies there, are hopeful pointers for the future. The studies on scrub control with goats at Smithcombe may also lead to the development of sustainable and cost-effective techniques. It is ironical that the decline of the rabbit in the 1950s led to the decline and extinction of several species of butterfly in the County, and may well have been a contributory factor in all cases, while at present rabbit populations have increased to such an extent on some sites that they are regarded as a threat in themselves. Effective management of rabbits is essential for their grazing to make a useful contribution to maintaining a mosaic of sward types without producing the dramatic destruction of which they are capable.

The restoration of herb-rich grassland from improved pasture or arable is a very long-term process. According to some authorities, it may take several decades or even a century before the number of species will approach that of an undisturbed sward. Nevertheless, artificial seeding with wild flowers and some larval foodplants of the Lepidoptera can produce useful results in the short term, provided the seed is from native stock. Evidence for this can be seen in the abundance of butterflies and day-flying moths on recently reclaimed sites, such as Bromham Lake nature reserve (21 butterfly species).

In recent years, the appearance of the agricultural landscape has been altered considerably by the introduction of 'set-aside'. The objective of this European Community scheme was not wildlife conservation but the reduction of surplus stocks of agricultural produce, especially cereals. Although the 'set-aside' may provide additional breeding areas for the commoner and more mobile species of Lepidoptera, the scheme is too short-term in nature and too liable to change to contribute much to the conservation of the more endangered species. A long-term scheme to encourage farmers to leave a few metres uncultivated around field margins, and perhaps to allow hedgerows to spread out by even a metre on each side, would have greater value for conservation in general and for Lepidoptera in particular.

Woodlands

In woodlands, canopy, coppice and ride management need to be reinstated where appropriate. Again much more needs to be learned before sustainable management techniques can be evolved for each site. First attempts at re-introducing coppice cycles often seem disappointing. Instead of the hoped-for abundant violets and other food and nectar plants, a ground cover of brambles and grasses develops but these too are foodplants for several species, some of them uncommon. The Mere Wainscot whose larvae feed on *Calamagrostis* species is an example. (For a review of the effect of coppicing on woodland Lepidoptera see Waring & Haggett, 1991.)

The long period of time since woods in the County were last coppiced has resulted in coppice which is over-mature for cutting. Some stools may have died out and need replacing. Deer, especially muntjac, browse the regrowth. The regrowth may not be as vigorous after the first cut as it would be in coppice cut on a regular cycle. If the coppice stools are not protected, the browsing will stunt the regrowth and may even kill the stools. But fencing coppice blocks is expensive and using the brash to make a dead hedge is labour-intensive. Protecting the coppice stools with brash is effective but may itself shade out the smaller plants. Many Bedfordshire woods are not large enough to allow several hectares to be cut at one time, a practice which minimises the intensity of damage by deer.

Similar problems arise in ride restoration and widening. The rides become choked with rank grass and flowers are much scarcer than expected. Before myxomatosis, rabbits may have played an important part in keeping the sward short in rides. Appropriate mowing and removal of cuttings may produce a similar result if continued over 10 years or more. In the long term, some form of grazing may be more cost-effective.

Whatever techniques are developed for coppice and ride management, they will have to be economic and sustainable in the long term, otherwise the initial efforts to restore the woodlands to their former glory will be wasted.

One factor which may compound the problems of managing coppice and rides as well as open grassland, is the deposition of increasing amounts of nitrogenous compounds from the air. This favours the growth of grasses at the expense of most flowering plants and hinders efforts to reduce the nutritional status of soils on such sites.

Fragmentation

The sites with the greatest number of species of Lepidoptera are now mostly fragments of what were once much larger areas of suitable habitat. This fragmentation can lead to three distinct problems. Firstly, many sites are too small to sustain a mosaic of interlinked populations so a single catastrophe may result in the local extinction of a species. Secondly, sites may be so isolated from one another that populations of a species cannot interbreed. This can lead to inbreeding within a site, loss of genetic variability, genetic drift, inability to adapt to changes in the environment and, again, local extinction. Thirdly, sites bounded by intensive arable agriculture may be subject to aerial drift or run-off of agricultural chemicals which could be deleterious in various ways. There is little direct information on the effects of pesticides on the butterfly and moth species that are not pests. We can only assume that pesticides may have played some part in the apparent reduction in abundance of species along hedgerows in arable areas. Fertilisers are applied to pastures in order to encourage the growth of grasses as opposed to broad-leaved plants. Fertiliser leaching from farmland into natural habitats may have similar effects. There is therefore a great need both for buffer zones around important sites and for the creation of corridors which will allow individuals to move between sites.

Corridors

Hedgerows, road verges and green lanes are the main linear habitats that form corridors between natural butterfly and moth sites in Bedfordshire. Many miles of hedgerow were removed during the 1950s, '60s and '70s. Although many of these hedges would have dated only from the enclosures, their loss is almost as important as the loss of ancient hedges because of the loss of corridors along which wildlife can move between favourable sites. Current schemes to encourage the reinstatement of hedges may redress the loss in a small way but it will be a long time before the new hedges return to their former richness. As has been mentioned before, green lanes are to be especially treasured and damage by recreational activities and by heavy machinery should be minimised. Roadside verges would benefit from more imaginative management for the gain of the road users and the taxpayers as well as the flora and fauna. Applying topsoil to new verges, especially on bare chalk or limestone, merely encourages rank vegetation and increases the cost of maintenance. Leaving the cuttings to rot after mowing (Figure 36), which is current policy, smothers the smaller flowering plants, fertilises the soil and increases growth of grasses which then require yet more mowing. It may also contribute to the spread of nettles and cleavers which have come to dominate many verges. Some sections of road verge have been designated as nature reserves with controlled cutting regimes more congenial to wildlife.

Re-establishment

We started this chapter by listing the many species that have been lost from the County entirely and we end with the controversial question of reintroduction and re-establishment. Even if butterfly and moth populations benefit from the predicted climate change, the nearest colonies of some extinct species are many miles away from Bedfordshire and there are few suitable vacant sites to form 'stepping stones' for natural spread. So even if there was a concerted effort to restore favourable management to sites across the country, it could take many years before species such as the Pearl-bordered Fritillary returned naturally. We would therefore support planned reintroductions to sites that have been fully restored and can be suitably maintained in the long term. The Code for Insect Re-establishment produced by the Joint Committee for the Conservation of British Insects (JCCBI) sets out what is needed and should be followed in all cases. The casual release of a few individuals is not only a waste of livestock and effort but if repeated year by year can give the false impression that the site is suitable for the species and inhibit proper management.

Conclusion

Finally, although it may seem an impossible task to fully restore and link the butterfly and moth habitats in the County, one must acknowledge the great strides which have been made, especially during the last 10 to 15 years. Support for organisations such as the Wildlife Trusts and Butterfly Conservation has grown immensely. The National Trust, the Royal Society for the Protection of Birds, the Woodland Trust and other voluntary organisations involved in countryside and reserve management have become more aware of the needs of butterflies and moths as have Local Authorities, Forest Enterprise and many private landowners. If this momentum can be maintained there is very real hope for the future.

Monitoring Population Change and Diversity

I.P.Woiwod

Introduction

Although we can learn much about large scale changes in butterfly and moth populations by presence/absence recording at regular intervals, there are limitations to this approach particularly when it comes to assessing changes in the populations of the widespread or common species or obtaining information on more localised species in time for conservation measures to be implemented. For these purposes continuous estimates of populations over long periods of time are needed so that we can assess the background levels of year to year variability, and then go on to detect any significant trends as they occur. This is easy to say but the population sizes of all insect species are notoriously difficult to estimate, even for such a popular and well-studied order of insects as the Lepidoptera. One of the main problems, apart from the ability to identify the species, is the commitment of time required to carry out the necessary sampling on a regular basis over many years. However such monitoring is vital if we are to conserve the abundance and diversity of our insect fauna. It is also essential to enable us to utilise the sensitivity of insects to environmental change as an early warning system for deleterious changes to our natural environment.

Fortunately there are two national sampling schemes in existence for the Lepidoptera which have included records from Bedfordshire for 20 years or more. These are the British Butterfly Monitoring Scheme coordinated from the Institute of Terrestrial Ecology at Monks Wood (Pollard & Yates, 1993) and for moths, the light-trap network of the Rothamsted Insect Survey (Woiwod & Harrington, 1994). This chapter is largely based on the data obtained through these two schemes, in particular from the two longest sets of observations in the County, the butterfly transects recorded since 1974 in Potton Wood and the light-trap run at Cockayne Hatley since 1976.

Butterfly Monitoring

Background and Methodology

Although British butterflies are one of the easiest groups of insects to observe and identify as adults, it is still very difficult to obtain objective accurate quantitative measurements of population size, mainly because of the mobility and short lifespan of most species. Some of the most satisfactory methods are based on capture-mark-release-recapture techniques as these can provide estimates of actual population size, if certain assumptions are made. However such methods are very labour intensive and so can only be used for detailed studies of individual species. A more practical method is required for routine monitoring of populations over long periods of time. This was provided in the early 1970s by the development of the transect walk at Monks Wood National Nature Reserve (Pollard *et al.,*1975).

The transect walk consists of a fixed route, or transect, which is walked once a week between April and September. The route is divided into sections and all butterflies observed within 5 m of the recorder are identified and counted. The walks, which have come to be

1. Time of day: counts are made between 10.45 and 15.45 hours British Summer Time.
2. Weather: temperature must be above 13ºC.
   Between 13°C and 17°C there must be at least 60% sunshine.
   Above 17°C conditions may be cloudy or sunny but not rainy.
   Wind should not be above Beaufort scale 5.
3. Walk to take place at least once a week between 1 April and 29 September.
4. The transect to be walked at an even pace and all butterflies that come within 5 metres in front of the observer to be counted.

Table 1 Criteria for butterfly transect 'Pollard' walks – for details see Hall (1981).

known as 'Pollard walks', are made between 10.45 and 15.45 (British Summer Time) and only when weather conditions meet certain minimum criteria (Table 1) which ensure that most individual butterflies are active and so can be observed (Hall, 1981). Butterflies flying high above the recorders are not included in the counts so that certain species, such as the hairstreaks, tend to be under-recorded on the transects. However, the method has been shown to give consistent and repeatable estimates of relative abundance which can be used to study year-to-year fluctuations in butterfly numbers. The yearly index is obtained by adding all the weekly counts from each section. Weekly counts missing because of unsuitable weather or other unavoidable reasons are estimated by interpolation from existing counts.

From the initial work at Monks Wood, a national network of about 100 sites has been built up in the 18 years since 1976 to become the Butterfly Monitoring Scheme (BMS). This scheme has been jointly funded throughout by the Institute of Terrestrial Ecology (ITE) and the statutory conservation agency (currently the Joint Nature Conservation Committee (JNCC)). The original purpose of the scheme was to detect any underlying regional and national trends in butterfly abundance and also to relate differences from the overall trend to local factors such as management at individual sites. Many of the sites in the scheme are on nature reserves or similar areas where active management can be undertaken for conservation. Monitoring the effects of such work is vital. Two major summaries of the results from this national network have been produced (Pollard *et al.*, 1986; Pollard & Yates, 1993) as well as a number of papers on more detailed studies resulting from the BMS dataset (*e.g.* Pollard, 1988; 1991; Pollard *et al.*, 1984).

Butterfly Transects in Bedfordshire

One of the first butterfly transects to be set up after the initial development at Monks Wood was in Potton Wood. It was initiated in 1974 to test the technique and see if it was practical for an amateur to carry out such monitoring. Following the success of this pilot study a slightly extended transect was set up in 1976 and has continued ever since. This transect remains the only one in Bedfordshire which is part of the official national scheme, although a number of others are in operation using similar protocols, notably those coordinated by the Bedfordshire and Northamptonshire branch of Butterfly Conservation in the south-west of the County (Herbert,1995). All known transects in Bedfordshire with the conservation status of the site and the years of operation are given in Table 2.

The Potton Wood Transect

Potton Wood is a large (87.4 ha) boulder-clay wood on the border between Bedfordshire and Cambridgeshire. It is currently managed by Forest Enterprise and is an ancient

Site	Grid-ref.	Status	Years	Recorders
1. Potton Wood (BMS site)	TL2550	SSSI	1974 1976 →	I.P.Woiwod & B.Fensome
2. Rowney Warren	TL1241	—	1989-91	J.Adams & D.Parsons
3. Barton Hills	TL0930	NNR	1987-1988 1990 →	English Nature wardens
4. Dunstable Downs	TL0120	SSSI	1989 →	Countryside Rangers
5. Sharpenhoe Clappers	TL3006	SSSI	1989 →	) Members of
6. Totternhoe Old Chalk Quarry	SP9922	SSSI	1993 →	) Bedfordshire and
7. Whipsnade Downs (Bison Hill)	TL0019	SSSI	1987 →	) Northamptonshire
8. Blows Downs North	TL0322	SSSI	1994 →	) Branch of
9. Blows Downs West	TL0322	SSSI	1994 →	) Butterfly Conservation
10. Galley & Warden Hills	TL0926	SSSI	1995 →	T.Tween & M.McCarrick
11. Hill Rise LNR, Bedford	TL0551	SSSI	1994 →	B.Anderson & T.Greenwell
12. RSPB, The Lodge, Sandy	TL1948	SSSI	1989 -1995	M.Kemp
13. Priory Country Park Bedford	TL0749	CP	1992 →	Park Wardens

Table 2 Butterfly Transects in Bedfordshire.

woodland with SSSI status. Although substantial areas of ancient ash and hazel coppice remain, about a third of the wood in the south-west was planted with conifers about 1960. The wide main ride runs from south-west to north-east and is crossed by two other wide rides approximately at right angles (Figure 38). There is a much narrower and more overgrown track which runs parallel to the perimeter of the wood in most places. The Potton Wood butterfly transect originally consisted of 8 sections in 1974, section 9 was added in 1976 and all sections have been recorded since. Sections 1, 2 and 5 follow parts of the perimeter track, other sections follow various parts of the wider main rides (Figure 38).

During the 20 years of recording 31 species have been seen in the wood (Table 3). This is more than half the species on the current list of species regularly breeding in Britain (58 spp.) and all except six of those that breed in Bedfordshire (34 spp. including three migrants). The commonest species are Green-veined White, Ringlet and Meadow Brown, all with over 10,000 records, also notable populations of Peacock, Small White, Gatekeeper, Large White, Brimstone and Large Skipper occur, all with over 1000 records.

Figure 37 Ian Woiwod recording the Butterfly Transect in Potton Wood.

A few of the species in Table 3 are worthy of further comment. For example, the Wood White which was seen on two occasions in 1985 and was observed egg-laying on meadow vetchling during one of these sightings, although unfortunately the species did not reappear during the following year. The nearest known sighting of this species was an individual in 1978 in Wilstead Wood, 19 km south-west of Potton Wood, although the closest strong colony is at Salcey Forest, 44 km due west. A male Chalkhill Blue appeared in the wood in 1990, probably a wanderer from the colony at Royston Heath, Hertfordshire, which is 14 km south-east and within sight of the wood. I think it unlikely that either of these species made the journey to Potton Wood by unassisted low level flight but were probably wind-borne, possibly being caught up in strong thermals which were present at about the time they were seen.

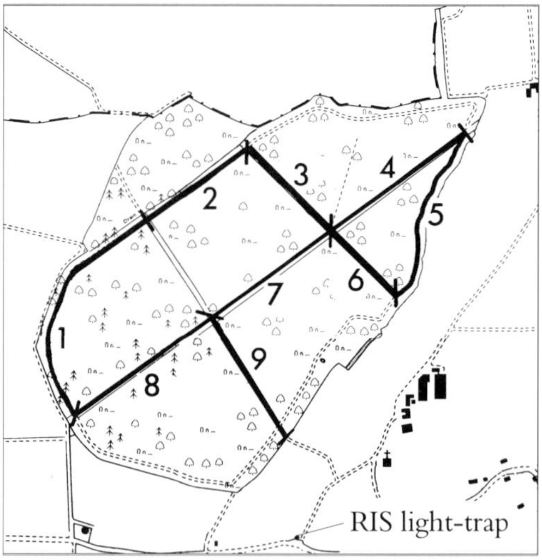

Figure 38 Map of the Butterfly Transect in Potton Wood.

In 1995 no less than four species were seen in Potton Wood for the first time since the transect was set up; Brown Argus, White Admiral, Silver-washed Fritillary and Marbled White. The Brown Argus was particularly noteworthy, as the 210 recorded in the second generation was the highest total for any site in the national network (Pollard & Greatorex-Davies, 1996). This species has been spreading in Bedfordshire and neighbouring counties into areas away from its normal chalkland habitats for reasons that are not yet understood and it will be very interesting to

Species recorded in Potton Wood 1974-1995	Transect total	Comments
1. Small Skipper *Thymelicus sylvestris*	629	both species present
2. Essex Skipper *Thymelicus lineola*		but not always separated
3. Large Skipper *Ochlodes venata*	1488	-
4. Wood White *Leptidea sinapis*	2	1985, single female laying eggs
5. Clouded Yellow *Colias croceus*	2	1983, the 'CloudedYellow' year
6. Brimstone *Gonopteryx rhamni*	1656	-
7. Large White *Pieris brassicae*	3893	-
8. Small White *Pieris rapae*	6871	-
9. Green-veined White *Pieris napi*	11385	-
10. Orange Tip *Anthocaris cardamines*	740	-
11. Purple Hairstreak *Quercusia quercus*	6	under-recorded on transect
12. White-letter Hairstreak *Satyrium w-album*	3	under-recorded on transect
13. Small Copper *Lycaena phlaeas*	91	-
14. Brown Argus *Aricia agestis*	210	first seen 1995
15. Common Blue *Polyommatus icarus*	625	-
16. Chalkhill Blue *Lysandra coridon*	1	Royston Heath colony,14 km away
17. Holly Blue *Celastrina argiolus*	153	-
18. White Admiral *Ladoga camilla*	1	1995
19. Red Admiral *Vanessa atalanta*	364	-
20. Painted Lady *Cynthia cardui*	161	-
21. Small Tortoiseshell *Aglais urticae*	993	-
22. Peacock *Inachis io*	7822	-
23. Comma *Polygonia c-album*	557	-
24. Silver-washed Fritillary *Argynnis paphia*	1	1995, male
25. Speckled Wood *Pararge aegeria*	1552	-
26. Wall *Lasiommata megera*	974	-
27. Marbled White *Melanargia galathea*	1	1995, not on transect
28. Gatekeeper *Pyronia tithonus*	5844	-
29. Meadow Brown *Maniola jurtina*	11277	-
30. Ringlet *Aphantopus hyperantus*	10922	-
31. Small Heath *Coenonympha pamphilus*	174	-

Table 3 Butterfly species list for Potton Wood.

see if the population in the wood prospers or disappears as suddenly as it arrived. The source of the three other new species in 1995 is unknown but hopefully they are an indication of increasing populations of these species more generally in the region.

In 1983 two specimens of the Clouded Yellow were unexpectedly seen flying through the wood, the first in May undoubtedly part of a large initial migration with the second later in the year probably one of the offspring of the earlier migrants. As a result of the many sightings 1983 became known as a 'Clouded Yellow' year and the Butterfly Monitoring Scheme provided valuable information on the timing of the invasion and its subsequent spread (Pollard *et al.*, 1984).

Two other species only recorded occasionally on the transect are worthy of note, these are the two hairstreaks, Purple and White-letter. As mentioned already, hairstreaks are likely to be under-recorded on 'Pollard' walks because of the habit of spending most of their adult lives at the tops of trees. The Purple Hairstreak appears to be well established in the wood and can be seen without difficulty in most years. The White-letter Hairstreak's status is less certain as elms, its only larval foodplant, have only a restricted distribution in the wood and are subject to the ravages of dutch elm disease.

Although continual long-term recording will nearly always provide such interesting records which often raise further questions, the main importance of the transect data lies in the detection of significant trends which may then be related to environmental change. The twenty years of recording in Potton Wood is probably about the minimum required to provide information on year-to-year variation and to ensure that any population changes detected are not just the result of short-term cycles which are part of the normal population dynamics of many species (Woiwod, 1991). Altogether eight of the twenty-one species tested exhibit statistically significant trends in annual index values between 1976-1994 (Table 4).

Species	Trends in numbers: Potton Wood	Trends in numbers: BMS Eastern Region	Comparison of trends between Potton Wood and Eastern Region
Large White	increase***	no trend (NS)	no difference (NS)
Common Blue	increase***	increase***	no difference (NS)
Red Admiral	increase***	increase***	no difference (NS)
Peacock	increase***	increase***	no difference (NS)
Speckled Wood	increase***	increase***	*
Gatekeeper	decrease**	no trend (NS)	*
Ringlet	increase**	increase***	no difference (NS)
Small Heath	decrease*	decrease*	no difference (NS)

Linear regression of log (N+1) on year, 1976-1994.
NS = not statistically significant; * = $p \leq 0.05$; ** = $p \leq 0.01$; *** = $p \leq 0.001$

Table 4 Statistically significant trends in butterfly abundance in Potton Wood compared with the trends in the eastern region of the BMS.

Perhaps rather surprisingly for most conservationists, all except two of these eight species have tended to become commoner over the time the recording has been done. The reason for this trend is not known. It may be a general response in those species to the series of milder winters and warmer summers at the end of the 1980s and the early 1990s, or it may be a more subtle response to recent management of the main rides in the wood. These have been mown more consistently and later in the year than previously. Also the ride edges have been cut back more regularly, keeping the rides open. However local management is probably not the main factor as, except for two species, the trends in Potton Wood are not significantly different from the regional trends (Table 4).

The two species which go against the general pattern are the Gatekeeper and Small Heath both of which show significant decreases in annual index values. Both of these decreases seem to be related to local environmental factors within the wood. The Small Heath is an open ground species which may have been commoner in the wood following management connected with replanting of some areas with conifers (Pollard *et al.,* 1986), although the decrease seems to have occurred more generally in the region (Table 4). The Gatekeeper on the other hand seems to have had a healthy population in the wood until 1987 when shrubs were severely cut back along the main ride in places where the species had been common. It was observed at the time that the management had affected the population badly. Although there has been some resurgence of the population since then it has not yet entirely recovered (Figure 39). As its other common name the Hedge Brown implies, this species is particularly associated with hedges and shrubby borders of sunny open rides although the larvae feed on grasses. The drastic or frequent ride management may not suit the Gatekeeper as much as the related Ringlet (population increasing) and Meadow Brown (population stable). The suggestion that the decline in the population of the Gatekeeper is mainly caused by local woodland management is confirmed by comparison with the regional BMS data which exhibits no significant change.

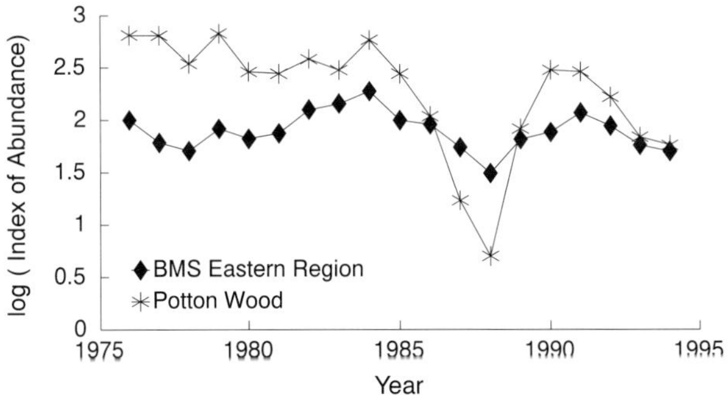

Figure 39 Gatekeeper – annual transect totals in Potton Wood, compared with other data from the eastern region of the BMS. There is a significant reduction in Potton Wood but not in the regional totals.

The only other species which goes noticeably against the regional trend is the Large White, which increased significantly in Potton Wood but has had no significant trend more widely. A possible explanation for this is local breeding on the extensive oilseed rape crops which are regularly grown on the fields surrounding the wood. Large White caterpillars have been seen in particular abundance on those occasions when some of the oilseed rape has been sown in the spring rather than in the autumn as is more usual.

The Speckled Wood Invasion

Of particular note is the very large increase in the population of the Speckled Wood (Table 4). The reason for this trend becomes apparent as soon as the annual transect counts for this species are plotted (Figure 40), for this is the only species that seems to have become established as a breeding population in the wood during the period monitored. Although single males were recorded holding territory in 1974, 1975 and 1984 there did not appear to be evidence of a viable population in the wood during that period. Presumably these individuals were casual wanderers from local populations in nearby woods possibly on the greensand which appears only some 800 m away towards Potton. However, in 1986 a single adult was again seen and for the next six years the species increased rapidly until a maximum of 399 were recorded in 1992. Since then numbers have decreased slightly but an established population remains and the Speckled Wood is notable in being the only species which can be recorded on every section of the transect during a single census. The reason for this sudden establishment and population explosion in Potton Wood is not clear although it appears to be part of a general expansion in the range of this species in East Anglia. Similar colonisations were observed at a number of the other BMS sites at about the same time (Figure 7.2 in Pollard & Yates, 1993), although a statistical comparison shows that the rate of increase was significantly higher in Potton Wood than in the Eastern region generally (Table 4).

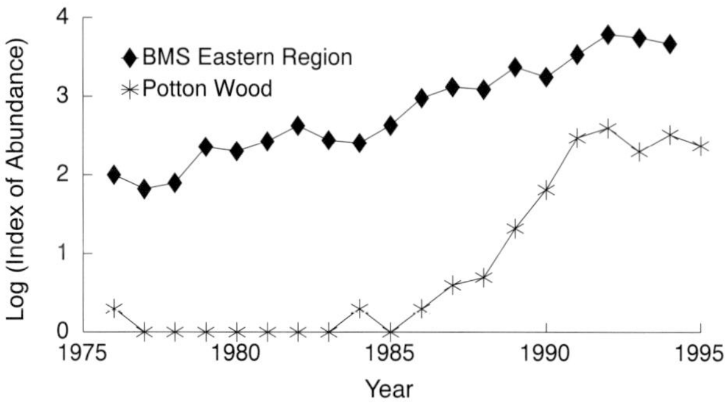

Figure 40 Speckled Wood – annual transect totals in Potton Wood, compared with BMS regional data. Although both show significant increases, the population in Potton Wood increased more rapidly between 1985 and 1991.

It is fortunate that the Speckled Wood is one of the few species for which we have a record from Potton Wood which pre-dates the butterfly transect. This comes from the Letchworth Natural History Society who were studying the spread of the species in their area and noted the presence of a 'few' individuals in the wood in May 1947 (Bowden, 1946, 1947). At that time the species was very rare around Letchworth generally but appeared to be expanding its range and so the observation was noteworthy particularly as it was a new site record. This record of an earlier colonisation of Potton Wood, followed presumably by an extinction, and the recolonisation during the present period of recording ties in very well with published observations from the neighbouring county of Hertfordshire where an expansion between 1939 and 1945 was recorded, followed by a noticeable decline between 1951 and 1969, which included many extinctions. Finally the beginning of the present period of expansion was observed from about 1970 onward from the south and west and was still continuing in 1986, about the time of the colonisation was first noticed on the transect (Sawford, 1987).

It may be that the Speckled Wood is a species that is particularly prone to local extinction and recolonisation even within its existing range so it will be interesting to continue to follow its fortunes in the wood and determine how often it becomes extinct.

Butterfly numbers in different sections of the Potton Wood transect.

All BMS transects are divided into sections so that the local distribution of butterflies can be studied and related to land use and management practices. Interpretation of these distributions for individual species is complex (Pollard & Yates, 1993) and therefore is not attempted here but it is instructive to look at the sections in relation to the total numbers of butterflies recorded. There is a significant ($p \leq 0.05$) increase in the total number of butterflies recorded in Potton Wood between 1976 and 1994. This confirms the results for individual species in Table 4 where a number of very abundant species such as Peacock and Ringlet have increased and many of the other dominant species have not changed significantly. However, individual sections do not all conform to this pattern. Sections 3,4,5,7,8 and 9 all showed significant increases, section 6 had no trend but sections 1 and 2 actually showed significant decreases in abundance. All these trends were measured in the same way as in Table 4 between 1974 and 1994, except for section 9, which started in 1976.

As Figure 38 shows sections 1 and 2 lie along the perimeter path of Potton Wood which is narrow and tends to be overgrown and hence unsuitable for most butterfly species. When the transect was initiated both of these sections were more open because of woodland management at that time. This included some coppicing along section 1 and a large coppice area between sections 2 and 7 which was carried out in conjunction with some unsuccessful planting of larch. As these coppice areas have regrown sections 1 and 2 have become progressively less suitable for butterflies and hence the gradual downward trend. Also the growth of the coniferous plantation along the edge of parts of section 1 has also notably decreased numbers in that area. The other overgrown section is number 5 which has remained the least suitable for butterflies since recording began and has also been least affected by various changes in the wood. Numbers are always small in this section but there has been a significant increase over the last 20 years almost entirely due to the colonisation of the wood by the Speckled Wood. The males of this species will hold territory in any small patch of sunlight, even along very overgrown tracks and most records in section 5 derive from males behaving in this way.

Other Bedfordshire Transects and Surveys

There are currently 12 other 'Pollard walks' in operation in Bedfordshire (Table 2). Although not part of the national BMS scheme, they are already providing useful additional information on annual changes in the butterfly populations in Bedfordshire. Of particular importance is that they are mainly on the chalk grassland of the Chilterns which run through the south-west corner of the County. They therefore record many of the interesting species characteristic of this habitat and often of particular conservation interest such as Marbled White, Chalkhill Blue, Brown Argus, Green Hairstreak, Grizzled Skipper, Dingy Skipper and Duke of Burgundy. Yearly transect totals for Whipsnade Downs, Barton Hills and Potton Wood are given in the Appendix (pages 380-383).

In addition to the transects, two surveys have been started in Bedfordshire in recent years. The first was the Chalk Grasslands Butterfly Survey which was begun in 1992 as a cooperative effort between a number of organisations, including the Bedfordshire Natural History Society, Butterfly Conservation, the County Wildlife Trust, The National Trust and the County Council. The aim was for surveyors to visit a site on at least four occasions during the summer and record what butterflies they saw and where. This provides information for site managers and for possible future use in determining a suitable route for a transect walk. In 1995 a Woodland Butterfly Survey was started along similar lines.

Moth Monitoring

Background and Methodology.

Because they fly mainly at night and there are many more moth than butterfly species, the transect walk method is not feasible for quantitative moth recording. Trapping, identifying and counting regular samples taken in light-traps is the obvious way of obtaining information on changes in populations and this has been the approach of the national scheme for monitoring the more abundant and widespread species, the light-trap network of the Rothamsted Insect Survey (RIS) (Woiwod & Harrington, 1994). This network originated at and is coordinated from Rothamsted Experimental Station (IACR-Rothamsted) at Harpenden in Hertfordshire which is only about 8 km south of the Bedfordshire county border.

Most of the light-trapping used for routine recording of moths in Bedfordshire has been done using mercury-vapour (MV) lamps or actinic tubes, either hung from a tripod over a white sheet (Figure 41) or in various forms of proprietary and home-made trap.

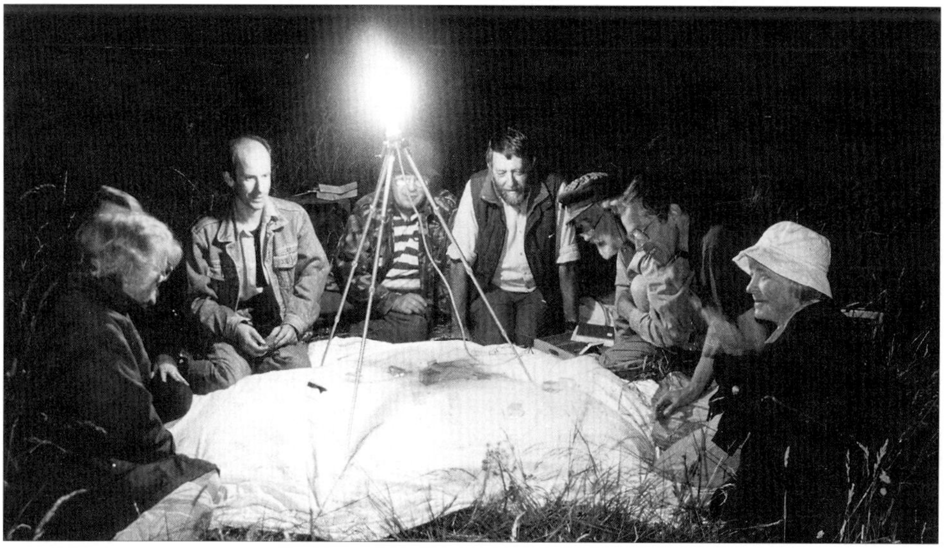

Figure 41 Moth trapping over a sheet at a meeting of the Bedfordshire Natural History Society. Vic Arnold is on the immediate right of the light with David Manning on his left.

The RIS light-trap is a standard Rothamsted design which uses a 200 watt clear tungsten bulb (Figure 42). The traps are operated every night of the year from dusk to dawn by volunteers and all the macrolepidoptera are identified, often by the trap operators. The trap design originates from the 1920s but has proved to be good one, providing small but consistent samples. The relatively small sample size, particularly compared with traps using MV bulbs which are often employed in moth collecting and recording, is important from two aspects. It reduces the identification task to a manageable level and also ensures that the sampling has no deleterious effect on natural populations. This is clearly important from a conservation angle but also scientifically there would be little point in monitoring populations if they were being affected by the sampling method. Careful analysis of data from the network over many years has confirmed the lack of any effect of removing the small sample

Figure 42 The Rothamsted Insect Survey light-trap at Cockayne Hatley. Potton Wood can be seen in the background separated from the garden trap by an arable field.

obtained by this method. This is as expected with insects which are relatively mobile, have very high potential rates of natural increase in population and also have to withstand very high levels of natural mortality.

Although some of the records of the Rothamsted Insect Survey go back to the 1930s, the national network was developed from about 1965 and there are currently about 100 traps in operation throughout Britain. Unlike the Butterfly Monitoring Scheme which is specifically orientated towards conservation questions, the light-trap network was originally developed to study fundamental questions concerned with the way insect populations function. It is also closely linked to the national network of suction traps for aphids which has an agricultural emphasis. However, as data have accumulated, the moth records have been used for a wide range of studies covering fundamental questions relating to population dynamics, agricultural pests, and patterns of biodiversity and conservation aspects, such as the effects of changes in land use (Woiwod & Harrington, 1994).

RIS light-traps in Bedfordshire

Altogether 9 sites have operated RIS light-traps in Bedfordshire as part of the national scheme though there are currently only two in operation, one at Cockayne Hatley which has run continuously for 20 years and the other at Eaton Bray which has now been running for 2 years (Table 5). The first trap in the County was operated within the grounds of the RSPB reserve at Sandy. Although resited in 1974, it ran continuously for a period of 7 years until an unfortunate change of policy led to its closure in 1975. Other sites of note were the two in Whipsnade Wild Animal Park and one in Shuttleworth College grounds. Records of note from all these traps are included in the species accounts later in this volume.

Cockayne Hatley light-trap records 1976-1995

As with the Potton Wood butterfly data, the light-trap has been run at Cockayne Hatley for long enough to provide some information on population changes that may indicate

Site No.	Site Name	Grid Ref.	Years Operated	Complete Years (to 1995)	Trap Operator
125	Sandy I	TL 187478	1969-1973	5	RSPB
208	Whipsnade I	TL 002179	1971-1973	2	Graham Buss
229	Whipsnade II	TL 001660	1973 (incomplete)	0	Graham Buss
283	Shuttleworth	TL 148444	1974-1980	6	Shuttleworth College
290	Sandy II	TL 188478	1974-1975	2	RSPB
336	Cockayne Hatley	TL 253494	1976→	20	Ian Woiwod
412	Eaton Bray	SP 976207	1980-1989	8	Graham Buss
452	Houghton Regis I	TL 028247	1985	1	Adrian Riley
522	Houghton Regis II	TL 023249	1991-1994	4	Graham Buss
559	Eaton Bray II	SP 967207	1994→	2	Graham Buss

Table 5 Rothamsted Insect Survey light-traps in Bedfordshire.

significant long-term trends. The trap is situated in a private garden about 300 m south east of Potton Wood (Figure 38) and is surrounded by the intensively cultivated fields of the CWS farm at Cockayne Hatley.

Altogether 338 species of macrolepidoptera and 355 species of microlepidoptera have been recorded from the Cockayne Hatley trap since 1976, although only the macrolepidoptera have been identified and counted daily over the whole period. New species are still being recorded even after 20 years of continuous operation, emphasising the mobility of moths and difficulty in obtaining complete species inventories for any site. Species of note which occur regularly in the Cockayne Hatley trap but are considered more unusual elsewhere in the County include the Oak Eggar, Round-winged Muslin, Dingy Footman, Least Black Arches, Mere Wainscot, Least Yellow Underwing and Large Thorn. In addition several species on the Bedfordshire list have only been recorded from this trap site, for example the Feathered Ranunculus, Pinion-streaked Snout and many species of micro-lepidoptera.

Only 87 species of macrolepidoptera have been recorded between 1976 and 1995 in sufficient numbers to test for significant trends in population. For 56 of the 87 species tested the trend was downwards (regression coefficients negative), implying reduction in population. This is much more than would be expected by chance ($p \leq 0.01$), even taking into account that many of these trends are not statistically significant individually. Of the 25 species which showed statistically significant change, 7 species increased and 18 decreased (Table 6; Figure 43).

The reason for this overall decline is not known and is in sharp contrast to the butterfly situation in nearby Potton Wood, so it is unlikely to be related directly to climate. The garden area in the immediate vicinity of the trap has become more diverse with many trees and shrubs becoming established and if anything it is now more 'moth friendly' than previously. However, the area of semi-natural habitat on the farm surrounding the garden declined in the years immediately following the establishment of the trap. The arable agriculture on the farm became more intensive, with ditches being filled in and field verges ploughed up so that cultivation could be taken right to the field margins. Also chemical pest control used to take place much more routinely and prophylactically than at present. Recently there has been some amelioration of these agricultural trends with trees and hedgerows being planted and pest control carried out in a more integrated and environmentally sensitive manner.

Species	Common name	Direction of Change	Significance
Habrosyne pyritoides	Buff Arches	decrease	*
Trichiura crataegi	Pale Eggar	decrease	***
Eilema lurideola	Common Footman	increase	*
Spilosoma lutea	Buff Ermine	decrease	**
Arctia caja	Garden Tiger	decrease	*
Agrotis segetum	Turnip Moth	decrease	*
Xestia c-nigrum	Setaceous Hebrew Character	increase	***
Xestia xanthographa	Square-spot Rustic	decrease	*
Orthosia gothica	Hebrew Character	increase	**
Orthosia cruda	Small Quaker	increase	**
Mythimna ferrago	The Clay	decrease	***
Caradrina morpheus	Mottled Rustic	decrease	**
Oligia fasciuncula	Middle-barred Minor	decrease	**
Phlogophora meticulosa	Angle Shades	increase	*
Thalpophila matura	Straw Underwing	decrease	**
Photedes minima	Small Dotted Buff	decrease	***
Hydraecia micacea	Rosy Rustic	decrease	***
Amphipyra tragopoginis	Mouse Moth	decrease	**
Dryobotodes eremita	Brindled Green	increase	***
Diloba caeruleocephala	Figure of Eight	decrease	**
Autographa gamma	Silver Y	increase	*
Xanthorhoe ferrugata	Dark-barred Twin-spot Carpet	decrease	*
Eulithis pyraliata	Barred Straw	decrease	*
Ennomos fuscantiaria	Dusky Thorn	decrease	***
Selenia dentaria	Early Thorn	decrease	*

Regression of log (N+1) on year
Significant regressions: *, **, *** = $p \leq 0.05, 0.01, 0.001$ respectively

Table 6 Moth species showing statistically significant trends in the numbers caught each year between 1976 and 1995 in the light-trap at Cockayne Hatley.

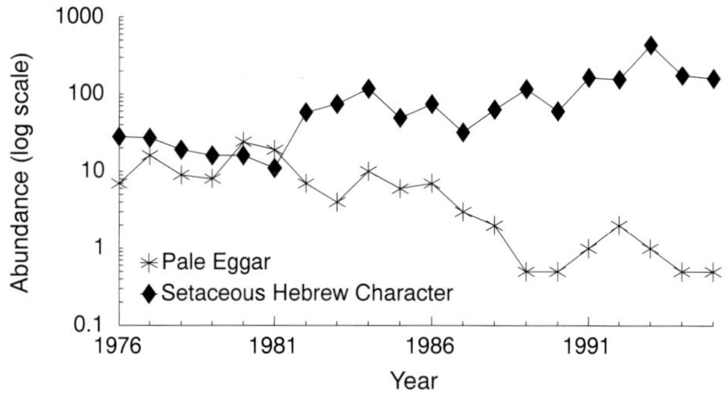

Figure 43 Trends in abundance of two moth species as observed in the light-trap at Cockayne Hatley.

It will be interesting to see if these welcome new policies reverse the downward trend in the populations of many species indicated by trap catches over the last 20 years.

Several species have become established in the area during the sampling period the most notable being Blair's Shoulder-knot which was first recorded in 1988 and since 1990 has been seen every year. This fits in well with the known expansion of this species northwards through Britain with the larvae feeding on non-native cypress trees. Another species of interest was the Dotted Rustic which first appeared in 1982. It was caught regularly between 1985 and 1991 but not again until 1996 when a single moth was caught. This reflects an expansion and contraction in the range and abundance of this species observed elsewhere, although the cause is still completely unknown.

Rather surprisingly, despite these changes in the abundance of individual species, there has been no significant change in the annual total numbers of macrolepidoptera in the vicinity of the Cockayne Hatley light-trap. Increases and decreases in individual species seem to have counteracted each other and prevented the overall change over 20 years being separated from the large year to year variation. Only with an even longer run of data will any overall trend become apparent.

Climate Change and Moths

There is increasing concern both amongst scientists and the general public over predicted climate change induced by human activities, particularly the burning of fossil fuel since the industrial revolution and the resultant increase in atmospheric levels of CO_2, an important greenhouse gas. Although there is still some controversy, the general opinion of experts is that such concerns are valid and that we may already be seeing some of the effects of such change (Houghton *et al.*, 1996). Any change, particularly in temperature, may be particularly important for our insect fauna (Harrington & Woiwod, 1995). Long term monitoring is vital if we are to detect the effect of such changes as they occur. One of the important questions to be asked of such long term datasets is whether they are already beginning to show evidence of climate change effects.

One predicted effect of any increase in temperature is that there could be an increase of range northward of southern species which are presently restricted in range by climate. However, changes in distribution are very difficult to interpret and there are nearly always some species whose ranges are contracting at the same time as others are expanding. In the past many of these changes have been put down to climate change, usually with very little evidence except the lack of any other explanation. Detailed ecological studies on some of our rarer and declining butterfly and moth species have now shown the importance of changes in land use and land management. Often such changes result in alteration of the micro-climate experienced by butterflies and moths and this in turn affects their numbers (Woiwod & Thomas, 1993). At the same time, several species which have expanded their ranges recently have only been able to do so because of the previous establishment of non-native foodplants, for example Blair's Shoulder-knot on cypresses.

One result of climate change that seems to be more amenable to analysis and interpretation is that affecting the time of the year when the adults fly (flight phenology). The adult flight times are part of the life history strategy of each species and are usually genetically determined. However, it is known from work on pest species that the flight times vary from year to year depending on the temperatures experienced by the immature stages. Any general trend in flight times is therefore likely to be dependent on temperature and might be one sign that climate change is actually taking place.

Species Common name	No. of years in analysis	Estimated no. of days earlier(-) or later (+) when given percentage of population was caught in 1995 as compared with 1975.				
		5%	25%	50%	75%	95%
Eilema lurideola Common Footman	19	-9.0	-11.2	-9.4	-9.6	-16.4**
Spilosoma lubricipeda White Ermine	19	-10.4	-8.6	-7.2	-6.0	-11.2
Xestia xanthographa Square-spot Rustic	20	+3.6	+4.8	+6.8	+8.8*	+9.0*
Orthosia gothica Hebrew Character	18	-30.6**	-38.4**	-37.0***	-27.8**	-23.8**
Mythimna impura Smoky Wainscot	19	-8.4	-7.8	-7.6	-7.8	-2.0
Caradrina morpheus Mottled Rustic	16	-8.4	-9.0	-10.0	-10.2	-7.2
Hoplodrina alsines The Uncertain	15	-8.2	-11.6	-10.8	-8.4	-3.4
Apamea anceps Large Nutmeg	18	-21.2*	-16.4*	-18.6	-18.0	-17.4*
Mesoligia furuncula Cloaked Minor	16	-3.8	+0.4	+0.2	-2.4	-6.0
Luperina testacea Flounced Rustic	20	-7.2	-6.8	-5.4	-3.6	-4.2
Rusina ferruginea Brown Rustic	15	-11.6	-5.8	-6.0	-2.0	-3.8
Omphaloscelis lunosa Lunar Underwing	19	-2.8	-3.2	-3.0	-4.0	-2.8
Agrochola lychnidis Beaded Chestnut	18	-1.8	-2.6	-3.0	-2.8	-1.8
Idaea dimidiata Single-dotted Wave	17	-1.0	-6.8	-5.2	-4.8	+1.4
Idaea aversata Riband wave	16	-9.6	-10.6	-1.8	-0.8	-7.4
Xanthorhoe montanata Silver-ground Carpet	17	-15.4*	-12.4*	-10.2	-8.4	-16.8
Eulithis pyraliata Barred Straw	20	-7.6	-9.6	-10.2	-9.2	-9.0
Hydriomena furcata July Highflyer	13	-3.2	-6.4	-1.0	-8.4	-17.2*
Epirrhoe alternata Common Carpet	13	-15.8	-31.8	-12.6	-12.0	-1.4

Significant regressions: *, **, *** = $p \leq 0.05, 0.01, 0.001$ respectively

Table 7 Estimates of the change in flight times between 1976 and 1995 as observed in the light-trap at Cockayne Hatley.

To look for such trends among the data from the Cockayne Hatley light-trap, species were selected which had a single generation each year and an annual catch of at least 20 individuals for most of the 20 years that the trap has been run. First and last dates are often used in such studies. Unfortunately these are often very variable and badly influenced by the numbers recorded in a particular year. To overcome this problem we often use the dates on which a particular proportion of the catch has been caught, which are much less dependent on the numbers caught. For this study, dates by which 5, 25, 50, 75 and 95% of the total annual catch had been recorded were used in the analysis.

Sufficient data for analysis was available for 19 species of moths and the results are presented in Table 7. For only one species, the Hebrew Character, was the change significant across all five points in the flight period, averaging between 23.8 and 38.4 days earlier over the last 20 years. It therefore seems to be flying about a month earlier than 20 years ago (Figure 44). This species flies earlier in the year than any other in the analysis. It has probably been particularly affected by the recent series of mild winters. The other species that stands out is the Large Nutmeg which now seems to be flying about 2 to 3 weeks earlier than previously.

Although only a few of the changes in flight are statistically significant, nearly all the other species are tending to fly earlier in the year. If there was no overall pattern we would expect an equal number flying earlier and later. However, only 8 of the 95 values for number of days in Table 7 are positive, *i.e.* later. This can be tested formally and shown to be a highly

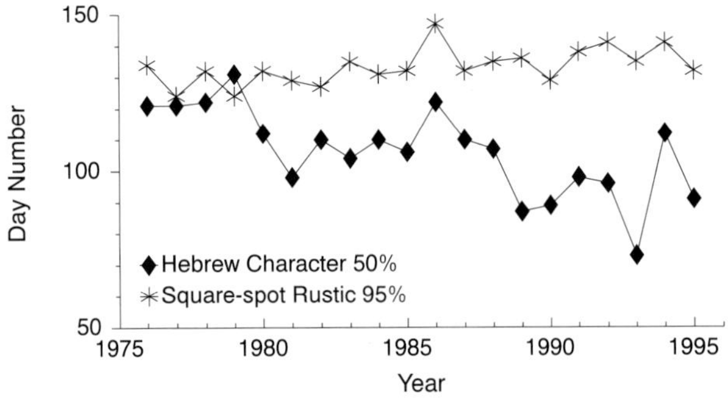

Figure 44 The time of year when the Hebrew Character appears in the light trap at Cockayne Hatley has changed over the last 20 years, becoming about a month earlier. In contrast that of the Square-spot Rustic has moved later by about a week.
Day number is from 1 January but the Square-spot Rustic has been scaled (minus 130 days) to fit the graph.

significant difference from what would happen by chance. From this it seems that most species for which there is sufficient data are now tending to fly earlier in Bedfordshire than they did 20 years ago. This is consistent with predictions about likely effects of climate warming, although with only 20 years data these results must still be regarded as preliminary. The lack of statistical significance of individual values (regressions) underlines the difficulty of these types of analysis as the signal can easily get lost in the natural year-to-year variability. The only solution to this problem is to collect data over an even longer time which emphasizes again the importance of long-term studies.

A notable exception to the tendency towards earlier flight times is the Square-spot Rustic which appears now to be flying about a week later than 20 years ago (Table 7; Figure 44). Perhaps not all species will react in the same way to climate change, and it may be that some species that fly later in the year will tend to fly even later and other species may well start to produce additional generations if climate change becomes a reality.

Biodiversity of the Bedfordshire Moth Fauna

The term biodiversity has rapidly become part of our everyday vocabulary since its invention by E.O.Wilson in 1988. Many books and articles have now been written about it. Ecologists, the public and even politicians, call for its conservation, and funding bodies support research into it. The popularity of the word derives partly from the wide variety of ideas and areas it encompasses so that it can mean different things to different people. Generally the word refers to the rich variety contained within the natural biological world. This is often equated solely to the number of species but it can also refer to the genetic variability within species. Whatever the context there is a general perception that we have lost or are in process of losing a lot of this natural variety and that such loss is at the very least undesirable and may have serious consequences in the longer term.

Site	No. of years	Diversity Index (mean α) ± Standard Error	Number of moths (mean N)	Number of species (mean S)
125 Sandy I	5	47.5 ± 3.8	3362	202
208 Whipsnade	2	38.3 ± 3.5	2336	158
283 Shuttleworth	6	46.5 ± 1.6	2177	179
290 Sandy II	2	44.1 ± 2.9	1698	162
336 Cockayne Hatley				
macrolepidoptera	19	35.3 ±0.8	3256	159
microlepidoptera	2	45.6 ± 2.5	5938	217
412 Eaton Bray	8	38.0 ± 1.2	2204	154
452 Houghton Regis I	1	23.7 ± 2.9	946	88
522 Houghton Regis II	4	27.1 ± 2.9	2002	117
559 Eaton Bray II	1	38.8 ± 4.0	1124	132

Table 8 Biodiversity indices for macro- and microlepidoptera caught in RIS light-traps in Bedfordshire.

From an ecological point of view it is important to be able to measure the existing biodiversity, study changes and ultimately conserve and even enhance it. However, despite the simplicity of the concept, diversity is very difficult to measure in practice, particularly in relatively species-rich and mobile groups such as the moths. The problem can be illustrated by taking the simplest measure, the number of species recorded in a particular area. It is a well-known feature of such measures of species-richness that they are very dependent on the effort and expertise of recorders in the particular locality. Even if the same effort is used, for example a light-trap is run for exactly the same period in two different years, then the biodiversity as measured by number of species recorded may be considerably different just because more individuals might be recorded in one year compared with the other. To overcome this problem we therefore need a way of correcting our species lists for the numbers of individuals examined. An 'index of diversity' [★] (α) is given in Table 8.

[★] For the statistically-minded, the number of species can be corrected for sample size if we know something about the underlying species frequency distribution, that is the relative abundances of the different species in the samples. It has been found from extensive analysis of light-trap samples that a particular statistical distribution, the log-series, often fits such data and that α, a parameter from this distribution makes a very useful diversity statistic which has a number of desirable properties. These include: independence from sample size, response to known environmental change, robustness to the fit of the model, lack of undue influence of the most abundant or rarest species, and perhaps most importantly an ability to discriminate between sample sites. It has also been shown that this index performs consistently better than many other commonly used diversity indices (Taylor, Kempton & Woiwod, 1976). As with most such measures of diversity, α combines two aspects of the species frequency distribution, species richness and the evenness of abundances between species. In effect it gives us a measure of the rate at which new species are likely to be added as sample size increases and is calculated from the relatively simple equation: $\mathbf{S} = \alpha \log(1+\mathbf{n}/\alpha)$ where **S** is the number of species in the sample and **N** is the number of individuals.

Using this measure, the greatest moth diversity recorded from the nine Bedfordshire RIS sites was at the original RSPB Sandy I, with very similar values at the Sandy II and Shuttleworth traps (Table 8). These high values seem to be particularly related to the well drained greensand soils. The Whipsnade and Eaton Bray sites are in the chalk region of the County and have almost identical diversities. The diversity of 35.4, recorded from the Cockayne Hatley trap, is very close to the national average from all RIS samples. Presumably it is related to the poorly drained Boulder Clay soil and the intensive agriculture surrounding the trap site. The two Houghton Regis sites have diversities well below average as one might expect from these urban sites on the outskirts of the Luton and Dunstable conurbation.

How the pattern of moth diversity fits into the surrounding counties can be seen from the diversity contour map centred on Bedfordshire but produced from the all data from the national light-trap network (Plate 104). Although at this scale the trap distribution is somewhat patchy and the pattern in areas without samples must therefore be treated with caution it seems that Bedfordshire lies on the edge of an area of high diversity with areas of lower diversity on the Oxford clay to the west and towards the London urban area to the south. The trap sites on the greensand display particularly large values not dissimilar to samples on the light soils of the Breckland and the Surrey sites, also on light sandy soils. Just why sandy soils should be so productive for moth species is a mystery, particularly when compared to the chalk, which is so rich in butterfly species. Part of the reason may be directly related to differences in vegetation but there may be some more subtle ecological factors at work. Certain species may be unable to pupate successfully in waterlogged soils, perhaps because they succumb to fungal disease or to insect-eating nematodes in such soils. Many clay soils become hard when dry and larvae seeking pupation sites may not be able to burrow into them.

Only the trap at Cockayne Hatley has run consistently and long enough to look for changes in moth diversity through time. However, despite some evidence that more species have been declining rather than increasing at this site over the last 20 years, there is only a slight and non-significant decrease in overall numbers and there is no sign of any change at all in the annual diversity values. Whether changes in climate, agricultural practice, land use or other factors will bring about future changes in the abundance and diversity of the butterfly and moth fauna of Bedfordshire will only be fully appreciated if the long-term recording outlined in this chapter can be continued.

It is unusual to have estimates of diversity for microlepidoptera for any sites in the national RIS network. Taxonomic problems mean that it is more difficult and time-consuming to identify and count them than the macros which are done routinely. However, thanks to the hard work of David Manning, we do have this information for the Cockayne Hatley trap based on two years, 1994 and 1995 (Table 8). Numbers of individuals, species and diversity are considerably greater for the micros than for the macrolepidoptera. This probably reflects the larger overall species-pool of microlepidoptera in the County. More species of micros have been recorded already from the Cockayne Hatley trap, even though micro-moths have not been identified from all 20 years. This high diversity also suggests that there may still be plenty of species which await discovery.

The Primitive Moths

(Micropterigidae and Eriocraniidae)

D.V.Manning

Micropteryx calthella (x 4)

Family: **Micropterigidae**

A family of small primitive moths with metallic bronze and purple forewings. Wingspan 6-11 mm. The moths have mandibles rather than probosces and are found feeding on pollen during the day, sometimes in large numbers. The life histories are little known. Three of the five British species have been found in the County.

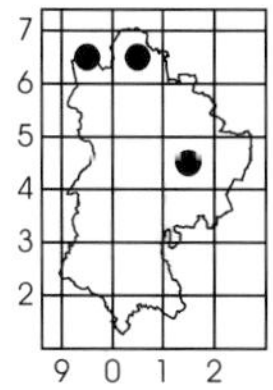

***Micropterix tunbergella* (Fabricius) (1)**
Post VCH: Recorded only from West Wood, Coppice Wood and Chicksands Wood.
Flight: May (weeks 18 to 21)*, June.
Larval Foodplants: Not known.

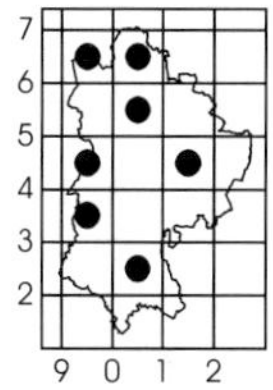

***Micropterix aruncella* (Scopoli) (4)**
VCH: (as *Eriocrania seppella* Fab.) "Bedford, Luton; on *Veronica chamaedrys*".
Post VCH: Local and uncommon, but possibly overlooked: Jackdaw Hill, Marston Thrift, West Wood, Sharpenhoe Clappers, Thurleigh Cutting, Coppice Wood and Old Warden Tunnel.
Flight: May, June (weeks 20 to 26)*, July and August.
Larval Foodplants: Not known for certain.

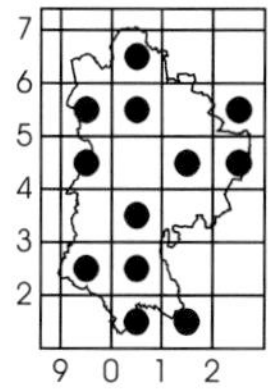

***Micropterix calthella* (Linnaeus) (5)** (Plate 42)
VCH: "Bedford, Luton; among *Caltha*".
Post VCH: Widespread and common, often in some numbers on flowers of buttercups and sedges during late May and June.
Flight: May, June (weeks 18 to 26)*.
Larval Foodplants: Not known for certain.

Family: **Eriocraniidae**

Small day-flying moths which emerge in early spring. The forewings are metallic bronze and purple. Wingspan 9-16 mm. The birch-feeding species are mainly recorded from the conspicuous blotch mines in the leaves. Determination of the species is difficult, depending on small differences in larval details and the form of the mine. Seven of the eight British species are recorded in the County.

For key to moth maps see page 3.

Eriocrania subpurpurella **(Haworth) (6)** (Plate 43)
VCH: "Bedford, Luton; among oak".
Post VCH: Widespread and common. The moth appears to be present wherever the foodplant occurs.
Flight: April to June (weeks 16 to 24)*.
Larval Foodplants: Oaks*, in a leaf-mine.

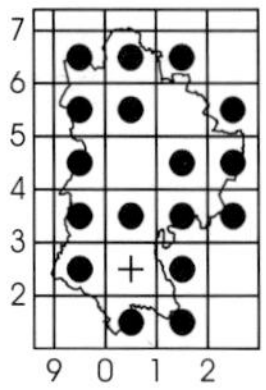

Eriocrania unimaculella **(Zetterstedt) (8)**
Post VCH: Local and uncommon: Marston Thrift, Park Wood and Flitwick Moor.
Flight: March, April.
Larval Foodplants: Birches*, in a leaf-mine.

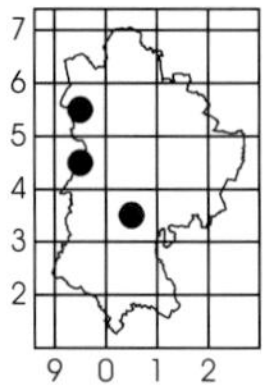

Eriocrania sparrmannella **(Bosc) (9)**
Post VCH: Local and uncommon: Marston Thrift, Flitwick Moor and Sutton Fen.
Flight: April (week 17)*, May.
Larval Foodplants: Birches*, in a leaf-mine.

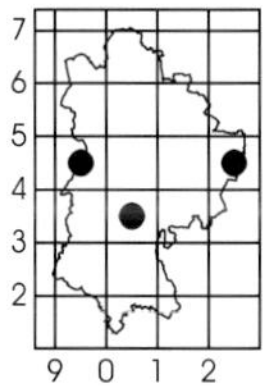

Eriocrania salopiella **(Stainton) (10)**
Post VCH: Widespread and common: Marston Thrift, Park Wood, Flitwick Moor, Coppice Wood, Rowney Warren and Sutton Fen.
Flight: April, May.
Larval Foodplants: Birches*, in a leaf-mine.

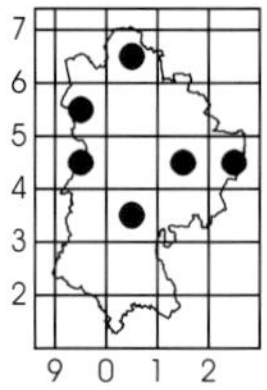

Eriocrania haworthi **(Bradley) (11)**
Post VCH: Widespread and common: Marston Thrift, Park Wood, Flitwick Moor, Old Warden and Sutton Fen.
Flight: April.
Larval Foodplants: Birches*, in a leaf-mine.

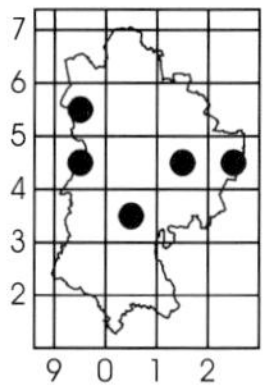

Eriocrania sangii **(Wood) (12)**
Post VCH: Widespread and common: King's Wood (Heath and Reach), Park Wood, West Wood, Flitwick Moor, Rowney Warren and Sutton Fen.
Flight: March, April.
Larval Foodplants: Birches*, in a leaf-mine.

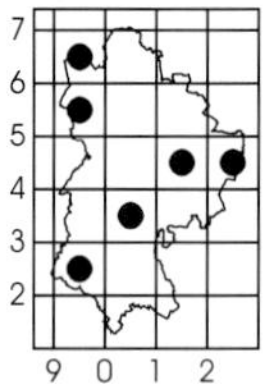

Eriocrania semipurpurella **(Stephens) (13)**
Post VCH: Locally common: Marston Thrift, Park Wood, Flitwick Moor, Rowney Warren and Sutton Fen.
Flight: March, April.
Larval Foodplants: Birches*, in a leaf-mine.

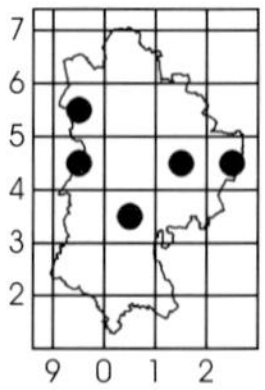

For details of standard weeks see page 6.

The Swift Moths

(Hepialidae)

V.W.Arnold

Map-winged Swift

Family: **Hepialidae**

The adult has no proboscis so cannot feed. The antennae are very short and the wings are long and narrow. Wingspan 25-48 mm. The males usually fly at dusk and are unusual in attracting the females by scent and by their bouncing display flight. The females broadcast their eggs in flight. The whitish larvae live in the soil and those of two species, the Ghost Moth and Common Swift, may damage crops. They may take more than one year to complete their development. The pupae often wriggle to the soil surface before the moths emerge. All five of the British species have been found in Bedfordshire.

Ghost Moth *Hepialus humuli* (Linnaeus) (14) (Plates 72 and 73)

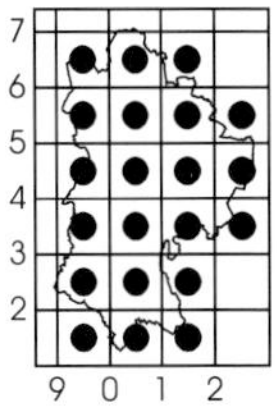

Pre VCH: Recorded in Abbot's notebook (MS1) for 2 June 1798 but without locality.
VCH: "Generally common."
Post VCH: Still common throughout the County. It can be seen flying over rough grasslands in the early evening.
Flight: June to August (weeks 22 to 33)*.
Larval Foodplants: Docks*, grasses and many other plants, feeding on and in the roots.

Orange Swift *Hepialus sylvina* (Linnaeus) (15)

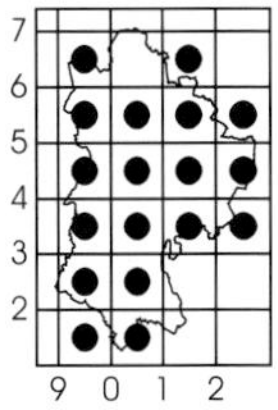

VCH: "Bedford and Luton."
Post VCH: Common throughout the County.
Flight: June to September (weeks 21 to 37, peak 31 to 36)*.
Larval Foodplants: Bracken and herbaceous plants such as docks, feeding on and in the roots.

Gold Swift *Hepialus hecta* (Linnaeus) (16)

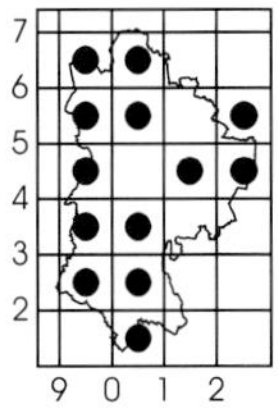

VCH: "Bedford and Luton; in woods."
Post VCH: A local species that can be found in woods especially where bracken occurs.
Flight: June and July (weeks 21 to 27, peak 24 to 25)*. One was found in the RIS trap at Eaton Bray on 10 September 1989, unusually late for this species.
Larval Foodplants: Bracken and other plants, feeding on and in the stems and roots.

For key to moth maps see page 3.

Common Swift *Hepialus lupulinus* (Linnaeus) (17)

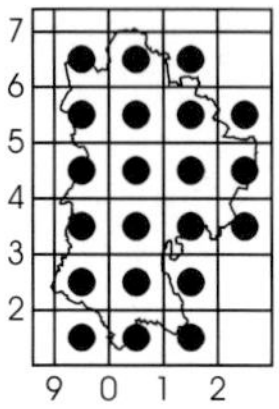

VCH: "Generally abundant in meadows."
Post VCH: Common throughout the County.
Flight: May to July (weeks 18 to 28, peak 21 to 26)*.
Larval Foodplants: Grasses and many wild and cultivated plants, feeding on and in the roots.

Map-winged Swift *Hepialus fusconebulosa* (De Geer) (18) (Drawing on page 81)
VCH: (as *Hepialus velleda* Esp.) "Bedford and Luton."

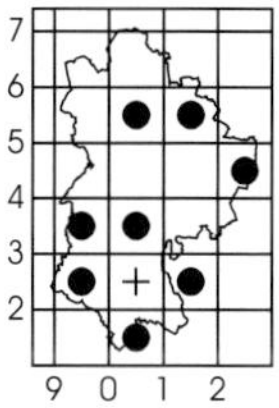

Post VCH: An uncommon and local species. It has been found in the following locations, all in light-traps: Aspley Heath (1937, 1948, 1958, 1981, 1986, 1987), Biddenham (1979), Great Barford (1982), Maulden Wood (1979), Pegsdon Hills (1986), Stockgrove Country Park (1983), Woburn (1992) and the RIS traps at Whipsnade Wild Animal Park (1972, 1973) and Cockayne Hatley (1981).
Flight: June and July (weeks 23 to 27, peak 24 to 25)*.

Larval Foodplant: Bracken, feeding in the stems and roots.

For details of standard weeks see page 6.

Some Leaf-miners and Longhorns

(Nepticulidae to Heliozelidae)

D.V.Manning

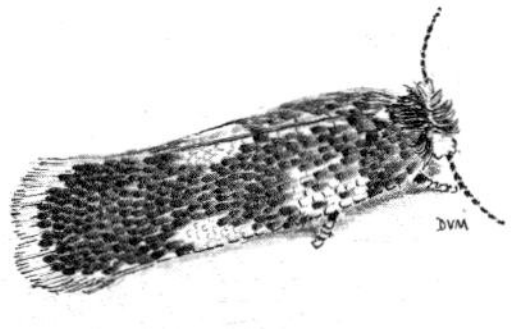

Ectoedemia turbidella (x 8)

Mine of Ectoedemia occultella in a birch leaf

Family: **Nepticulidae**

A large family of very small moths, most with wingspans between 4 and 6 mm. Although many are brightly coloured, with metallic markings, they are rarely seen. The larvae of most species make conspicuous leaf-mines, and it is from these mines that most records have been obtained. There are about 100 British species, of which 64 have been found in the County.

Flight periods are not generally shown, as the adults are very rarely encountered and successfully identified.

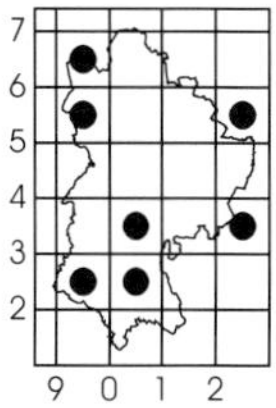

Bohemannia pulverosella **(Stainton) (40)**
Post VCH: Local and fairly common: King's Wood (Heath and Reach), Sharnbrook, Barton Hills, Maulden Wood, Stotfold, and Cockayne Hatley Wood.
Larval Foodplant: Apple*, in a leaf-mine.

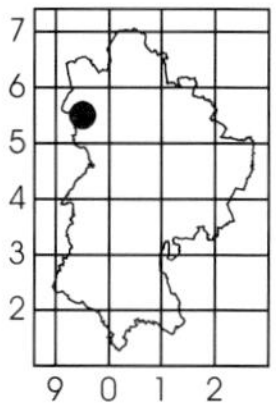

Etainia decentella **(Herrich-Schäffer) (20)**
Post VCH: A single record of the moth at MV light at Sharnbrook on 17 July 1978.
Larval Foodplant: Sycamore, feeding on the seeds.

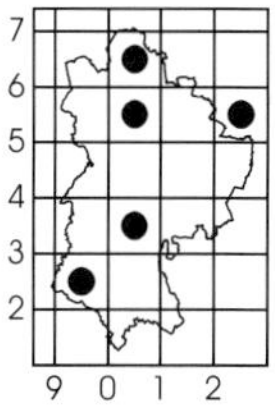

Etainia louisella **(Sircom) (=** ***sphendamni*** **(Hering)) (22)**
Post VCH: Local and fairly common: King's Wood (Heath and Reach), Maulden Wood, Putnoe Wood, Sharnbrook and Potton Wood.
Larval Foodplant: Field maple*, feeding on the seeds.

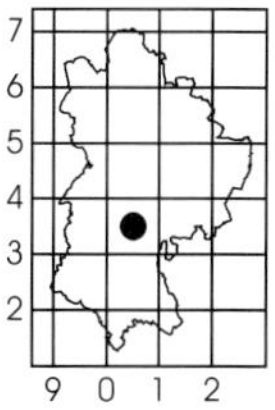

Ectoedemia atrifrontella **(Stainton) (41)**
Post VCH: A single record from Maulden Wood on 14 October 1984 by A.M.Emmet.
Larval Foodplants: Oaks*, beneath young green bark.

For key to moth maps see page 3.

***Ectoedemia argyropeza* (Zeller) (23)**
Post VCH: Widespread and common: Cranfield, Odell Great Wood, Colworth Estate, Chicksands Wood and Potton Wood.
Larval Foodplant: Aspen*, in a leaf-mine.

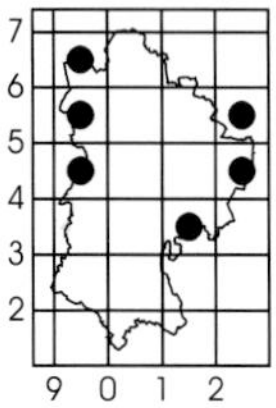

***Ectoedemia turbidella* (Zeller) (24)** (Drawing on page 83)
Post VCH: Stotfold, a single colony found in 1986 by T.S.Hollingworth. The trees have since been felled, and no other colony has been located.
Larval Foodplant: Grey poplar*, in a leaf-mine.

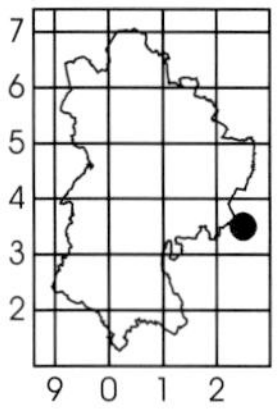

***Ectoedemia intimella* (Zeller) (25)**
Post VCH: Widespread and common: Marston Thrift, Felmersham Nature Reserve, Maulden Wood, Worley's Wood, Biggleswade Common and Potton Wood.
Larval Foodplants: Sallows* in woods, in a leaf-mine, not visible in the leaf until late October and November.

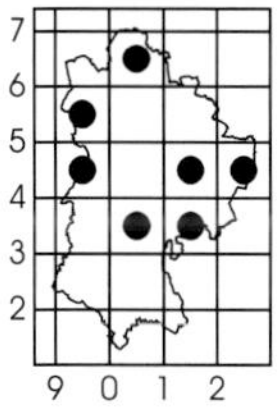

***Ectoedemia angulifasciella* (Stainton) (28)**
Post VCH: Widespread and common.
Larval Foodplants: Roses*, in a leaf-mine.

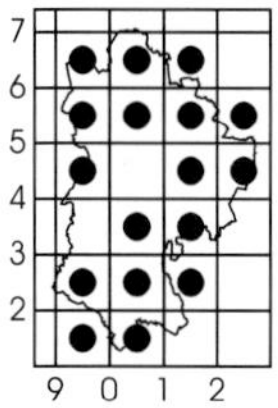

***Ectoedemia atricollis* (Stainton) (29)**
Post VCH: Widespread and common.
Larval Foodplants: Apple* and hawthorns*, in a leaf-mine.

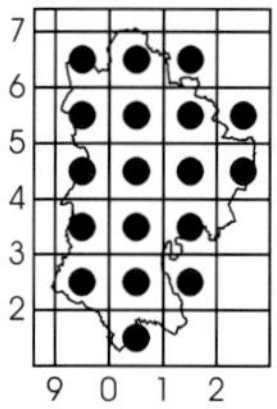

***Ectoedemia arcuatella* (Herrich-Schäffer) (30)**
Post VCH: Local and uncommon: Dunstable Downs and Pegsdon Hills.
Larval Foodplants: Wild strawberry* and barren strawberry*, in a leaf-mine.

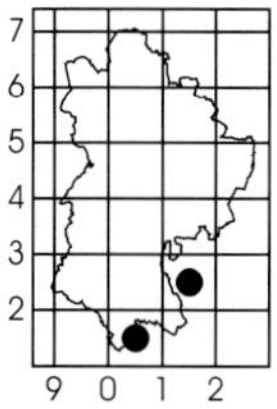

***Ectoedemia rubivora* (Wocke) (31)**
Post VCH: Local and uncommon: Cranfield, Worley's Wood, Blue Lagoon, Stanford Wood and Potton Wood.
Larval Foodplants: Brambles*, in a leaf-mine.

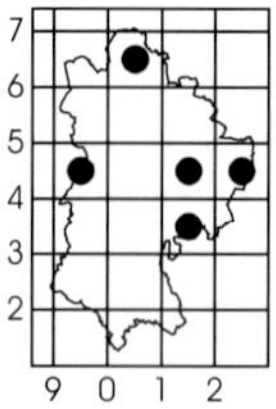

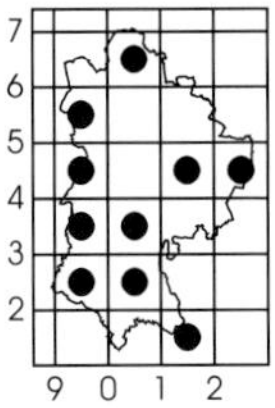

Ectoedemia occultella **(Linnaeus) (=** ***argentipedella*** **(Zeller)) (34)**
Post VCH: Widespread and common.
Larval Foodplants: Birches*, in a leaf-mine (drawing on page 83).

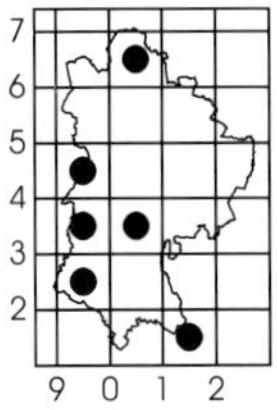

Ectoedemia minimella **(Zetterstedt) (=** ***mediofasciella*** **auctt.;** ***woolhopiella*** **(Stainton)) (35)**
Post VCH: Local and fairly common: King's Wood (Heath and Reach), Aspley Heath, Marston Thrift, Maulden Wood, Sharnbrook and Luton Hoo.
Larval Foodplants: Birches*, in a leaf-mine.

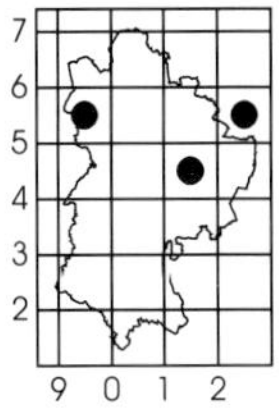

Ectoedemia quinquella **(Bedell) (36)**
Post VCH: Local and uncommon: Sharnbrook, Biggleswade and Cockayne Hatley Wood.
Larval Foodplants: Oaks*, in a leaf-mine.

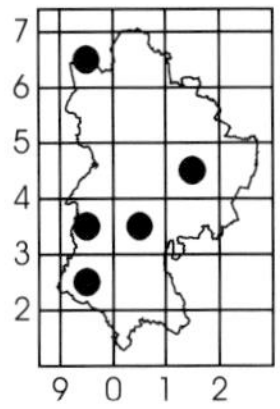

Ectoedemia albifasciella **(Heinemann) (37)**
Post VCH: Local and fairly common: King's Wood (Heath and Reach), Charle Wood, West Wood, Maulden Wood and Old Warden.
Larval Foodplants: Oaks*, in a leaf-mine.

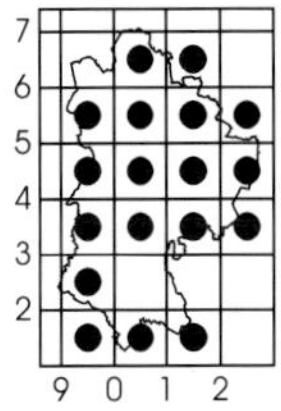

Ectoedemia subbimaculella **(Haworth) (38)**
Post VCH: Widespread and common.
Larval Foodplants: Oaks*, in a leaf-mine.

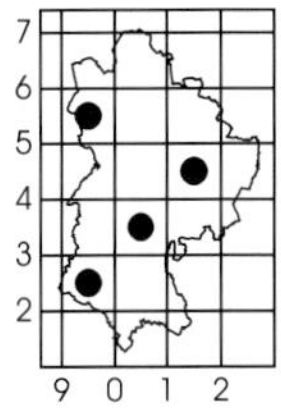

Ectoedemia heringi **(Toll) (39)**
Post VCH: Local and fairly common: King's Wood (Heath and Reach) and Sharnbrook.
Larval Foodplants: Oaks*, in a leaf-mine.

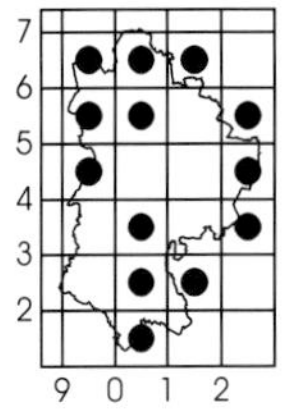

Fomoria septembrella **(Stainton) (42)**
Post VCH: Widespread and common.
Larval Foodplants: St John's-worts*, in a leaf-mine.

For key to moth maps see page 3.

***Trifurcula immundella* (Zeller) (46)**
Post VCH: Local and fairly common: Maulden Wood and The Lodge, Sandy.
Larval Foodplant: Broom*, in mines on twigs.

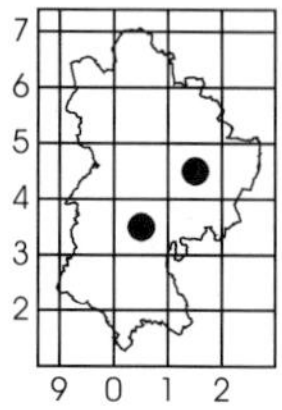

***Stigmella aurella* (Fabricius) (50)**
VCH: "Luton, among bramble".
Post VCH: Widespread and common. A very conspicuous mine, recorded from all 10 km squares.
Larval Foodplants: Brambles*, in a leaf-mine.

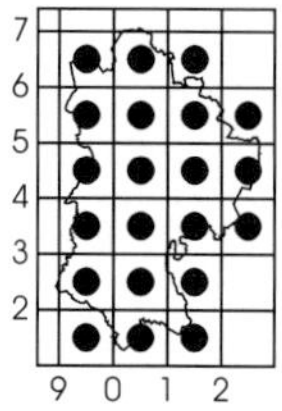

***Stigmella fragariella* (Heyden) (51)**
Post VCH: Widespread and fairly common.
Larval Foodplant: Agrimony*.
Note: This is now regarded as a form of *Stigmella aurella*.

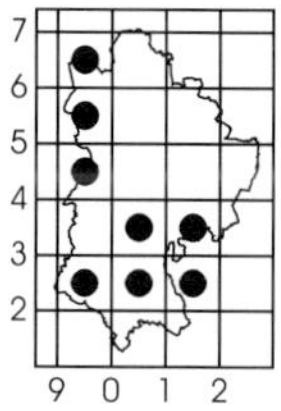

***Stigmella splendidissimella* (Herrich-Schäffer) (53)**
Post VCH: Widespread and fairly common: Whipsnade, Totternhoe Knolls, Maulden Wood, Putnoe Wood and Potton Wood.
Larval Foodplants: Dewberry, and other species of bramble*, in a leaf-mine.

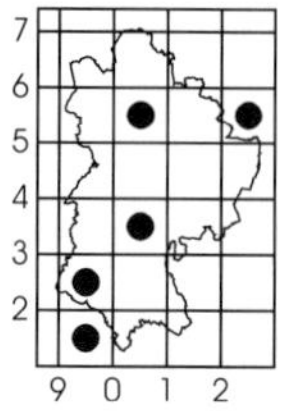

***Stigmella dulcella* (Heinemann) (52)**
Post VCH: Local and uncommon: King's Wood (Heath and Reach), Felmersham Nature Reserve, Dunstable Downs and Bedford.
Larval Foodplant: Wild strawberry*.
Note: This is now regarded as a form of *Stigmella splendidissimella*.

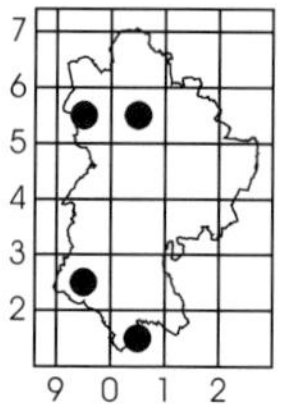

***Stigmella aeneofasciella* (Herrich-Schäffer) (55)**
Post VCH: Scarce: Waterloo Thorns.
Larval Foodplant: Agrimony*, in a leaf-mine.

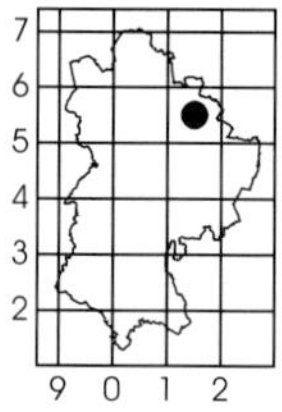

***Stigmella ulmariae* (Wocke) (58)**
Post VCH: A single record from Stockgrove Country Park on 9 October 1985 by A.M.Emmet.
Larval Foodplant: Meadowsweet*, in a leaf-mine.

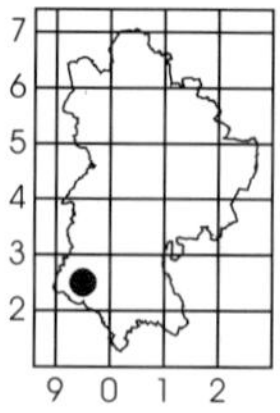

For details of standard weeks see page 6.

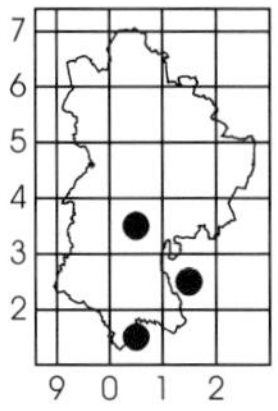

***Stigmella poterii* (Stainton) (59)**
Post VCH: Locally common: Dunstable Downs, Sharpenhoe Clappers and Pegsdon Hills.
Larval Foodplant: Salad burnet*, in a leaf-mine.

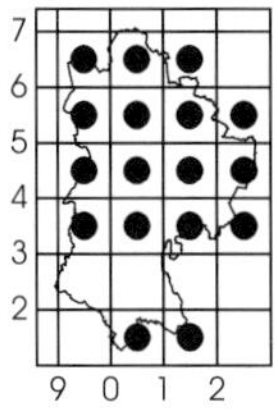

***Stigmella marginicolella* (Stainton) (63)**
Post VCH: Widespread and common.
Larval Foodplants: Elms*, in a leaf-mine.

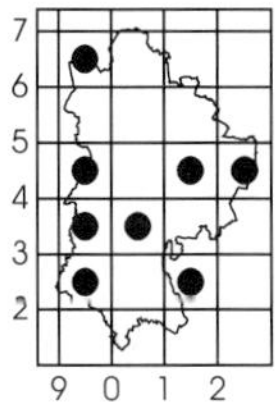

***Stigmella continuella* (Stainton) (64)**
Post VCH: Local and fairly common: Salford, Marston Thrift, West Wood, Pegsdon Hills, Sandy and Sutton Fen.
Larval Foodplants: Birches*, in a leaf-mine.

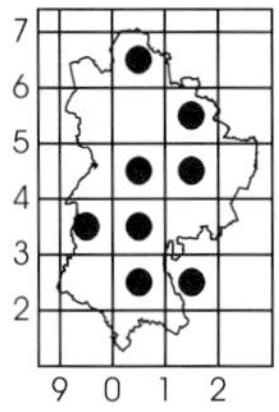

***Stigmella speciosa* (Frey) (65)**
Post VCH: Widespread and fairly common: Aspley Heath, Barton Hills, Maulden Wood, Priory Country Park, Sharnbrook, Pegsdon Hills, Great Barford and The Lodge, Sandy.
Larval Foodplant: Sycamore*, in a leaf-mine.

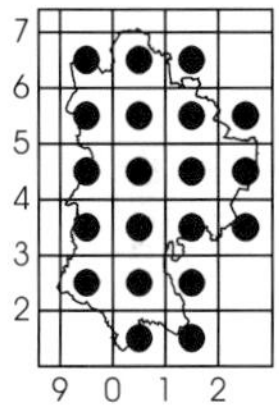

***Stigmella plagicolella* (Stainton) (67)**
Post VCH: Widespread and common.
Larval Foodplants: Blackthorn* and other *Prunus* spp.*, in a leaf-mine.

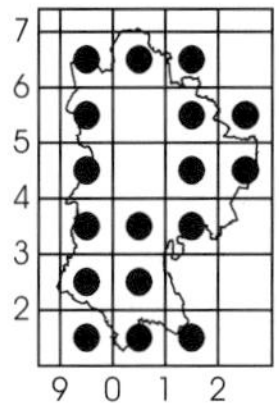

***Stigmella salicis* (Stainton) (68)**
Post VCH: Widespread and common.
Flight: Specimens dissected (weeks 30,32)*.
Larval Foodplants: Sallows*, in a leaf-mine.

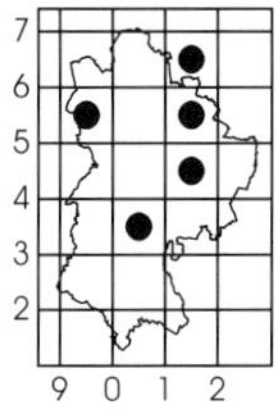

***Stigmella obliquella* (Heinemann) (70)**
Post VCH: Widespread and fairly common: Felmersham Nature Reserve, Cooper's Hill, Cople Pits, Willington Lock and Little Staughton.
Larval Foodplants: Willows*, in a leaf-mine.

For key to moth maps see page 3.

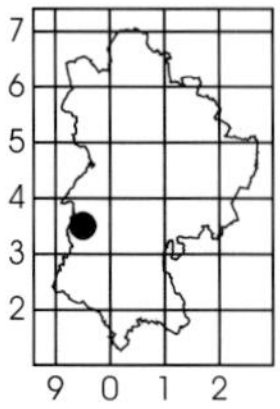

Stigmella myrtillella **(Stainton) (72)**
Post VCH: Local and uncommon: Old Wavendon Heath.
Larval Foodplant: Bilberry*, in a leaf-mine.

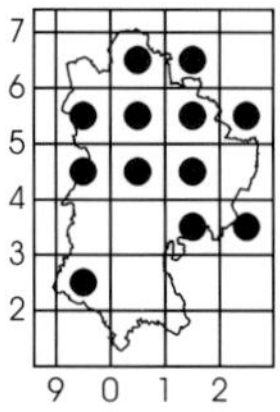

Stigmella trimaculella **(Haworth) (73)**
Post VCH: Widespread and common.
Larval Foodplants: Black poplar* and Lombardy poplar, in a leaf-mine.

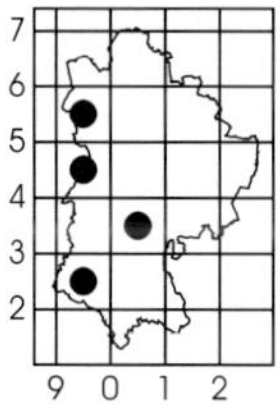

Stigmella assimilella **(Zeller) (74)**
Post VCH: Local and uncommon: Stockgrove Country Park, Marston Thrift, Sharnbrook and Maulden Wood.
Larval Foodplant: Aspen*, in a leaf-mine.

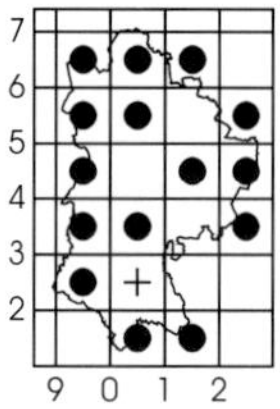

Stigmella floslactella **(Haworth) (75)**
VCH: "Luton".
Post VCH: Widespread and common.
Larval Foodplants: Hazel* and hornbeam*, in a leaf-mine.

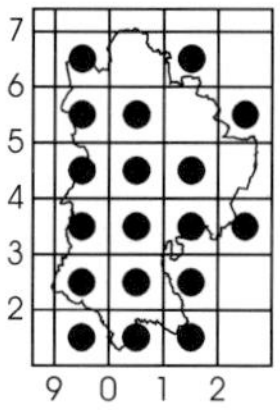

Stigmella tityrella **(Stainton) (77)**
Post VCH: Widespread and common.
Larval Foodplant: Beech*, in a leaf-mine (Plate 50).

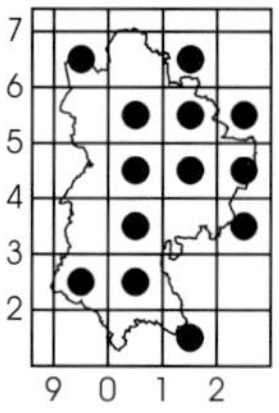

Stigmella perpygmaeella **(Doubleday) (79)**
Post VCH: Widespread and common.
Flight: Specimens dissected (weeks 30, 31)*.
Larval Foodplants: Hawthorns*, in a leaf-mine.

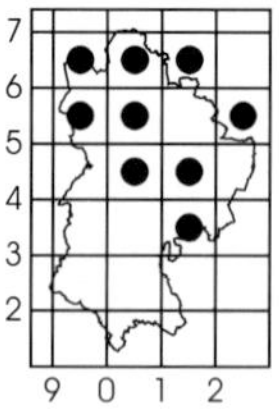

Stigmella ulmivora **(Fologne) (80)**
Post VCH: Widespread and common.
Larval Foodplants: Elms*, in a leaf-mine.

For details of standard weeks see page 6.

Stigmella hemargyrella **(Kollar) (81)**
Post VCH: Widespread and common.
Larval Foodplant: Beech★, in a leaf-mine.

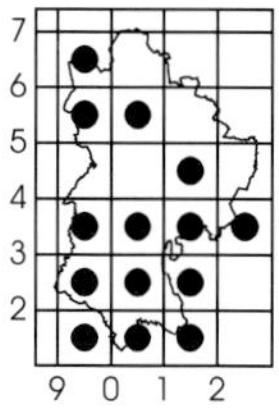

Stigmella paradoxa **(Frey) (82)**
Post VCH: Local and scarce: Barton Hills and Pegsdon Hills.
Larval Foodplants: Hawthorns★, in a leaf-mine.

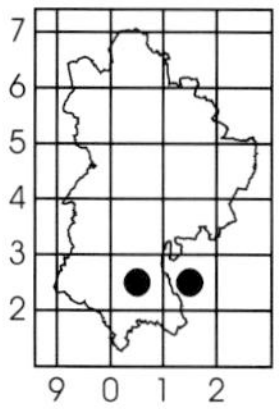

Stigmella atricapitella **(Haworth) (83)**
Flight: Specimens dissected (week 30)★.
Larval Foodplants: Oaks★, in a leaf-mine. #

Note: the distribution of species 83 and 86 has not been satisfactorily determined. The leaf-mines cannot be reliably separated, and the species must be bred to maturity. The distribution maps in Heath (1976) indicate that both species have been reared from the County by A.M.Emmet.

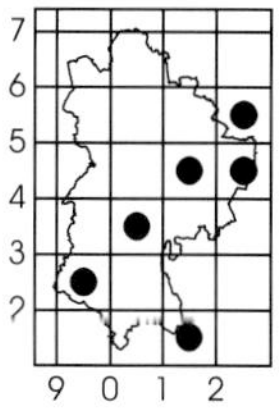

Stigmella ruficapitella **(Haworth) (84)**
Post VCH: Widespread and common.
Larval Foodplants: Oaks★, in a leaf-mine.

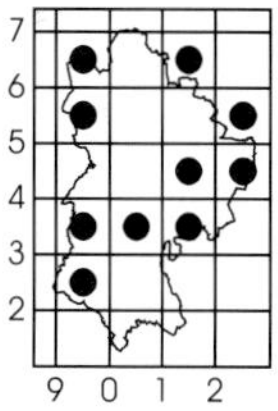

Stigmella suberivora **(Stainton) (85)**
Post VCH: A single record from Woburn on 21 September 1986 by T.S.Hollingworth.
Larval Foodplant: Evergreen oak★, in a leaf-mine.

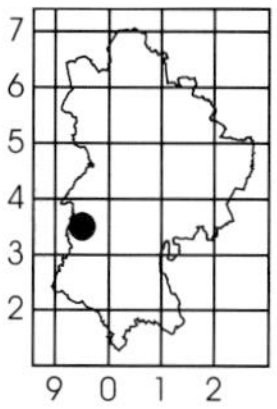

Stigmella roborella **(Johansson) (86)**
Larval Foodplants: Oaks★, in a leaf-mine. #

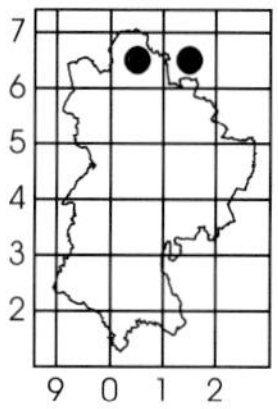

Stigmella samiatella **(Zeller) (88)**
Post VCH: Scarce. One leaf-mine on chestnut from Woodbury Park on 10 November 1990, and one moth in the RIS trap at Cockayne Hatley in the week 23 - 29 July 1995.
Flight: July (week 30)★(specimen dissected).
Larval Foodplants: Sweet chestnut★ and oaks, in a leaf-mine.

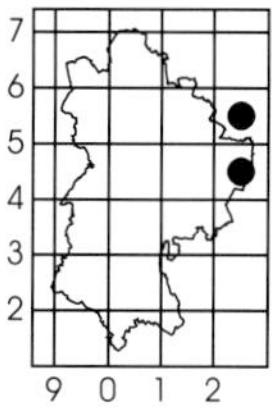

For key to moth maps see page 3.

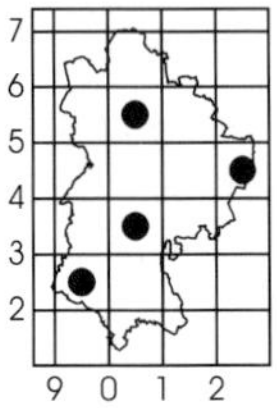

Stigmella basiguttella **(Heinemann) (89)**
Post VCH: Local and fairly common: King's Wood (Heath and Reach), Maulden Wood, Putnoe Wood and Sutton Fen.
Larval Foodplants: Oaks*, in a leaf-mine.

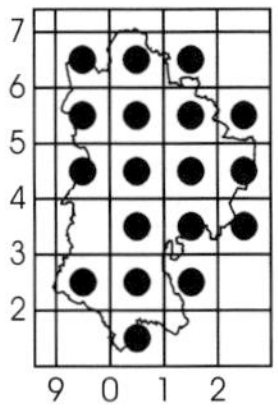

Rose Leaf-miner *Stigmella anomalella* (Goeze) (92)
Post VCH: Widespread and common.
Larval Foodplants: Roses*, in a leaf-mine.

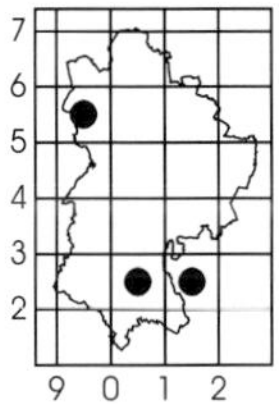

Stigmella centifoliella **(Zeller) (93)**
Post VCH: Local and uncommon: Sharnbrook, Icknield Way, Pegsdon Hills. The mines are so similar to one of the mine-forms of *Stigmella anomalella* that the records of this species are in some doubt.
Larval Foodplants: Roses*, in a leaf-mine.

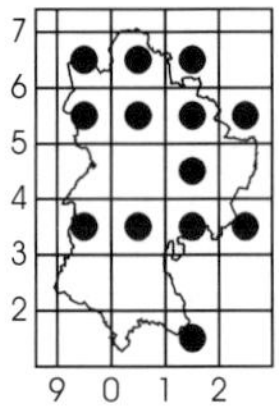

Stigmella viscerella **(Stainton) (95)**
Post VCH: Widespread and common.
Larval Foodplants: Elms*, in a leaf-mine.

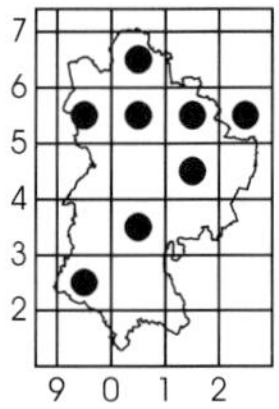

Stigmella malella **(Stainton) (97)**
Post VCH: Widespread and common.
Larval Foodplant: Apple*, in a leaf-mine.

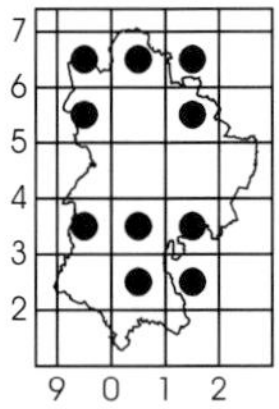

Stigmella catharticella **(Stainton) (98)**
Post VCH: Local and fairly common.
Larval Foodplant: Buckthorn*, in a leaf-mine.

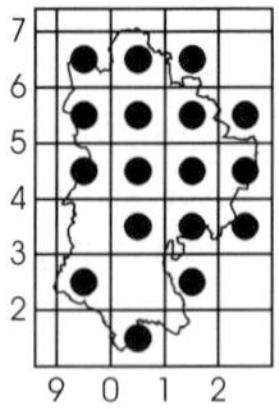

Stigmella hybnerella **(Hübner) (99)**
Post VCH: Widespread and common.
Flight: Specimens dissected (week 31)*.
Larval Foodplants: Hawthorns*, in a leaf-mine.

For details of standard weeks see page 6.

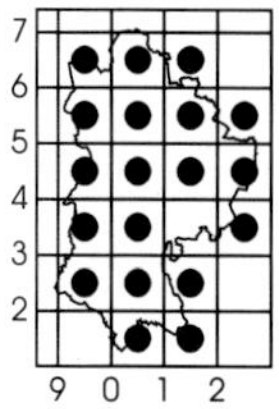

***Stigmella oxyacanthella* (Stainton) (100)**
Post VCH: Widespread and common.
Larval Foodplants: Hawthorns★, apple★ and pear, in a leaf-mine.

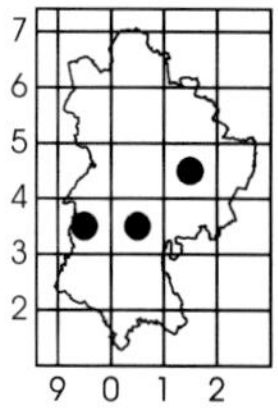

***Stigmella nylandriella* (Tengström) (= *aucupariae* (Frey)) (103)**
Post VCH: Local and uncommon: Aspley Heath, Flitwick Moor and The Lodge, Sandy.
Larval Foodplant: Rowan★, in a leaf-mine.

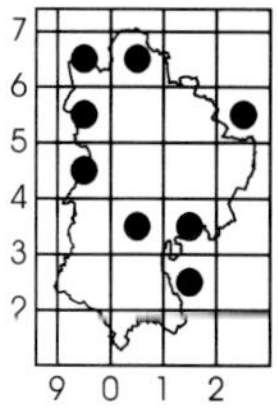

***Stigmella regiella* (Herrich-Schäffer) (107)**
Post VCH: Widespread and common.
Larval Foodplants: Hawthorns★, in a leaf-mine.

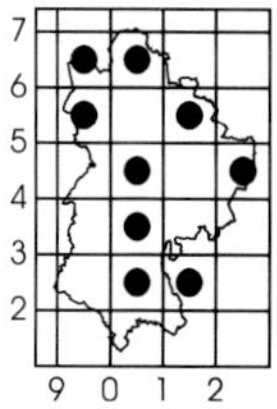

***Stigmella crataegella* (Klimesch) (108)**
Post VCH: Widespread and common.
Larval Foodplants: Hawthorns★, in a leaf-mine.

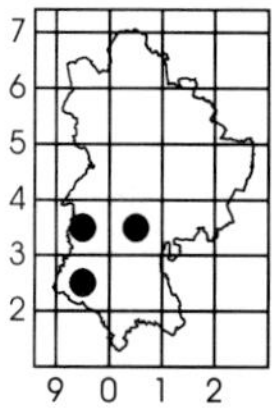

***Stigmella betulicola* (Stainton) (110)**
Post VCH: Local and uncommon: Aspley Heath.
Larval Foodplants: Birches★, in a leaf-mine.

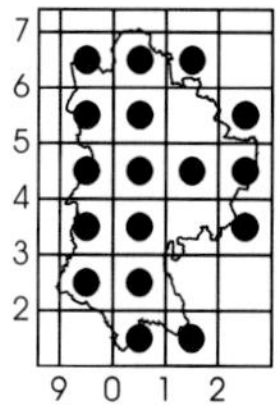

***Stigmella microtheriella* (Stainton) (111)**
Post VCH: Widespread and common.
Larval Foodplants: Hazel★ and hornbeam, in a leaf-mine.

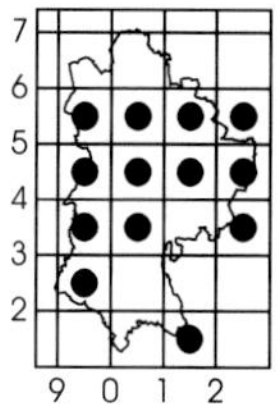

***Stigmella luteella* (Stainton) (112)**
Post VCH: Widespread and common.
Larval Foodplants: Birches★, in a leaf-mine.

For key to moth maps see page 3.

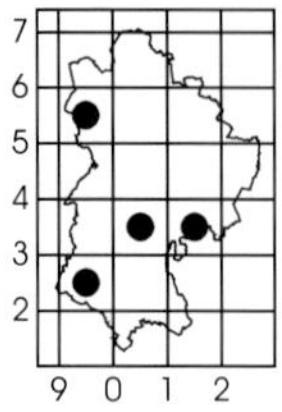

Stigmella glutinosae **(Stainton) (114)**
Post VCH: Local and uncommon: Felmersham Nature Reserve.
Larval Foodplant: Alder*, in a leaf-mine.

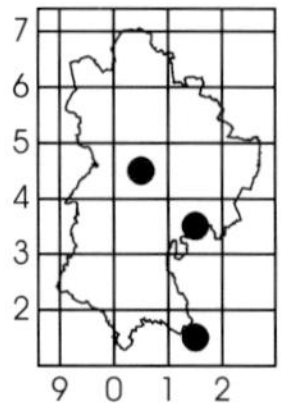

Stigmella alnetella **(Stainton) (115)**
Post VCH: Local and uncommon: Bedford and Newmill End.
Larval Foodplant: Alder*, in a leaf-mine.

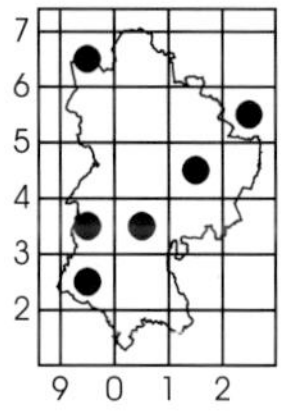

Stigmella lapponica **(Wocke) (116)**
Post VCH: Widespread and fairly common: Stockgrove Country Park, Aspley Heath, West Wood, Maulden Wood, Old Warden and Potton Wood.
Larval Foodplants: Birches*, in a leaf-mine.

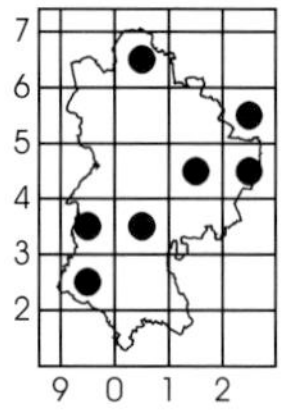

Stigmella confusella **(Wood) (117)**
Post VCH: Local and uncommon: King's Wood (Heath and Reach), Charle Wood, Maulden Wood, Coppice Wood, Sandy, Sutton Fen and Potton Wood.
Larval Foodplants: Birches*, in a leaf-mine.

Family: **Opostegidae**

Small, pale-coloured moths (wingspan 7-10 mm). They fly at dusk and are attracted to light, but are seldom seen. The early stages are unknown. Of the four British species, two have been found in Bedfordshire.

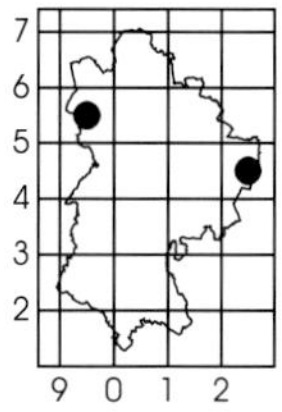

Opostega salaciella **(Treitschke) (119)**
Post VCH: Scarce: Sharnbrook and the RIS trap at Cockayne Hatley.
Flight: June, July (week 30)*.
Larval Foodplants: Docks (?).

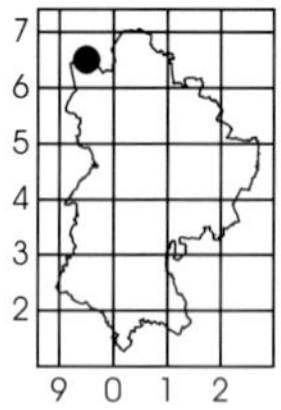

Opostega crepusculella **Zeller (121)**
Post VCH: Scarce: West Wood.
Flight: June, July (weeks 25, 30)*.
Larval Foodplants: Mints (?).

For details of standard weeks see page 6.

Family: **Tischeriidae**

Small, plain-coloured moths. Wingspan 7-11 mm. The larvae make conspicuous blotch mines in leaves, ejecting their frass. Of the six British species, three have been found in Bedfordshire.

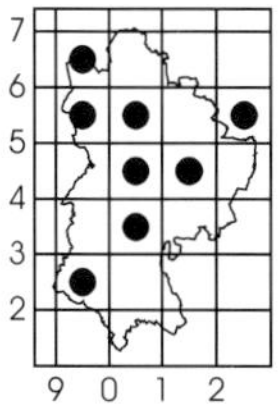

***Tischeria ekebladella* (Bjerkander) (123)**
VCH: (as *T. complanella* Hb.) "Bedford".
Post VCH: Widespread and common.
Flight: June, July (week 29)*.
Larval Foodplants: Oaks*, in a leaf-mine.

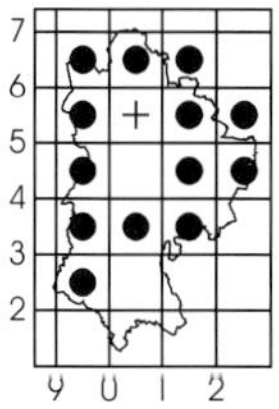

***Emmetia marginea* (Haworth) (125)**
VCH: "Bedford".
Post VCH: Widespread and common.
Flight: May to September (weeks 22 to 32, 35,36)*.
Larval Foodplants: Brambles*, in a leaf-mine.

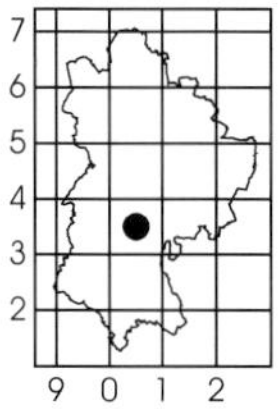

***Emmetia angusticollella* (Duponchel) (127)**
Post VCH: Local and uncommon: Maulden Wood.
Flight: June, July.
Larval Foodplants: Roses*, in a leaf-mine.

Family: **Incurvariidae**

All modern records are of the day-flying moths. Wingspan 7-23 mm. The males of the genera *Nematopogon*, *Nemophora* and *Adela* ('the longhorns')have antennae several times longer than the body. The larvae feed as stem-borers, leaf-miners or in portable cases on the ground made from soil or leaf-fragments, and have not yet been studied in Bedfordshire. There are 28 British species, of which 15 have been found in the County.

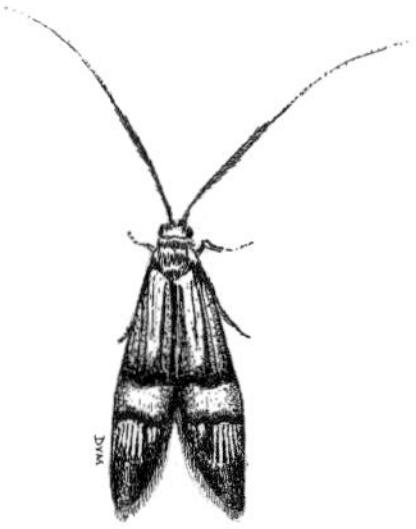

Nemophora degeerella (female x 1.5)

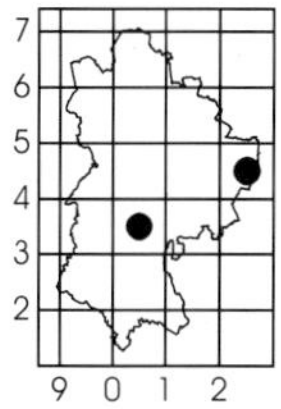

***Phylloporia bistrigella* (Haworth) (128)**
Post VCH: Local and uncommon: Flitwick Moor and Sutton Fen.
Flight: May to July.
Larval Foodplants: Birches*, in a leaf-mine from which a case is excised for pupation.

For key to moth maps see page 3.

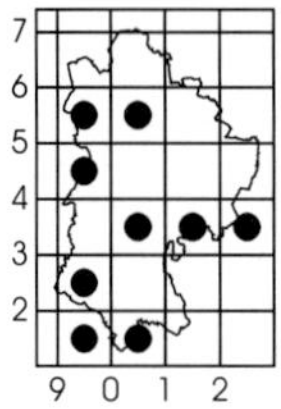

Incurvaria masculella **([Denis & Schiffermüller]) (130)**
VCH: "Generally common".
Post VCH: Widespread and common.
Flight: April, May (weeks 17-21)★.
Larval Foodplants: Hawthorns, later in leaf-litter in a case.

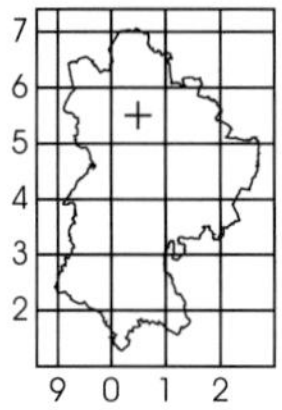

Lampronia luzella **(Hübner) (135)**
VCH: "Bedford".
Post VCH: No recent record.
Flight: May to July.
Larval Foodplants: Uncertain but possibly *Rubus* spp.

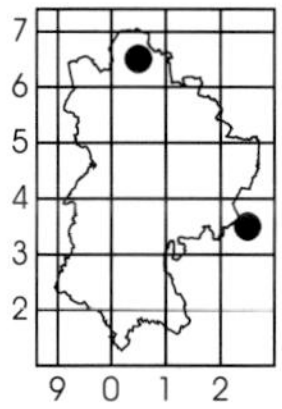

Raspberry Moth *Lampronia rubiella* (Bjerkander) (136)
Post VCH: Scarce: Coppice Wood on 29 June 1985 and Stotfold on 8 July 1992.
Flight: May to July (weeks 26, 28)★.
Larval Foodplant: Raspberry.

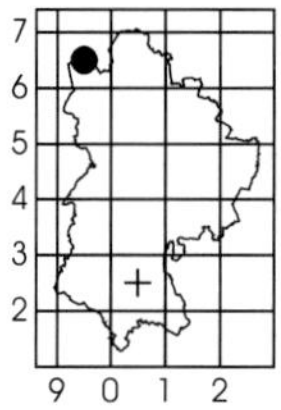

Lampronia morosa **Zeller (137)**
VCH: (as *L. quadripunctella* Fab.) "Luton".
Post VCH: A single modern record from West Wood on 20 May 1989.
Flight: May (week 20)★, June.
Larval Foodplants: Roses.

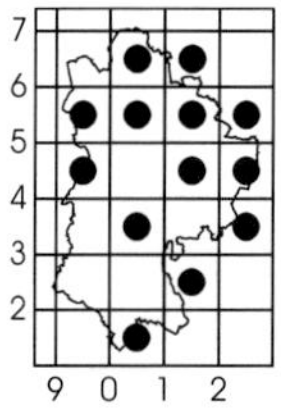

Nematopogon swammerdamella **(Linnaeus) (140)**
VCH: "Bedford, in woods".
Post VCH: Widespread and common.
Flight: May, June (weeks 19 to 25)★.
Larval Food: Leaf-litter, where larval cases can be found.

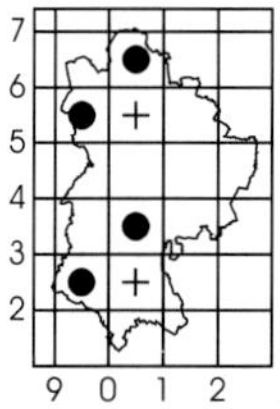

Nematopogon schwarziellus **(Zeller) (=** ***panzerella*** **auctt.) (141)**
VCH: "Bedford, Luton".
Post VCH: Local and uncommon: Sewell Cutting, Felmersham Nature Reserve, Flitwick Moor and Worley's Wood.
Flight: May to July (weeks 21 to 24, 27)★.
Larval Food: Leaf-litter, where larval cases can be found.

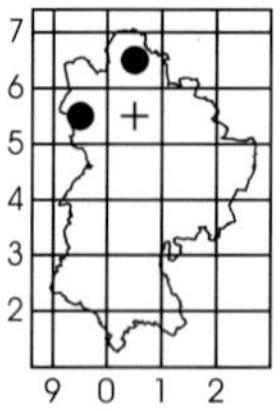

Nematopogon metaxella **(Hübner) (143)**
VCH: "Bedford, in marshy places".
Post VCH: Local and uncommon: Felmersham Nature Reserve and Worley's Wood.
Flight: May to July (weeks 23 to 29)★.
Larval Food: Leaf-litter, where larval cases can be found.

For details of standard weeks see page 6.

Nemophora cupriacella **(Hübner) (146)**
Post VCH: Local and uncommon: Pegsdon Hills.
Flight: July (week 28)*.
Larval Foodplants: Field scabious, small scabious and devils'-bit scabious, in a larval case.

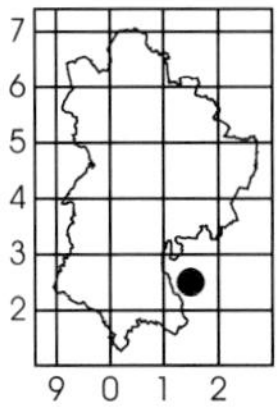

Nemophora metallica **(Poda) (147)**
Post VCH: Locally common: Totternhoe Knolls, Dunstable Downs, Sharpenhoe and Pegsdon Hills.
Flight: July, August (weeks 28, 29, 33)*.
Larval Foodplants: Field scabious and small scabious, in a larval case.

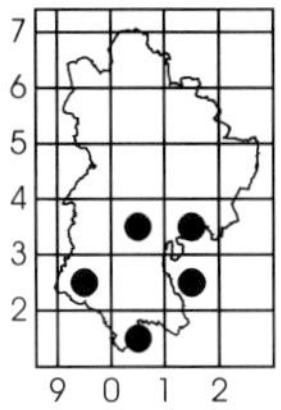

Nemophora degeerella **(Linnaeus) (148)** (Drawing on page 93)
VCH: "Bedford, in woods".
Post VCH: Locally common.
Flight: May, June (weeks 23 to 26)*.
Larval Food: Leaf-litter, where larval cases can be found.

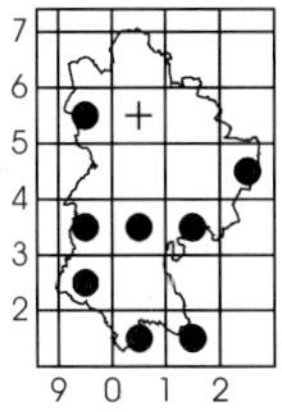

Adela reaumurella **(Linnaeus) (150)** (Plate 77)
VCH: (as *A. viridella* Linn.) "Generally common in woods".
Post VCH: Widespread and common.
Flight: May, June (weeks 18 to 23)*.
Larval Food: Leaf-litter, where larval cases can be found.

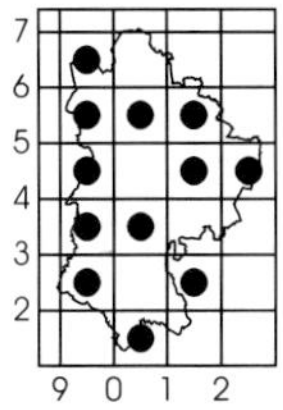

Adela croesella **(Scopoli) (151)**
Post VCH: Local and uncommon: Barton Hills.
Flight: June, July*.
Larval Food: Leaf-litter, where larval cases can be found.

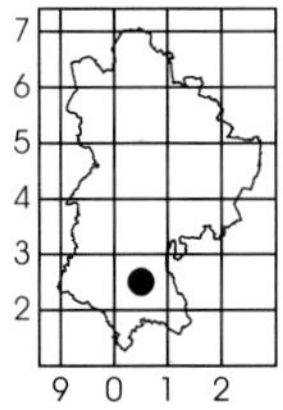

Adela rufimitrella **(Scopoli) (152)**
Post VCH: Local and uncommon: Marston Thrift and Sharnbrook.
Flight: May, June (week 23)*.
Larval Foodplant: Cuckooflower, in a larval case.

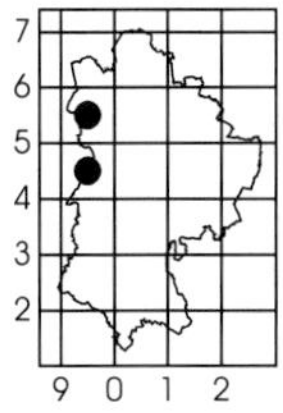

Adela fibulella **([Denis & Schiffermüller]) (153)**
Post VCH: Locally common: moths found resting on flowers of germander speedwell. Sewell Cutting, Dunstable Downs, Great Early Grove, Pegsdon Hills, Chicksands Wood and Potton Wood.
Flight: May, June (weeks 20 to 23)*.
Larval Foodplant: Germander speedwell*, in a larval case.

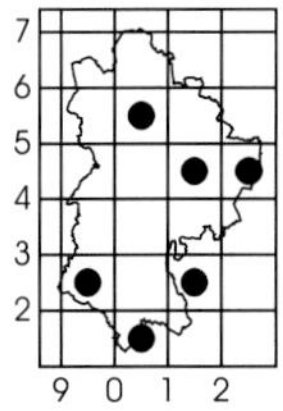

For key to moth maps see page 3.

Family: **Heliozelidae**

Small moths (wingspan 5-9 mm) which fly in afternoon sunshine, but which are seldom seen. The larvae form mines in the petioles and leaves of the foodplant, and pupate on the ground in portable cases detached from the mine. All five British species have been found in Bedfordshire, but have not been studied in the County and are under-recorded.

Heliozela sericiella **(Haworth) (154)**
VCH: "Bedford".
Post VCH: Local and uncommon: Maulden Wood, Putnoe Wood and Rowney Warren.
Flight: April, May (week 19)*.
Larval Foodplant: Oaks*, in a mine, mainly in the petiole.

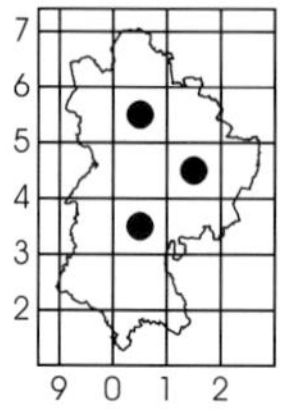

Heliozela resplendella **(Stainton) (156)**
Post VCH: Local and uncommon: Felmersham Nature Reserve.
Flight: May to July.
Larval Foodplant: Alder*, in a mine, mainly in leaf-veins.

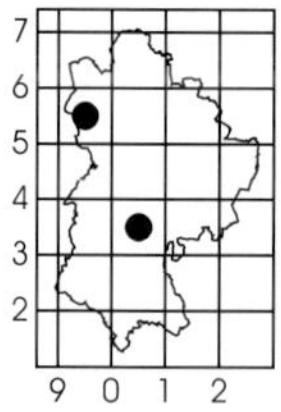

Heliozela hammoniella **Sorhagen (157)**
Post VCH: Local and uncommon: King's Wood (Heath and Reach) and West Wood.
Flight: May, June.
Larval Foodplants: Birches*, in a mine, mainly in the petiole.

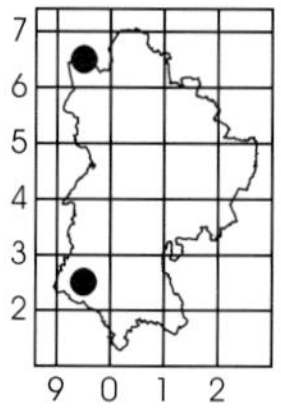

Antispila metallella **([Denis & Schiffermüller]) (= *pfeifferella* (Hübner)) (158)**
Post VCH: Local and uncommon: Putnoe Wood.
Flight: May*.
Larval Foodplant: Dogwood, in a leaf-mine.

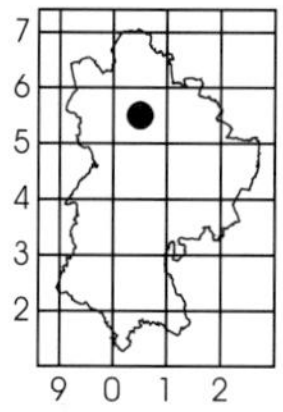

Antispila petryi **Martini (159)**
Post VCH: A single record from Felmersham Nature Reserve on 14 October 1984 by A.M.Emmet.
Flight: June, July.
Larval Foodplant: Dogwood*, in a leaf-mine.

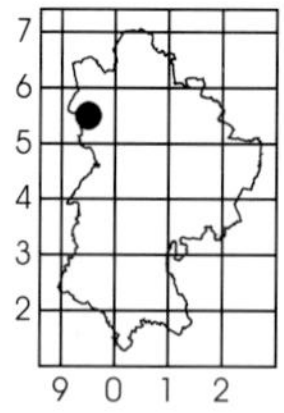

For details of standard weeks see page 6.

Leopard and Goat Moths, Foresters and Burnets

(Cossidae and Zygaenidae)

V.W.Arnold

Leopard Moth

Family: **Cossidae**

A small group of species whose larvae bore in the stems of plants where they may live and feed for more than one year. The moths fly at night.

Subfamily: **Zeuzerinae The Leopard Moths**

Only one of the two British species, the Leopard Moth, is found in Bedfordshire. The moth is white with bluish-black spots, wingspan 30-56 mm. Its larvae bore into the stems and branches of several different trees and shrubs and pupate in the feeding tunnel.

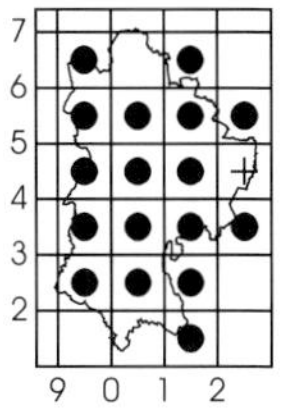

Leopard Moth *Zeuzera pyrina* (Linnaeus) (161)
VCH: "Bedford, Woburn, Potton; not plentiful."
Post VCH: Found throughout the County, usually as single specimens. This species comes readily to light.
Flight: June to early August (weeks 25 to 33)*.
Larval Foodplants: A variety of trees and shrubs, feeding inside the stems and branches.

Subfamily: **Cossinae The Goat Moths**

The only British species, the Goat Moth, occurs in Bedfordshire. The greyish-brown moth has no proboscis. It has a wingspan of 68-84 mm. The large reddish-brown larvae smell of goat and are most often seen when they leave their feeding tunnels in trees to pupate.

Goat Moth *Cossus cossus cossus* (Linnaeus) (162)
Pre VCH: J.C.Dale (MS2) recorded receiving this species from Abbot's collection, "nr Bedford" but not dated. Abbot (MS1) noted rearing it in 1799.

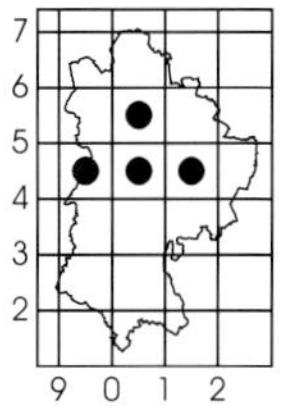

VCH: (as *C. ligniperda* Fab.) "Generally distributed."
Post VCH: R.M.Craske recalled that this species was common in Bedford between 1918 and 1927. Since then it has become much scarcer. In 1956 when a damaged specimen was found in Cardington Road, Bedford, it was claimed that "the larva is a pest in riverside willows" (West, 1957). Larvae were found at Stagsden (1970), on the Embankment in Bedford (1978, 1980) and were photographed in 1983 at Cople Pits Nature Reserve by Mrs B.Bowskill.
Flight: June and July (all recent records were of larvae).

For key to moth maps see page 3.

Larval Foodplants: Willows, ash, poplars, various fruit trees and many other trees, feeding in the living wood.
Notes: The larva overwinters three or four times. It emits a strong smell of goat.

Family: **Zygaenidae**

A group of day-flying moths which have well-developed probosces and slightly clubbed antennae. They are often seen feeding at flowers.

Subfamily: **Procridinae The Foresters**

These beautiful moths have bright metallic green forewings and grey hindwings.The wingspan is 18-31 mm. The larvae start feeding as leaf-miners but later feed externally on the upperside of leaves. They pupate among the foodplant. All three British species have been found in Bedfordshire.

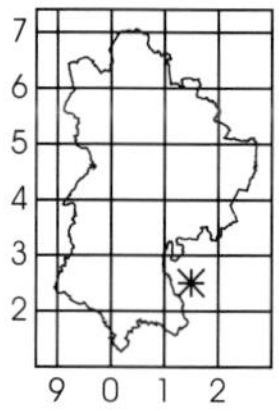

Scarce Forester *Adscita globulariae* (Hübner) (165)
Post VCH: One record only, a specimen labelled "15/06/1917 Pegsdon. W.G.Nash" in the Kershaw collection.
Flight: June. Flies in the daytime.
Larval Foodplants: Greater knapweed and common knapweed.

Cistus Forester *Adscita geryon* (Hübner) (164) (Plate 10)
Post VCH: There are two specimens in the Oxford County Museum collection labelled "Bedford District 17/06/1909" and "Pegsdon 15/06/1917", both collected by W.G.Nash. The Kershaw collection contains a specimen from Barton Hills dated 1911 which may also have been collected by Nash and also two from Sharpenhoe (1933, 1948). R.M.Craske recalled that between 1918 and 1927 the Cistus Forester was "common on Sharpenhoe". A.H.Foster (1934) described it as "often abundant on Pegsdon Hills about midsummer". The last known record from Pegsdon was 23 June 1946 by S.R. Bowden (1965). R.Palmer (MS2) noted it as "fairly abundant" on Barton Hills on 13 June 1943. Now recorded in most years, flying in sunshine, on Bison Hill and Dunstable Downs.

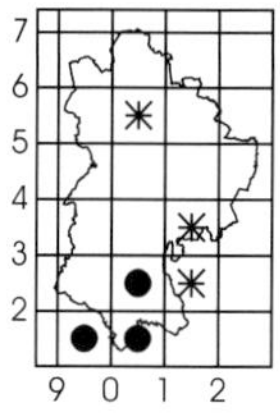

Flight: June and July (weeks 23 to 26)★. Flies in the daytime.
Larval Foodplant: Common rock-rose.

The Forester *Adscita statices* (Linnaeus) (163)
Pre VCH: J.C.Dale (MS2) recorded receiving this species from Abbot's collection, "nr Bedford" but not dated.
VCH: "Luton."
Post VCH: Recorded only twice since the publication of the VCH. Once by S.H. Kershaw from Aspley Heath and also by V.H.Chambers from King's Wood, Heath and Reach. Both records were in 1950.

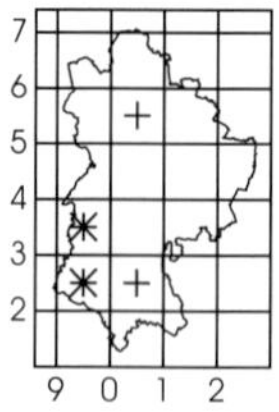

Flight: June★ and July. Flies in the daytime.
Larval Foodplants: Sheep's sorrel and common sorrel.

For details of standard weeks see page 6.

Subfamily: **Zygaeninae The Burnets**

The moths are red and black in colour with a wingspan of 24-40 mm. The larvae feed on vetches and make characteristic papery cocoons, often on grass stems. Of the seven British species, three have been found in Bedfordshire.

Six-spot Burnets

Six-spot Burnet *Zygaena filipendulae* (Linnaeus) ssp. *stephensi* Dupont (169)

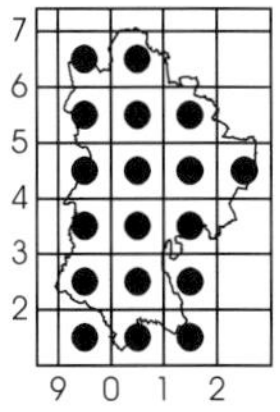

VCH: "Bedford, Luton, Potton; common."
Post VCH: Widespread and common. Found on grassy banks, waste areas and on the downs in the south of the County. A specimen in G.Ping's collection from Marston Thrift (1980), is f. *flava* in which the red colour is replaced by yellow.
Flight: July and August (weeks 26 to 33)*. Flies in the daytime.
Larval Foodplant: Common bird's-foot-trefoil*.

Five-spot Burnet *Zygaena trifolii* (Esper) ssp. *decreta* Verity (170)

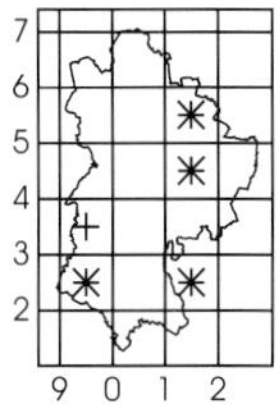

VCH: "Found by Mr. H.Studman near Woburn."
Post VCH: Foster (1917) recorded this species from Pegsdon Hills. Also found at Totternhoe Knolls in 1944 (Kershaw) and 1958 (West, 1959) and in water-meadows near Barford Bridge and Willington in 1962 (West, 1963).
Flight: July and August. Flies in the daytime.
Larval Foodplant: Greater bird's-foot-trefoil.
Notes: It is possible that the above were misidentified *Z. lonicerae* (Scheven), which is the more common and widespread species.

Narrow-bordered Five-spot Burnet *Zygaena lonicerae* (Scheven) ssp. *latomarginata* Tutt (171) (Plate 11)

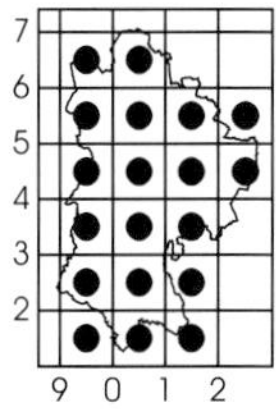

Post VCH: Widespread and common. Found on grassy banks, waste ground and on the downs in the south of the County.
Flight: Late June and July (weeks 26 to 30)*. Flies in the daytime.
Larval Foodplants: Clovers, trefoils and vetches.
Notes: This species may have been confused with *Z. trifolii* (Esper) in the past but in the absence of any specimens it is impossible to know just what has been recorded.

For key to moth maps see page 3.

Bagworms and more Leaf-miners

(Psychidae to Gracillariidae)

D.V.Manning

Family: **Psychidae** **The bagworms.**

A neglected family in Bedfordshire, with records of only four of the twenty British species. The larvae feed from portable cases (Plate 45) on lichens, algae, dead insects or leaf-litter. Wingspan of males 7-20 mm. The female moths are generally wingless and do not leave the larval case. Some species, including *Luffia ferchaultella*, are parthenogenetic (*i.e.* males do not occur).

***Narycia monilifera* (Geoffroy) (175)**
Post VCH: Local and uncommon: West Wood, Flitwick and Rowney Warren.
Flight: June, July.
Larval Foodplants: Lichens. Larval cases found on tree-trunks★ and fences.

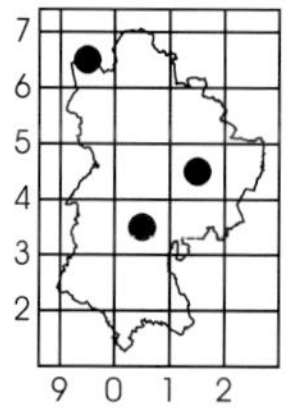

***Taleporia tubulosa* (Retzius) (181)**
VCH: (as *T. pseudo-bombycella* Ochs.) "Bedford".
Post VCH: Local and uncommon: King's Wood (Heath and Reach), Flitwick and Putnoe Wood.
Flight: May, June.
Larval Foodplants: Lichens and leaf-litter. Larval cases found on tree-trunks★.

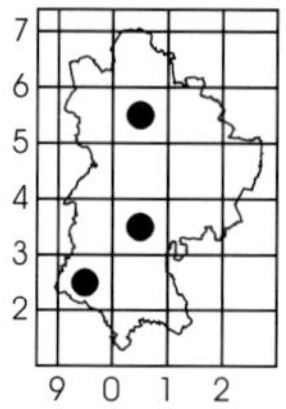

***Luffia ferchaultella* (Stephens) (185)**
Post VCH: A single colony found in a garden in Stotfold on Turkey oak in 1987. Specimens were identified by the Forestry Commision Research Station, Farnham, Hants.
Flight: June, July.
Larval Foodplants: Lichens. Larval cases found on tree-trunks★.

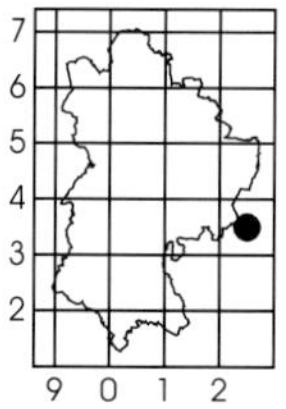

***Psyche casta* (Pallas) (186)**
Post VCH: Widespread and common: King's Wood (Heath and Reach), Sharnbrook, Flitwick Moor, Clapham Park Wood, Sandy and Willington.
Flight: June, July.
Larval Foodplants: Lichens. Larval cases (Plate 44) found on tree-trunks★, fence-posts★ and, for pupation, on leaves of many plants★.

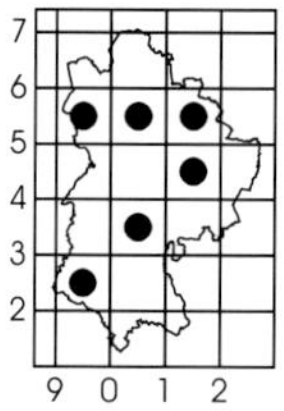

For details of standard weeks see page 6.

Family: **Tineidae**

A family of small to medium-sized moths (wingspan 9-30 mm), whose larvae feed on stored products of both vegetable and animal origin, or on fungi or dead wood. Some larvae feed in birds nests. The family includes the clothes moths, which appear to be much less common than when they were listed in VCH. The British list of over fifty species includes a number of casual imports. Twenty-one species have been found in Bedfordshire. Two of these have not been seen since publication of VCH.

Morophaga choragella **([Denis & Schiffermüller]) (196)**
Post VCH: Local and scarce. Pegsdon Hills (15 July 1986) and in the RIS trap at Cockayne Hatley.
Flight: July (week 28)*, August.
Larval Food: Bracket fungi and rotten wood.

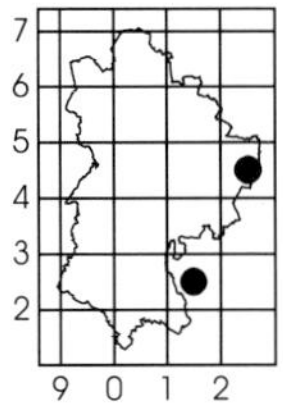

Psychoides verhuella **(Bruand) (199)**
Post VCH: A single record from Stotfold on 7 June 1982 by T.S.Hollingworth.
Flight: June (week 23)*, July.
Larval Foodplants: Ferns.

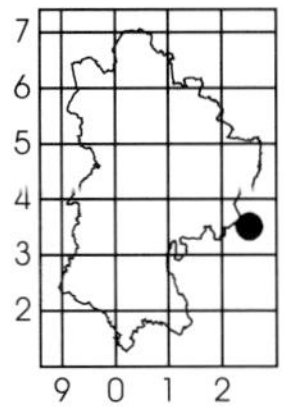

Corn Moth *Nemapogon granella* (Linnaeus) (215)
Post VCH: A single record from Bedford on 19 June 1985 by T.S.Hollingworth.
Flight: Continuous brooded (week 25)*.
Larval Food: Stored vegetable products and outdoors on bracket fungi.

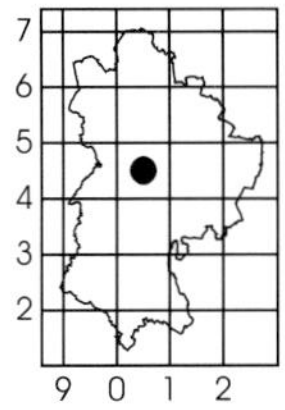

Cork Moth *Nemapogon cloacella* (Haworth) (216)
VCH: "Bedford; Luton".
Post VCH: Widespread and common.
Flight: May to August (weeks 22 to 33)*, September.
Larval Food: Bracket fungi, sometimes on stored vegetable products indoors.

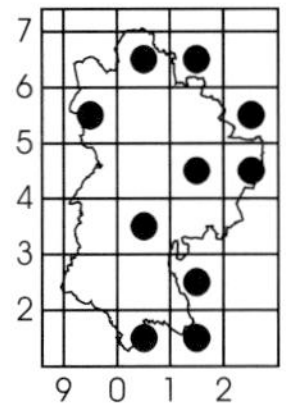

Nemapogon wolffiella **Karsholt & Nielsen (217)**
Post VCH: Local and uncommon: Worley's Wood, Cockayne Hatley and Cockayne Hatley Wood.
Flight: June (week 26)*, July, August (weeks 32, 33)*.
Larval Food: Bracket fungi and rotten wood.

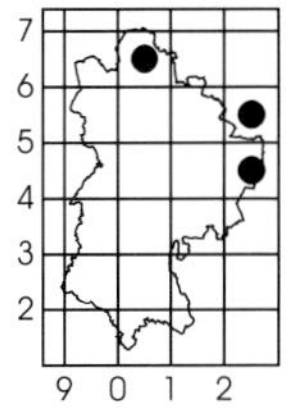

Nemapogon ruricolella **(Stainton) (219)**
Post VCH: A single record from Cockayne Hatley Wood on 25 June 1992.
Flight: June (week 26)*, July, August.
Larval Food: Bracket fungi and fungi in rotten wood.

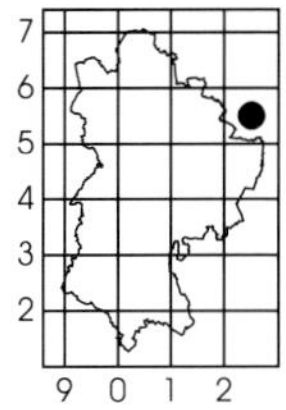

For key to moth maps see page 3.

Nemapogon clematella **(Fabricius) (220)**
VCH: (as *Scardia arcella* Fab.) "Luton".
Post VCH: Local and scarce: Worley's Wood on 8 August 1986 and RIS trap at Cockayne Hatley, 30 July to 5 August 1995.
Flight: June to August (weeks 31 and 32)*.
Larval Food: Bracket fungi and fungi in dead wood.

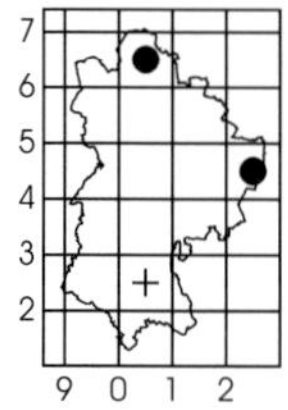

Triaxomera parasitella **(Hübner) (224)**
Post VCH: Local and uncommon: Marston Thrift, Felmersham Nature Reserve, Putnoe Wood and Cockayne Hatley.
Flight: May, June (weeks 24 to 26)*.
Larval Food: Bracket fungi and dead wood.

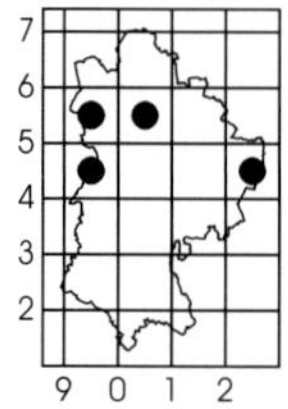

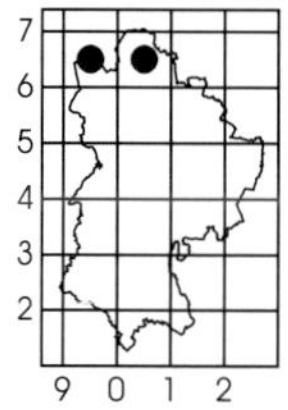

Triaxomera fulvimitrella **(Sodoffsky) (225)**
Post VCH: Local and uncommon: West Wood and Coppice Wood.
Flight: May, June (week 24)*, July.
Larval Food: Bracket fungi and dead wood.

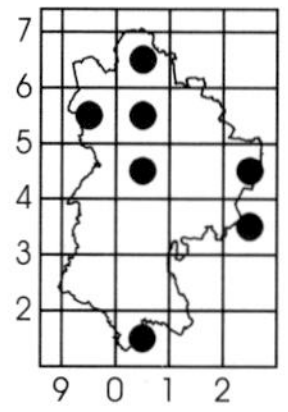

Skin Moth ***Monopis laevigella*** **([Denis & Schiffermüller]) (227)**
VCH: (as *Tinea rusticella* Hb.) "Bedford".
Post VCH: Widespread and common.
Flight: May to July (weeks 19 to 28)*, August (week 35)*, September.
Larval Food: Birds' nests and animal products and debris.

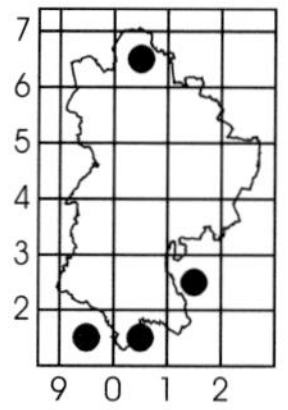

Monopis weaverella **(Scott) (228)** (Plate 21)
Post VCH: Local and uncommon: Bison Hill, Studham, Coppice Wood and Pegsdon Hills.
Flight: May, June (weeks 19 to 23)*, July, August (weeks 30 to 33)*.
Larval Food: Dead mammals and faeces.

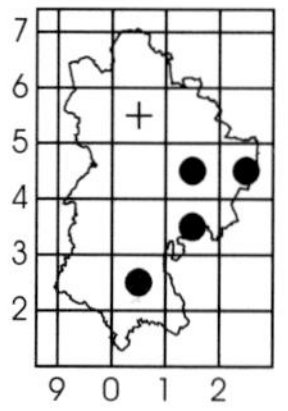

Monopis obviella **([Denis & Schiffermüller]) (229)**
VCH: (as *Tinea ferruginella* Hb.) "Bedford".
Post VCH: Local and uncommon: Dunstable, Arlesey, Biggleswade and Cockayne Hatley.
Flight: May to October (weeks 25 to 32)*.
Larval Food: Animal and vegetable refuse.

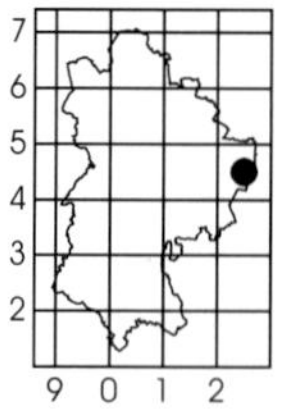

Monopis crocicapitella (Clemens) **(230)**
Post VCH: A single record from the RIS trap at Cockayne Hatley, 24-30 September 1994 .
Flight: June to October (week 39)*.
Larval Food: Animal and vegetable refuse.

For details of standard weeks see page 6.

***Monopis imella* (Hübner) (231)**
VCH: "Recorded at Bedford by Mr. Sharpin".
Post VCH: No recent record.
Flight: June to September.
Larval Food: Animal and vegetable refuse.

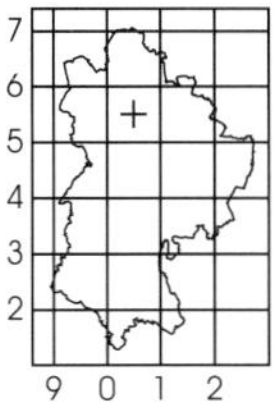

Tapestry Moth *Trichophaga tapetzella* (Linnaeus) (234)
VCH: "Everywhere in harness rooms and houses".
Post VCH: No recent record.
Flight: May to August.
Larval Food: Birds' nests, animal refuse and stored products.

Common Clothes Moth *Tineola bisselliella* (Hummel) (236)
VCH: "Bedford, in houses".
Post VCH: Local and uncommon: Sharnbrook and Bedford.
Flight: Continuous brooded (weeks 10 to 18, 35)*.
Larval Food: Woollens*, stored products of animal origin.

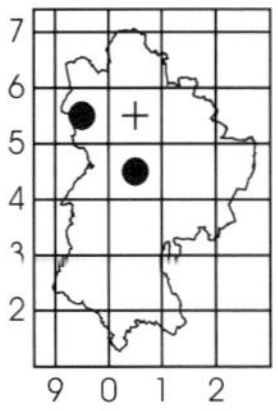

Brown-dotted Clothes Moth *Niditinea fuscella* (Linnaeus) (237)
VCH: (as *Tinea fuscipunctella* Haw.) "Bedford, Luton".
Post VCH: A single record from Sharnbrook on 31 July 1995.
Flight: May to September (week 31)*.
Larval Food: Birds' nests and animal refuse.

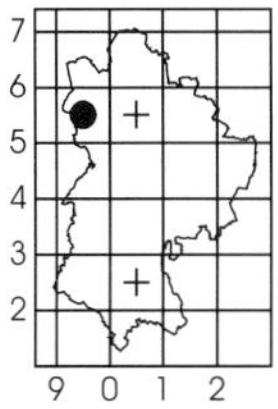

Case-bearing Clothes Moth *Tinea pellionella* (Linnaeus) (240)
VCH: "(The common clothes-moth.) In houses everywhere".
Post VCH: Local and uncommon: Cranfield, Studham and Stotfold.
Flight: June (weeks 24, 25)* to October.
Larval Food: Woollens and stored products.

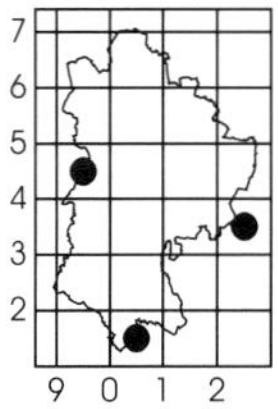

Large Pale Clothes Moth *Tinea pallescentella* Stainton (245)
VCH: "Bedford, Luton".
Post VCH: Local and uncommon: Bedford and Stotfold.
Flight: Continuous brooded (week 30)*.
Larval Food: Stored products of animal origin and animal refuse.

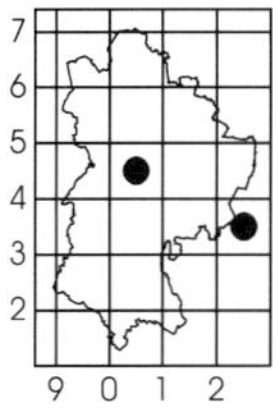

***Tinea semifulvella* Haworth (246)**
Post VCH: Widespread and common.
Flight: May to August (weeks 22 to 32)*, September.
Larval Food: Birds' nests and animal refuse.

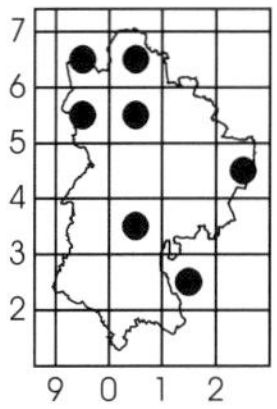

For key to moth maps see page 3.

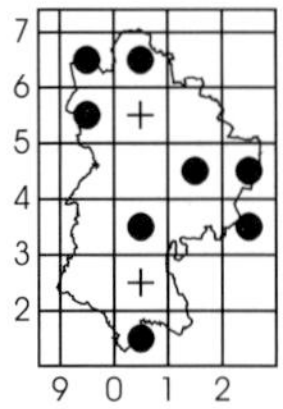

Tinea trinotella **Thunberg (247)**
VCH: (as *T. lappella* Stt.) "Bedford, Luton".
Post VCH: Widespread and common.
Flight: April to August (weeks 18 to 24, 28 to 35)*.
Larval Food: Birds' nests and animal refuse.

Family: **Lyonetiidae**

Small, mainly pale-coloured moths (wingspan 5-10 mm) which fly by day. Some species are shining white with a radial pattern of black and yellow stripes at the tip of the forewing. The larvae mine leaves or the bark of twigs. Eleven species are included on the British list of which six have been found in Bedfordshire.

Mine of Leucoptera malifoliella in a hawthorn leaf.

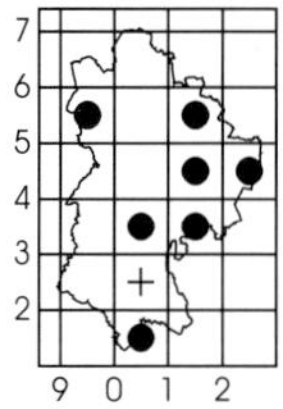

Laburnum Leaf-miner *Leucoptera laburnella* (Stainton) (254)
VCH: "Luton".
Post VCH: Widespread and common.
Flight: May, July to September (weeks 28 to 30, 36, 37)*.
Larval Foodplant: Laburnum*, in a leaf-mine.

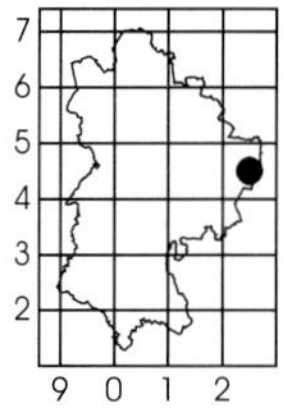

Leucoptera wailesella **(Stainton) (255)**
Post VCH: A single record from the RIS trap at Cockayne Hatley, 16-22 July 1994, identified by dissection.
Flight: May, July (week 29)*.
Larval Foodplant: Dyer's greenweed, in a leaf-mine.

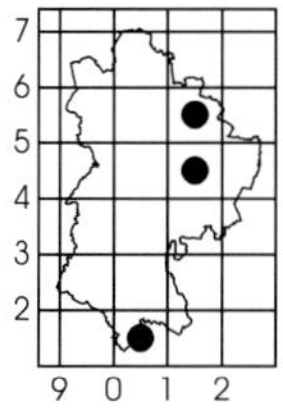

Leucoptera spartifoliella **(Hübner) (256)**
Post VCH: Local and uncommon: Studham, Sandy and Waterloo Thorns.
Flight: June to August (weeks 28, 33)*.
Larval Foodplant: Broom*, in mines in twigs.

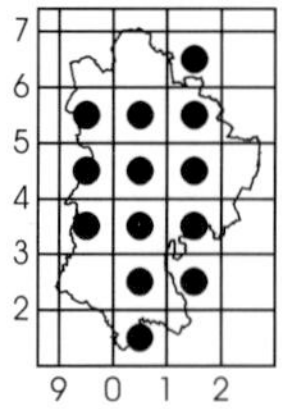

Pear Leaf Blister Moth *Leucoptera malifoliella* (Costa) (= *scitella* (Zeller)) (260)
Post VCH: Widespread and common.
Flight: June, July.
Larval Foodplants: Rosaceous trees and shrubs*, in a leaf-mine.

For details of standard weeks see page 6.

Apple Leaf-miner *Lyonetia clerkella* (Linnaeus) (263)
VCH: "Bedford".
Post VCH: Widespread and common.
Flight: Continuous (weeks 22 to 27, 31, 32)★.
Larval Foodplants: Birches★, and rosaceous trees and shrubs★, in a leaf-mine.

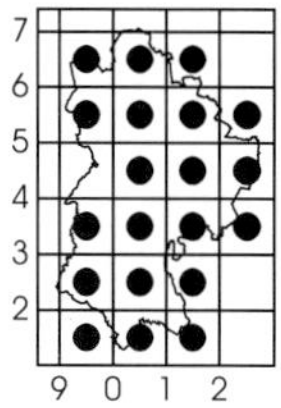

***Bedellia somnulentella* (Zeller) (264)**
Post VCH: Known only from the RIS trap at Cockayne Hatley.
Flight: July, August (weeks 28 to 30, 33)★, October to May.
Larval Foodplant: Convolvulus, in leaf-mines.

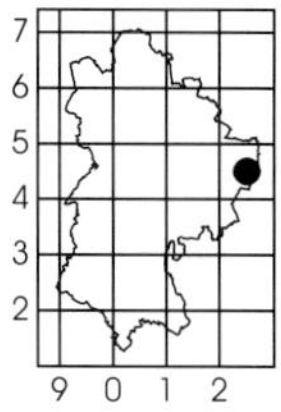

Family: **Bucculatricidae**

Small moths (wingspan 6-9 mm) which fly mainly in the evening. The larvae mine the leaves of the foodplant in early instars. Later feeding results in pale windows in the leaves with the upper surface of the leaf left intact. There are twelve British species, of which six have been found in Bedfordshire. The family has been somewhat neglected in the county, and all species are under-recorded.

***Bucculatrix cristatella* Zeller (265)**
Post VCH: Local and uncommon: RIS trap at Cockayne Hatley.
Flight: June, July★, August.
Larval Foodplant: Yarrow.

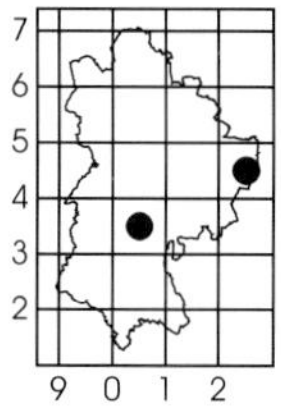

***Bucculatrix nigricomella* Zeller (266)**
VCH: (as *B. aurimaculella* Stt.) "Luton, among ox-eye daisy".
Post VCH: Local and uncommon: Sharnbrook and in the RIS trap at Cockayne Hatley.
Flight: May, June (week 23)★, July, August (weeks 30, 31)★.
Larval Foodplant: Oxeye daisy.

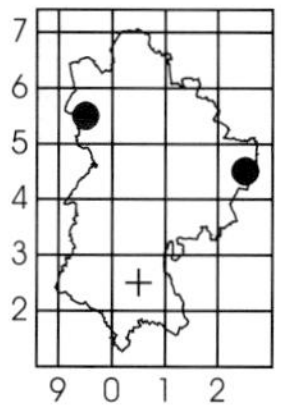

***Bucculatrix albedinella* Zeller (271)**
Post VCH: Local and uncommon: found on the Stotfold-Ampthill-Woburn road (A.M.Emmet) and in the RIS trap at Cockayne Hatley.
Flight: June (weeks 23, 24)★.
Larval Foodplants: Elms★.

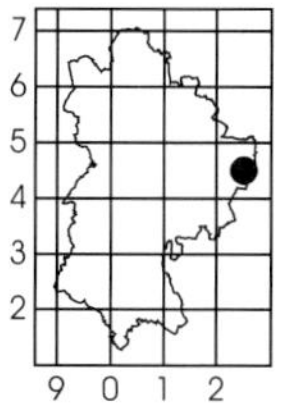

***Bucculatrix thoracella* (Thunberg) (273)**
Post VCH: Local and uncommon: King's Wood (Heath and Reach) and Sharnbrook.
Flight: June.
Larval Foodplants: Limes★.

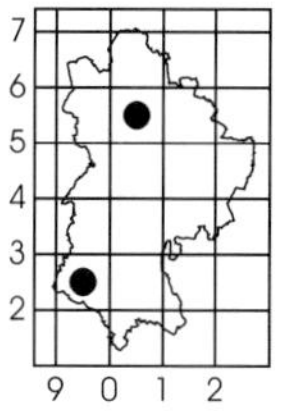

For key to moth maps see page 3.

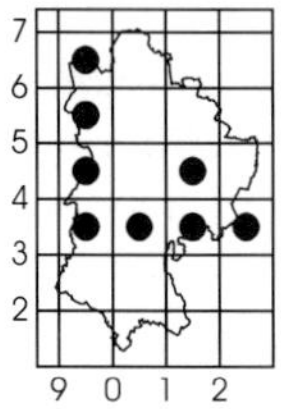

***Bucculatrix ulmella* Zeller (274)**
Post VCH: Widespread and common.
Flight: May, June, August.
Larval Foodplants: Oaks*.

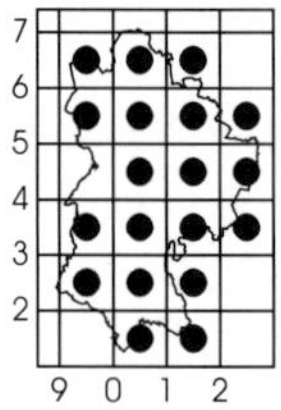

***Bucculatrix bechsteinella* (Bechstein & Scharfenberg) (275)**
VCH: (as *B. crataegi* Zell.) "Luton, about hawthorn".
Post VCH: Widespread and common.
Flight: May, June (week 24)*.
Larval Foodplants: Hawthorns*.

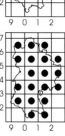

Family: **Gracillariidae**

Subfamily: **Gracillariinae**

Small moths (wingspan 9-16 mm), some of which have striking wing patterns. At rest the moths stand in a characteristic posture, with the front raised and the legs displayed (Plate 47). The larvae at first mine leaves, sap-feeding on the epidermis in early instars. Later feeding is in a full-depth mine. Most species complete their feeding on the surface of the leaf, constructing folds or cones of the leaf edge. Thirty-five species are on the British list, of which 20 have been found in Bedfordshire.

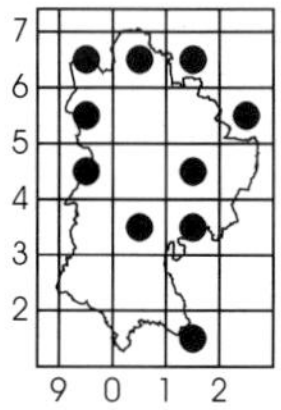

***Caloptilia elongella* (Linnaeus) (282)**
Post VCH: Widespread and common.
Flight: June, August (week 31)* to April.
Larval Foodplant: Alder*.

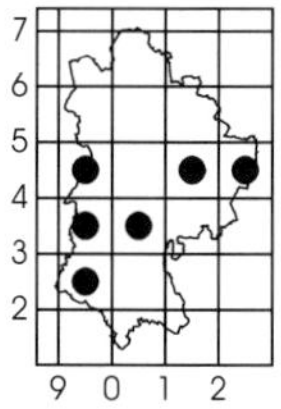

***Caloptilia betulicola* (Hering) (283)**
Post VCH: Widespread, fairly common: Charle Wood, Marston Thrift and in the RIS trap at Cockayne Hatley.
Flight: June, August (week 32)* September (week 37)* to April.
Larval Foodplants: Birches*.

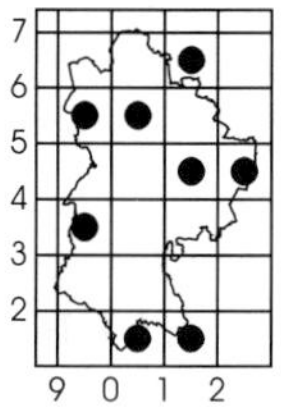

***Caloptilia rufipennella* (Hübner) (284)**

Post VCH: Local and uncommon, but becoming more widespread: the conspicuous larval cones on leaves were not found until 1990. Since then they have been recorded from several sites in both rural and urban areas, and the moth has appeared in light-traps. New Wavendon Heath, Sharnbrook, Studham, Bedford, Luton Hoo, Sandy, Little Staughton and in the RIS trap at Cockayne Hatley.

Flight: August (week 31)*, October (week 44)* to May.
Larval Foodplants: Sycamore.*

For details of standard weeks see page 6.

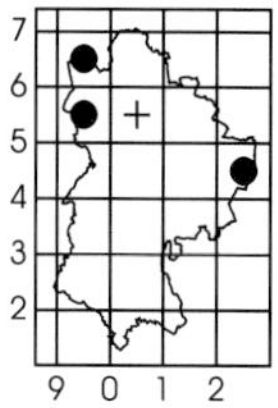

***Caloptilia alchimiella* (Scopoli) (286)**
VCH: (as *Gracilaria swederella* Thunb.) "Bedford, among oak".
Post VCH: Probably widespread and common. The larval feeding of this species or the next is widespread, but the two are not reliably separable. Only confirmed records are shown here, mainly from light-trap captures: Carlton, West Wood and in the RIS trap at Cockayne Hatley.
Flight: May (week 22)★, June.
Larval Foodplants: Oaks★, feeding July to September.

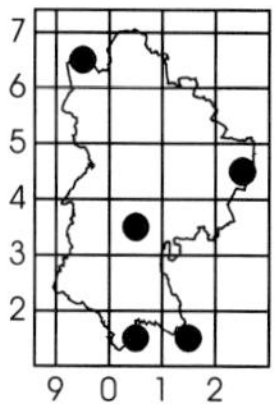

***Caloptilia robustella* Jäckh (287)** (Plate 47)
Post VCH: Probably widespread and common: West Wood, Studham, Flitwick Moor, Luton Hoo and in the RIS trap at Cockayne Hatley.
Flight: April, May (weeks 23, 24)★, July to September (weeks 30 to 36)★.
Larval Foodplants: Oaks★, May to July and September to October.

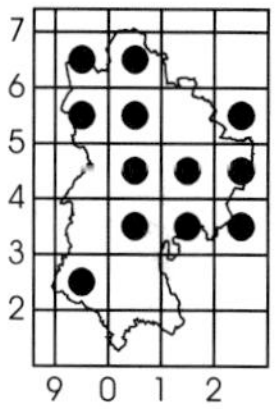

***Caloptilia stigmatella* (Fabricius) (288)**
Post VCH: Widespread and common.
Flight: July to May (weeks 27 to 35, 39, 40, 15)★.
Larval Foodplants: Poplars and willows.

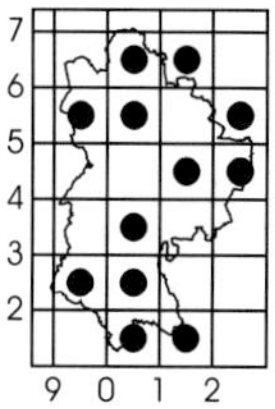

***Caloptilia syringella* (Fabricius) (293)**
VCH: "Bedford, Luton; in gardens".
Post VCH: Widespread and common.
Flight: April, May to July (weeks 20 to 26)★.
Larval Foodplants: Ash★, lilac★ and privets★.

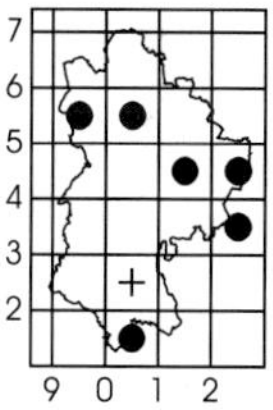

***Aspilapteryx tringipennella* (Zeller) (294)**
VCH: "Luton, among ribwort plantain".
Post VCH: Local and uncommon: Sharnbrook, Studham, Thurleigh Cutting, Biggleswade, Stotfold and in the RIS trap at Cockayne Hatley.
Flight: May, June (weeks 20 to 23)★, July, August (weeks 27 to 34)★.
Larval Foodplant: Ribwort plantain.

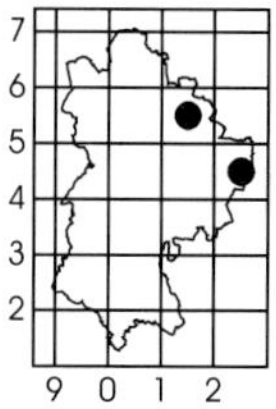

***Calybites phasianipennella* (Hübner) (296)**
Post VCH: Local and uncommon: Tempsford and in the RIS trap at Cockayne Hatley.
Flight: August (weeks 31 to 35)★ to May.
Larval Foodplants: Sorrels, water dock, redshank, water-pepper and yellow loosestrife.

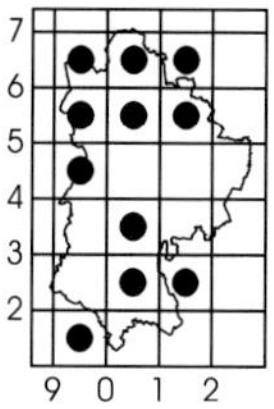

***Calybites auroguttella* (Stephens) (297)**
Post VCH: Widespread and common.
Flight: May (week 22)★, July, August (weeks 29 to 32, 35)★.
Larval Foodplants: St John's-worts★.

For key to moth maps see page 3.

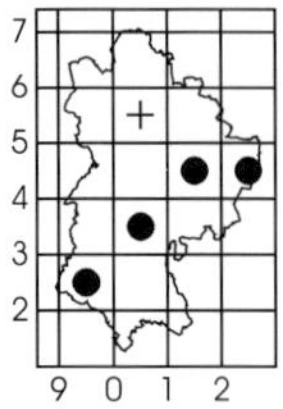

Parornix betulae **(Stainton) (301)**
VCH: "Bedford, among birch".
Post VCH: Local and uncommon: King's Wood (Heath and Reach), Flitwick Moor, Old Warden and Sutton Fen.
Flight: May, August.
Larval Foodplants: Birches★.

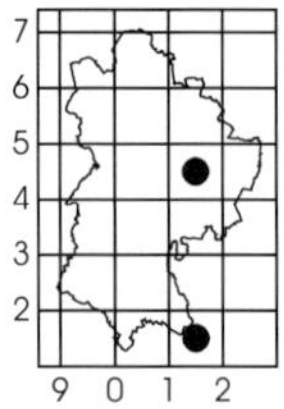

Parornix fagivora **(Frey) (302)**
Post VCH: Scarce: Luton Hoo and Old Warden.
Flight: May, August.
Larval Foodplant: Beech★.

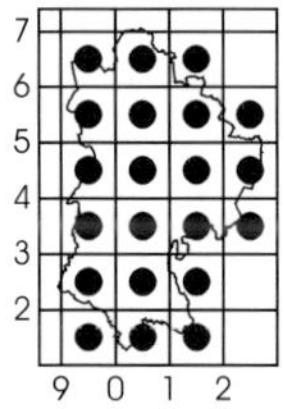

Parornix anglicella **(Stainton) (303)**
VCH: "Luton, Bedford; among hawthorn".
Post VCH: Widespread and common.
Flight: May (week 21)★, July, August (weeks 28 to 34)★.
Larval Foodplants: Hawthorns★.

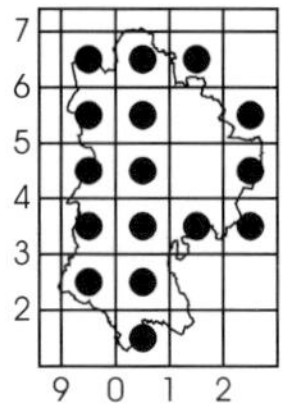

Parornix devoniella **(Stainton) (304)**
VCH: (as *Ornix avellanella* Stt.) "Luton, Bedford; among hazel".
Post VCH: Widespread and common.
Flight: May, July, August (weeks 28 to 35)★.
Larval Foodplant: Hazel★.

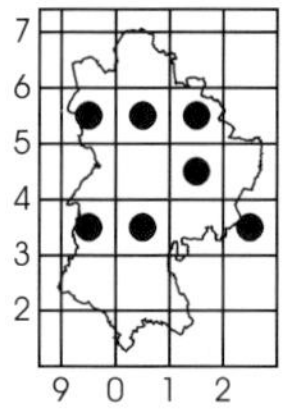

Parornix scoticella **(Stainton) (305)**
Post VCH: Local and fairly common.
Flight: May, August.
Larval Foodplants: Apple★, rowan and common whitebeam★.

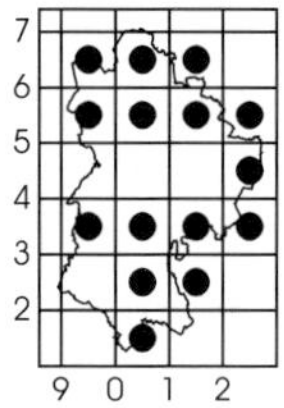

Parornix finitimella **(Zeller) (308)**
Post VCH: Widespread and common.
Flight: May (weeks 19 to 22)★, June to August (weeks 26 to 35)★.
Larval Foodplants: Blackthorn★ and wild plum.

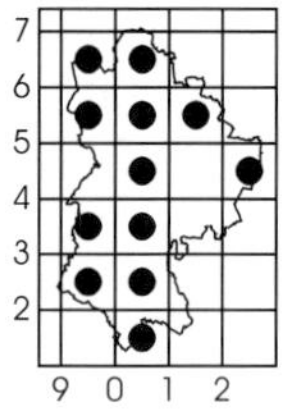

Parornix torquillella **(Zeller) (309)**
VCH: "Bedford, among blackthorn".
Post VCH: Widespread and common.
Flight: May, June to August (weeks 23, 28 to 32)★.
Larval Foodplants: Blackthorn★ and wild plum.

For details of standard weeks see page 6.

Callisto denticulella **(Thunberg) (310)**
VCH: (as *Ornix guttea* Haw.) "Bedford, among apple".
Post VCH: Widespread and common.
Flight: May (week 21)*, June.
Larval Foodplant: Apple*.

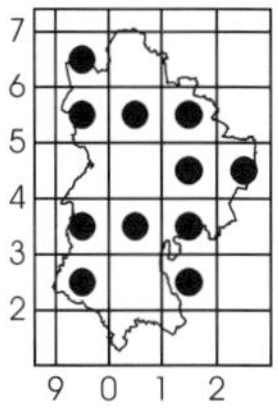

Acrocercops brongniardella **(Fabricius) (313)**
VCH: "Bedford, among oak".
Post VCH: Scarce until 1991 when it became fairly common at some sites. Numbers have since declined again. Probably widespread, but not yet confirmed. Sharnbrook, Cooper's Hill, Sandy and Cockayne Hatley Wood.
Flight: July to May.
Larval Foodplants: Oaks*, in a leaf-mine.

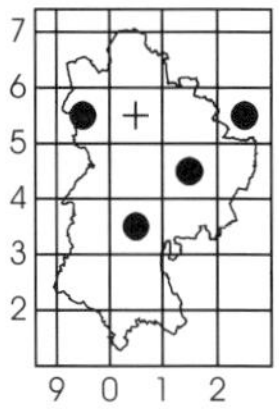

Leucospilapteryx omissella **(Stainton) (314)**
Post VCH: Local and uncommon: Stotfold and in the RIS trap at Cockayne Hatley.
Flight: May, August.
Larval Foodplant: Mugwort*, in a leaf-mine.

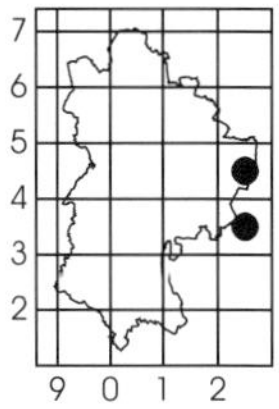

Subfamily: **Lithocolletinae**

Small moths (wingspan 6-10 mm) generally with a pattern of white streaks (strigulae) on a brown or orange ground colour. The larvae feed within a leaf-mine, most of which have characteristic "concertina" type folds caused by silk spinning contracting the surface of the leaf. The British list includes over 50 species, of which 37 have been found in Bedfordshire.

Phyllonorycter blancardella
(approx. x 5.5)

Phyllonorycter harrisella **(Linnaeus) (315)**
VCH: (as *Lithocolletis cramerella* Fab.) "Everywhere common among oak".
Post VCH: Widespread and common.
Flight: May, June (weeks 20 to 26)*, July to September (weeks 30 to 36)*.
Larval Foodplants: Oaks*, in a leaf-mine.

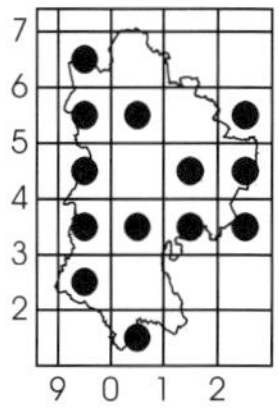

Phyllonorycter heegeriella **(Zeller) (317)**
Post VCH: Widespread and fairly common.
Flight: May, August.
Larval Foodplants: Oaks*, in a leaf-mine.

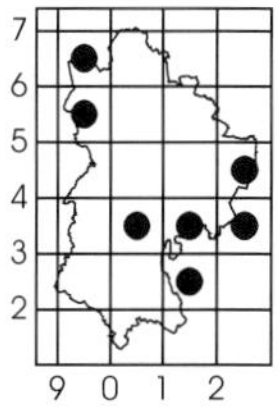

For key to moth maps see page 3.

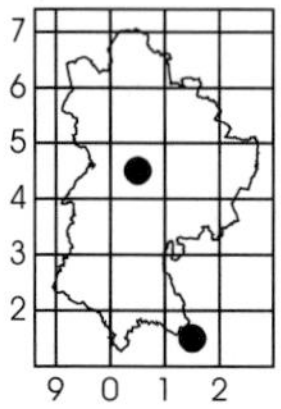

***Phyllonorycter tenerella* (Joannis) (318)**
Post VCH: Local and uncommon: Bedford and Luton Hoo.
Flight: May, August.
Larval Foodplant: Hornbeam★, in a leaf-mine.

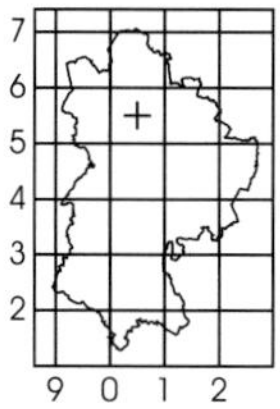

***Phyllonorycter saportella* (Duponchel) (319)**
VCH: (as *Lithocolletis hortella* Fab.) "Bedford".
Post VCH: No recent record.
Flight: May, August.
Larval Foodplants: Oaks, in a leaf-mine.

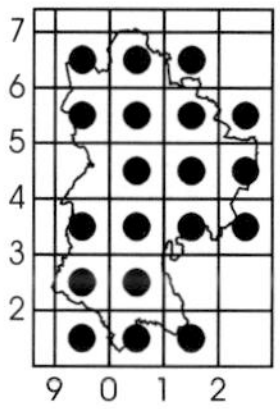

***Phyllonorycter quercifoliella* (Zeller) (320)**
VCH: "Everywhere abundant among oak".
Post VCH: Widespread and common.
Flight: April to June (weeks 17 to 24)★, July to October (weeks 30 to 44)★.
Larval Foodplants: Oaks★, in a leaf-mine.

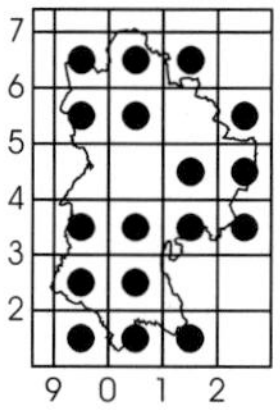

***Phyllonorycter messaniella* (Zeller) (321)**
Post VCH: Widespread and common.
Flight: May, June to November (weeks 26 to 48)★.
Larval Foodplants: Oaks★, holm-oak★, sweet chestnut★ and beech★, in a leaf-mine.

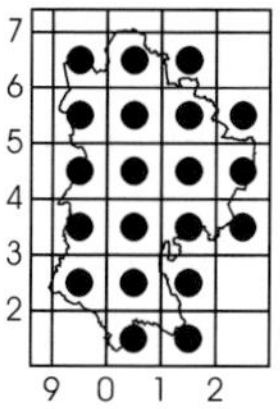

***Phyllonorycter oxyacanthae* (Frey) (323)**
Post VCH: Widespread and common.
Flight: April, May (weeks 16 to 18)★, June to August (weeks 26, 29 to 31, 35)★.
Larval Foodplants: Hawthorns★, in a leaf-mine.

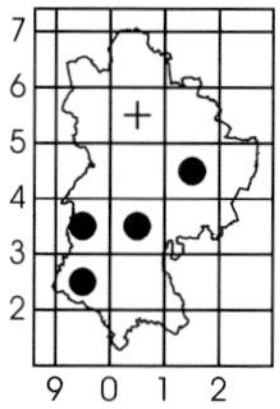

***Phyllonorycter sorbi* (Frey) (324)**
VCH: "Bedford".
Post VCH: Local and uncommon: King's Wood (Heath and Reach), Charle Wood, Maulden Wood and Rowney Warren.
Flight: April, May, July (week 30)★, August.
Larval Foodplant: Rowan★, in a leaf-mine.

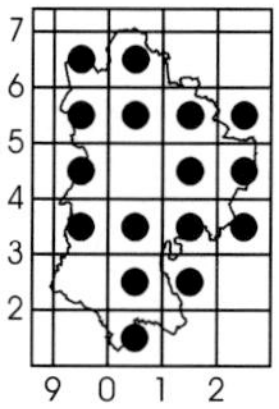

***Phyllonorycter blancardella* (Fabricius) (= *concomitella* (Bankes)) (326)** (Drawing on page 109)
Post VCH: Widespread and common. Larvae of this and the next species cannot be separated. Adults netted and bred have all been this species, so all records have been placed here, but must be treated with caution.
Flight: May (weeks 20, 21)★, July (weeks 28 to 30)★, August, September (week 38)★.
Larval Foodplant: Apple★, in a leaf-mine.

For details of standard weeks see page 6.

Phyllonorycter cydoniella **([Denis & Schiffermüller]) (=** ***blancardella*** **(Pierce & Metcalfe)** ***et*** **auctt.)) (327)**
Post VCH: The record in Heath and Emmet (1985) has been confirmed by A.M.Emmet "per Ian Watkinson". See previous species.
Flight: May, August.
Larval Foodplants: Apple, quince and wild service-tree.

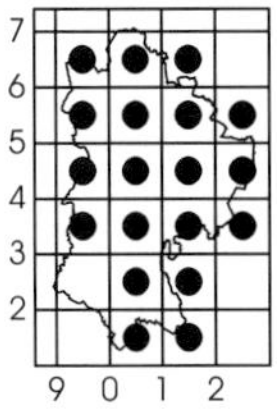

Phyllonorycter spinicolella **(Zeller) (=** ***pomonella*** **auctt.) (329)**
Post VCH: Widespread and common.
Flight: May, August.
Larval Foodplant: Blackthorn*, in a leaf-mine.

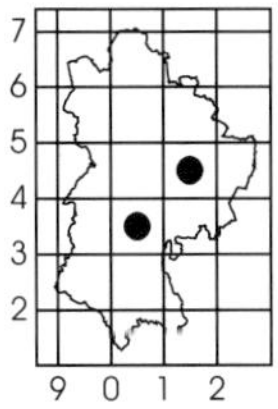

Phyllonorycter cerasicolella **(Herrich-Schäffer) (330)**
Post VCH: Local and uncommon: Maulden Wood and Sandy.
Flight: May, August.
Larval Foodplants: Wild cherry* and bird cherry, in a leaf-mine.

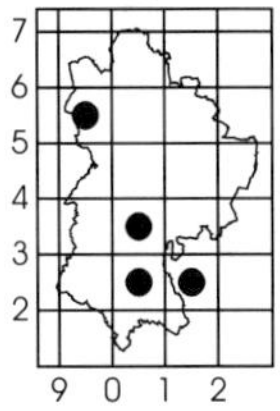

Phyllonorycter lantanella **(Schrank) (331)**
Post VCH: Local and uncommon: Sharnbrook, Icknield Way and Sharpenhoe.
Flight: May, August.
Larval Foodplant: Wayfaring-tree*, in a leaf-mine.

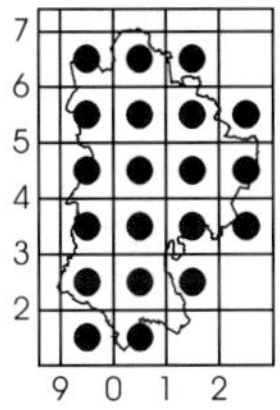

Phyllonorycter corylifoliella **(Hübner) (332)**
Post VCH: Widespread and common.
Flight: May (week 21)*, June, July to August (weeks 30 to 33)*.
Larval Foodplants: Hawthorns*, apple* and rowan*, in a leaf-mine.

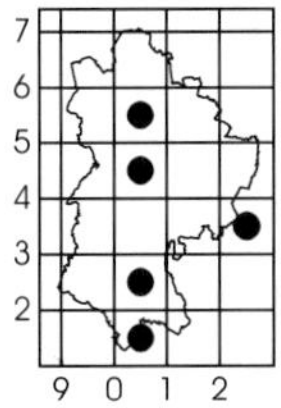

Firethorn Leaf-miner ***Phyllonorycter leucographella*** **(Zeller) (332a)**
Post VCH: A recent introduction to the British list, first found in the county in the winter of 1991/2. Locally common and likely to spread. Studham, Dunstable, Bedford and Stotfold. (Plate 97)
Flight: April, May, July to October.
Larval Foodplants: *Pyracantha* spp.*, in a leaf-mine.

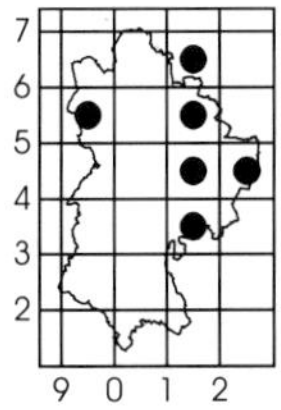

Phyllonorycter viminiella **(Sircom) (333)**
Post VCH: Widespread and common.
Flight: May to August (weeks 21, 28 to 31, 35)*.
Larval Foodplant: Crack willow*, in a leaf-mine.

For key to moth maps see page 3.

***Phyllonorycter salicicolella* (Sircom) (335)**
Post VCH: Widespread and common.
Flight: May (week 21)*, July (week 28)*, August.
Larval Foodplants: Sallows*, in a leaf-mine.

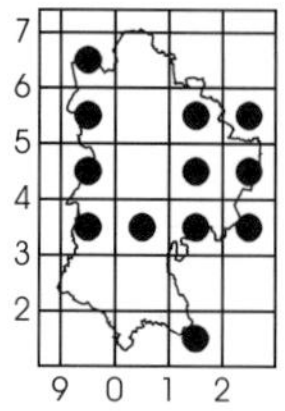

***Phyllonorycter dubitella* (Herrich-Schäffer) (336)**
Post VCH: A single record from the RIS trap at Cockayne Hatley in July 1992.
Flight: May, June, July*, August.
Larval Foodplants: Sallows.

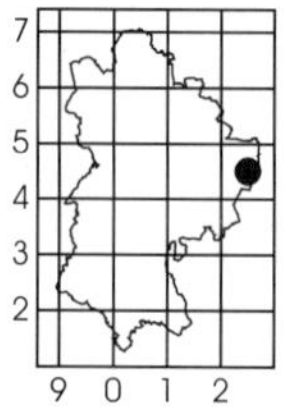

***Phyllonorycter hilarella* (Zetterstedt) (= *spinolella* (Duponchel)) (337)**
Post VCH: Local and uncommon: Bison Hill, Felmersham Nature Reserve, West Wood, Flitwick Moor, Henlow and Biggleswade Common.
Flight: May, August.
Larval Foodplants: Willows and sallows*, in a leaf-mine.

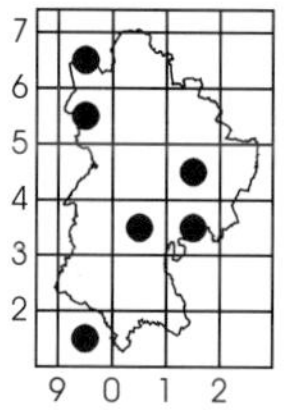

***Phyllonorycter cavella* (Zeller) (338)**
Post VCH: Local and uncommon: Bedford Park and Old Warden.
Flight: June, July.
Larval Foodplants: Birches*, in a leaf-mine.

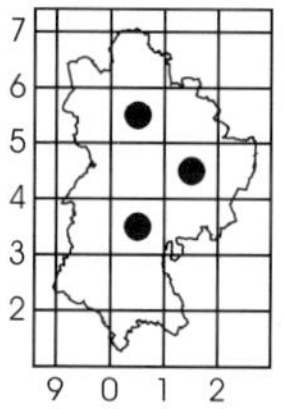

***Phyllonorycter maestingella* (Müller) (= *faginella* (Zeller)) (341)**
Post VCH: Widespread and common.
Flight: May, June, August.
Larval Foodplant: Beech*, in a leaf-mine.

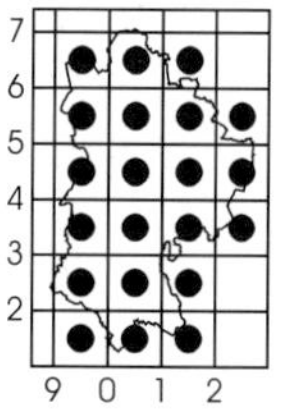

Nut Leaf Blister Moth *Phyllonorycter coryli* (Nicelli) (342)
VCH: "Luton, among hazel".
Post VCH: Widespread and common.
Flight: May, August, September (week 38)*.
Larval Foodplant: Hazel*, in a leaf-mine.

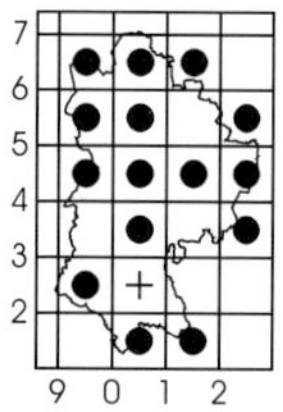

***Phyllonorycter quinnata* (Geoffroy) (= *carpinicolella* (Stainton)) (343)**
Post VCH: Local and uncommon: Woburn, Clapham Park Wood, Luton Hoo, Old Warden and Stotfold.
Flight: May, August.
Larval Foodplant: Hornbeam*, in a leaf-mine.

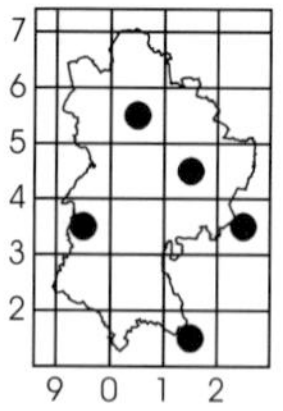

For details of standard weeks see page 6.

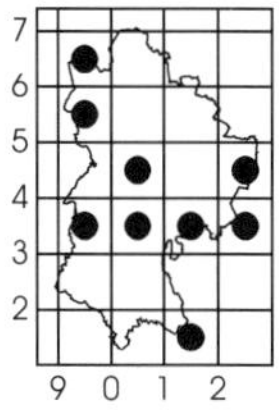

Phyllonorycter rajella **(Linnaeus) (=** ***alnifoliella*** **(Hübner)) (345)**
Post VCH: Widespread. fairly common.
Flight: May, July (week 28)*, August.
Larval Foodplant: Alder*, in a leaf-mine.

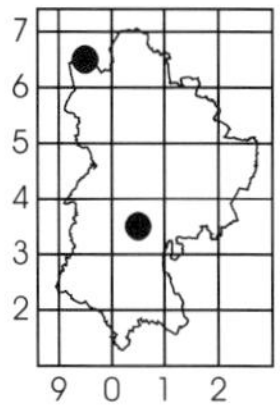

Phyllonorycter lautella **(Zeller) (351)**
Post VCH: Local and uncommon: West Wood and Maulden Wood.
Flight: May, August.
Larval Foodplants: Oaks*, in a leaf-mine.

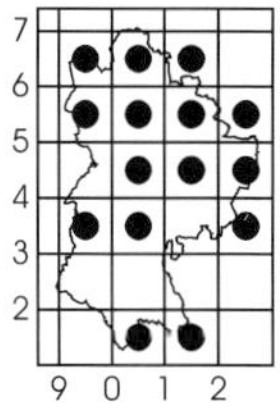

Phyllonorycter schreberella **(Fabricius) (352)**
Post VCH: Widespread and common.
Flight: May, August (week 31)*.
Larval Foodplants: Elms*, in a leaf-mine.

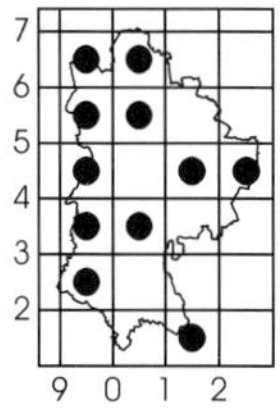

Phyllonorycter ulmifoliella **(Hübner) (353)**
Post VCH: Widespread and common.
Flight: May, August.
Larval Foodplants: Birches*, in a leaf-mine.

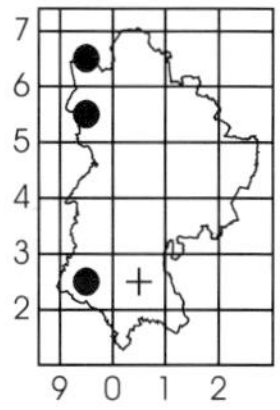

Phyllonorycter emberizaepenella **(Bouché) (354)**
VCH: "Luton, among honeysuckle".
Post VCH: Local and uncommon: King's Wood (Heath and Reach), Sharnbrook and West Wood.
Flight: May, August.
Larval Foodplant: Honeysuckle* and snowberry, in a leaf-mine.

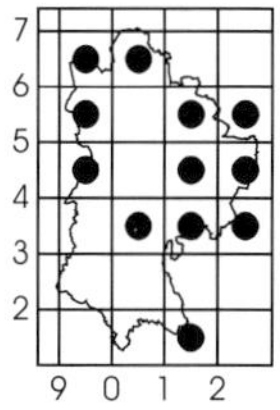

Phyllonorycter tristrigella **(Haworth) (356)**
Post VCH: Widespread and common.
Flight: May, August.
Larval Foodplants: Elms*, in a leaf-mine.

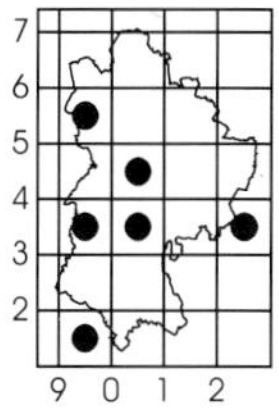

Phyllonorycter stettinensis **(Nicelli) (357)**
Post VCH: Local and uncommon: Whipsnade, Yelnow New Wood, Flitwick Moor, Bedford and Stotfold.
Flight: May, August.
Larval Foodplant: Alder*, in a leaf-mine.

For key to moth maps see page 3.

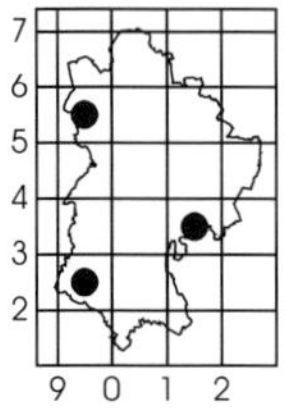

Phyllonorycter froelichiella **(Zeller) (358)**
Post VCH: Local and uncommon: Stockgrove Country Park and Felmersham Nature Reserve.
Flight: July, August.
Larval Foodplant: Alder*, in a leaf-mine.

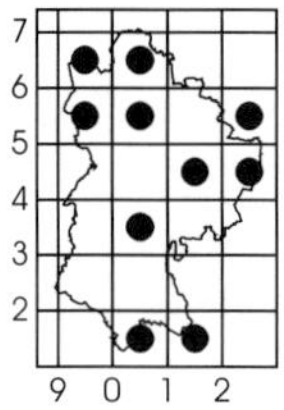

Phyllonorycter nicellii **(Stainton) (359)**
Post VCH: Widespread and common.
Flight: May, August (week 31)*.
Larval Foodplant: Hazel*, in a leaf-mine.

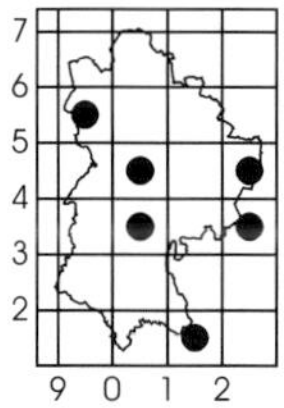

Phyllonorycter kleemannella **(Fabricius) (360)**
Post VCH: Widespread, fairly common: Felmersham Nature Reserve, Flitwick Moor, Bedford, Luton Hoo, Stotfold and in the RIS trap at Cockayne Hatley.
Flight: August.
Larval Foodplant: Alder*, in a leaf-mine.

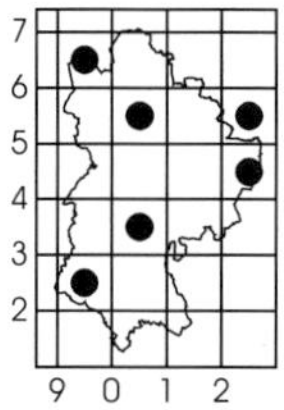

Phyllonorycter trifasciella **(Haworth) (361)**
Post VCH: Widespread and common.
Flight: May, August (weeks 31, 32, 35)*, October (week 40)*.
Larval Foodplant: Honeysuckle*, in a leaf-mine.

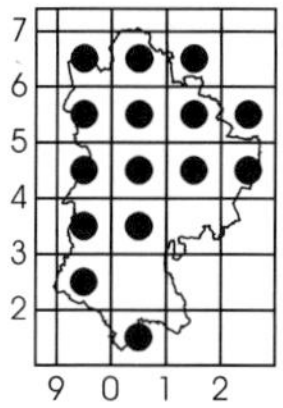

Phyllonorycter acerifoliella **(Zeller) (=** ***sylvella*** **(Haworth)) (362)**
Post VCH: Widespread and common.
Flight: May (week 20)*, July, August (weeks 28 to 31)*.
Larval Foodplant: Field maple*, in a leaf-mine.

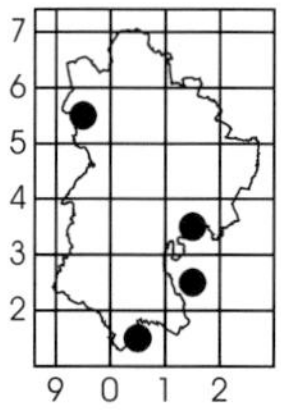

Phyllonorycter platanoidella **(Joannis) (363)**
Post VCH: Local and uncommon: Sharnbrook, Dunstable Downs and Pegsdon Hills.
Flight: May, August.
Larval Foodplant: Norway maple*, in a leaf-mine.

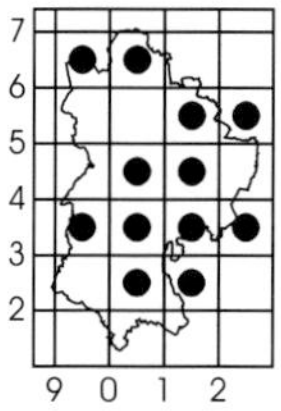

Phyllonorycter geniculella **(Ragonot) (364)**
Post VCH: Widespread and common.
Flight: May, August.
Larval Foodplant: Sycamore*, in a leaf-mine.

For details of standard weeks see page 6.

Subfamily: **Phyllocnistinae**

Small moths (wingspan 7-8 mm), whose larvae mine twigs or the epidermis of leaves. There are three British species, of which one has been found in Bedfordshire.

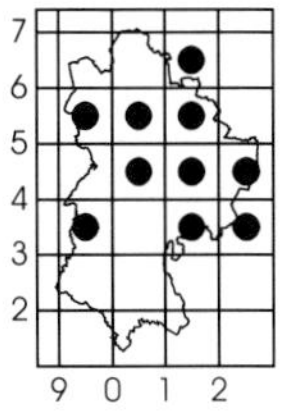

Phyllocnistis unipunctella **(Stephens) (368)**
Post VCH: Widespread and common.
Flight: July, September to April.
Larval Foodplants: Black poplar* and lombardy poplar, in a leaf-mine.

For key to moth maps see page 3.

Clearwings

(Sesiidae)

V.W.Arnold

Family: **Sesiidae**

The adults mimic wasps. On emergence the wings are usually covered with a thin layer of scales which are lost when the moth becomes active, leaving the wings transparent apart from a dark border. Size varies with wingspans ranging from 15 to 46 mm. The moths fly by day but are rarely noticed. The larvae of most species bore in stems and roots of shrubs and trees and may spend more than one year as a larva. Pupation is within the feeding tunnel. There are 15 British species of which nine have been found in Bedfordshire.

Hornet Moth *Sesia apiformis* (Clerck) (370)
Pre VCH: Emily Shore (Anon, 1891) noted seeing *Sphinx apiformis* on 16 May 1835, presumably near Everton, but we cannot be sure whether she really meant the Hornet Moth or was using the name loosely for one of the Bee Hawk-moths.
VCH: "Bedford, Woburn; on poplars."

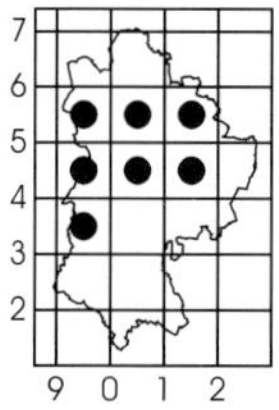

Post VCH: R.M.Craske recalled that this species was common in the Bedford area between 1918 and 1927. A specimen in B.B.West's collection is labelled "Bedford 1st July 1924. W.G.Nash". Specimens in the Kershaw collection are labelled "Bedfordshire July 1924 and July 1930 W.G.Nash". More recently this species has been recorded from: Bedford area (1959, 1960, 1979, 1984), Biggleswade (1989), Blunham (1983), Brogborough (1984), Clapham (1964), Felmersham Nature Reserve (1984), Langford (1972), Salford (1996), Sandy (1981) and Tempsford (1994). The Hornet Moth is almost certainly under-recorded in the County.
Flight: June and July. Flies during the day.
Larval Foodplants: Black poplar★ and sometimes other species of poplar, feeding in the lower trunk and roots .

Lunar Hornet Moth *Sesia bembeciformis* (Hübner) (371)
VCH: "Bedford."

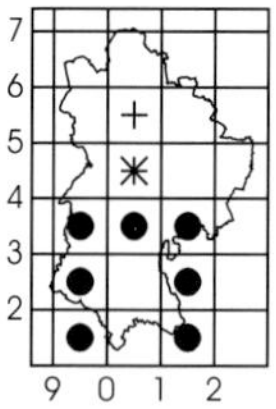

Post VCH: There are specimens in the Rylands collection from Kempston in 1911. Collected in 1983 as larvae from East Hyde and bred by K.F.Webb (Webb, 1984c). The following records are all for exit holes in the base of sallow bushes: Aspley Guise (1992), Henlow, Sewell and Maulden Wood (1984); Luton Hoo, Bison Hill and King's Wood, Heath and Reach (1985); Pegsdon (1991-1992). Another under-recorded species.
Flight: July to August. Flies during the day but the adults are rarely seen.
Larval Foodplant: Sallow★, feeding in the roots and trunks.

For details of standard weeks see page 6.

Currant Clearwing *Synanthedon tipuliformis* (Clerck) (373) (Plate 89)
VCH: "Generally common about currant bushes."

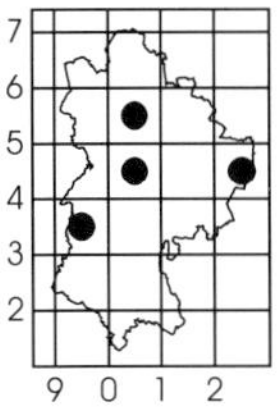

Post VCH: A moth that is rarely seen in the County. Found at Aspley Guise (1992), Aspley Heath (1938), Bedford (1960, 1971, 1984, 1987, 1990-96) and Biggleswade (1982). This is another species that is probably overlooked and may be more common than is indicated by the records.
Flight: June and July (weeks 24 to 26)★. Flies during the day.
Larval Foodplants: Black currant★, red currant★ and gooseberry, feeding inside the stems.

Yellow-legged Clearwing *Synanthedon vespiformis* (Linnaeus) (374)
Pre VCH: Found by J.C.Dale in Clapham Park Wood on 31 May, 1 and 2 June 1820 "under ye bark of Oak stump" (Dale, MS3 under the name Sesia Ostriformis). There are four specimens in the Dale collection side-labelled "Bedford" which may date from this occasion.
VCH: (as *Sesia cynipiformis* Esp.) "Recorded by Westwood in Clapham Park Woods."

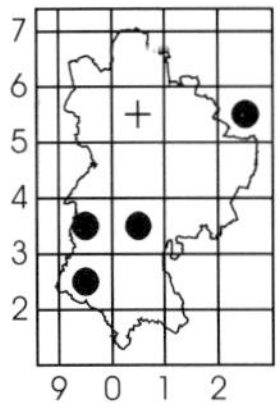

Post VCH: A scarce species in Bedfordshire. Found at Aspley Heath (1971), Maulden Wood (1974 and 1977), Potton Wood (1977) and Sewell (1978). Chambers (1948) found the Yellow-legged Clearwing in Forty Foot Lane on 28 June 1947. However, he used the Latin name *Aegeria andreniformis* which refers to the Orange-tailed Clearwing. What the specimen was will never be known for certain.
Flight: May to August. Flies during the day.
Larval Foodplants: Oaks★, elms, cherry, birches and sometimes sweet chestnut, feeding under the bark.

Orange-tailed Clearwing *Synanthedon andrenaeformis* (Laspeyres) (= *anthraciniformis* (Esper)) (378)

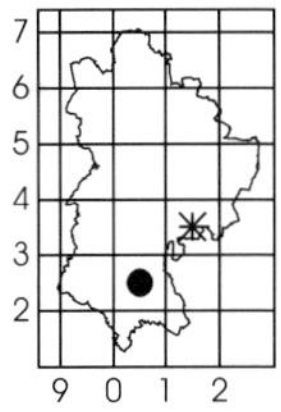

Post VCH: Anon (1907) mentions *Aegeria andreniformis* bred from Bedfordshire specimens. R.Palmer "took a number of larvae in stems of Viburnum at Tingley Plantation" on 15 April 1943 (Palmer, MS2). Reared by S.H.Kershaw from Barton in 1945. More recently collected from stems of wayfaring tree on Markham Hills by K.F.Webb. The adults emerged during June and July 1984 (Webb, 1985a). See also the section on the Yellow-tailed Clearwing for the record by Chambers (1948).
Flight: May, June★, July★. Flies during the day.
Larval Foodplants: Wayfaring-tree★ and guelder-rose, feeding in the stems.

Red-belted Clearwing *Synanthedon myopaeformis* (Borkhausen) (379)
VCH: "Taken by Mr. W.Bond-Smith at Potton."

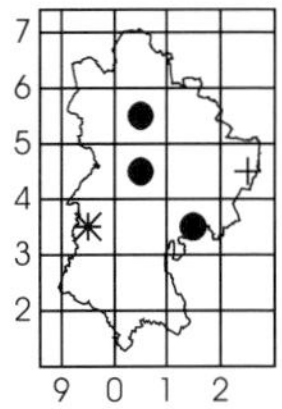

Post VCH: A scarce species in Bedfordshire. A specimen in the Kershaw collection is labelled "Woburn Sands 1933, G.Hawes". As no exact location is given, this could have been found just over the county boundary in Buckinghamshire. Kershaw found it in apple branches at Aspley Heath in 1935.The only recent records are from Bedford (1960, 1961, 1977, 1978 and 1983) and Shillington (1996). Mostly found in gardens and orchards.

For key to moth maps see page 3.

Flight: June★ and July. Flies during the day.
Larval Foodplants: Apple★, pear and other fruit trees, feeding under the bark.

Red-tipped Clearwing *Synanthedon formicaeformis* (Esper) (380)

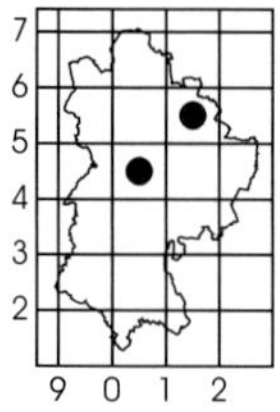

Post VCH: There is a label in the Rylands collection with the entry "Kempston" but no date. As with the previous species, there is a specimen in the Kershaw collection labelled "Woburn Sands 1933, G.Hawes". Again no exact location is given, so we do not know on which side of the county boundary it was found. S.Cham found a single specimen resting on foliage on the bank of the River Ouse, north of Great Barford on the 14 July 1989. W.J.Champkin found another specimen on a sallow bush by the Ouse in Bedford in July 1995.
Flight: June, July (week 28)★. Flies during the day.
Larval Foodplants: Osier and other species of willow and sallow, feeding in the stems.

Large Red-belted Clearwing *Synanthedon culiciformis* (Linnaeus) (381)

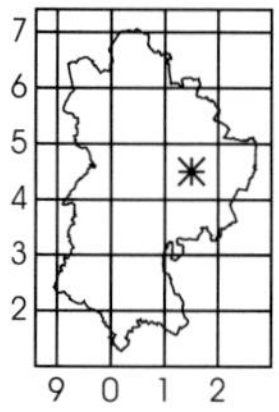

Post VCH: A very scarce species in Bedfordshire. A specimen was found in Rowney Warren in May 1956 by V.H.Chambers. There are many areas in Bedfordshire where the foodplants of the Large Red-belted Clearwing are common so it may well have been overlooked.
Flight: May★ and June. Flies during the day.
Larval Foodplants: Birches and possibly alder, feeding under the bark.

Six-belted Clearwing *Bembecia scopigera* (Scopoli) (382)

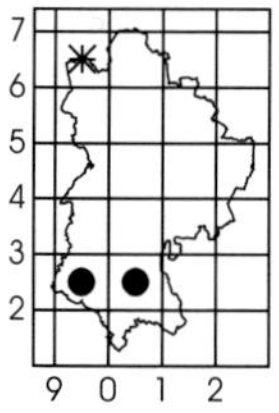

Post VCH: Found by searching or sweeping its foodplants and adjacent areas. Recorded from Sewell (1978 and 1984), Sharnbrook Summit (1965), Stanbridgeford (1982)and Sundon Hills Country Park (1990).
Flight: June, July (week 27)★, August. Flies during the day.
Larval Foodplants: Bird's-foot-trefoils and kidney vetch, feeding in the roots.

For details of standard weeks see page 6.

Small Ermines and their Allies

(Choreutidae to Schreckensteiniidae)

D.V.Manning

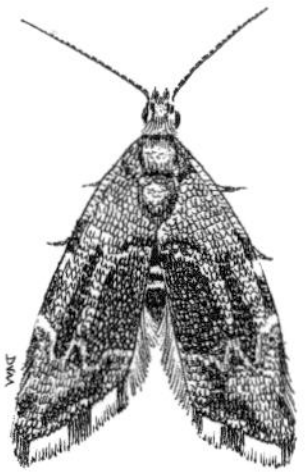

Anthophila fabriciana
(*x 3*)

Family: **Choreutidae**

Small day-flying moths (wingspan 9-15 mm). The larvae feed in webs on the leaves of the foodplant. There are seven British species, of which four have been found in Bedfordshire.

Anthophila fabriciana **(Linnaeus) (385)** (Plate 46)
VCH: "Over nettles everywhere".
Post VCH: Widespread and common.
Flight: May to October (weeks 19 to 42)★, November. Flies actively in sunshine and walks jerkily on flowers and leaves.
Larval Foodplants: Nettles★.

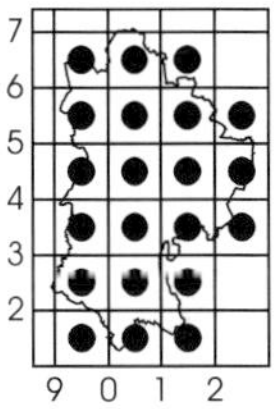

Prochoreutis sehestediana **(Fabricius) (387)**
Post VCH: At Cooper's Hill on 14 August 1992 several hundred moths were seen feeding on gipsywort, apparently freshly emerged. This is the only record for this species in Bedfordshire.
Flight: May, July, August (week 33)★.
Larval Foodplant: Skullcap.

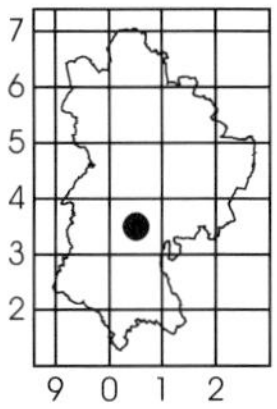

Prochoreutis myllerana **(Fabricius) (388)**
Post VCH: A few moths at Felmersham Nature Reserve on 4 September 1985.
Flight: July to September (week 36)★.
Larval Foodplant: Skullcap.

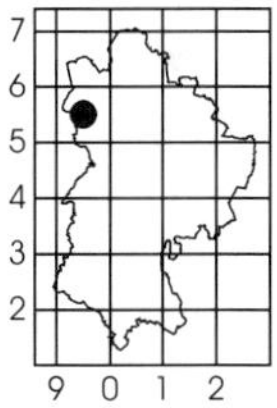

Apple Leaf Skeletonizer ***Choreutis pariana*** **(Clerck) (389)**
Post VCH: Local and uncommon: Sharnbrook, Maulden Wood and Biggleswade.
Flight: July, September to March.
Larval Foodplants: Apple★, hawthorns and rowan.

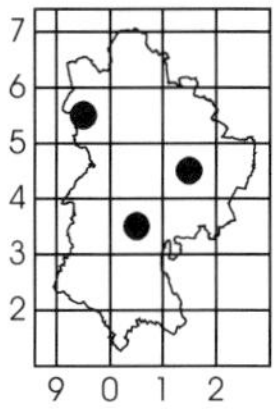

For key to moth maps see page 3.

Family: **Glyphipterigidae**

Small day-flying moths (wingspan 6-9 mm). There are seven British species. Of the four species recorded from Bedfordshire, two have not been seen since they were listed in VCH.

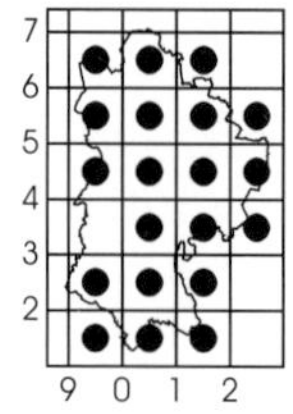

Cocksfoot Moth *Glyphipterix simpliciella* (Stephens) (391)
VCH: (as *G. fischerella* Zell.) "Luton; probably everywhere".
Post VCH: Widespread and common. The moths can often be seen in numbers in the flowers of dandelions and buttercups.
Flight: May, June (weeks 20 to 26)*.
Larval Foodplants: Cock's-foot feeding on the seeds. Also on some species of fescue.

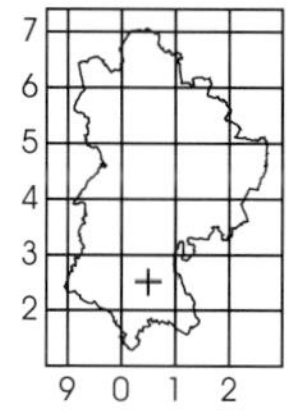

***Glyphipterix equitella* (Scopoli) (= *minorella* (Snellen)) (393)**
VCH: "Luton, in gardens about stonecrop".
Post VCH: No recent record.
Flight: June, July.
Larval Foodplants: *Sedum* spp.

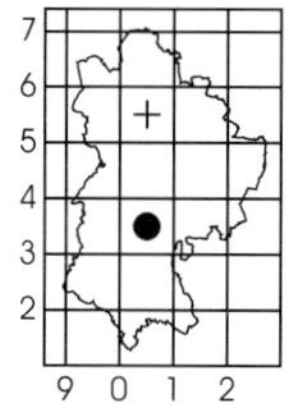

***Glyphipterix fuscoviridella* (Haworth) (396)**
VCH: "Bedford".
Post VCH: Flying in large numbers in one of the fields in Maulden Wood on 2 June 1996 (C.R.B.Baker).
Flight: May, June (week 22)*.
Larval Foodplants: Wood-rushes.

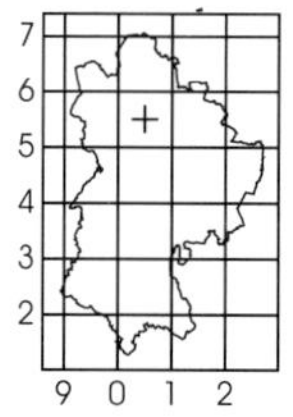

***Glyphipterix thrasonella* (Scopoli) (397)**
VCH: "Bedford, doubtless about rushes everywhere".
Post VCH: No recent record.
Flight: May to August.
Larval Foodplants: Not known, possibly *Juncus* spp.

Family: **Yponomeutidae**

A large and varied family of small to medium-sized moths. The larval feeding includes borers in buds, shoots or catkins (*Argyresthia*), in communal webs (*Yponomeuta*), or singly on the surface of leaves. Of the 80 British species, 47 have been found in Bedfordshire.

For details of standard weeks see page 6.

Subfamily: **Argyresthiinae**

The moths of the genus *Argyresthia* rest in a characteristic 'head-down' position with the hind legs held tightly against the raised abdomen. Wingspan 7-14 mm.

Argyresthia pruniella
(approx x 5.5)

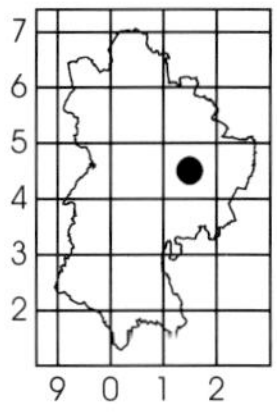

Argyresthia laevigatella **Herrich-Schäffer (401)**
Post VCH: A single record from Rowney Warren in May 1982 by E.C. Pelham-Clinton.
Flight: May, June.
Larval Foodplants: Larches*.

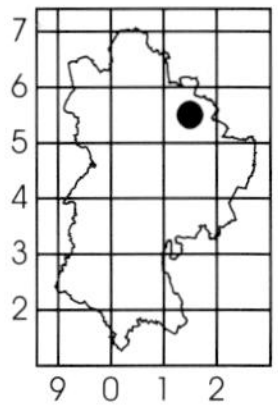

Argyresthia glabratella **(Zeller) (403)**
Post VCH: A single record from Willington on 16 June 1983.
Flight: June (week 24)*.
Larval Foodplant: Norway spruce.

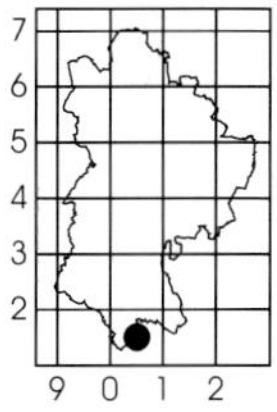

Argyresthia dilectella **Zeller (407)**
Post VCH: A single record from a garden at Studham on 13 July 1994 by C.R.B.Baker.
Flight: July (week 28)*, August.
Larval Foodplant: Juniper, including garden varieties.

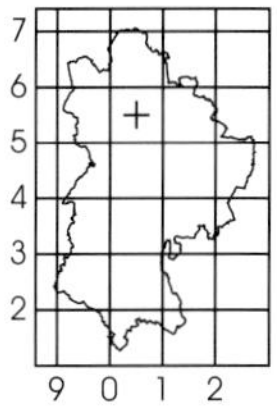

Argyresthia ivella **(Haworth) (409)**
VCH: (as *A. anderegiella* Fisch.) "Reported at Bedford by Mr. Sharpin".
Post VCH: No recent record.
Flight: July, August.
Larval Foodplants: Apple and hazel.

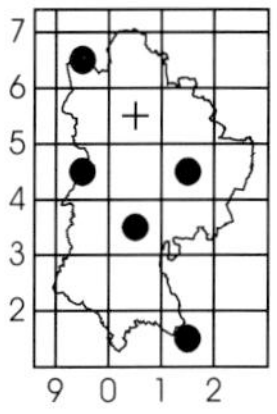

Argyresthia brockeella **(Hübner) (410)**
VCH: "Bedford, among alders".
Post VCH: Locally common: Marston Thrift, West Wood, Flitwick Moor, Luton Hoo and Rowney Warren.
Flight: June to August (weeks 25 to 33)*.
Larval Foodplants: Birches and alder.

For key to moth maps see page 3.

Argyresthia goedartella **(Linnaeus) (411)**
VCH: "Bedford, among alders".
Post VCH: Widespread and common.
Flight: June to September (weeks 25 to 39)*.
Larval Foodplants: Birches and alder.

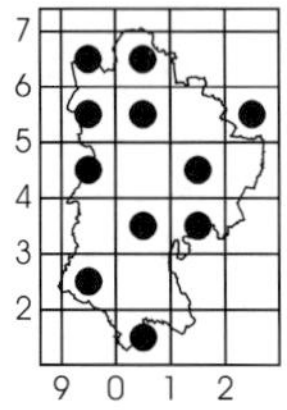

Argyresthia pygmaeella **([Denis & Schiffermüller]) (412)**
VCH: "Bedford, among sallow".
Post VCH: Local and uncommon: Felmersham Nature Reserve, Worley's Wood and in the RIS trap at Cockayne Hatley.
Flight: June, July (weeks 25 to 28)*, August.
Larval Foodplants: Sallows.

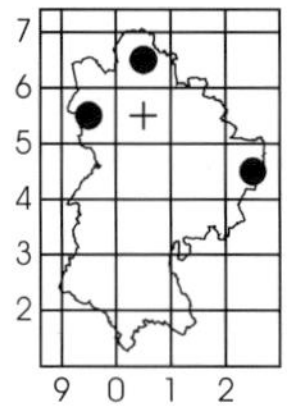

Argyresthia curvella **(Linnaeus) (414)**
VCH: "Bedford, in orchards".
Post VCH: Local and uncommon: Felmersham Nature Reserve, Putnoe Wood and in the RIS trap at Cockayne Hatley.
Flight: June, July (weeks 23 to 28)*.
Larval Foodplant: Apple.

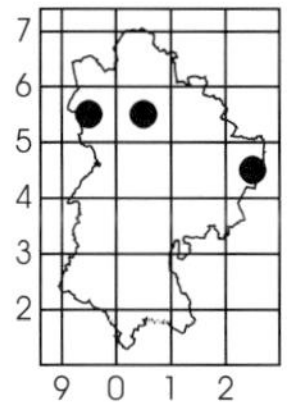

Argyresthia retinella **Zeller (415)**
Post VCH: Locally common.
Flight: June, July (weeks 24 to 29)*.
Larval Foodplants: Birches.

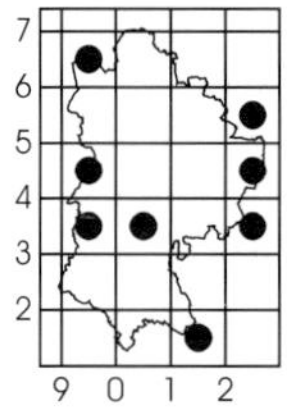

Argyresthia spinosella **(Stainton) (417)**
Post VCH: Widespread and common.
Flight: May (week 18)*, June, July (weeks 22 to 26, 30)*.
Larval Foodplant: Blackthorn.

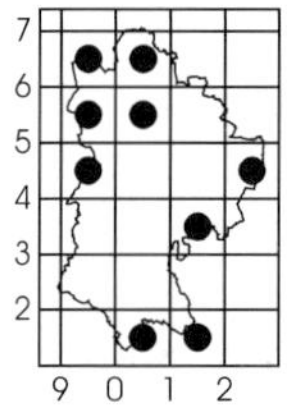

Apple Fruit Moth *Argyresthia conjugella* Zeller (418)
VCH: "Luton, among mountain ash".
Post VCH: Local and uncommon: Coppice Wood and Stotfold.
Flight: June (week 24)*, July (week 31)*.
Larval Foodplants: Rowan and apple.

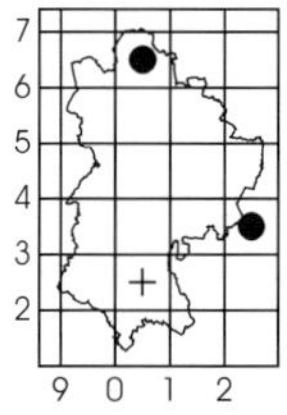

Argyresthia semifusca **(Haworth) (419)**
VCH: "Bedford".
Post VCH: Local and uncommon: West Wood and in the RIS trap at Cockayne Hatley.
Flight: August (weeks 31 to 34)*.
Larval Foodplants: Hawthorns and rowan.

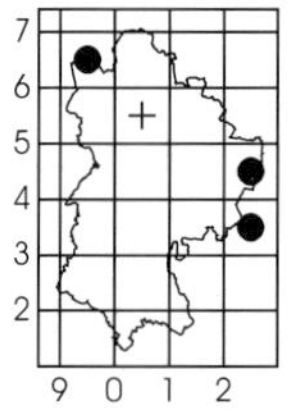

For details of standard weeks see page 6.

Cherry Fruit Moth *Argyresthia pruniella* (Clerck) (420)
(Plate 60 and drawing on page 121)
VCH: (as *A. ephippella* Fab.) "Bedford, about cherry trees".
Post VCH: Locally common.
Flight: June to August (weeks 24-33)★.
Larval Foodplant: Cherry.

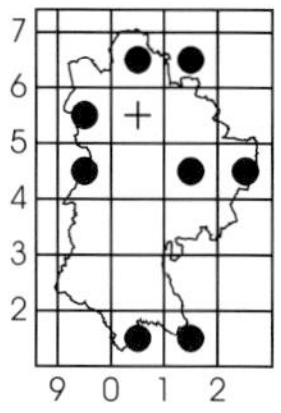

***Argyresthia bonnetella* (Linnaeus) (421)**
VCH: (as *A nitidella* Fab.) "Common in hedges everywhere".
Post VCH: Widespread and common.
Flight: June to September (weeks 26 to 37)★.
Larval Foodplants: Hawthorns.

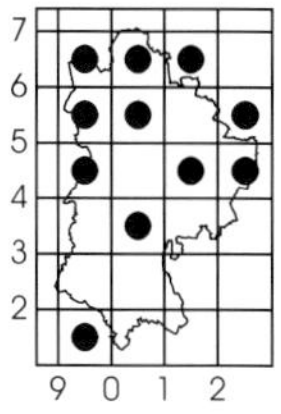

***Argyresthia albistria* (Haworth) (422)**
VCH: "Luton, in hedges".
Post VCH: Widespread and common.
Flight: July, August (weeks 28 to 35)★.
Larval Foodplant: Blackthorn★.

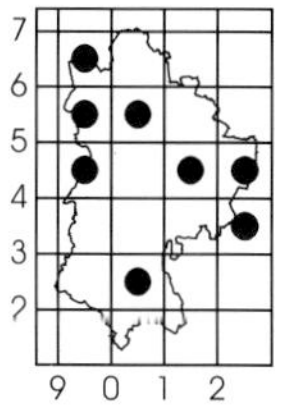

***Argyresthia semitestacella* (Curtis) (423)**
Post VCH: A single record from Stotfold on 29 August 1984 by T.S. Hollingworth.
Flight: August (week 35)★, September.
Larval Foodplant: Beech.

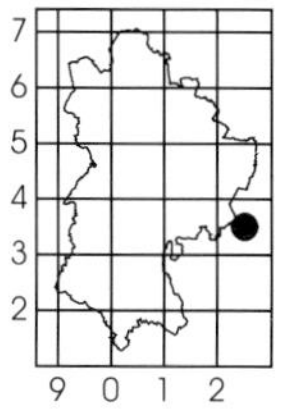

Subfamily: **Yponomeutinae**

The moths of this subfamily vary widely in colour and size (wingspan 10-25 mm). Those in the genus *Yponomeuta* are known as the 'small ermines' because of their white colour and pattern of small black dots (Plate 78). Their larvae feed gregariously in substantial webs and may defoliate bushes and even lengths of hedgerow (Plate 79).

Bird-cherry Ermine *Yponomeuta evonymella* (Linnaeus) (424)
Post VCH: Widespread and common.
Flight: July, August (weeks 27 to 33)★.
Larval Foodplants: Possibly *Prunus* species but most records may refer to migrants. The known foodplant, bird cherry, does not occur naturally in the County though there may be a few planted trees.

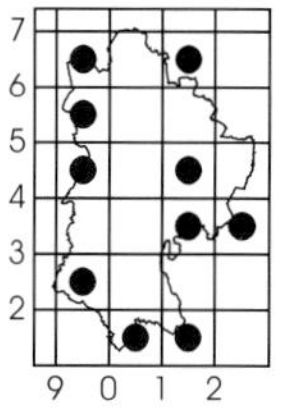

Orchard Ermine *Yponomeuta padella* (Linnaeus) (425)
VCH: "Common everywhere in hawthorn hedges".
Post VCH: Widespread and common.
Flight: July, August (weeks 29 to 35)★.
Larval Foodplants: Hawthorns and blackthorn★ (Plate 79).

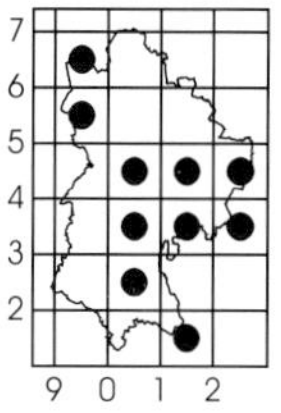

For key to moth maps see page 3.

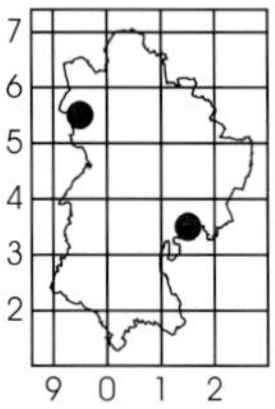

Apple Ermine *Yponomeuta malinellus* Zeller (426)
Post VCH: Scarce: first recorded in 1995 from Sharnbrook on 19 July and from Shillington on 29 July.
Flight: July, (weeks 29, 30)*, August.
Larval Foodplant: Apple.

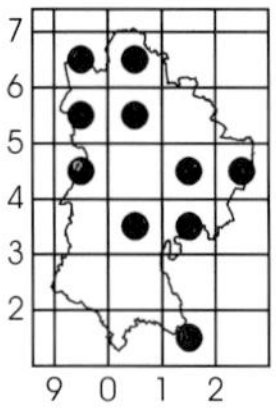

Spindle Ermine *Yponomeuta cagnagella* (Hübner) (427) (Plate 78)
Post VCH: Locally common.
Flight: July to September (weeks 29 to 36)*.
Larval Foodplant: Spindle*.

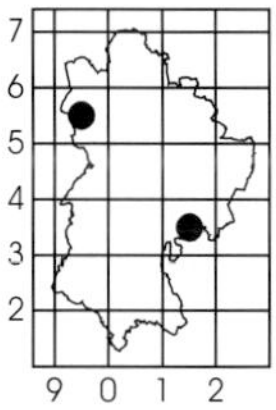

Willow Ermine *Yponomeuta rorrella* (Hübner) (428)
Post VCH: A scarce species, which appeared nationally in great numbers in 1989, probably as immigrants. Clifton on 23 July 1989 and Sharnbrook on 21 July 1990.
Flight: July (weeks 29, 30)*, August.
Larval Foodplant: White willow.

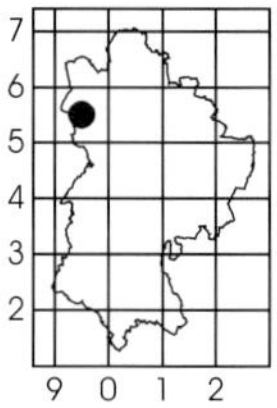

***Yponomeuta plumbella* ([Denis & Schiffermüller]) (430)**
Post VCH: Scarce: Sharnbrook.
Flight: July, August (weeks 30 to 35)*.
Larval Foodplant: Spindle.

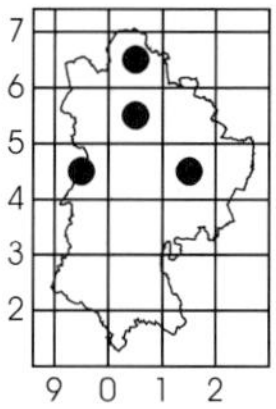

***Zelleria hepariella* Stainton (435)**

Post VCH: Local and uncommon: Marston Thrift, Putnoe Wood, Coppice Wood, Chicksands Wood.
Flight: August (weeks 31, 32)* to April.
Larval Foodplant: Ash.

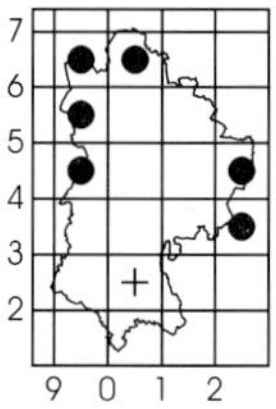

***Pseudoswammerdamia combinella* (Hübner) (436)**
VCH: (as *Swammerdamia apicella* Don.) "Luton, about blackthorn".
Post VCH: Widespread and fairly common.
Flight: May, June (weeks 18 to 23, 26)*.
Larval Foodplant: Blackthorn.

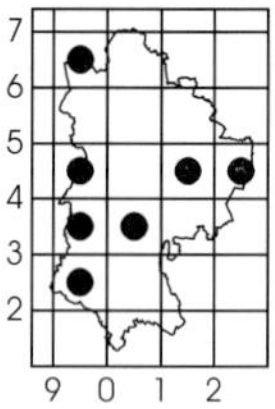

***Swammerdamia caesiella* (Hübner) (= *heroldella* (Hübner)) (437)**
Post VCH: Widespread and common.
Flight: May to August (weeks 28 to 32)*.
Larval Foodplants: Birches*.

For details of standard weeks see page 6.

Swammerdamia pyrella **(Villers) (438)**
VCH: "Luton, Bedford; about fruit trees".
Post VCH: Widespread and common.
Flight: May (weeks 19 to 22)★, July, August (weeks 28 to 32)★.
Larval Foodplants: Hawthorns★ and apple★.

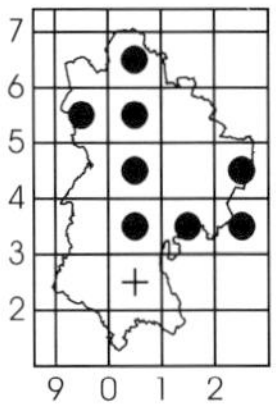

Paraswammerdamia albicapitella **(Scharfenberg) (440)**
VCH: (as *Swammerdamia spiniella* Zell.) "Luton, Bedford; about blackthorn".
Post VCH: Widespread and common.
Flight: June to October (weeks 23 to 37, 40)★.
Larval Foodplant: Blackthorn.

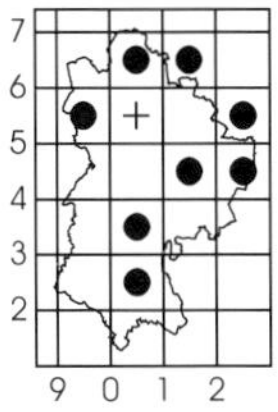

Paraswammerdamia lutarea **(Haworth) (441)**
VCH: (as *Swammerdamia oxyacanthella* Zell.) "Bedford, about hawthorn".
Post VCH: Widespread and common.
Flight: June to August (weeks 25 to 35)★.
Larval Foodplants: Hawthorns★ and rowan.

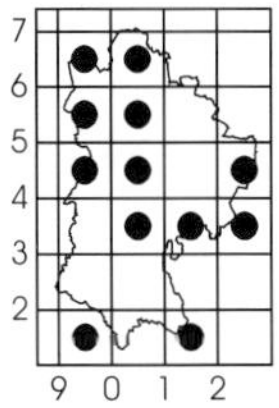

Cedestis gysseleniella **Zeller (442)**
Post VCH: Local and uncommon: Old Wavendon Heath, Maulden Wood, Rowney Warren and Potton Wood.
Flight: June to August (weeks 24 to 33)★.
Larval Foodplant: Scots pine★.

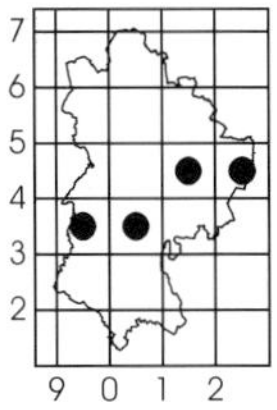

Cedestis subfasciella **(Stephens) (443)**
VCH: (as *C. farinatella* Zell.) "Bedford, Luton, among fir".
Post VCH: Local and uncommon: Luton Hoo and Potton Wood.
Flight: March to July (weeks 22, 25)★.
Larval Foodplants: Pines.

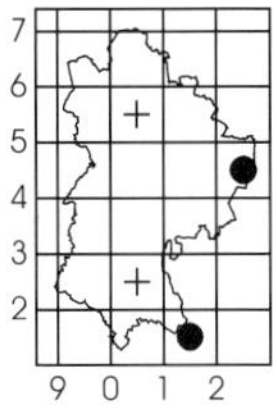

Ash Bud Moth *Prays fraxinella* (Bjerkander) (449)
VCH: (as *P. curtisella* Don.) "Bedford, among ash".
Post VCH: Widespread and common.
Flight: June, July (weeks 24 to 29)★, August, September (weeks 34, 36)★.
Larval Foodplant: Ash.

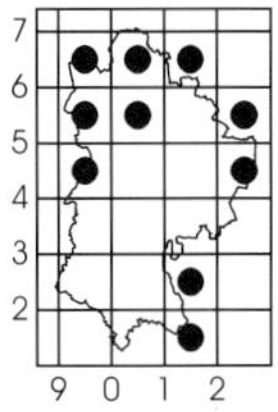

Hawthorn Moth *Scythropia crataegella* (Linnaeus) (450)
VCH: "Bedford".
Post VCH: Local and uncommon: Sharnbrook, Bedford, Stotfold and in the RIS trap at Cockayne Hatley.
Flight: June, July (weeks 26 to 30)★.
Larval Foodplants: Hawthorns and blackthorn.

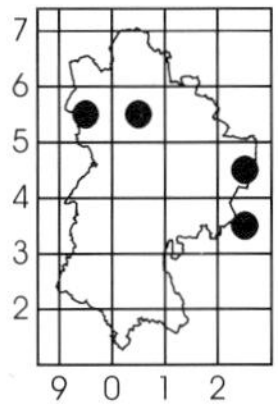

For key to moth maps see page 3.

Subfamily: **Plutellinae**

The moths in this subfamily rest in a characteristic position with the antennae pointing forward (porrect).

Ypsolopha sequella
(x 3)

***Ypsolopha mucronella* (Scopoli) (451)**
Post VCH: Local and uncommon: Cranfield, Felmersham Nature Reserve and Little Staughton.
Flight: August to April (week 16)★.
Larval Foodplant: Spindle★.

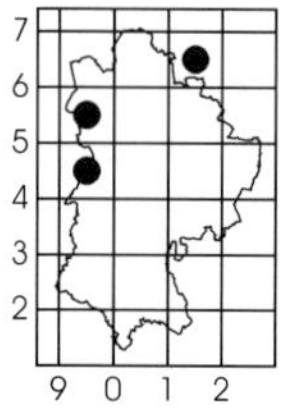

***Ypsolopha nemorella* (Linnaeus) (452)**
Post VCH: Two records in the RIS trap at Cockayne Hatley in August 1991 and in the week of 30 July to 5 August 1994.
Flight: July, August (week 31)★.
Larval Foodplant: Honeysuckle.

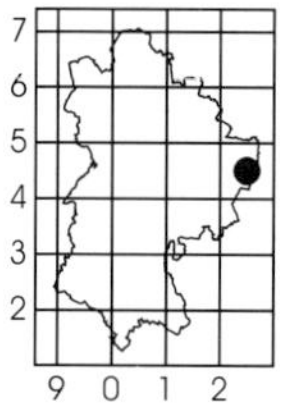

Honeysuckle Moth *Ypsolopha dentella* (Fabricius) (453)
VCH: (as *Harpipteryx xylostella* Schiff.) "Common about honeysuckle".
Post VCH: Widespread and fairly common.
Flight: July, August (weeks 28 to 35)★, September.
Larval Foodplant: Honeysuckle.

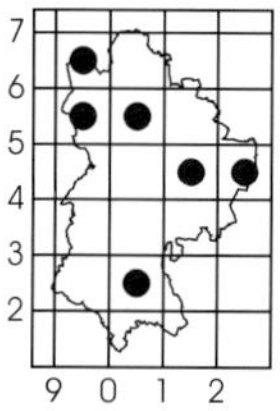

***Ypsolopha scabrella* (Linnaeus) (455)**
VCH: "Bedford".
Post VCH: Widespread and common.
Flight: July to September (weeks 29 to 37)★.
Larval Foodplants: Apple★ and hawthorns★.

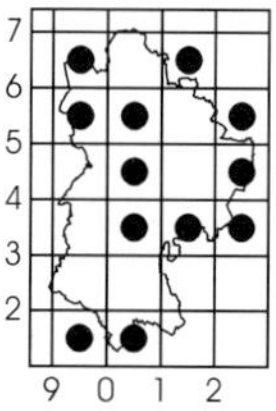

***Ypsolopha alpella* ([Denis & Schiffermüller]) (458)**
VCH: "Bedford".
Post VCH: Local, uncommon: Sharnbrook, West Wood, Putnoe Wood.
Flight: July, August (weeks 27, 31 to 35)★.
Larval Foodplants: Oaks.

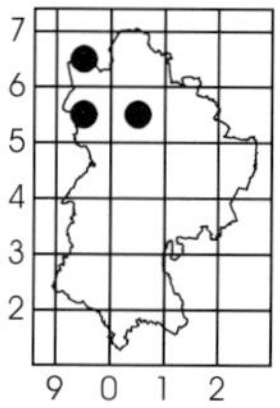

For details of standard weeks see page 6.

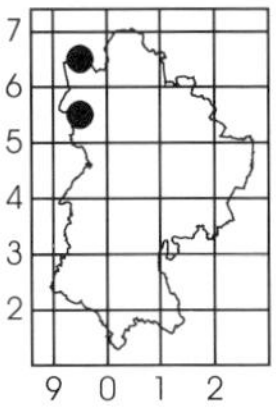

Ypsolopha sylvella (Linnaeus) (459)
Post VCH: Local and uncommon: Sharnbrook.
Flight: July, August (week 33)*.
Larval Foodplants: Oaks.

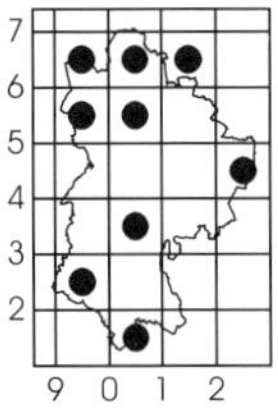

***Ypsolopha parenthesella* (Linnaeus) (460)**
VCH: (as *Cerostoma costella* Fab.) "Clapham Park near Bedford".
Post VCH: Widespread and common.
Flight: July to October (weeks 27 to 41)*.
Larval Foodplants: Oaks, birches, hazel*, hawthorns* and alder.

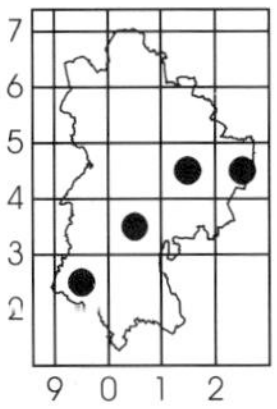

***Ypsolopha ustella* (Clerck) (461)**
VCH: (as *Cerostoma radiatella* Don.) "Common in all woods".
Post VCH: Locally common: King's Wood (Heath and Reach), Maulden Wood, Rowney Warren, RIS trap at Cockayne Hatley.
Flight: August to April (weeks 30 to 36, 41)*.
Larval Foodplants: Oaks*.

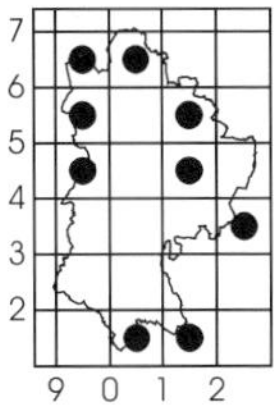

***Ypsolopha sequella* (Clerck) (462)** (Drawing on page 126)
Post VCH: Widespread and fairly common.
Flight: July to October (weeks 28-38, 42)*.
Larval Foodplants: Field maple and sycamore.

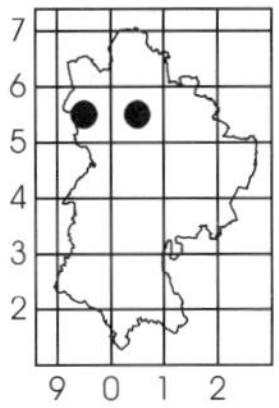

***Ypsolopha vittella* (Linnaeus) (463)**
Post VCH: Local and uncommon: Sharnbrook and Putnoe Wood.
Flight: July, August (weeks 28, 35)*.
Larval Foodplants: Elms and beech.

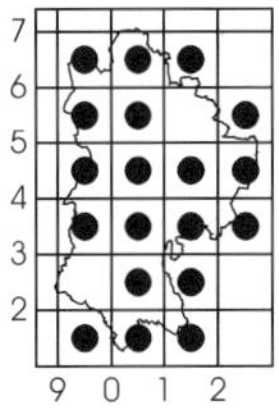

Diamond-back Moth *Plutella xylostella* (Linnaeus) (= *maculipennis* Curtis) (464)
VCH: (as *P. cruciferarum* Zell.) "abundant everywhere".
Post VCH: Widespread and very common. Numbers often increase sharply, probably as a result of immigration.
Flight: March to November (weeks 13 to 48)*.
Larval Foodplants: Cabbage and other Cruciferae.

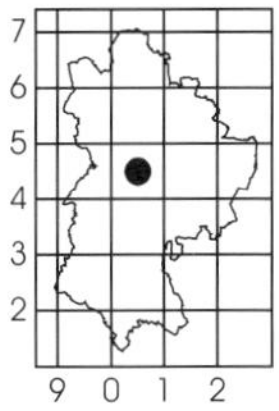

***Plutella porrectella* (Linnaeus) (465)**
VCH: "Bedford, among *Hesperis matronalis*".
Post VCH: Bedford (Queen's Park), a single recent record on 31 May 1984.
Flight: May (week 22)*, July, September.
Larval Foodplant: Dame's-violet.

For key to moth maps see page 3.

***Eidophasia messingiella* (Fischer von Röslerstamm) (469)**
Post VCH: The RIS trap at Cockayne Hatley has provided the only specimens, between 1989 and 1991.
Flight: June★, July (week 27)★.
Larval Foodplants: Large bitter-cress and hoary cress.

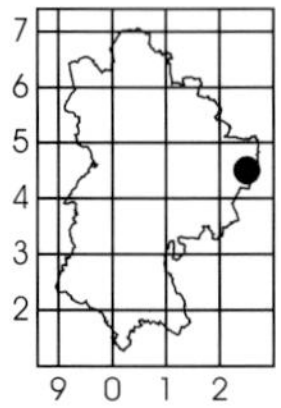

***Orthotelia sparganella* (Thunberg) (470)**
Post VCH: Local and uncommon: Sharnbrook, Flitwick Moor and Henlow.
Flight: March (week 11)★, July, August (week 31)★.
Larval Foodplants: Bur-reeds, irises and reed sweet-grass.

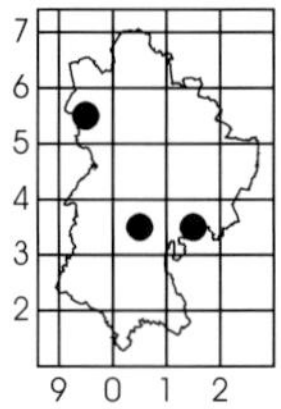

***Acrolepia autumnitella* Curtis (= *pygmaeana* (Haworth)) (476)**
Post VCH: A single record from Sharnbrook on 8 October 1981.
Flight: July, October (week 41)★ to April.
Larval Foodplants: Bittersweet and deadly nightshade.

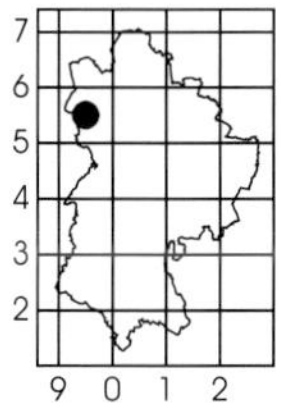

Family: **Roeslerstammiidae**

The following species and its relatives have recently been removed from the Yponomeutidae and placed in their own family. Its position in the systematic order is still uncertain. There are two British species, one of which has been found in Bedfordshire.

***Roeslerstammia erxlebella* (Fabricius) (447)**
Post VCH: Local and uncommon: King's Wood (Heath and Reach), Hinwick and Sharnbrook.
Flight: May, June, August, September.
Larval Foodplants: Limes★ and birches.

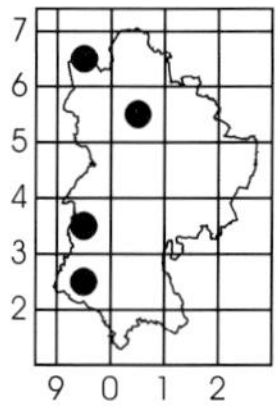

Family: **Epermeniidae**

A family of eight British species, of which only two have been found in Bedfordshire.

***Epermenia falciformis* (Haworth) (= *illigerella* auctt.) (481)**
Post VCH: Found only once, at Coppice Wood on 24 June 1986.
Flight: June (week 25)★, July, September.
Larval Foodplants: Wild angelica and ground-elder.

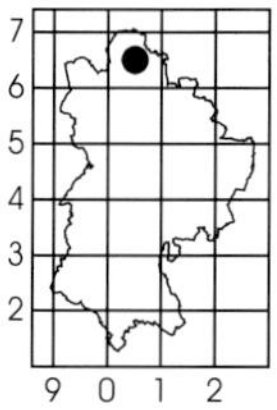

For details of standard weeks see page 6.

***Epermenia chaerophyllella* (Goeze) (483)**

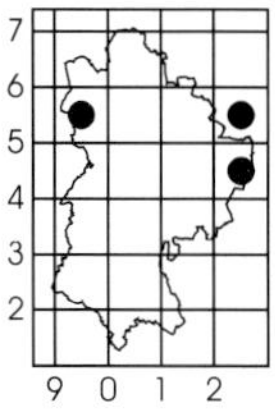

VCH: "Bedford, among Umbelliferae".
Post VCH: Local and uncommon: Felmersham Nature Reserve, RIS trap at Cockayne Hatley and Potton Wood.
Flight: July, August (weeks 27 to 34)*, September (week 39)* to May (week 20)*.
Larval Foodplants: Hogweed, wild parsnip, wild angelica and cow parsley.

Family: **Schreckensteiniidae**

There is only one species in this family in Britain. A small moth, wingspan 10-12 mm, with narrow forewings streaked with brown and yellow. It rests in a characteristic position using only its forelegs and midlegs. Its hindlegs are held raised in a V position over the abdomen.

***Schreckensteinia festaliella* (Hübner) (485)**

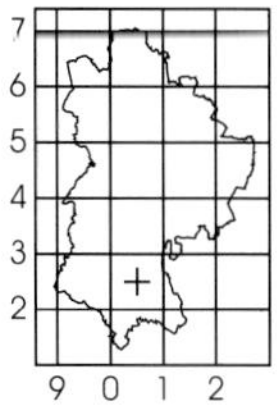

VCH: "Luton, among bramble".
Post VCH: No recent record.
Flight: May, June, August, September.
Larval Foodplants: *Rubus* spp.

For key to moth maps see page 3.

Case-bearers and their Allies.

(Coleophoridae to Elachistidae)

D.V.Manning

Family: **Coleophoridae**

Narrow-winged, mostly small moths (wingspan 7-22 mm), many of which must be dissected to determine the species. The larvae construct silk cases, often using portions of leaf or eaten-out seed-heads. Most species can be determined by the form of the case (beautifully illustrated in Emmet, 1996), and identification of the foodplant. There are more than 100 British species, of which 57 have been found in Bedfordshire.

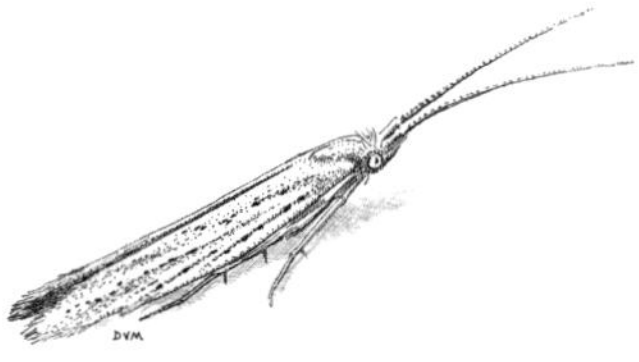

Coleophora adspersella
(*x 4*)

***Metriotes lutarea* (Haworth) (487)**
VCH: (as *Asychna modestella* Dup.) "Luton".
Post VCH: The only recent record is of the moth nectaring on stitchwort flowers in Putnoe Wood on 31 May 1984.
Flight: May (week 22)*, June.
Larval Foodplant: Greater stitchwort.

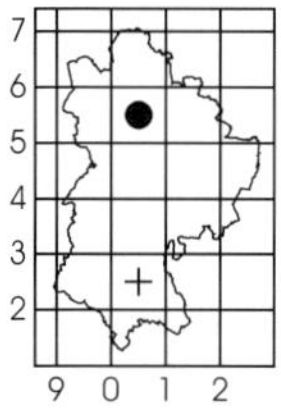

***Coleophora lutipennella* (Zeller) (490)**
VCH: "Bedford".
Post VCH: Probably widespread and common. It is not possible to separate this species and *C. flavipennella* without dissecting the adults. These two common species are therefore under-recorded.
Flight: June to August (weeks 27-31)*.
Larval Foodplants: Oaks*, in larval case.

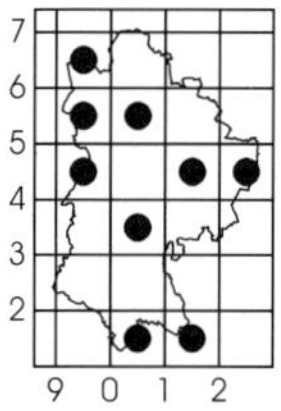

***Coleophora gryphipennella* (Hübner) (491)**
Post VCH: Widespread and common.
Flight: June, July (weeks 26-29)*.
Larval Foodplants: Roses*, in larval case (Plate 83).

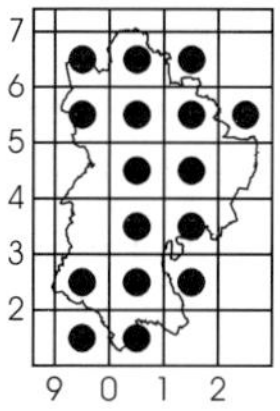

***Coleophora flavipennella* (Duponchel) (492)**
Post VCH: Probably widespread and common. This species is under-recorded (see *C. lutipennella* above).
Flight: June, July (weeks 26-30)*.
Larval Foodplants: Oaks*, in larval case.

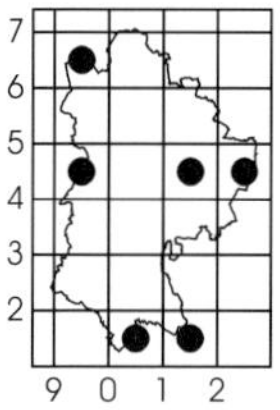

Coleophora serratella **(Linnaeus) (493)**
Post VCH: Widespread and common.
Flight: June to August (weeks 24, 27-32)*.
Larval Foodplants: Alder, birches*, hazel and elms, in larval case.

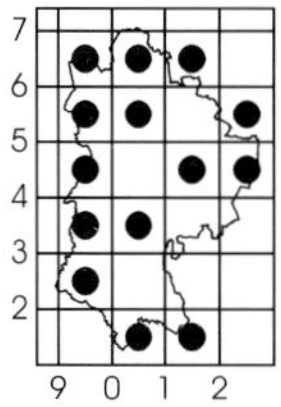

Coleophora coracipennella **(Hübner) (494)**
Post VCH: Scarce: RIS trap at Cockayne Hatley. Larval cases, probably of this species, have been found on blackthorn but not reared. It is not possible to separate this species and *C. spinella* without dissecting the adults.
Flight: June, July (week 29)*.
Larval Foodplants: Blackthorn and occasionally hawthorns and apple, in larval case.

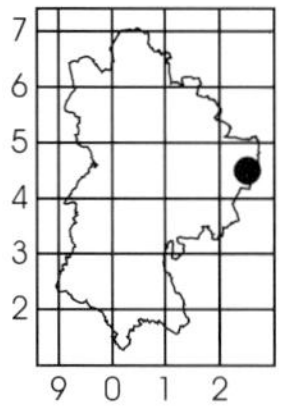

Apple & Plum Case-bearer *Coleophora spinella* (Schrank) (= *cerasivorella* Packard) (495)
VCH: (as *C. nigricella* Steph.) "Bedford, probably everywhere".
Post VCH: Larval cases on hawthorn have been assumed to be of this species. The only moth dissected is from Studham (bred).
Flight: June to August (weeks 27-32)*.
Larval Foodplants: Hawthorns* and apple, and less often on *Prunus* spp., in larval case.

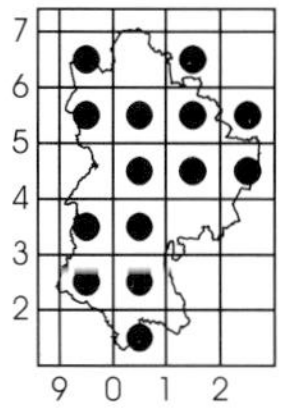

Coleophora milvipennis **Zeller (496)**
Post VCH: A single record from King's Wood (Heath and Reach) on 9 October 1985 by A.M.Emmet.
Flight: May, June.
Larval Foodplants: Birches*, in larval case.

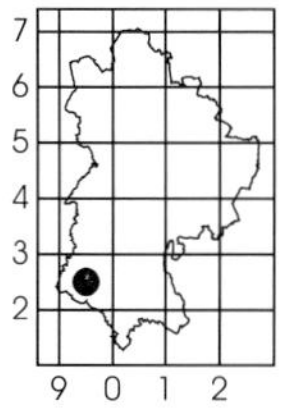

Coleophora adjectella **Herrich-Schäffer (496a)**
Post VCH: A single record from West Wood on 27 September 1992 by A.M.Emmet and J.R.Langmaid.
Flight: July.
Larval Foodplant: Blackthorn*, in larval case.

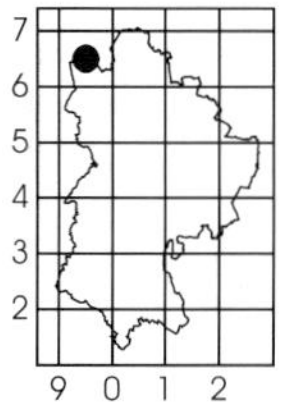

Coleophora badiipennella **(Duponchel) (497)**
Post VCH: Local and uncommon: Putnoe Wood, Sheerhatch Wood, Little Staughton, Chicksands Wood and Cockayne Hatley Wood.
Flight: July.
Larval Foodplants: Elms*, in larval case.

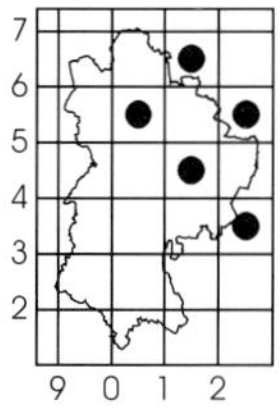

Coleophora limosipennella **(Duponchel) (499)**
Post VCH: Local and uncommon: Salford, Sharnbrook, West Wood, Putnoe Wood and Chicksands Wood.
Flight: June, July.
Larval Foodplants: Elms*, in larval case.

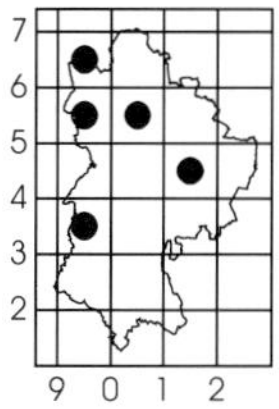

For key to moth maps see page 3.

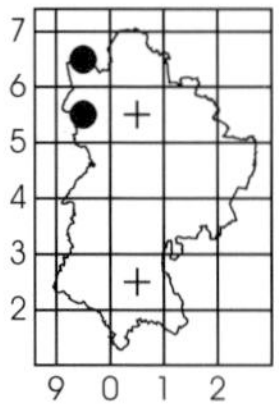

Coleophora siccifolia **Stainton (501)**
VCH: "Bedford, Luton".
Post VCH: Local and uncommon: Sharnbrook and West Wood.
Flight: June.
Larval Foodplants: Birches, hawthorns★, apple and rowan, in larval case.

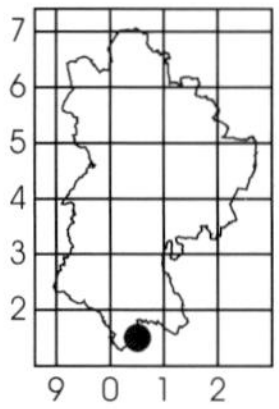

Coleophora trigeminella **Fuchs (502)**
Post VCH: Whipsnade Heath, a single record on 21 October 1983, by R.W.J.Uffen.
Flight: June.
Larval Foodplants: Hawthorns★ and apple, in larval case.

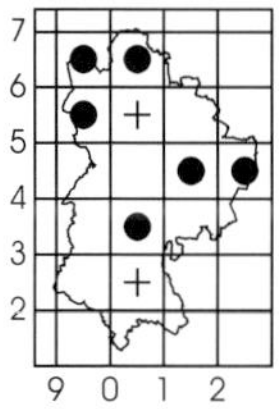

Coleophora lusciniaepennella **(Treitschke)(=** ***viminetella*** **Zeller) (504)**
VCH: "Bedford, Luton".
Post VCH: Local and uncommon: Felmersham Nature Reserve, West Wood, Maulden Wood, Worley's Wood, Sandy and in the RIS trap at Cockayne Hatley.
Flight: June, July (weeks 26-29)★.
Larval Foodplants: Sallows★, in larval case.

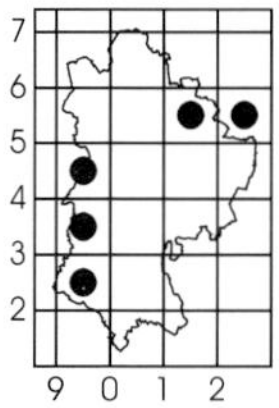

Coleophora violacea **(Ström)(=** ***paripennella*** **auctt.) (509)**
Post VCH: Local and uncommon: King's Wood (Heath and Reach), Cranfield, Waterloo Thorns and Cockayne Hatley Wood.
Flight: May, June.
Larval Foodplants: Various shrubs and trees, in larval case.

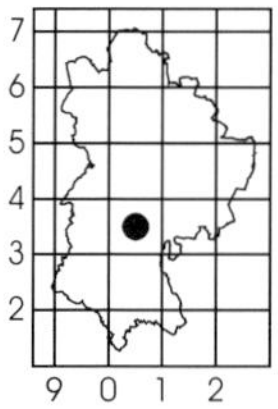

Coleophora juncicolella **Stainton (510)**
Post VCH: A few larval cases swept from heather at Cooper's Hill on 3 April 1993.
Flight: June, July.
Larval Foodplant: Heather★, in larval case.

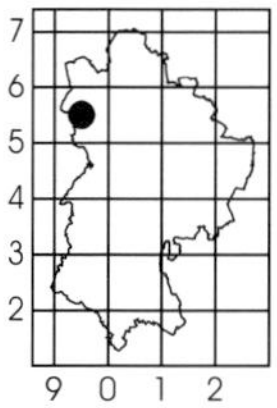

Coleophora orbitella **Zeller (511)**
Post VCH: A single larval case recorded from White Lane (Odell Great Wood) on 13 October 1985.
Flight: May, June.
Larval Foodplants: Birches★, in larval case.

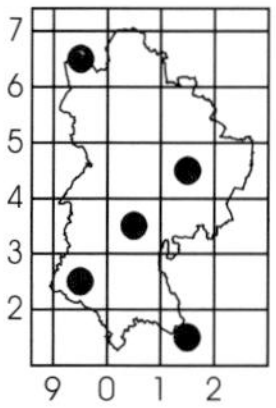

Coleophora binderella **(Kollar) (512)**
Post VCH: Local and uncommon: King's Wood (Heath and Reach), West Wood, Flitwick Moor, Luton Hoo and Chicksands Wood.
Flight: June (week 23)★, July.
Larval Foodplants: Alder, birches★ and hazel★, in larval case.

For details of standard weeks see page 6.

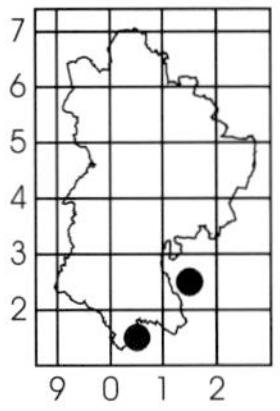

***Coleophora potentillae* Elisha (513)**
Post VCH: Scarce: Larvae found on Dunstable Downs on 21 October 1983 and Pegsdon Hills on 21 October 1985.
Flight: June.
Larval Foodplants: Brambles★, herbaceous Rosaceae and various shrubs, in larval case.

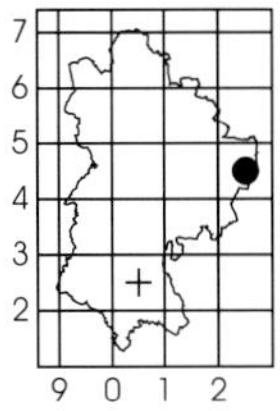

***Coleophora albitarsella* Zeller (515)**
VCH: "Luton, among ground ivy".
Post VCH: Locally common: RIS trap at Cockayne Hatley has produced many specimens.
Flight: June to August (weeks 28-32)★.
Larval Foodplants: Calamints, wild basil, ground-ivy, selfheal, mints and marjoram, in larval case.

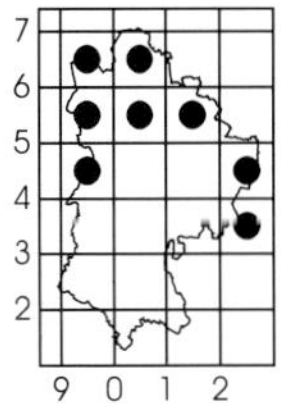

***Coleophora trifolii* (Curtis)(=*frischella* auctt.) (516)**
Post VCH: Widespread and common.
Flight: June, July (weeks 23-30)★.
Larval Foodplants: Melilots, in larval case.

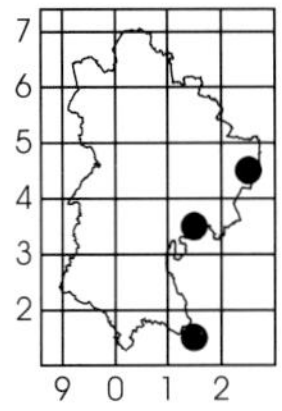

Small Clover Case-bearer *Coleophora frischella* (Linnaeus) (517)
Post VCH: Local and uncommon: Luton Hoo, Shillington and in the RIS trap at Cockayne Hatley.
Flight: May to September (weeks 22-24, 29-35)★.
Larval Foodplant: White clover, in larval case.

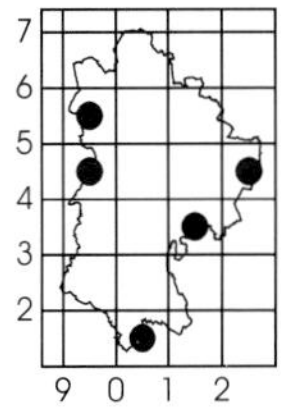

***Coleophora mayrella* (Hübner) (= *spissicornis* (Haworth)) (518)**
Post VCH: Local and uncommon: Cranfield, Sharnbrook, Studham, Pegsdon Hills and in the RIS trap at Cockayne Hatley.
Flight: June to August (weeks 25-32)★.
Larval Foodplant: White clover, in larval case.

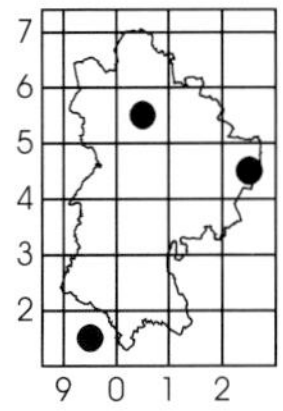

***Coleophora deauratella* Lienig & Zeller (519)**
Post VCH: Local and uncommon: Bison Hill, Thurleigh Cutting and in the RIS trap at Cockayne Hatley.
Flight: June to August (weeks 26-31)★.
Larval Foodplant: Red clover, in larval case.

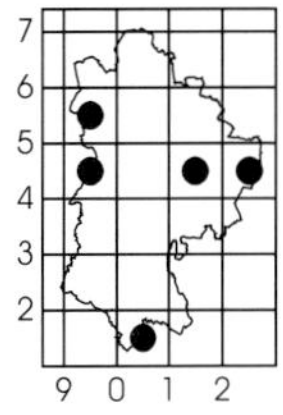

***Coleophora lineolea* (Haworth) (= *crocogramma* Zeller) (522)**
Post VCH: Widespread and common.
Flight: June to August (weeks 25-31)★.
Larval Foodplants: Black horehound★, lamb's-ear, hedge woundwort, betony and white horehound, in larval case.

For key to moth maps see page 3.

***Coleophora hemerobiella* (Scopoli) (523)**
Post VCH: A single record, from Luton Hoo on 25 July 1995.
Flight: July (week 30)*.
Larval Foodplants: Hawthorns, apple, pear, wild plum and wild cherry.

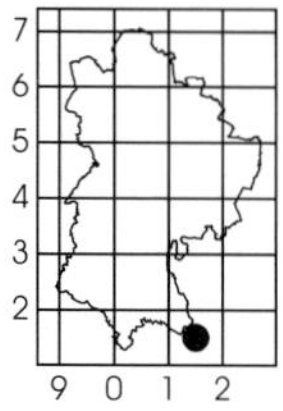

***Coleophora solitariella* Zeller (525)**
Post VCH: Local and uncommon: Sharnbrook and Worley's Wood.
Flight: July.
Larval Foodplant: Greater stitchwort*, in larval case.

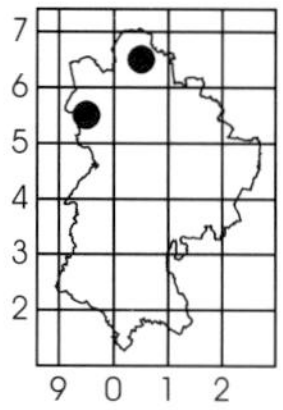

Larch Case-bearer *Coleophora laricella* (Hübner) (526)
VCH: "Bedford, upon larch".
Post VCH: Widespread and common.
Flight: June, July (week 27)*.
Larval Foodplants: Larches*, in larval case.

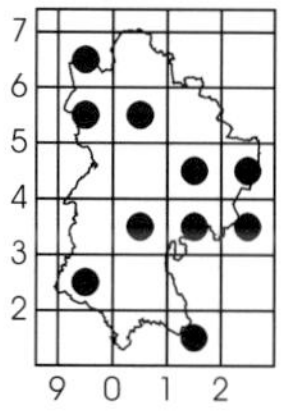

***Coleophora lixella* Zeller (530)**
Post VCH: Found only once, at Bison Hill on 20 July 1984 by T.S.Hollingworth.
Flight: July (week 29)*.
Larval Foodplants: Thymes, in larval case.

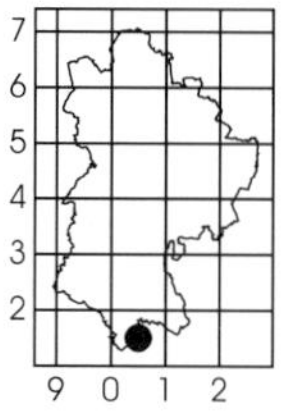

***Coleophora albidella* ([Denis & Schiffermüller]) (532)**
Recorded in Manning (1992) but now deleted as a mis-identification.

Pistol Case-bearer *Coleophora anatipennella* (Hübner) (533)
Post VCH: Widespread and common.
Flight: June, July (weeks 28, 31)*.
Larval Foodplants: Hawthorns, apple and blackthorn*, in larval case.

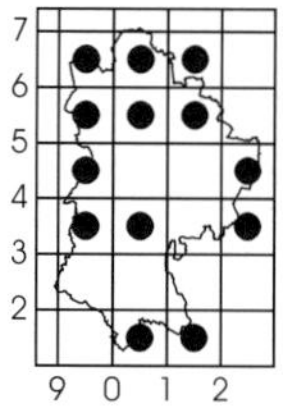

***Coleophora ibipennella* Zeller (= *ardeaepennella* Scott) (535)**
Post VCH: Widespread and common.
Flight: July (weeks 27-30)*, August.
Larval Foodplants: Oaks*, in larval case.

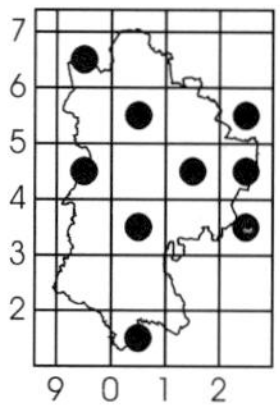

***Coleophora betulella* Heinemann & Wocke (= *ibipennella* auctt.) (536)**
Post VCH: Widespread and common.
Flight: July.
Larval Foodplants: Birches*, in larval case.

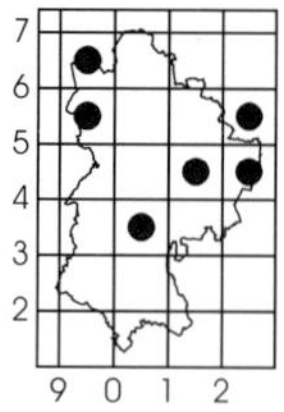

For details of standard weeks see page 6.

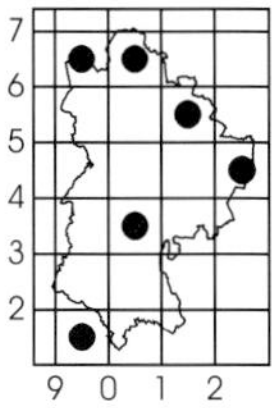

***Coleophora palliatella* (Zincken) (537)**
Post VCH: Widespread and fairly common.
Flight: June, July (weeks 26-30)★.
Larval Foodplants: Oaks★, in larval case.

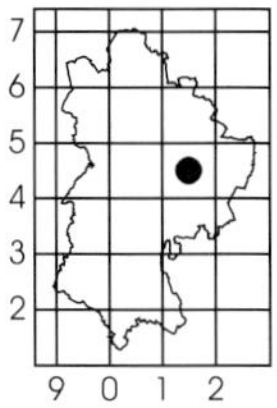

***Coleophora pyrrhulipennella* Zeller (541)**
Post VCH: A single larval case swept from heather at The Lodge, Sandy, on 2 November 1987.
Flight: July.
Larval Foodplant: Heather★, in larval case.

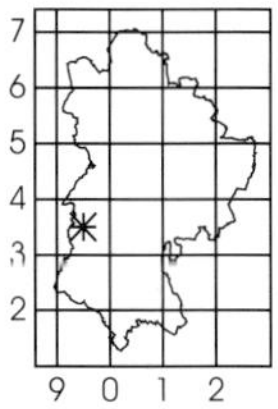

***Coleophora albicosta* (Haworth) (544)**
Post VCH: A single record from Aspley Heath on 17 June 1962 by R.W.J.Uffen.
Flight: May, June (week 24)★.
Larval Foodplant: Gorse, in larval case.

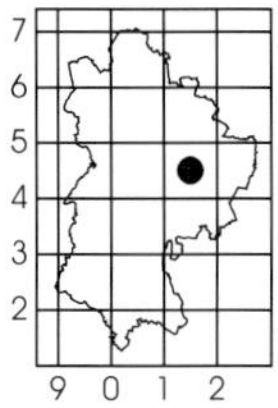

***Coleophora saturatella* Stainton (545)**
Post VCH: Scarce: larval cases recorded from Sandy in 1971 by R.W.J.Uffen.
Flight: July.
Larval Foodplants: Broom★ and dyer's greenweed, in larval case.

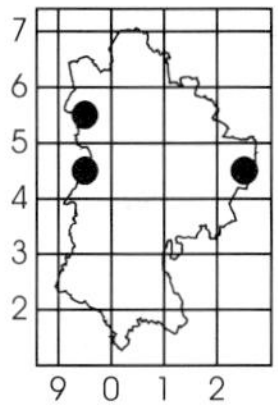

***Coleophora discordella* Zeller (547)**
Post VCH: Local and uncommon: Cranfield, Felmersham Nature Reserve and in the RIS trap at Cockayne Hatley.
Flight: June (week 24)★, July (week 29)★.
Larval Foodplants: Bird's-foot-trefoils, in larval case.

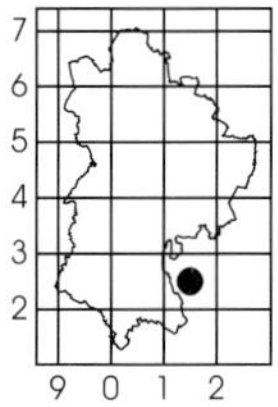

***Coleophora niveicostella* Zeller (548)**
Post VCH: A single record from Pegsdon Hills, 15 July 1992.
Flight: June, July (week 28)★.
Larval Foodplants: Thymes, in larval case.

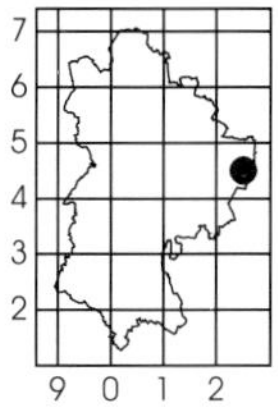

***Coleophora striatipennella* (Nylander) (= *lineolea* auctt.) (553)**
Post VCH: Scarce: RIS trap at Cockayne Hatley, June 1989 and in the week of 4 - 10 June 1995.
Flight: June (week 23)★, July.
Larval Foodplants: Lesser stitchwort, common chickweed and common mouse-ear, in larval case.

For key to moth maps see page 3.

Coleophora follicularis **(Vallot)(=** ***troglodytella*** **(Duponchel)) (555)**
Post VCH: A single record from Bedford on 15 July 1984 by T.S.Hollingworth.
Flight: July (week 28)*, August.
Larval Foodplants: Creeping thistle, hemp-agrimony, ploughman's-spikenard and common fleabane, in larval case.

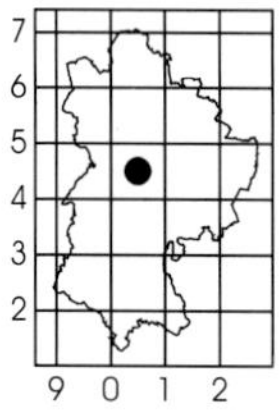

Coleophora peribenanderi **Toll (=** ***therinella*** **auctt.) (559)**
Post VCH: Widespread and fairly common.
Flight: June to August (weeks 23, 26-31)*.
Larval Foodplant: Creeping thistle*, in larval case.

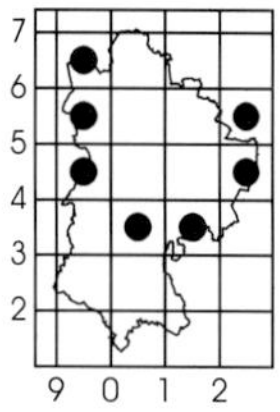

Coleophora paripennella **Zeller (560)** (Plates 81 and 82)
Post VCH: Local and uncommon: Sharnbrook, Upper Dean and Tempsford Airfield.
Flight: June (week 25)*, July.
Larval Foodplants: Knapweeds*, in larval case.

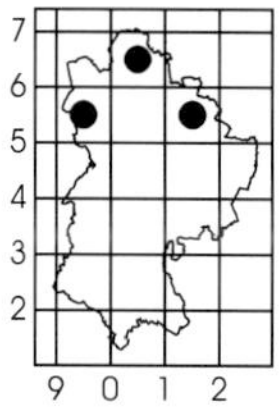

Coleophora therinella **Tengström (561)**
Post VCH: Local and uncommon: This nationally scarce species has been obtained in the RIS trap at Cockayne Hatley in 1986, and 1989-95, the specimens determined by dissection. One specimen was obtained from Stotfold on 18 July 1985.
Flight: June to August (weeks 27-33)*.
Larval Foodplant: Black-bindweed, in larval case.

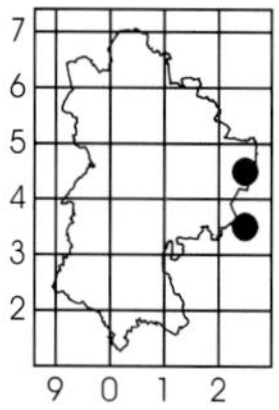

Coleophora argentula **(Stephens) (563)**
Post VCH: Widespread and common.
Flight: July (weeks 28-30)*, August.
Larval Foodplant: Yarrow*, in larval case.

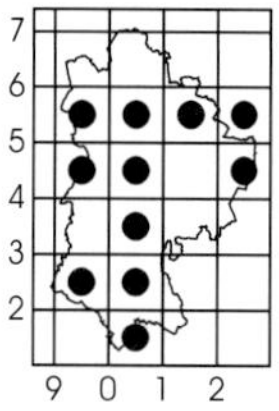

Coleophora saxicolella **(Duponchel)(=** ***benanderi*** **Kanerva,** ***annulatella*** **auctt.) (565)**
Post VCH: Widespread and probably common: Sharnbrook, Flitwick Moor and in the RIS trap at Cockayne Hatley. This and the following species which feed on seeds of Chenopodiaceae cannot be separated without dissection. All species are therefore probably under-recorded.
Flight: June to August (weeks 25, 28-32, 35)*.
Larval Foodplants: Goosefoots, fat-hen* and oraches, in larval case, feeding on the seeds.

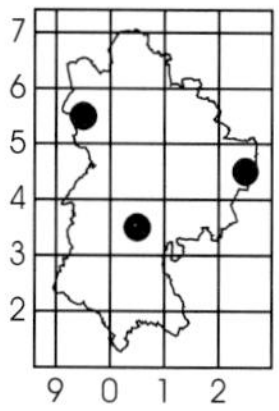

Coleophora sternipennella **(Zetterstedt) (566)**
Post VCH: See 565 above. Sharnbrook, Shillington and in the RIS trap at Cockayne Hatley.
Flight: June*, July (weeks 28, 29)*, August (weeks 33, 34)*.
Larval Foodplants: Goosefoots, fat-hen and oraches, in larval case.

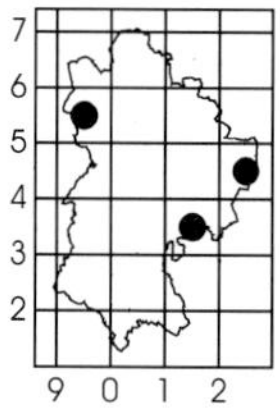

For details of standard weeks see page 6.

***Coleophora adspersella* Benander (567)** (Drawing on page 130)

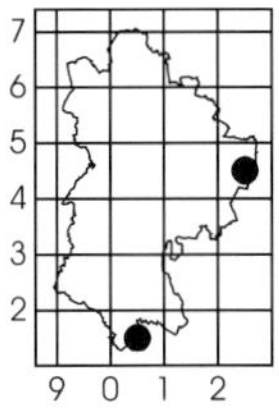

Post VCH: See 565 above. Studham on 11 July 1995 and the RIS trap at Cockayne Hatley in the week 9 -15 July 1995.
Flight: June, July (week 28)★.
Larval Foodplants: Oraches, in larval case.

***Coleophora versurella* Zeller (568)**

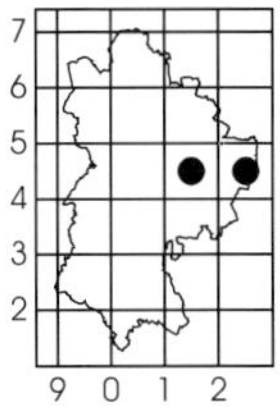

Post VCH: See 565 above. Sandy and in the RIS trap at Cockayne Hatley.
Flight: June to September (weeks 27-36)★.
Larval Foodplants: Goosefoots and fat-hen, in larval case.

***Coleophora vestianella* (Linnaeus) (= *laripennella* Zetterstedt) (572)**

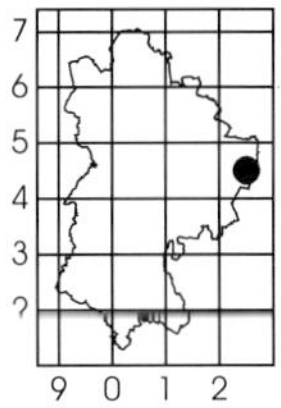

Post VCH: See 565 above. Two specimens have been obtained from the RIS trap at Cockayne Hatley, identified by dissection.
Flight: June, July and August★.
Larval Foodplant: Common orache, in larval case.

***Coleophora artemisicolella* Bruand (577)**

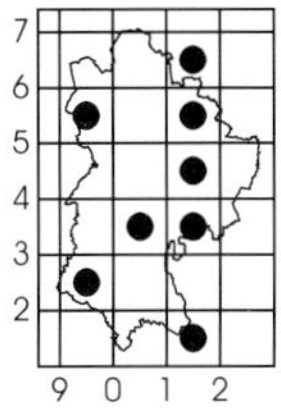

Post VCH: Widespread and common.
Flight: June, July (weeks 26, 30)★, August.
Larval Foodplant: Mugwort★, in larval case.

***Coleophora otidipennella* (Hübner) (= *murinipennella* (Duponchel)) (578)**

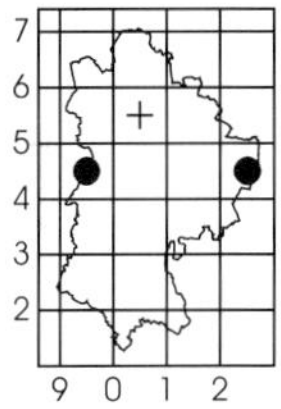

VCH: "Bedford".
Post VCH: Local and uncommon: Cranfield and in the RIS trap at Cockayne Hatley.
Flight: May to July (week 27)★.
Larval Foodplants: Wood-rushes, in larval case.

***Coleophora taeniipennella* Herrich-Schäffer (581)**

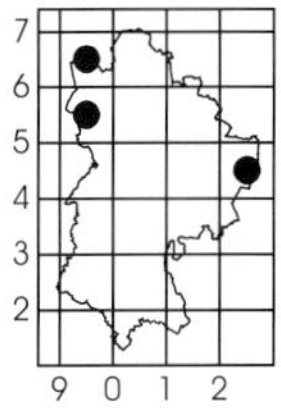

Post VCH: Locally common: Felmersham Nature Reserve, West Wood and in the RIS trap at Cockayne Hatley.
Flight: June, July (weeks 26-28)★.
Larval Foodplants: Jointed rush★ and sharp-flowered rush, in larval case.

***Coleophora glaucicolella* Wood (582)**

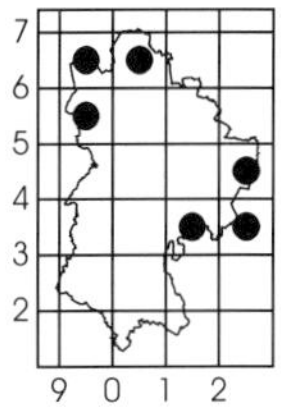

Post VCH: Locally common: Sharnbrook, West Wood, Melchbourne, Shillington, Stotfold and in the RIS trap at Cockayne Hatley.
Flight: June, July (weeks 26-30)★, August.
Larval Foodplants: Rushes★, in larval case.

For key to moth maps see page 3.

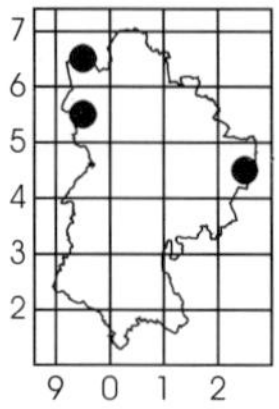

Coleophora tamesis **Waters (583)**
Post VCH: Local and uncommon: Felmersham Nature Reserve, West Wood and in the RIS trap at Cockayne Hatley.
Flight: June to August.
Larval Foodplant: Jointed rush*, in larval case.

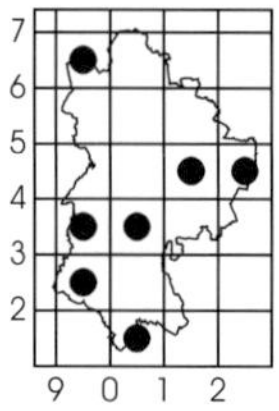

Coleophora alticolella **Zeller (=** ***caespititiella*** **auctt.) (584)**
Post VCH: Locally common.
Flight: June to August (weeks 22-31)*.
Larval Foodplants: Rushes*, in larval case.

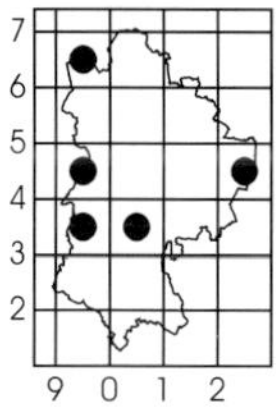

Coleophora caespititiella **Zeller (=** ***agrammella*** **Wood) (587)**
Post VCH: Locally common.
Flight: May, June (weeks 21-26)*.
Larval Foodplants: Compact rush, occasionally other rushes, in larval case.

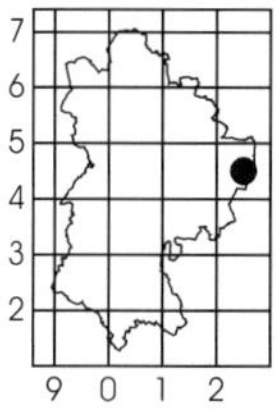

Coleophora clypeiferella **Hofmann (589)**
Post VCH: A single record from the RIS trap at Cockayne Hatley in 1991.
Flight: July and August*.
Larval Foodplant: Fat-hen, in larval case.

Family: **Elachistidae**

Small moths (wingspan 7-12 mm) which are not often seen. Many are obscurely marked and identifiable only by dissection. The larvae are mainly leaf-miners on grasses and sedges. Most records are of moths netted or attracted to light. Little work has been done on the leaf-mines. There are 47 British species, of which 22 have been found in Bedfordshire.

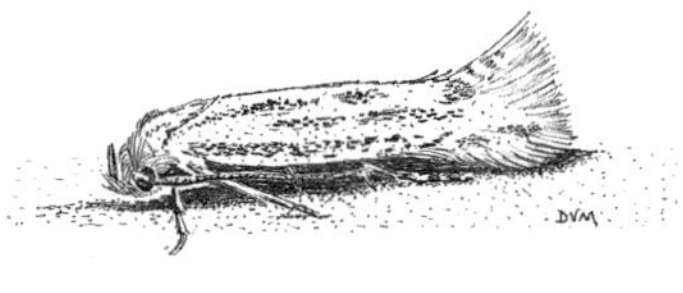

Elachista rufocinerea
(*x* 6.5)

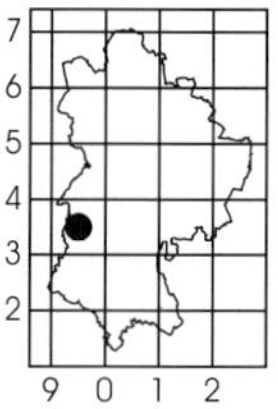

Perittia obscurepunctella **(Stainton) (590)**
Post VCH: Aspley Heath (a single specimen, found dead in light-trap, 8 June 1986).
Flight: May, June (week 23)*.
Larval Foodplant: Honeysuckle.

For details of standard weeks see page 6.

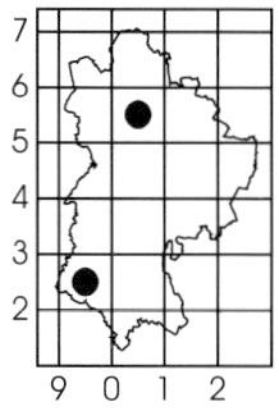

Stephensia brunnichella **(Linnaeus) (592)**
Post VCH: Locally common: Sewell Cutting and Thurleigh Cutting.
Flight: May, June (weeks 19-26)*, August.
Larval Foodplant: Wild basil.

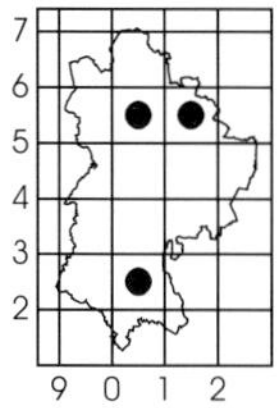

Elachista gleichenella **(Fabricius) (594)**
Post VCH: Locally common: Sharpenhoe, Thurleigh Cutting and Willington.
Flight: June to August (weeks 26, 30, 31)*.
Larval Foodplants: Sedges and wood-rushes.

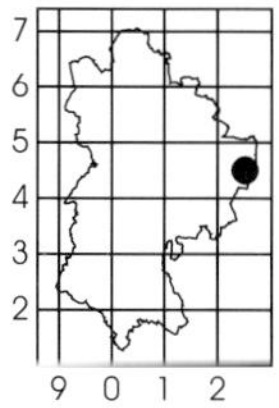

Elachista biatomella **(Stainton) (595)**
Post VCH: A single record from the RIS trap at Cockayne Hatley, 13-19 August 1994.
Flight: May, June, August (week 33)*.
Larval Foodplant: Glaucous sedge.

Elachista poae **(Stainton) (596)**

A record from Sharnbrook in 1984 is now regarded as doubtful.

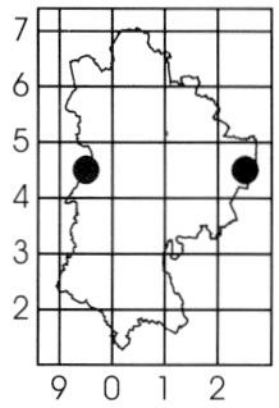

Elachista atricomella **Stainton (597)**
Post VCH: Local and uncommon: Cranfield and in the RIS trap at Cockayne Hatley.
Flight: June to September (weeks 24-28)* .
Larval Foodplant: Cock's-foot.

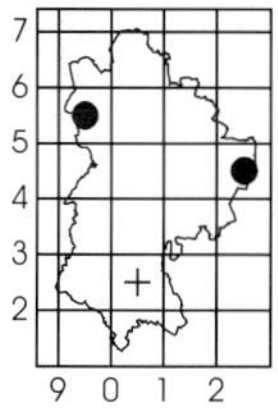

Elachista luticomella **Zeller (600)**
VCH: "Luton".
Post VCH: Local and uncommon: Sharnbrook and in the RIS trap at Cockayne Hatley.
Flight: June (week 25)* to August.
Larval Foodplant: Cock's-foot.

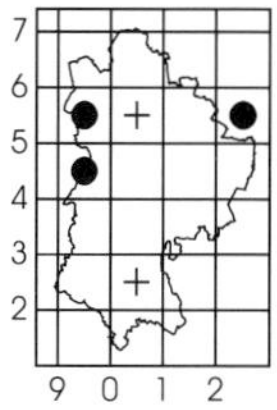

Elachista albifrontella **(Hübner) (601)**
VCH: "Bedford, Luton".
Post VCH: Local and uncommon: Marston Thrift, Sharnbrook and Potton Wood.
Flight: June, July (weeks 24-27)*.
Larval Foodplants: Grasses.

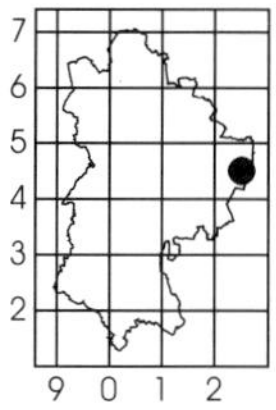

Elachista apicipunctella **Stainton (602)**
Post VCH: Found commonly in the RIS trap at Cockayne Hatley.
Flight: April, May (week 17-19)*, July, August (weeks 28-31)*.
Larval Foodplants: Grasses.

For key to moth maps see page 3.

***Elachista humilis* Zeller (606)**
Post VCH: A single record from Potton Wood.
Flight: May, June (week 24)*, July.
Larval Foodplant: Tufted hair-grass.

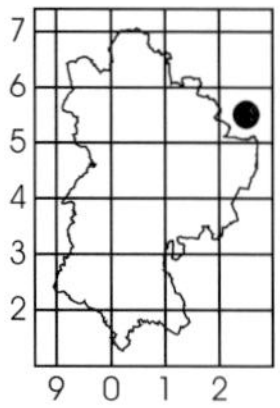

***Elachista canapennella* (Hübner) (= *obscurella* Stainton) (607)**
Post VCH: Local and uncommon: Bison Hill, Cranfield, Studham and in the RIS trap at Cockayne Hatley.
Flight: May to September (weeks 18-32, 35, 38)*.
Larval Foodplant: Tufted hair-grass.

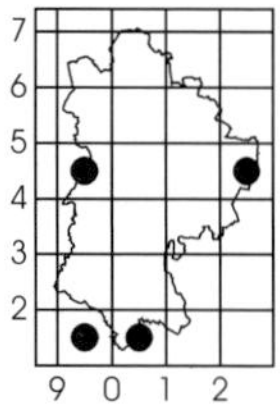

***Elachista rufocinerea* (Haworth) (608)** (Drawing on page 138)
VCH: "Common everywhere".
Post VCH: Widespread and common.
Flight: April to June (weeks 18-22, 26)*.
Larval Foodplants: Creeping soft-grass, false oat-grass and tall fescue.

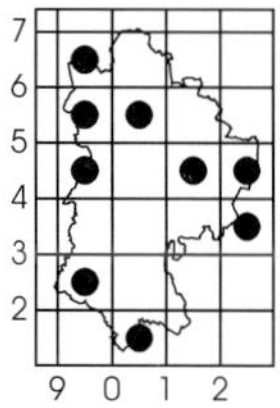

***Elachista monosemiella* Rössler (= *cerusella* (Hübner)) (609)**
Post VCH: Local and uncommon: Stotfold and in the RIS trap at Cockayne Hatley.
Flight: May to September (weeks 20-22, 29-31, 36).
Larval Foodplants: Reed canary-grass and common reed.

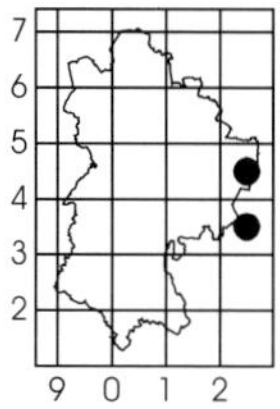

***Elachista argentella* (Clerck) (610)**
VCH: (as *E. cygnipennella* Hb.) "Bedford, Luton".
Post VCH: Widespread and common.
Flight: May to July (weeks 20-28)*.
Larval Foodplants: Grasses.

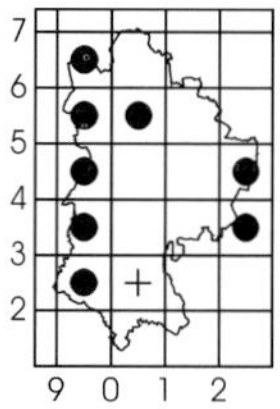

***Elachista triatomea* (Haworth) (611)**
VCH: "Bedford".
Post VCH: Widespread and fairly common: Cranfield, Felmersham Nature Reserve, Thurleigh Cutting, Pegsdon Hills and Henlow.
Flight: May to July (weeks 21-25, 29)*.
Larval Foodplants: Sheep's- fescues.

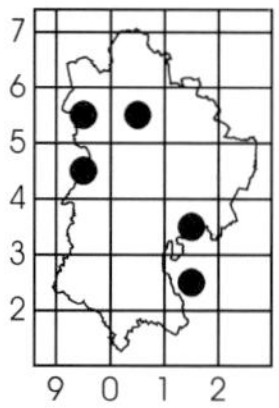

***Elachista subocellea* (Stephens) (613)**
Post VCH: A single record from Sharnbrook in July 1975.
Flight: June, July*.
Larval Foodplant: False brome.

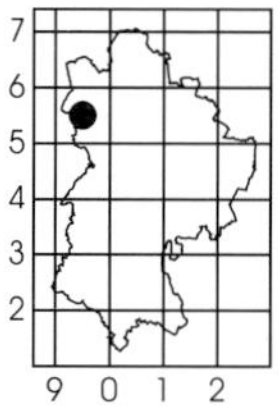

For details of standard weeks see page 6.

***Elachista megerlella* (Hübner) (= *gangabella* auctt.) (617)**
VCH: "Bedford".
Post VCH: Local and uncommon: Bison Hill and Marston Thrift.
Flight: May to September (weeks 23, 29, 37)*.
Larval Foodplant: False brome.

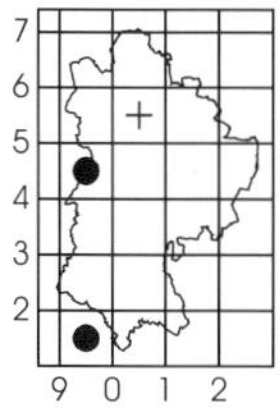

***Elachista gangabella* Zeller (= *taeniatella* Stainton) (620)**
Post VCH: Local and uncommon: Maulden Wood and Worley's Wood.
Flight: May, June.
Larval Foodplant: False brome*.

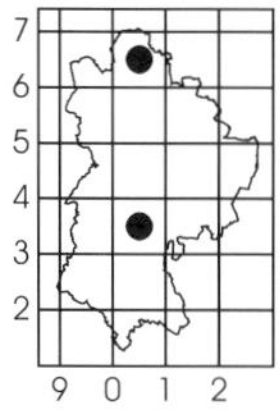

***Elachista bisulcella* (Duponchel) (623)**
Post VCH: Local and uncommon: RIS trap at Cockayne Hatley and Potton Wood.
Flight: May to August (weeks 29, 35)*.
Larval Foodplants: Tufted hair-grass and tall fescue.

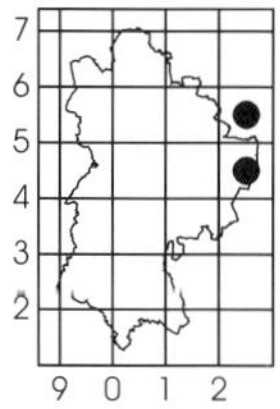

***Biselachista utonella* (Frey) (629)**
Post VCH: RIS trap at Cockayne Hatley, a single record in the week of 23 - 29 July 1995.
Flight: May to July (week 30)*.
Larval Foodplants: Sedges.

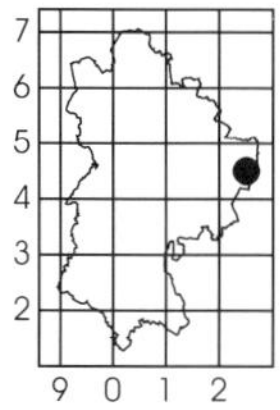

***Cosmiotes freyerella* (Hübner) (631)**
VCH: (as *Elachista nigrella* Hb.) "Luton; probably everywhere".
Post VCH: Local and uncommon: Sharnbrook and Stotfold.
Flight: April, May (weeks 18, 19)*, June, August.
Larval Foodplants: Meadow-grasses.

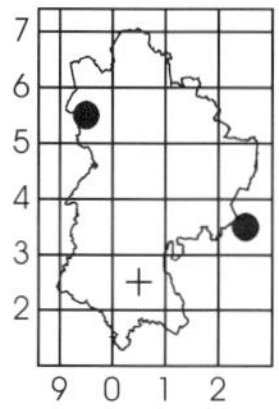

***Cosmiotes consortella* (Stainton) (632)**
Post VCH: Local and uncommon: RIS trap at Cockayne Hatley.
Flight: March to September (weeks 31, 32, 35, 39)*.
Larval Foodplants: Grasses.

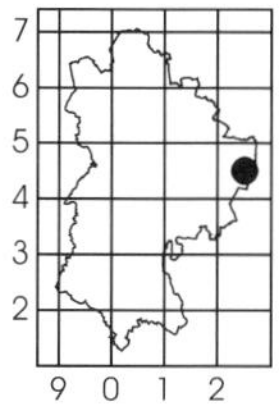

***Cosmiotes stabilella* (Stainton) (633)**
Post VCH: Local and uncommon: Sharnbrook, Studham, Cooper's Hill and in the RIS trap at Cockayne Hatley.
Flight: April to August (weeks 20, 21, 28-31)*.
Larval Foodplants: Bents and tall fescue.

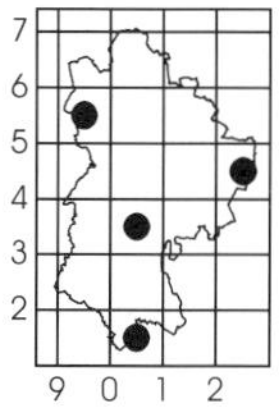

For key to moth maps see page 3.

Mainly Spinners

(Oecophoridae to Scythrididae)

D.V.Manning

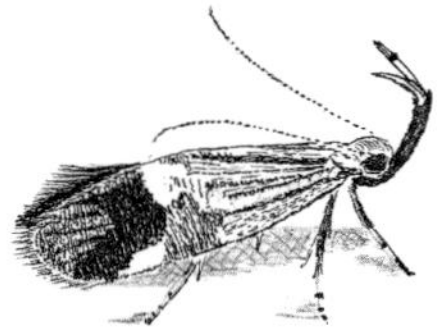

Alabonia geoffrella
(*x 2.5*)

Family: **Oecophoridae**

An extensive family of moths, here divided into five subfamilies, although in the latest classification (Emmet, 1996) these are accorded family status. The differences between the subfamilies are of interest mainly to the specialist so they are not included here. Wingspans 10-31 mm. There are 91 British species, of which 44 have been found in Bedfordshire. Several of these have not been seen since they were recorded in VCH. The larvae of several species feed on fungi, dead wood, etc. Two species are common household pests.

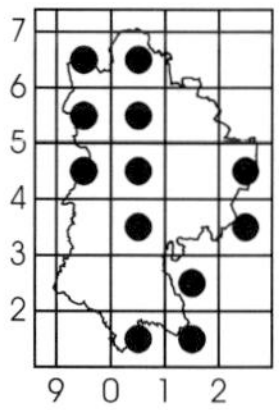

Batia lunaris **(Haworth) (640)** (Plate 61)
VCH: "Bedford".
Post VCH: Widespread and common.
Flight: July, August (weeks 27-32)*.
Larval Food: Larvae found under dead bark of trees and shrubs.

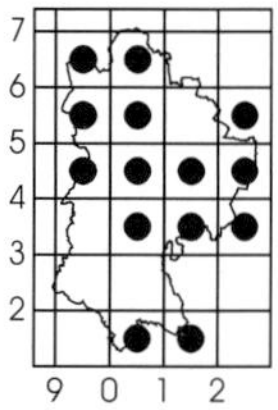

Batia unitella **(Hübner) (642)**
VCH: "Bedford".
Post VCH: Widespread and common.
Flight: June to September (weeks 26-37)*.
Larval Food: Larvae found on dead wood under bark of trees.

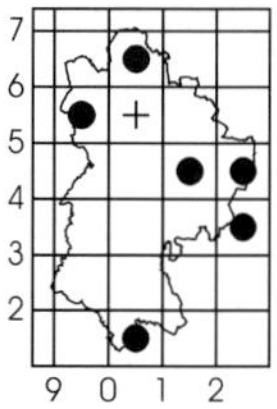

Borkhausenia fuscescens **(Haworth) (644)**
VCH: "Bedford".
Post VCH: Widespread and common.
Flight: July, August (weeks 28-34)*.
Larval Food: Larvae found on decaying leaves and in birds' nests.

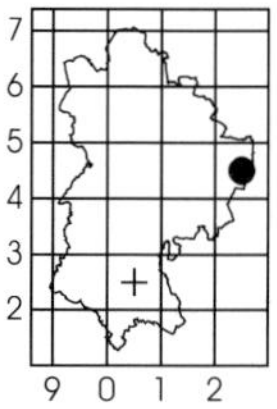

Borkhausenia minutella **(Linnaeus) (645)**
VCH: "Luton".
Post VCH: Scarce: RIS trap at Cockayne Hatley.
Flight: May, June, August*.
Larval Food: Seeds and dry vegetable matter.

For details of standard weeks see page 6.

Brown House-moth *Hoffmannophila pseudospretella* (Stainton) (647)
VCH: "Generally too common".
Post VCH: Widespread and common.
Flight: Continuous brooded (weeks 9-12, 18-37)★.
Larval Food: Dried vegetable and animal matter. In houses on textiles etc. and also in birds' nests★. At Sharnbrook, larvae found feeding on commercial slug-pellets★ were bred to maturity.

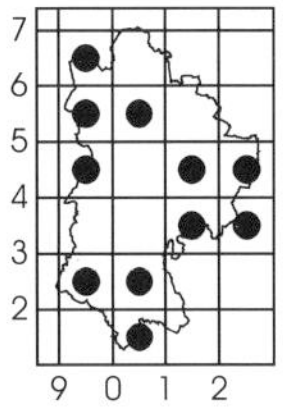

White-shouldered House-moth *Endrosis sarcitrella* (Linnaeus) (648)
VCH: (as *E. fenestrella* Scop.) "Generally too common in houses".
Post VCH: Widespread and common. (Plate 103)
Flight: Continuous brooded (weeks 3-45, 50)★.
Larval Food: Dried vegetable and animal matter. Also in birds' nests★ and bee-hives.

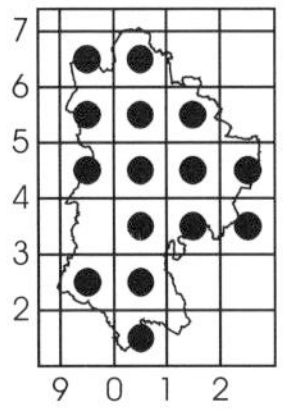

***Esperia sulphurella* (Fabricius) (649)**
VCH: "Common everywhere among decayed wood".
Post VCH: Widespread and common.
Flight: May, June (weeks 19-26)★.
Larval Food: Dead wood and under bark of trees.

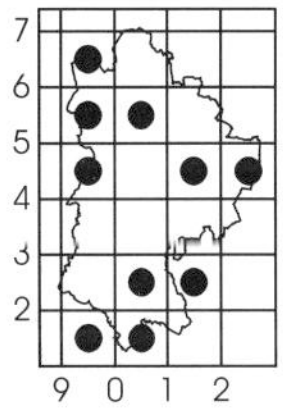

***Alabonia geoffrella* (Linnaeus) (652)** (Drawing on page 142)
VCH: "Bedford".
Post VCH: Putnoe Wood, a single record in 1978.
Flight: May, June.
Larval Food: Probably decayed wood.

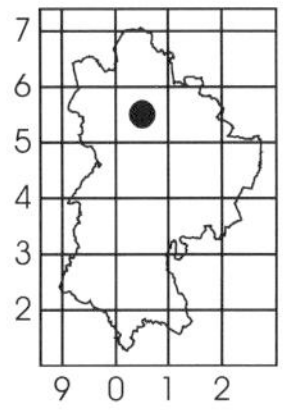

***Carcina quercana* (Fabricius) (658)** (Plate 48)
VCH: "Bedford, Luton; in oak woods".
Post VCH: Widespread and common.
Flight: July to September (weeks 27-37)★.
Larval Foodplants: Oaks, beech, apple, sycamore, etc.

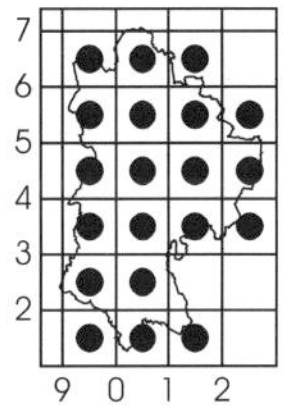

***Pseudatemelia flavifrontella* ([Denis & Schiffermüller]) (661)**
VCH: "Luton"
Post VCH: Stotfold, 31 May 1982, is the only recent record.
Flight: May, June (week 22)★.
Larval Food: Decaying leaves.

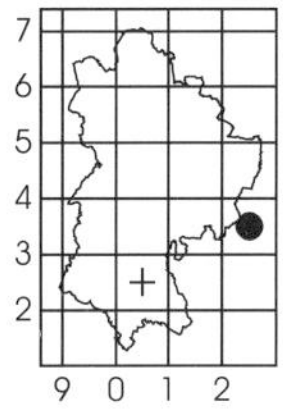

***Diurnea fagella* ([Denis & Schiffermüller]) (663)**
VCH: "On tree trunks generally".
Post VCH: Widespread and common.
Flight: March to May (weeks 10-18, 22)★.
Larval Foodplants: Oaks★, birches★, hornbeam★, blackthorn★, beech, sallows, etc.

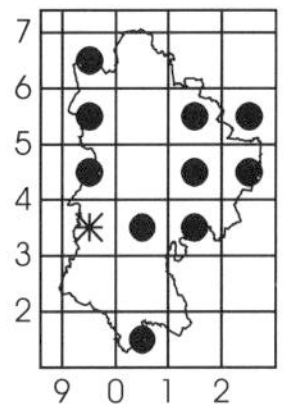

For key to moth maps see page 3.

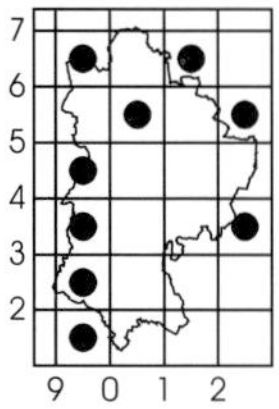

***Diurnea phryganella* (Hübner) (664)**
Post VCH: Widespread and common.
Flight: October, November (weeks 40-45)★.
Larval Foodplants: Oaks.

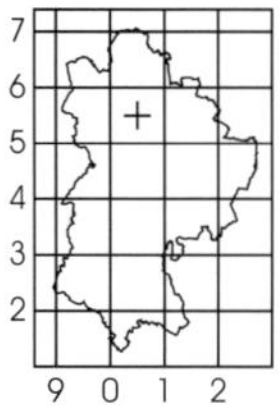

***Dasystoma salicella* (Hübner) (665)**
VCH: "Bedford".
Post VCH: No recent record.
Flight: April.
Larval Foodplants: Bog-myrtle, willows, blackthorn, buckthorns, herbaceous Rosaceae.

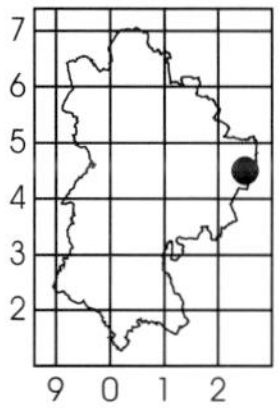

***Semioscopis avellanella* (Hübner) (666)**
Post VCH: RIS trap at Cockayne Hatley, a single record in April 1990.
Flight: March, April★.
Larval Foodplants: Small-leaved lime, birches and hornbeam.

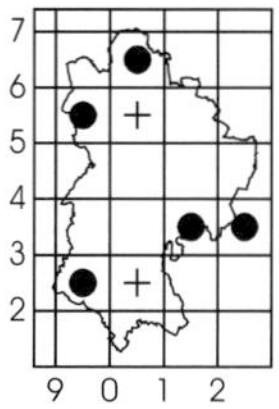

***Semioscopis steinkellneriana* ([Denis & Schiffermüller]) (667)**
VCH: "Bedford, Luton".
Post VCH: Local and uncommon.
Flight: April, May (weeks 18-21)★.
Larval Foodplants: Blackthorn, rowan and hawthorns.

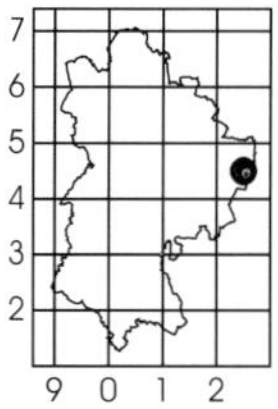

***Enicostoma lobella* ([Denis & Schiffermüller]) (668)**
Post VCH: RIS trap at Cockayne Hatley, a single record in June 1990.
Flight: June★.
Larval Foodplant: Blackthorn.

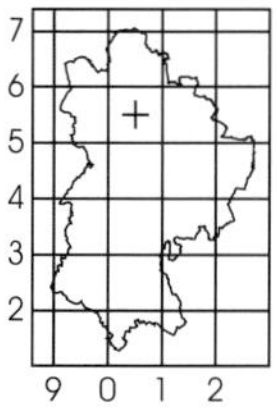

***Depressaria daucella* ([Denis & Schiffermüller]) (670)**
VCH: (as *D. nervosa* Haw.) "Bedford".
Post VCH: No recent record.
Flight: September to April.
Larval Foodplant: Water-dropworts and whorled caraway.

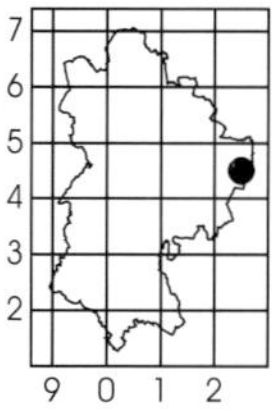

***Depressaria ultimella* Stainton (671)**
Post VCH: RIS trap at Cockayne Hatley, a single record in 1976.
Flight: August to April.
Larval Foodplants: Fool's water-cress and fine-leaved water-dropwort.

For details of standard weeks see page 6.

Parsnip Moth *Depressaria pastinacella* (Duponchel) (672)
VCH: (as *D. heracliana* De Geer.) "Bedford, Luton".
Post VCH: Widespread and common.
Flight: September to May (weeks 33-41, 9-18)★.
Larval Foodplants: Hogweed and wild parsnip.

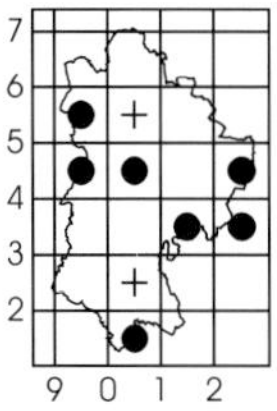

***Depressaria badiella* (Hübner) (674)**
VCH: "Bedford, Luton".
Post VCH: Cople Pits, a few on 10 September 1988.
Flight: July to October (week 37)★.
Larval Foodplants: Cat's-ears, perennial sow-thistle and dandelions.

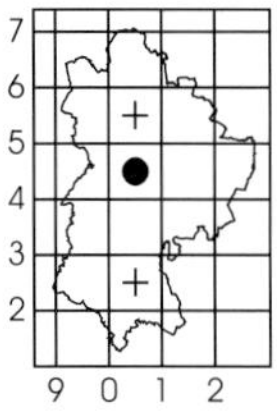

***Depressaria pulcherrimella* Stainton (676)**
Post VCH: Fairly common in the RIS trap at Cockayne Hatley.
Flight: July, August (weeks 28-32)★, September.
Larval Foodplants: Burnet-saxifrage, wild carrot and pignut.

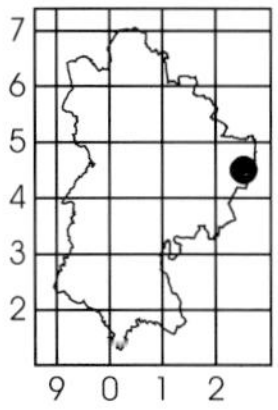

***Depressaria weirella* Stainton (678)**
VCH: "Bedford".
Post VCH: Scarce: Sharnbrook and in the RIS trap at Cockayne Hatley.
Flight: July★, August★.
Larval Foodplants: Cow parsley, chervils and hemlock.

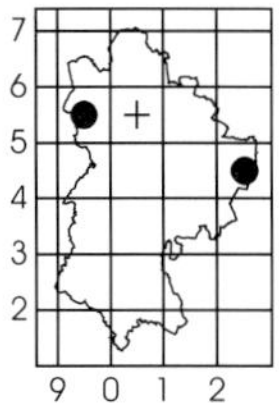

***Depressaria chaerophylli* Zeller (682)**
VCH: "Luton".
Post VCH: A single record from the RIS trap at Cockayne Hatley in August 1986.
Flight: August★ to April.
Larval Foodplant: Rough chervil.

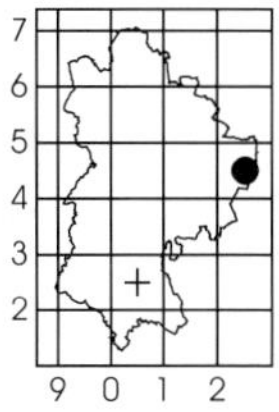

***Agonopterix heracliana* (Linnaeus) (688)**
VCH: (as *Depressaria applana* Fab.) "Abundant everywhere".
Post VCH: Widespread and common.
Flight: July to May (weeks 28-48, 1-21)★.
Larval Foodplants: Umbelliferae.

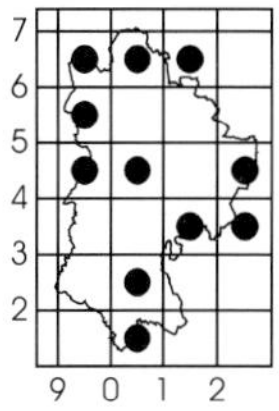

***Agonopterix ciliella* (Stainton) (689)**
Post VCH: A single record from the RIS trap at Cockayne Hatley in July 1988.
Flight: July★ to May.
Larval Foodplants: Umbelliferae.

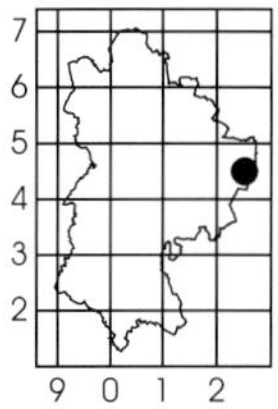

For key to moth maps see page 3.

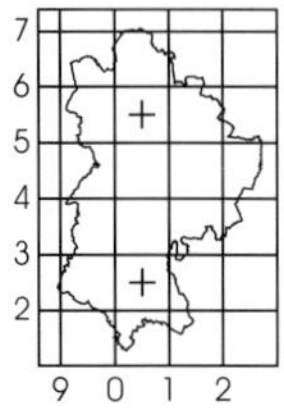

Agonopterix purpurea **(Haworth) (691)**
VCH: "Bedford, Luton".
Post VCH: No recent record.
Flight: April to June.
Larval Foodplants: Umbelliferae.

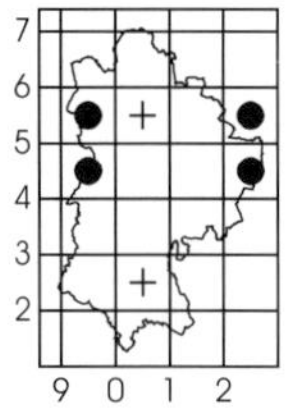

Agonopterix subpropinquella **(Stainton) (692)**
VCH: "Bedford, Luton".
Post VCH: Local and uncommon: Cranfield, Sharnbrook, Potton Wood and in the RIS trap at Cockayne Hatley.
Flight: August to April (weeks 29-42)*.
Larval Foodplants: Knapweeds and thistles.

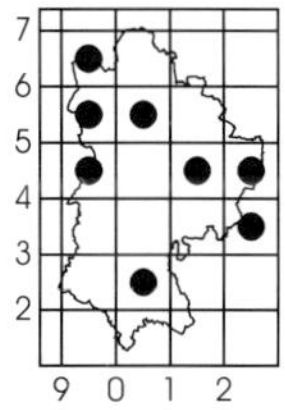

Agonopterix alstromeriana **(Clerck) (695)**
VCH: "Bedford, Luton".
Post VCH: Widespread and common.
Flight: July to May (weeks 30-42, 15-21)*.
Larval Foodplant: Hemlock.

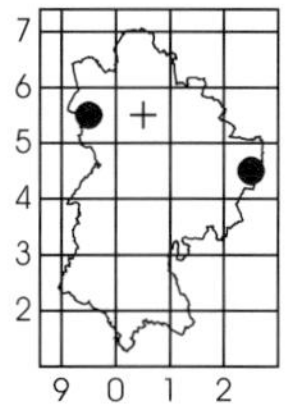

Agonopterix propinquella **(Treitschke) (696)**
VCH: "Bedford".
Post VCH: Local and uncommon: Sharnbrook and in the RIS trap at Cockayne Hatley.
Flight: August to July (weeks 35, 17)*.
Larval Foodplants: Creeping thistle and spear thistle.

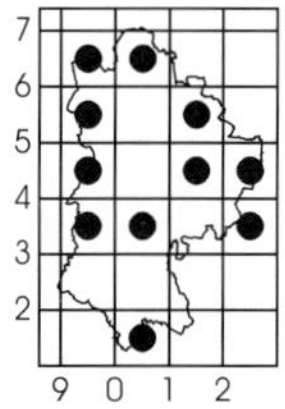

Agonopterix arenella **([Denis & Schiffermüller]) (697)**
VCH: "Generally common".
Post VCH: Widespread and common.
Flight: August to May, but recorded locally in weeks 15-40*.
Larval Foodplants: Knapweeds, thistles, burdocks and saw-wort.

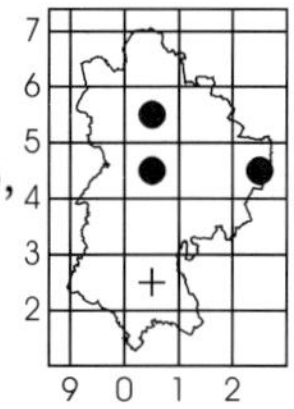

Agonopterix kaekeritziana **(Linnaeus) (698)**
VCH: (as *Depressaria liturella* Schiff.) "Bedford, Luton; among *Centaurea*".
Post VCH: Local and uncommon: King's Wood (Houghton Conquest), Thurleigh Cutting and in the RIS trap at Cockayne Hatley.
Flight: July, August (weeks 28, 31)*.
Larval Foodplants: Knapweeds.

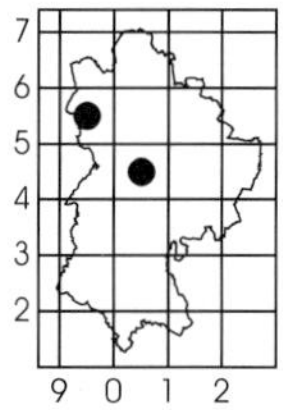

Agonopterix ocellana **(Fabricius) (701)**
Post VCH: Scarce: Felmersham Nature Reserve and Bedford. Not recorded since 1975.
Flight: August (week 32)* to May.
Larval Foodplants: Willows and sallows.

For details of standard weeks see page 6.

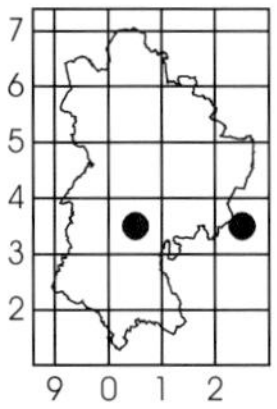

Agonopterix assimilella **(Treitschke) (702)**
Post VCH: Local and uncommon: Maulden Wood and Stotfold.
Flight: June to August.
Larval Foodplant: Broom*.

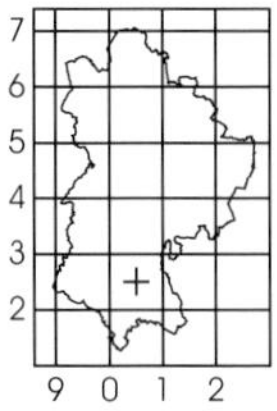

Agonopterix scopariella **(Heinemann) (=** ***atomella*** **auctt.) (704)**
VCH: "Luton".
Post VCH: No recent record.
Flight: August to April.
Larval Foodplant: Broom.

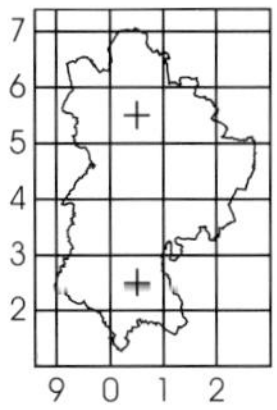

Agonopterix ulicetella **(Stainton) (705)**
VCH: (as *Depressaria umbellana* Steph.) "Bedford, Luton; among furze".
Post VCH: No recent record.
Flight: August to April.
Larval Foodplant: Gorse.

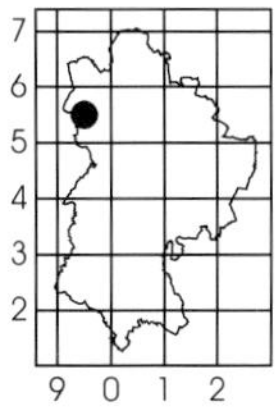

Agonopterix nervosa **(Haworth) (706)**
VCH: (as *Depressaria costosa* Haw.) "Generally common among furze".
Post VCH: Local and uncommon: Sharnbrook.
Flight: July to September (weeks 31-37)*
Larval Foodplants: Gorse, broom and dyer's greenweed.

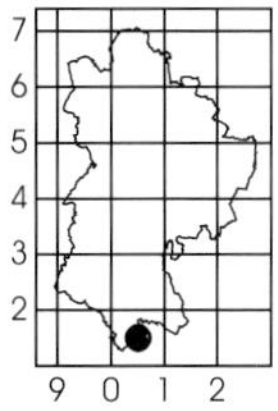

Agonopterix carduella **(Hübner) (708)**
Post VCH: A single record from Studham, 16 August 1995, by C.R.B. Baker.
Flight: July to August (week 33)*.
Larval Foodplants: Common knapweed and thistles.

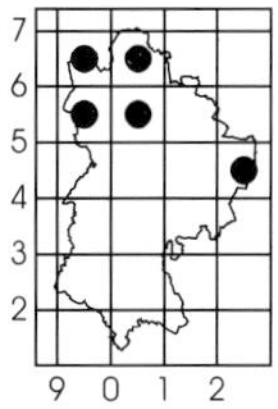

Agonopterix liturosa **(Haworth) (=** ***hypericella*** **Hübner) (709)**
Post VCH: Local and uncommon: Sharnbrook, West Wood, Clapham Park Wood, Coppice Wood and in the RIS trap at Cockayne Hatley.
Flight: July, August (weeks 28, 32-35)*, October (week 41)*, November (week 46)*.
Larval Foodplants: St John's-worts*.

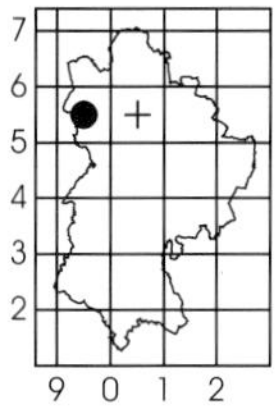

Agonopterix conterminella **(Zeller) (710)**
VCH: "Bedford".
Post VCH: A single record from Felmersham Nature Reserve.
Flight: July (week 28)* to September.
Larval Foodplants: Willows and sallows.

For key to moth maps see page 3.

***Agonopterix angelicella* (Hübner) (713)**
Post VCH: Local and uncommon: Felmersham Nature Reserve, West Wood and in the RIS trap at Cockayne Hatley.
Flight: July to September (weeks 30, 33, 34)*.
Larval Foodplants: Wild angelica and hogweed.

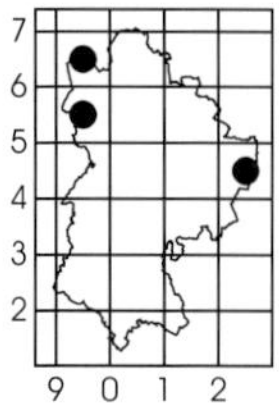

***Agonopterix yeatiana* (Fabricius) (714)**
VCH: "Bedford".
Post VCH: No recent record.
Flight: September to June.
Larval Foodplants: Umbelliferae.

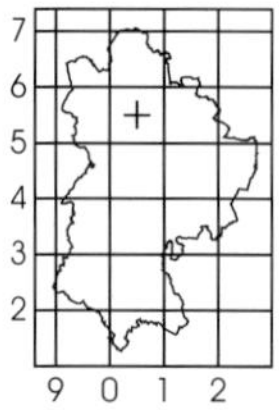

***Ethmia dodecea* (Haworth) (= *decemguttella* (Hübner)) (718)**
Post VCH: West Wood, a single record on 26 June 1987.
Flight: May, June (week 26)*, August.
Larval Foodplant: Common gromwell.

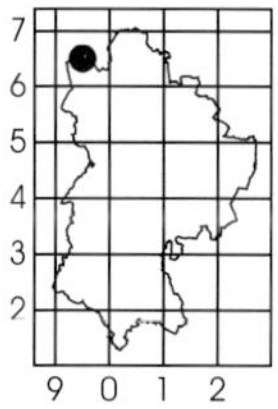

***Ethmia funerella* (Fabricius) (719)**
Post VCH: A single record from Biggleswade in 1994, by R.C.Revels.
Flight: May to July.
Larval Foodplants: Comfreys, lungwort.

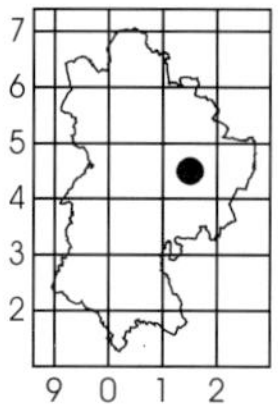

***Stathmopoda pedella* (Linnaeus) (877)**
Post VCH: Found only once at Flitwick Moor on 31 July 1985 by T.S. Hollingworth.
Flight: June, August (week 31)*.
Larval Foodplant: Alder.

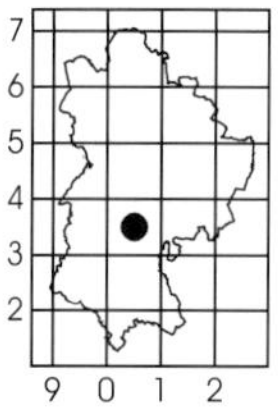

Family: **Gelechiidae**

A large family with about 150 British species, of which only 60 have been found in Bedfordshire. Wingspans 9-22 mm. The moths are rarely seen except at light, and the larvae have not been studied to date. There is no comprehensive current literature on this family. Publication of Volume 4 of *The Moths and Butterflies of Great Britain and Ireland* will make more detailed recording possible.

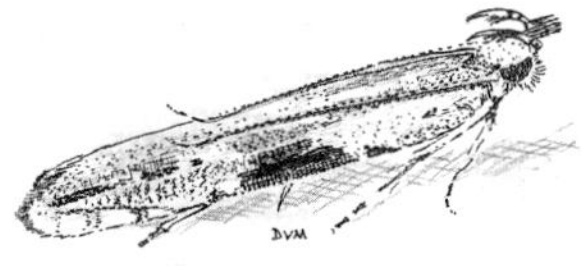

Hypatima rhomboidella
(x 4)

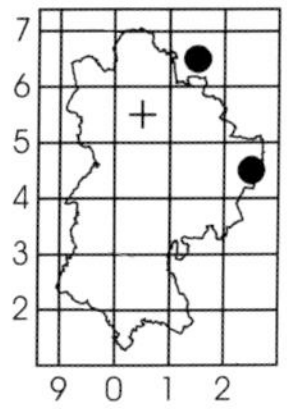

Metzneria lappella **(Linnaeus) (724)**
VCH: "Bedford".
Post VCH: Local and uncommon: Bushmead and in the RIS trap at Cockayne Hatley.
Flight: June, July (weeks 25-30)*.
Larval Foodplant: Greater burdock.

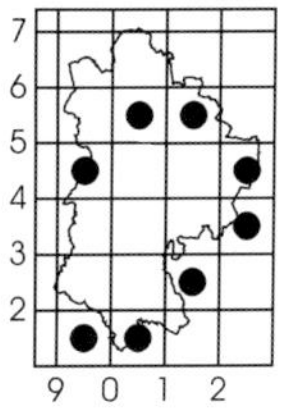

Metzneria metzneriella **(Stainton) (726)** (Plate 16)
Post VCH: Widespread and common.
Flight: June, July (weeks 24-29)*, August.
Larval Foodplants: Common knapweed and saw-wort.

Metzneria neuropterella **(Zeller) (727)**
Post VCH: Meyrick [1928] lists the distribution as "Kent, Sussex, Surrey, Bedford, Westmorland, local". No recent record. Parsons (1995) lists the confirmed records for this species which was previously confused with *M. aprilella*. He wrote "a record from Bedfordshire is also considered to be in error".

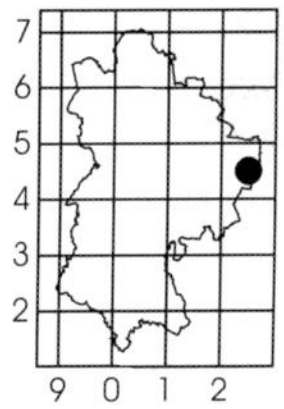

Metzneria aprilella **(Herrich-Schäffer) (727a)**
Post VCH: Scarce: RIS trap at Cockayne Hatley, first recorded on 1 July 1986 and occasional specimens since.
Flight: June*, July (week 26)*, August.
Larval Foodplant: Greater knapweed.

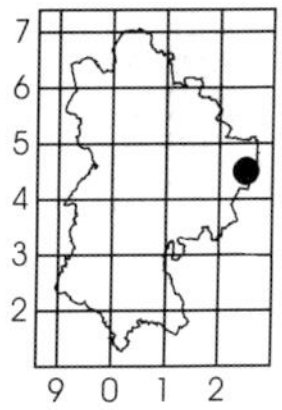

Isophrictis striatella **([Denis & Schiffermüller]) (729)**
Post VCH: A single record from the RIS trap at Cockayne Hatley, August 1991.
Flight: July, August*.
Larval Foodplants: Tansy and sneezewort.

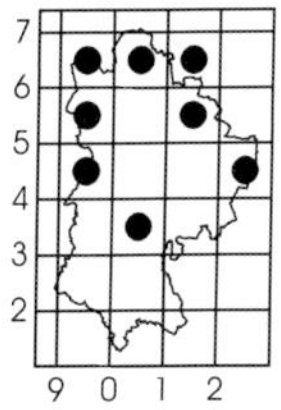

Eulamprotes atrella **([Denis & Schiffermüller]) (731)**
Post VCH: Widespread and common.
Flight: June to August (weeks 26-33)*.
Larval Foodplants: St John's-worts.

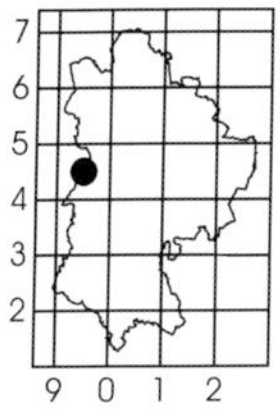

Eulamprotes unicolorella **(Duponchel) (732)**
Post VCH: Cranfield, a single record on 8 June 1983 by T.S.Hollingworth.
Flight: June (week 23)*, July.
Larval Foodplants: Unknown.

For key to moth maps see page 3.

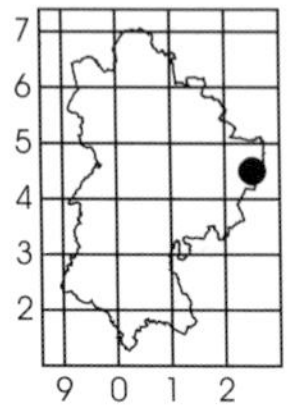

***Monochroa lucidella* (Stephens) (736)**
Post VCH: A single record from the RIS trap at Cockayne Hatley in the week 9 - 15 July 1995.
Flight: June, July (week 28)*.
Larval Foodplant: Common spike-rush.

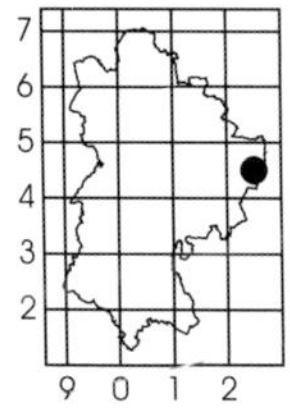

***Monochroa palustrella* (Douglas) (737)**
Post VCH: A single record from the RIS trap at Cockayne Hatley, June 1992.
Flight: June to August (weeks 27, 31)*.
Larval Foodplant: Curled dock.

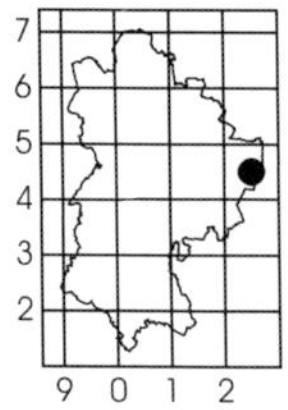

***Monochroa conspersella* (Herrich-Schäffer) (739)**
Post VCH: A single record from the RIS trap at Cockayne Hatley in the week 9 - 15 July 1995.
Flight: June (week 28)*, August.
Larval Foodplant: Yellow loosestrife.

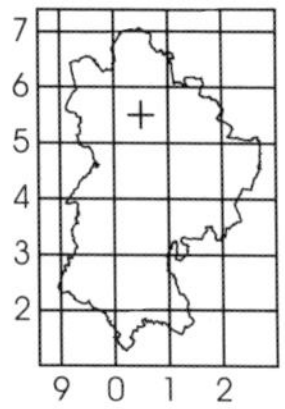

***Chrysoesthia drurella* (Fabricius) (746)**
VCH: (as *Nannodia hermannella* Fab.) "Bedford".
Post VCH: No recent record.
Flight: June, August, September.
Larval Foodplants: Goosefoots, fat-hen and oraches.

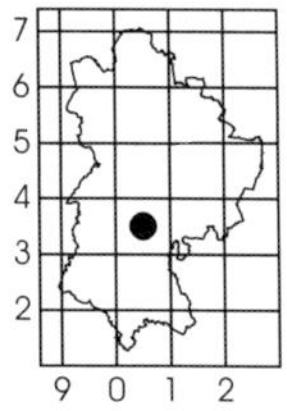

***Chrysoesthia sexguttella* (Thunberg) (747)**
Post VCH: Flitwick Moor, a single record, 28 September 1985.
Flight: May, June, August, September (week 39)*.
Larval Foodplants: Goosefoots, fat-hen and oraches.

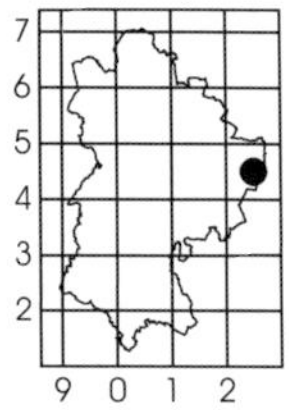

***Ptocheuusa paupella* (Zeller) (748)**
Post VCH: RIS trap at Cockayne Hatley, a single record in August 1991.
Flight: June, August*, September.
Larval Foodplants: Common fleabane, ploughman's-spikenard, common knapweed and mints.

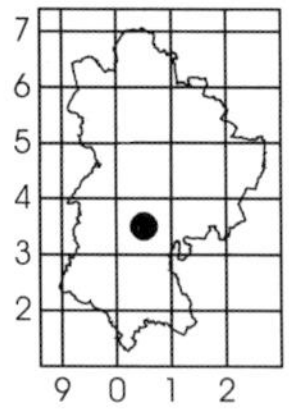

***Aristotelia ericinella* (Zeller) (752)**
Post VCH: Locally common: Cooper's Hill.
Flight: July (week 30)*, August.
Larval Foodplant: Heather.

For details of standard weeks see page 6.

***Stenolechia gemmella* (Linnaeus) (755)**
VCH: "Bedford".
Post VCH: Local and uncommon: West Wood.
Flight: August, September (weeks 33-36)★, October.
Larval Foodplants: Oaks.

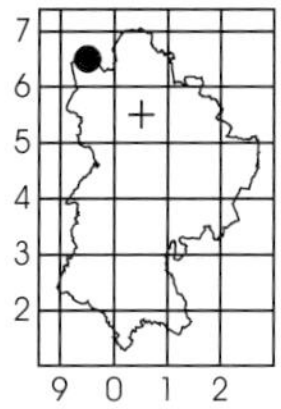

***Parachronistis albiceps* (Zeller) (756)**
VCH: "Bedford".
Post VCH: No recent record.
Flight: July, August.
Larval Foodplant: Hazel.

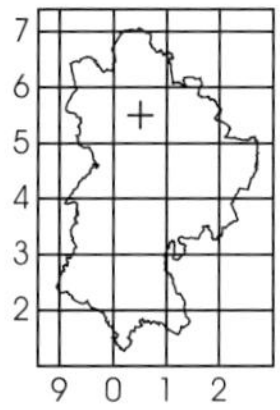

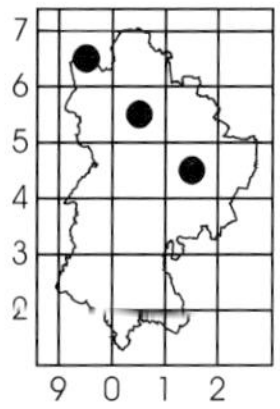

***Recurvaria nanella* ([Denis & Schiffermüller]) (757)**
Post VCH: Local and uncommon: West Wood, Bedford and Biggleswade.
Flight: June, July (weeks 26, 28)★
Larval Foodplants: Apple, plum and blackthorn.

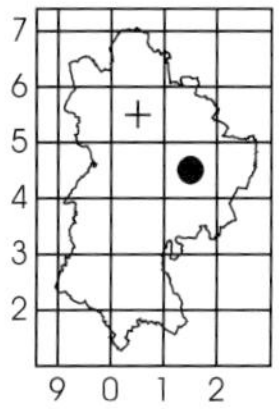

***Exoteleia dodecella* (Linnaeus) (760)**
VCH: "Bedford".
Post VCH: A single record from Rowney Warren on 15 July 1983.
Flight: June, July (week 28)★.
Larval Foodplant: Scots pine.

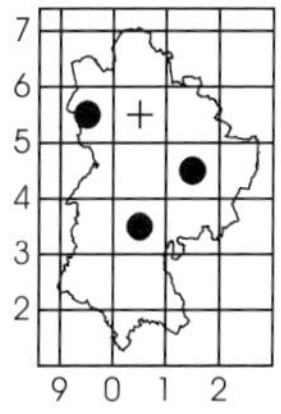

***Athrips mouffetella* (Linnaeus) (762)**
VCH: "Bedford".
Post VCH: Local and uncommon: Sharnbrook, Flitwick Moor and Biggleswade.
Flight: July, August (weeks 30, 31)★, September.
Larval Foodplant: Honeysuckle.

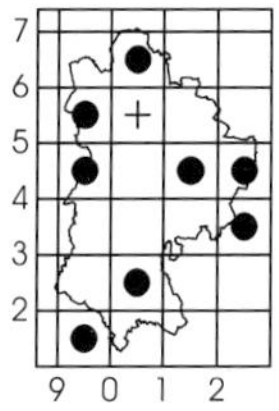

***Teleiodes vulgella* (Hübner) (765)**
VCH: "Bedford, Luton".
Post VCH: Widespread and common.
Flight: June, July (weeks 26-30)★.
Larval Foodplants: Hawthorns and blackthorn.

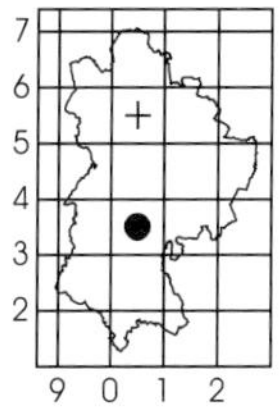

***Teleiodes decorella* (Haworth) (767)**
VCH: (as *Teleia humeralis* Zell.) "Bedford".
Post VCH: A single record from Flitwick Moor on 31 July 1985 by T.S.Hollingworth.
Flight: July, August (week 31)★ to April.
Larval Foodplants: Oaks and dogwood.

For key to moth maps see page 3.

Teleiodes notatella **(Hübner) (768)**
VCH: "Bedford".
Post VCH: Sutton Fen, a single record on 27 May 1982 by T.S.Hollingworth.
Flight: May (week 21)*, June.
Larval Foodplant: Sallow.

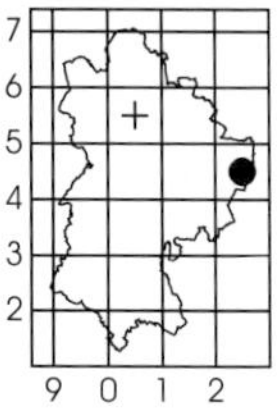

Teleiodes proximella **(Hübner) (770)**
Post VCH: Local and uncommon: Sharnbrook and Sutton Fen.
Flight: May (week 21)* to July (week 28)*.
Larval Foodplants: Birches and alder.

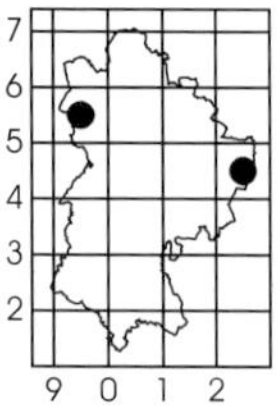

Teleiodes alburnella **(Zeller) (771)**
Post VCH: Rowney Warren, a single record on 15 July 1983 by T.S. Hollingworth.
Flight: June, July (week 28)* to September.
Larval Foodplants: Birches.

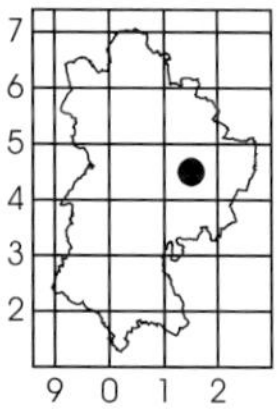

Teleiodes fugitivella **(Zeller) (772)**
Post VCH: Local and uncommon: Felmersham Nature Reserve and Little Staughton.
Flight: June, July (weeks 27-29)*.
Larval Foodplants: Elms.

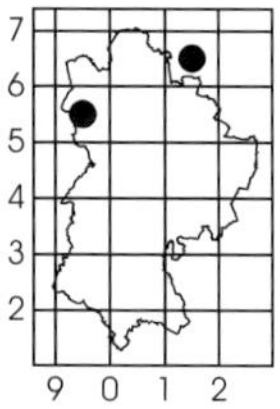

Teleiodes paripunctella **(Thunberg) (773)**
VCH: (as *Teleia triparella* Zell.) "Bedford".
Post VCH: No recent record.
Flight: May, June.
Larval Foodplants: Oaks.

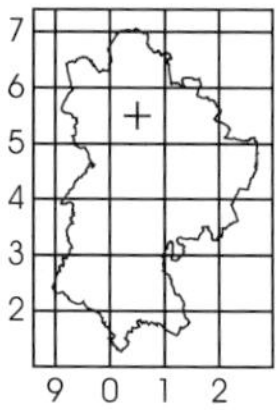

Teleiodes luculella **(Hübner) (774)**
Post VCH: Locally common: West Wood and Maulden Wood.
Flight: May to July (weeks 20, 24-30)*.
Larval Foodplants: Oaks.

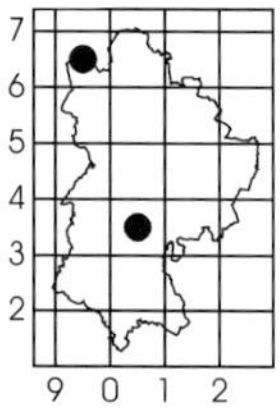

Teleiodes sequax **(Haworth) (775)**
Post VCH: A specimen in the collection at Rothamsted Experimental Station (Harpenden) is labelled "Whipsnade vii.1924 J.C.F.Fryer". No recent record.
Flight: July.
Larval Foodplant: Common rock-rose.

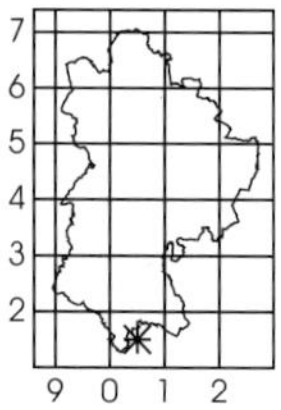

For details of standard weeks see page 6.

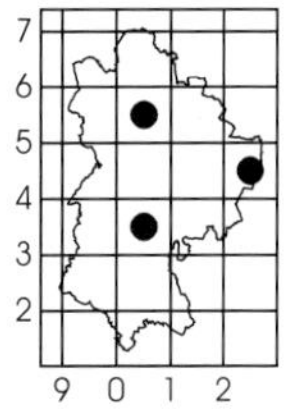

Teleiopsis diffinis **(Haworth) (776)**
VCH: "Bedford".
Post VCH: Locally common: Maulden Wood, Putnoe Wood and in the RIS trap at Cockayne Hatley.
Flight: May, June (weeks 23-26)*, September, October.
Larval Foodplant: Sheep's sorrel.

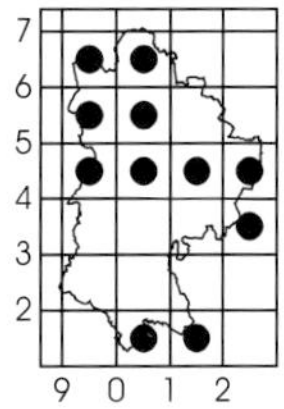

Bryotropha affinis **(Haworth) (779)**
Post VCH: Widespread and common.
Flight: May to August (weeks 22-35)*.
Larval Foodplants: Mosses on walls.

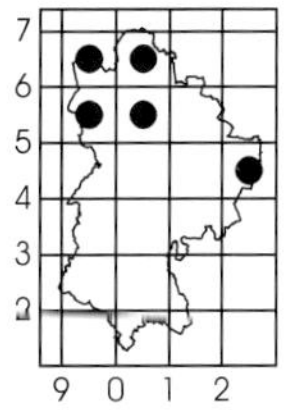

Bryotropha senectella **(Zeller) (782)**
Post VCH: Locally common.
Flight: June to August (weeks 26-33)*
Larval Foodplants: Mosses on the ground.

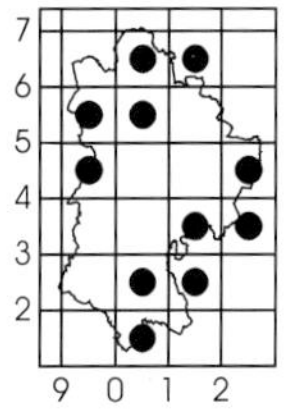

Bryotropha terrella **([Denis & Schiffermüller]) (787)**
VCH: "Abundant everywhere".
Post VCH: Widespread and common.
Flight: June to August (weeks 24-34)*.
Larval Foodplants: Grasses.

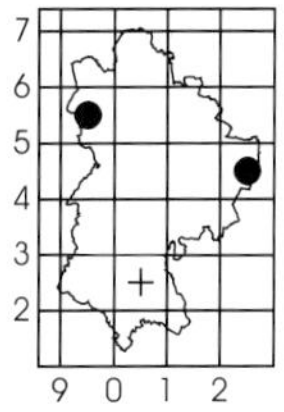

Bryotropha domestica **(Haworth) (789)**
VCH: "Luton".
Post VCH: Local and uncommon: Sharnbrook and in the RIS trap at Cockayne Hatley.
Flight: July, August (weeks 29-33)*.
Larval Foodplants: Mosses.

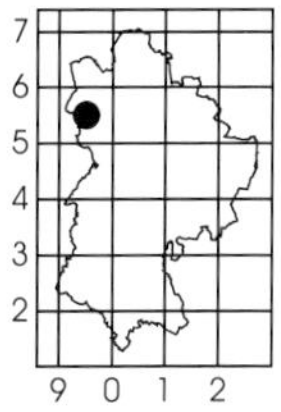

Chionodes fumatella **(Douglas) (790)**
Post VCH: Found only once, at Sharnbrook on 27 July 1992.
Flight: June, July (week 30)*, August.
Larval Foodplants: Mosses.

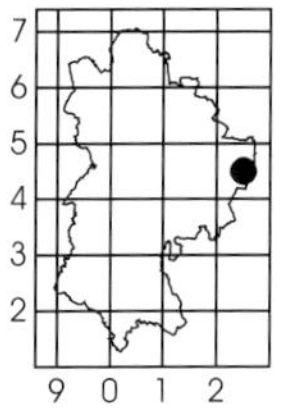

Mirificarma mulinella **(Zeller) (792)**
Post VCH: Common in the RIS trap at Cockayne Hatley.
Flight: July, August (weeks 32-34)*.
Larval Foodplants: Gorse, broom and lupins.

For key to moth maps see page 3.

***Neofaculta ericetella* (Geyer) (797)**
Post VCH: Locally common: Cooper's Hill.
Flight: May, June (weeks 20, 23)*.
Larval Foodplant: Heather.

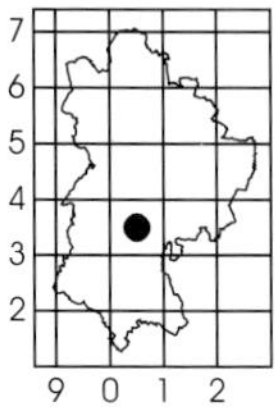

***Neofriseria singula* (Staudinger) (799)**
VCH: (as *Gelechia pelliella* Zett.) "Bedford, taken by Mr. Sharpin".
Post VCH: No recent record.
Flight: July.
Larval Foodplant: Sheep's sorrel.

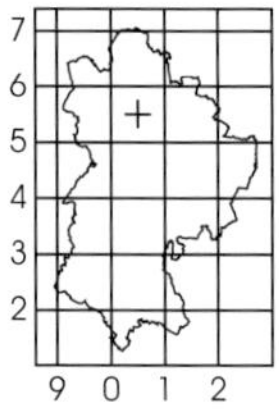

***Gelechia rhombella* ([Denis & Schiffermüller]) (800)**
Post VCH: A single record from Sharnbrook, 27 July 1986.
Flight: July (week 30)*, August.
Larval Foodplant: Apple.

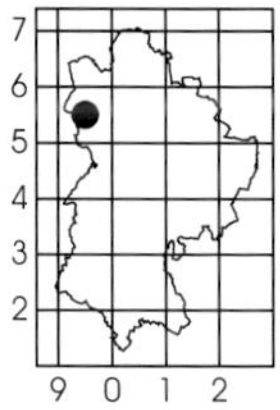

***Gelechia sororculella* (Hübner) (802a)**
Post VCH: Local and uncommon: Worley's Wood and in the RIS trap at Cockayne Hatley.
Flight: July, August (weeks 30, 32)*.
Larval Foodplants: Sallows and willows*.

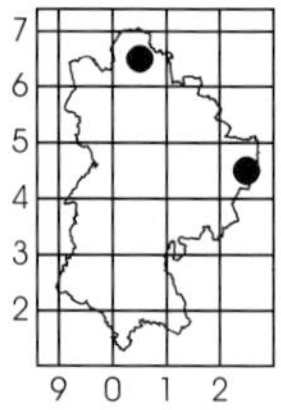

***Gelechia turpella* ([Denis & Schiffermüller]) (807)**
Post VCH: A single record from Sharnbrook, 28 July 1985.
Flight: July (week 30)*.
Larval Foodplant: Black poplar.

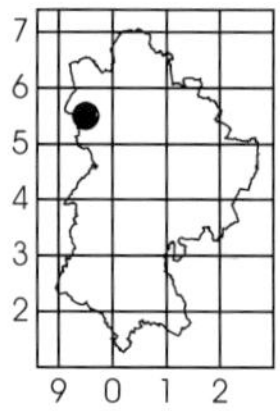

Hollyhock Seed Moth *Pexicopia malvella* (Hübner) (809)
Post VCH: Recorded on vice-county distribution maps held by A.M.Emmet, with the caption "1936 (Neville Birket)".
Flight: June, July.
Larval Foodplants: Marsh-mallow and cultivated hollyhock.

***Scrobipalpa atriplicella* (Fischer von Röslerstamm) (818)**
Post VCH: Local and uncommon: RIS trap at Cockayne Hatley.
Flight: July, August (week 31)*, September (week 34)*, October*.
Larval Foodplants: Goosefoots, fat-hen and oraches.

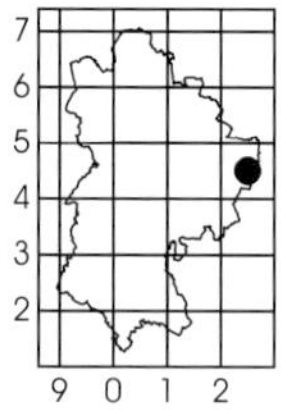

For details of standard weeks see page 6.

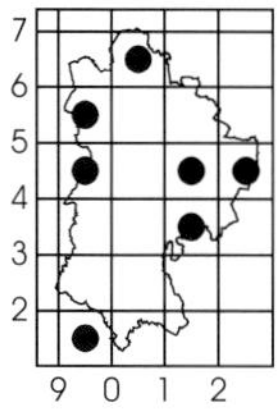

***Scrobipalpa costella* (Humphreys & Westwood) (819)**
Post VCH: Widespread and common.
Flight: June to May (weeks 24-27, 30-45, 18)*.
Larval Foodplant: Bittersweet.

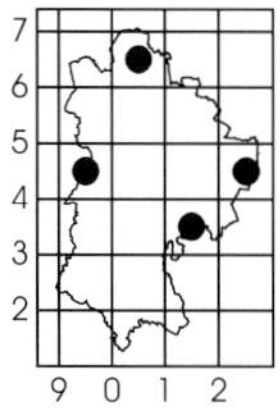

***Scrobipalpa acuminatella* (Sircom) (822)**
Post VCH: Locally common: Hanger Wood, Coppice Wood, Shillington and in the RIS trap at Cockayne Hatley.
Flight: May, June (weeks 18, 23)*, July to September (weeks 29-37)*.
Larval Foodplants: Thistles and knapweeds.

Potato Tuber Moth *Phthorimaea operculella* (Zeller) (825)
Post VCH: Larvae found at Studham in imported potatoes by C.R.B.Baker (no date available). This is not a resident British species but is found occasionally on imported potatoes and tomatoes.

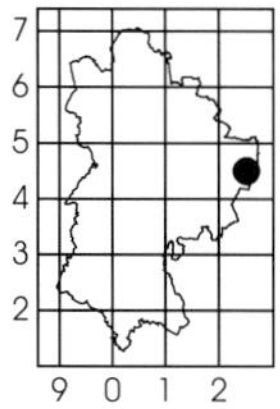

***Caryocolum fraternella* (Douglas) (830)**
Post VCH: Local and uncommon: RIS trap at Cockayne Hatley.
Flight: June, July (week 31)*.
Larval Foodplants: Lesser stitchwort, bog stitchwort, common mouse-ear and field mouse-ear.

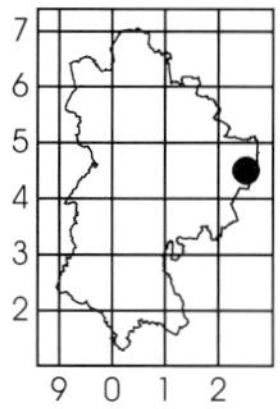

***Caryocolum proximum* (Haworth) (831)**
Post VCH: A single record from the RIS trap at Cockayne Hatley, 16-22 July 1994.
Flight: July (week 29)*.
Larval Foodplant: Common mouse-ear.

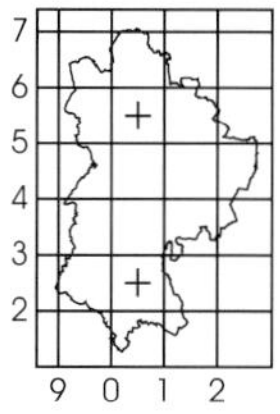

***Caryocolum blandella* (Douglas) (832)**
VCH: (as *Lita maculea* Haw.) "Bedford, Luton".
Post VCH: No recent record.
Flight: July, August.
Larval Foodplant: Greater stitchwort.

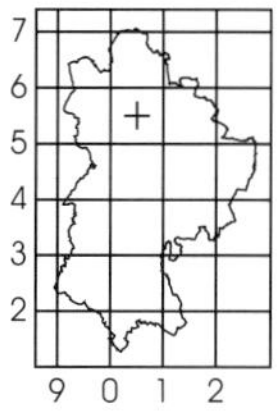

***Caryocolum tricolorella* (Haworth) (834)**
VCH: "Bedford".
Post VCH: No recent record.
Flight: July to September.
Larval Foodplant: Greater stitchwort.

For key to moth maps see page 3.

Caryocolum kroesmanniella **(Herrich-Schäffer) (836)**
VCH: (as *Lita hubneri* Haw.) "Recorded at Bedford by Mr. Sharpin".
Post VCH: No recent record.
Flight: July, August.
Larval Foodplant: Greater stitchwort.

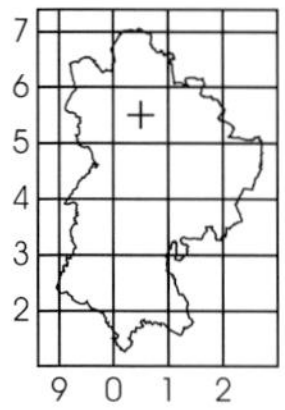

Sophronia semicostella **(Hübner) (841)**
Post VCH: Local and uncommon: Bison Hill, Stockgrove Country Park and The Lodge, Sandy.
Flight: June to August (weeks 28, 31)*.
Larval Foodplants: Not known in Britain.

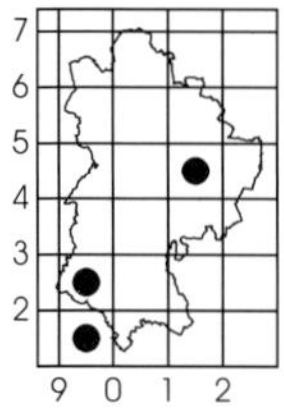

Aproaerema anthyllidella **(Hübner) (843)**
Post VCH: RIS trap at Cockayne Hatley, a single record, September 1990.
Flight: May, June, August, September*.
Larval Foodplants: Kidney vetch, sainfoin and clovers.

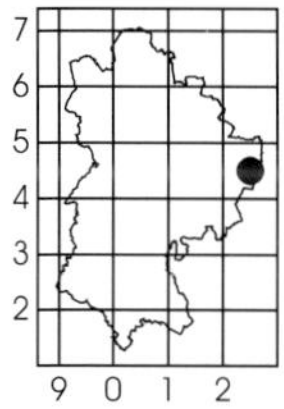

Anacampsis populella **(Clerck) (853)**
VCH: "Luton".
Post VCH: Locally common.
Flight: July to September (weeks 28-36)*.
Larval Foodplants: Aspen, sallows and willows.

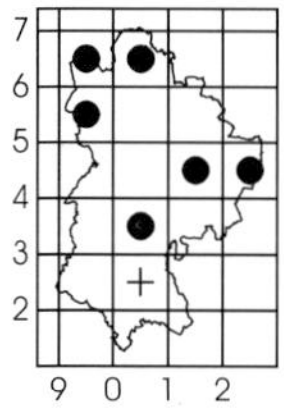

Acompsia cinerella **(Clerck) (855)**
VCH: "Bedford".
Post VCH: Local and uncommon: Sharnbrook and in the RIS trap at Cockayne Hatley.
Flight: June to August (weeks 30, 31)*.
Larval Foodplants: Mosses on trees.

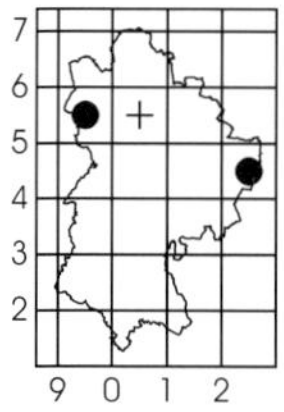

Anarsia spartiella **(Schrank) (856)**
Post VCH: Local and uncommon: Cranfield and Sharnbrook.
Flight: July, August (weeks 30, 31)*.
Larval Foodplants: Gorse, broom and dyer's greenweed.

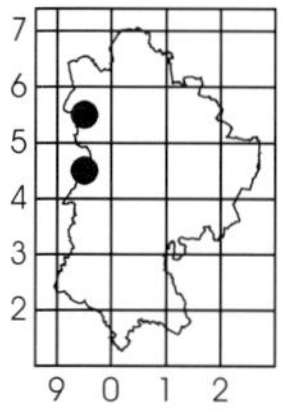

Peach Twig Borer *Anarsia lineatella* (Zeller) (857)
Post VCH: Larvae found at Studham in imported peaches by C.R.B.Baker (no date available). This is not a resident British species but is found occasionally on imported peaches and other fruit.

For details of standard weeks see page 6.

***Hypatima rhomboidella* (Linnaeus) (858)** (Drawing on page 148)
VCH: as *Chelaria hubnerella* "Luton".
Post VCH: Locally common: Marston Thrift, West Wood, King's Wood (Houghton Conquest) and in the RIS trap at Cockayne Hatley.
Flight: June to October (weeks 31-40)*.
Larval Foodplants: Birches and hazel*.

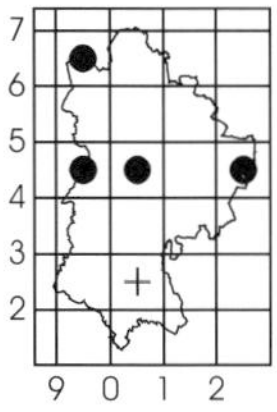

Juniper Webber *Dichomeris marginella* (Fabricius) (862) (Plate 99)
Post VCH: Local and uncommon: Sharnbrook, Houghton Regis, Clifton, Biggleswade and in the RIS trap at Cockayne Hatley.
Flight: June to August (weeks 25-31)*.
Larval Foodplant: Juniper, including garden varieties.

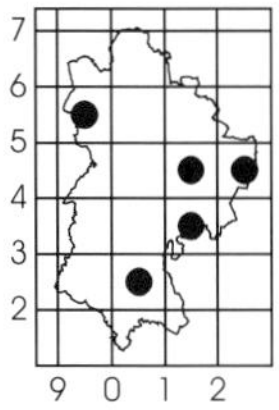

***Brachmia blandella* (Fabricius) (= *gerronella* (Zeller)) (866)**
Post VCH: Widespread and common.
Flight: June to August (weeks 27-32, 35)*.
Larval Foodplant: Gorse, but also occurs where gorse is absent.

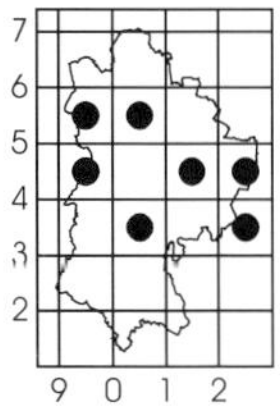

***Brachmia rufescens* (Haworth) (868)**
VCH: "Luton".
Post VCH: Widespread and common.
Flight: June to August (weeks 23-34)*.
Larval Foodplants: Grasses.

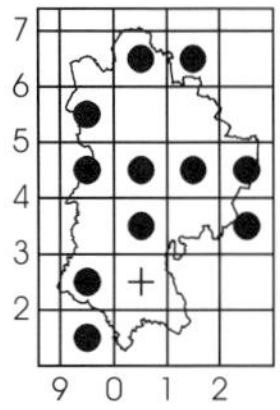

***Oegoconia deauratella* (Herrich-Schäffer) (871)**
Post VCH: Locally common: Cranfield, Sharnbrook, Bedford, Biggleswade and in the RIS trap at Cockayne Hatley.
Flight: June to August (weeks 25-32)*.
Larval Food: Decaying vegetable matter.

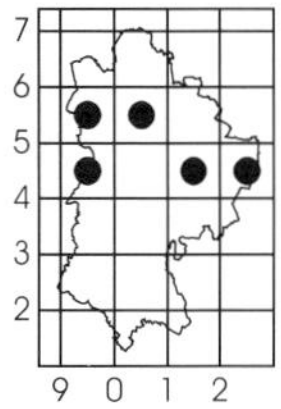

Family: **Blastobasidae**

There are four species on the British list. All are foreign introductions, of which two have become established and occur in Bedfordshire. Wingspans 15-21 mm.

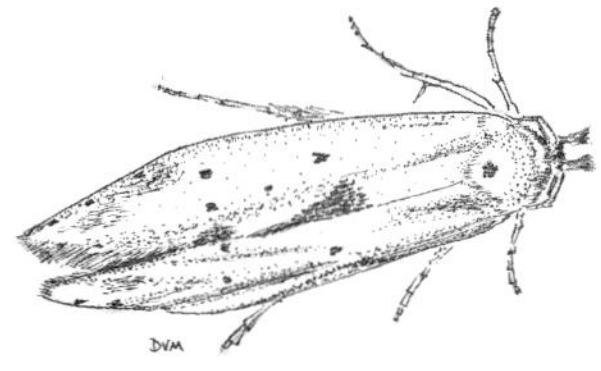

Blastobasis decolorella
(x 4)

For key to moth maps see page 3.

Blastobasis lignea **Walsingham (873)**
Post VCH: Locally common: until recently known only at one site, but during 1994 and 1995 it was recorded from a further six 10k m squares.
Flight: July, August (weeks 29-31)*.
Larval Foodplants: Yew, spruces, firs, etc. on fresh and decaying leaves.

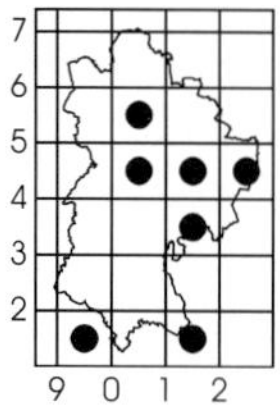

Blastobasis decolorella **(Wollaston) (874)** (Drawing on page 157)
Post VCH: Widespread and common: This species was, until recent years, restricted to London and the Thames estuary. The first record in Bedfordshire was in 1978, since when it appears to have spread throughout the county.
Flight: May to September (weeks 21-36)*, October, November (weeks 40-45)*.

Larval Foodplants: Fresh and decaying vegetable matter*.

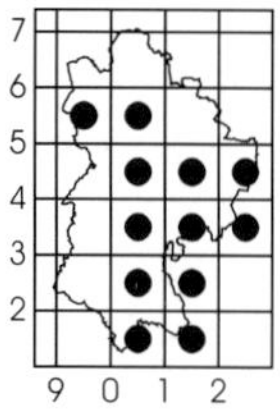

Family: **Momphidae**

Small moths (wingspans 7-16 mm), often brightly coloured. Many species have larvae associated with willowherbs. Of the sixteen British species, eight occur in Bedfordshire.

Batrachedra praeangusta **(Haworth) (878)**
Post VCH: Local and uncommon: Cranfield, Sharnbrook and in the RIS trap at Cockayne Hatley.
Flight: July, August (weeks 28-32)*.
Larval Foodplants: Poplars, sallows and willows.

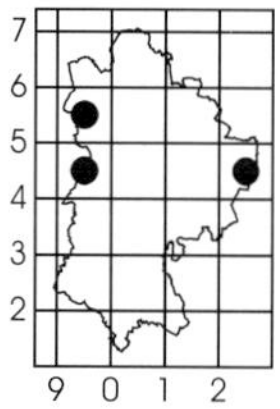

Batrachedra pinicolella **(Zeller) (879)** Plate 59
Post VCH: Scarce: Maulden Wood on 26 June 1983 and Studham on 20 June 1995.
Flight: June (weeks 25, 26)*, July.
Larval Foodplants: Norway spruce and Scots pine.

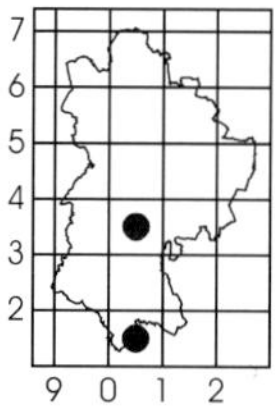

Mompha raschkiella **(Zeller) (883)**
Post VCH: Widespread and common.
Flight: May, June (week 25)*, July, August (weeks 30-32)*.
Larval Foodplant: Rosebay willowherb*.

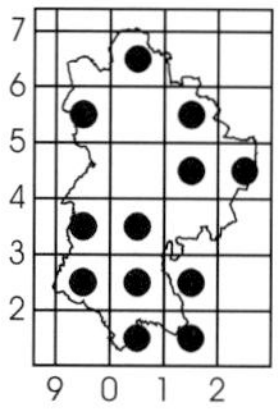

Mompha miscella **(Denis & Schiffermüller) (884)**
Post VCH: A single record (details not known) by R.W.J.Uffen.
Flight: May, June, August.
Larval Foodplant: Common rock-rose.

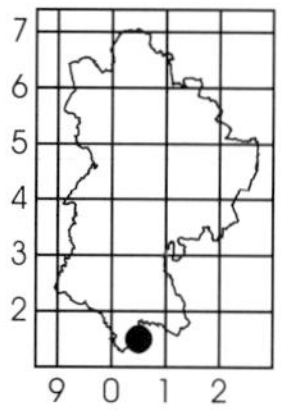

For details of standard weeks see page 6.

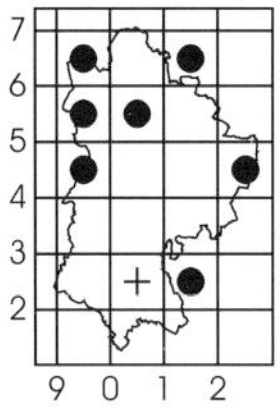

Mompha ochraceella **(Curtis) (886)**
VCH: "Luton, among *Epilobium*".
Post VCH: Widespread and common.
Flight: June, July (weeks 25-30)*.
Larval Foodplant: Great willowherb.

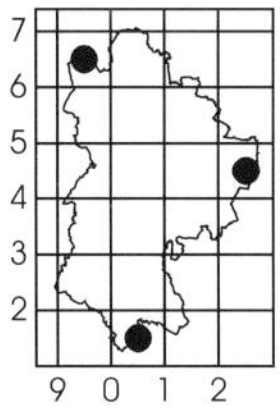

Mompha propinquella **(Stainton) (888)**
Post VCH: Local and uncommon: West Wood, Studham and in the RIS trap at Cockayne Hatley.
Flight: June to August (weeks 27-33)*.
Larval Foodplants: Willowherbs.

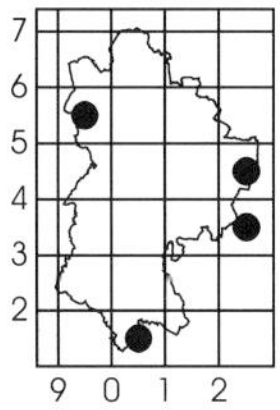

Mompha subbistrigella **(Haworth) (892)**
Post VCH: Local and uncommon: Sharnbrook, Studham, Stotfold and in the RIS trap at Cockayne Hatley.
Flight: July (week 29)*, August to May (weeks 34, 44, 47, 14, 21)*.
Larval Foodplant: Broad-leaved willowherb.

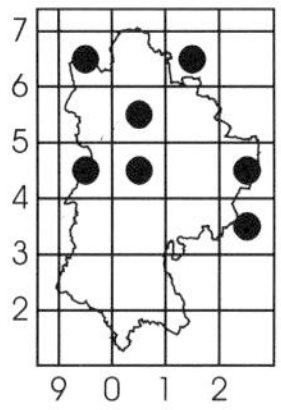

Mompha epilobiella **([Denis & Schiffermüller]) (893)**
VCH: (as *Laverna fulvescens* Haw.) "Bedford, among *Epilobium*".
Post VCH: Widespread and common.
Flight: July to June (weeks 29-33, 36, 15, 19-25)*.
Larval Foodplant: Great willowherb.

Family: **Cosmopterigidae**

Small, narrow-winged moths, some with metallic markings, others with tufts of scales on the forewings. Wingspans 8-21 mm. There are 17 British species, of which only six are recorded from Bedfordshire.

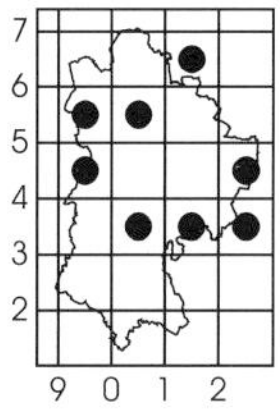

Limnaecia phragmitella **Stainton (898)**
Post VCH: Locally common.
Flight: July, August (weeks 27-33)*.
Larval Foodplants: Bulrushes*.

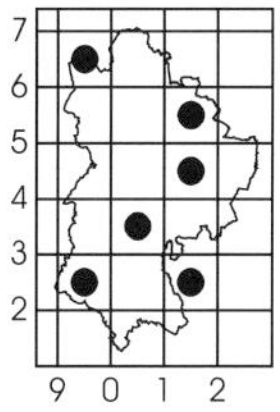

Pancalia leuwenhoekella **(Linnaeus) (899)**
Post VCH: Local and uncommon: Sewell Cutting, West Wood, Barton Hills, Pegsdon Hills, Old Warden Tunnel and Waterloo Thorns.
Flight: April to July (weeks 22-28)*.
Larval Foodplant: Hairy violet.

For key to moth maps see page 3.

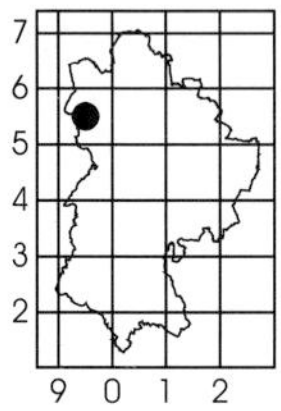

***Glyphipteryx linneella* (Clerck) (903)**
Post VCH: A single record from Sharnbrook on 16 August 1987.
Flight: July, August (week 33)★.
Larval Foodplants: Limes.

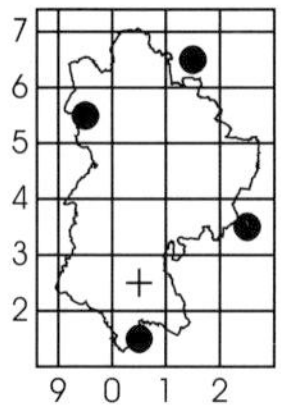

***Spuleria flavicaput* (Haworth) (904)**
VCH: "Luton, in hedges".
Post VCH: Local and uncommon: Carlton, Studham, Bushmead and Stotfold.
Flight: May, June (weeks 21-24)★.
Larval Foodplants: Hawthorns.

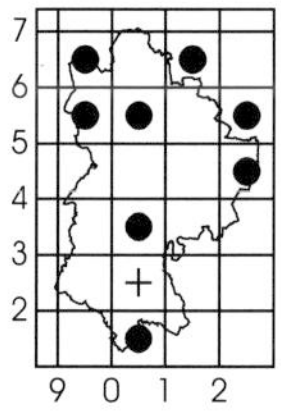

***Blastodacna hellerella* (Duponchel) (= *atra* auctt.) (905)**
VCH: "Bedford, Luton".
Post VCH: Widespread and common. (Plate 49)
Flight: June to August (weeks 23-32)★.
Larval Foodplants: Hawthorns.

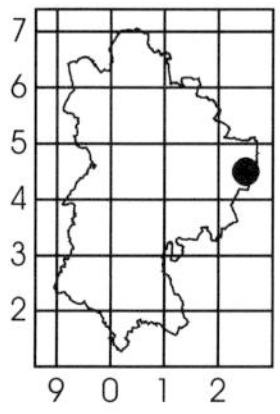

***Sorhagenia rhamniella* (Zeller) (908)**
Post VCH: RIS trap at Cockayne Hatley, three records in July and August 1995.
Flight: July, August (weeks 29-31)★.
Larval Foodplant: Alder Buckthorn.

Family: **Scythrididae**

Small, dull-coloured moths, wingspans 8-18 mm. The larvae feed on herbaceous plants. Only one of the twelve British species has been found in Bedfordshire.

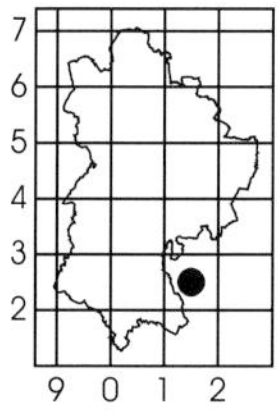

***Scythris crassiuscula* (Hübner) (= *fletcherella* Meyrick) (914)**
Post VCH: Common on Pegsdon Hills.
Flight: June, July (week 28)★.
Larval Foodplant: Common rock-rose.

The Tortrices - Part 1

(Tortricidae: Cochylinae to Chlidanotinae)

D.V.Manning

Family: **Tortricidae**

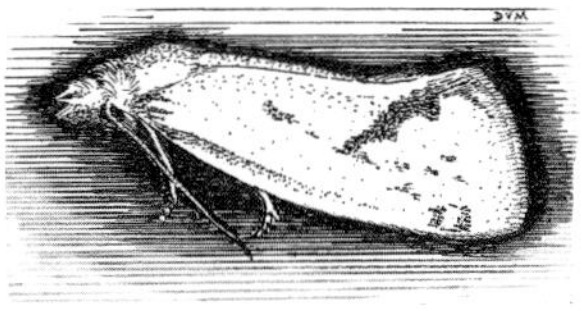

Agapeta hamana
(*x 3*)

Subfamily: **Cochylinae**

The moths are usually pale with darker markings. Wingspan 9-25 mm. Most larvae feed in spun flower-heads, stems or roots of Umbelliferae or Compositae. There are 48 British species, of which 25 have been found in Bedfordshire.

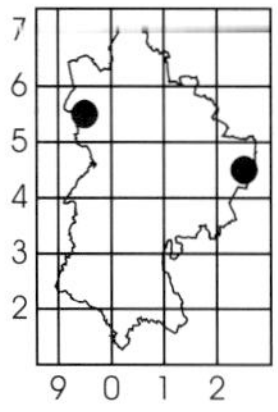

***Trachysmia inopiana* (Haworth) (921)**
Post VCH: Scarce: Sharnbrook in August 1975 and in the RIS trap at Cockayne Hatley in July 1995.
Flight: June to August (weeks 28-30, 34)*.
Larval Foodplant: Common fleabane.

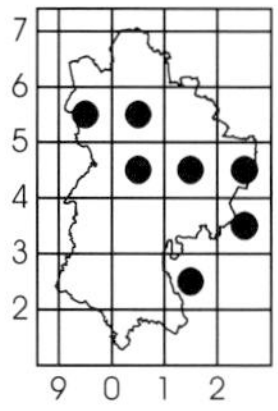

***Phtheochroa rugosana* (Hübner) (925)**
VCH: "Luton, among *Bryonia dioica*".
Post VCH: Widespread and fairly common.
Flight: May to July (weeks 20-29)*.
Larval Foodplant: White bryony.

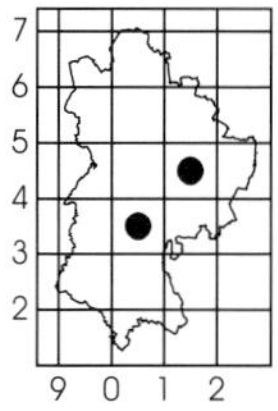

***Phalonidia manniana* (Fischer von Röslerstamm) (926)**
Post VCH: Scarce: Cooper's Hill and Stanford Wood.
Flight: May to July (weeks 21, 24)*.
Larval Foodplants: Water-mint and nipplewort.

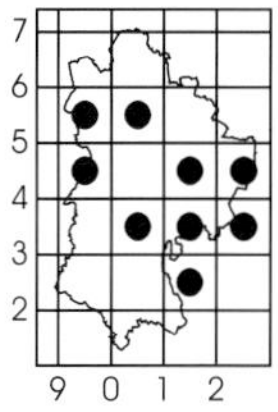

***Cochylimorpha straminea* (Haworth) (936)**
Post VCH: Widespread and common.
Flight: May to July (weeks 20-26)*, August, September (weeks 31-36)*.
Larval Foodplant: Common knapweed.

For key to moth maps see page 3.

***Agapeta hamana* (Linnaeus) (937)** (Drawing on page 161)
VCH: "Bedford, Luton; among knapweed".
Post VCH: Widespread and common.
Flight: May to September (weeks 22-38)*.
Larval Foodplants: Thistles.

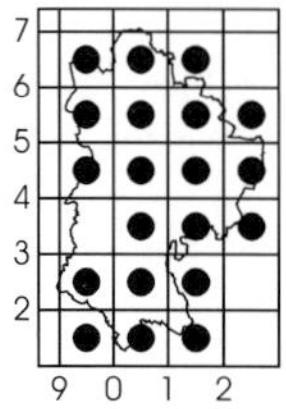

***Agapeta zoegana* (Linnaeus) (938)** (Plate 20)
VCH: "Bedford, Luton; among knapweed".
Post VCH: Widespread and common.
Flight: May to August (weeks 25-35)*.
Larval Foodplants: Common knapweed and small scabious.

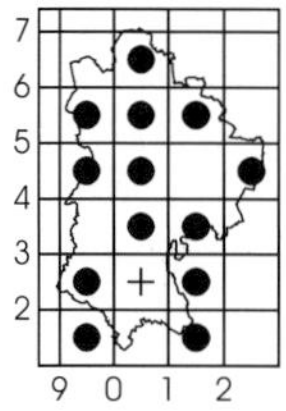

***Aethes tesserana* ([Denis & Schiffermüller]) (939)**
Post VCH: Locally common: Sewell Cutting, Thurleigh Cutting and Pegsdon Hills.
Flight: May to August (weeks 24-27)*.
Larval Foodplants: Oxtongues, hawkweeds, hawk's-beards and ploughman's-spikenard.

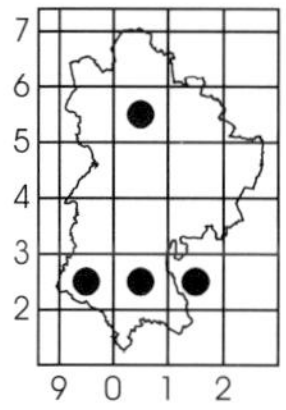

***Aethes hartmanniana* (Clerck) (941)**
VCH: (as *Argyrolepia sub-baumanniana* Dbld.) "Luton, among *Scabiosa columbaria*".
Post VCH: S.H.Kershaw found *sub-baumanniana* at Totternhoe on 30 May and 11 June 1946. Subseqently found at Sewell Cutting on 18 June 1987.
Flight: June (week 25)* to August.
Larval Foodplant: Small scabious.

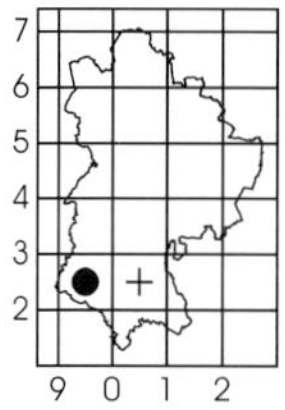

***Aethes williana* (Brahm) (944)**
VCH: (as *Argyrolepia zephyrana* Tr.) "On railway banks near Luton".
Post VCH: Thurleigh Cutting on 20 June 1985 and 19 May 1989.
Flight: May to August (weeks 20, 25)*.
Larval Foodplant: Wild carrot.

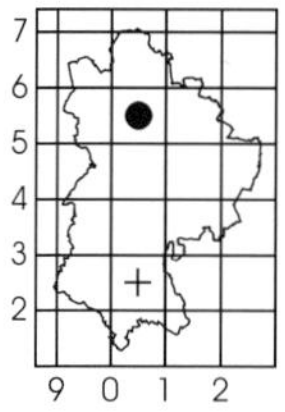

***Aethes cnicana* (Westwood) (945)**
VCH: "Luton, among marsh thistles".
Post VCH: Locally common: Marston Thrift, Felmersham Nature Reserve, West Wood, Coppice Wood, Sandy, RIS trap at Cockayne Hatley.
Flight: June, July (weeks 24-30)*.
Larval Foodplants: Thistles.

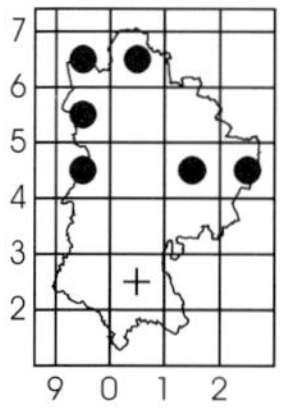

***Aethes rubigana* (Treitschke) (946)**
Post VCH: Locally common: Sharnbrook, West Wood, Bedford, Luton Hoo, Stotfold and in the RIS trap at Cockayne Hatley.
Flight: June to August (weeks 24-32)*.
Larval Foodplant: Greater burdock.

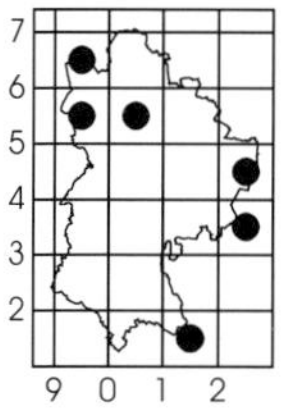

For details of standard weeks see page 6.

Aethes smeathmanniana **(Fabricius) (947)**
Post VCH: Locally common: Cranfield, Sharnbrook, Bedford, Henlow and in the RIS trap at Cockayne Hatley.
Flight: May to August (weeks 20-27, 30-35)*.
Larval Foodplants: Yarrow, knapweeds and corn chamomile.

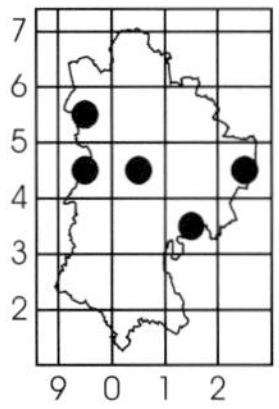

Aethes dilucidana **(Stephens) (949)**
Post VCH: Local and uncommon: Sharnbrook and in the RIS trap at Cockayne Hatley.
Flight: July, August (weeks 29-34)*.
Larval Foodplants: Wild parsnip and hogweed.

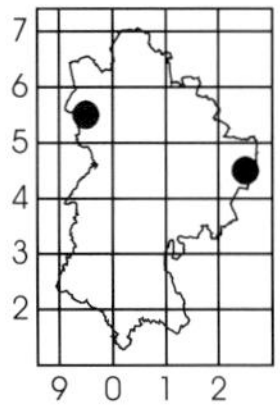

Aethes francillana **(Fabricius) (950)**
VCH: "Bedford, among wild carrot".
Post VCH: No recent record.
Flight: June to September.
Larval Foodplants: Wild carrot and milk-parsley

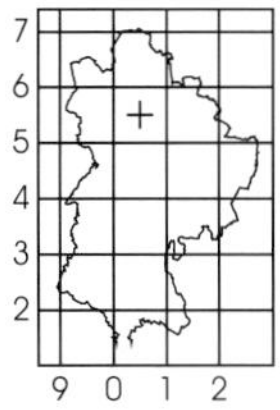

Aethes beatricella **(Walsingham) (951)**
Post VCH: Local and uncommon: Cranfield, Sharnbrook, Bushmead and in the RIS trap at Cockayne Hatley.
Flight: June to August (weeks 26-31)*.
Larval Foodplant: Hemlock.

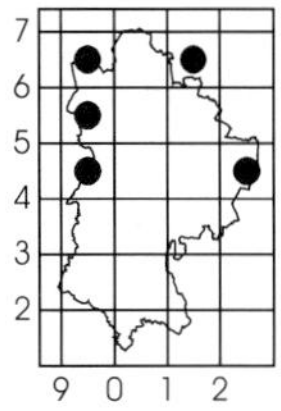

Commophila aeneana **(Hübner) (952)**
Post VCH: Local and uncommon: Sewell Cutting, Marston Thrift, Thurleigh Cutting and Old Warden Tunnel (Webb, 1983).
Flight: May to July (weeks 20-26)*.
Larval Foodplant: Common ragwort.

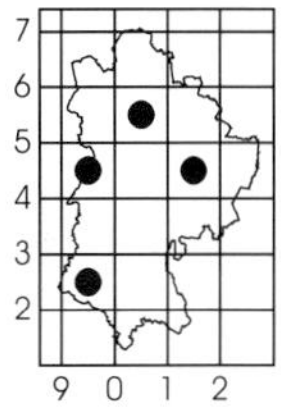

Eupoecilia angustana angustana **(Hübner) (954)**
VCH: "Luton".
Post VCH: Widespread and common.
Flight: June to September (weeks 23, 27-31)*.
Larval Foodplants: Plantains, yarrow, marjoram and thymes.

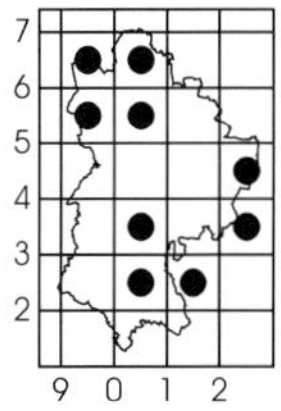

Cochylidia implicitana **(Wocke) (956)**
Post VCH: Local and uncommon: Cranfield, Bedford and in the RIS trap at Cockayne Hatley.
Flight: June to August (weeks 27-34)*.
Larval Foodplants: Scented mayweed, stinking chamomile and scentless mayweed.

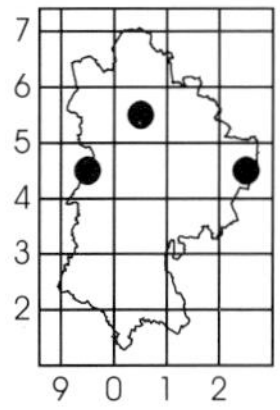

For key to moth maps see page 3.

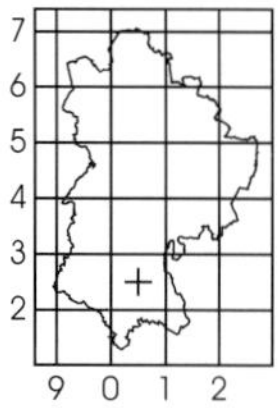

***Falseuncaria ruficiliana* (Haworth) (960)**
VCH: (as *Eupoecilia ciliella* Hb.) "Luton, among *Primula*".
Post VCH: No recent record.
Flight: May to August.
Larval Foodplants: Primrose, lousewort, goldenrod.

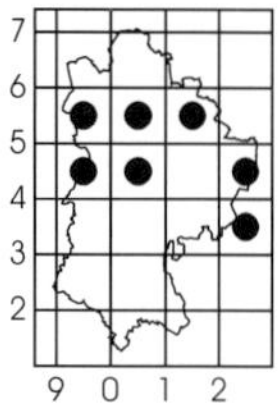

***Cochylis roseana* (Haworth) (962)**
Post VCH: Widespread and common.
Flight: May to August (weeks 27-33)*.
Larval Foodplant: Teasel*.

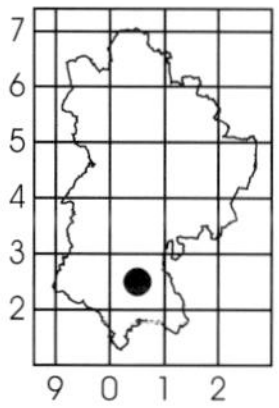

***Cochylis flaviciliana* (Westwood) (963)**
Post VCH: A single record from the RIS trap at Houghton Regis on 26 July 1985 (Riley, 1986).
Flight: June to August (week 30)*.
Larval Foodplant: Field scabious.

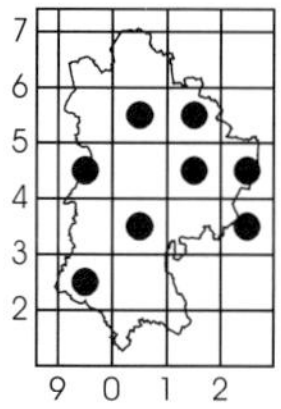

***Cochylis dubitana* (Hübner) (964)**
Post VCH: Widespread and common.
Flight: June (weeks 22-25)*, August, September (weeks 30-36)*.
Larval Foodplants: Common ragwort, hawk's-beards, hawkweeds and other Compositae.

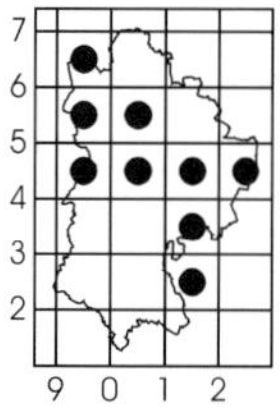

***Cochylis hybridella* (Hübner) (965)**
Post VCH: Widespread and common.
Flight: July, August (weeks 27-35)*.
Larval Foodplants: Oxtongues and hawk's-beards.

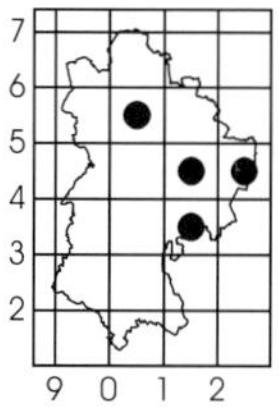

***Cochylis atricapitana* (Stephens) (966)**
Post VCH: Local and uncommon: Thurleigh Cutting, Shillington, Biggleswade and in the RIS trap at Cockayne Hatley.
Flight: May, June (weeks 22-26)*, July, August (week 35)*.
Larval Foodplant: Common ragwort.

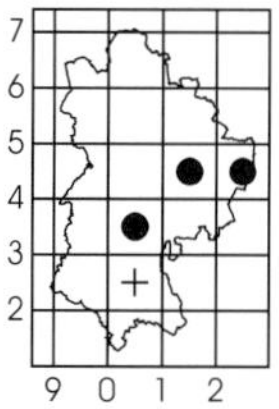

***Cochylis nana* (Haworth) (968)**
VCH: "Luton, among birch".
Post VCH: Local and uncommon: Flitwick Moor, Rowney Warren and Sutton Fen.
Flight: June, July (weeks 23-27)*.
Larval Foodplants: Birches.

For details of standard weeks see page 6.

Subfamily: **Tortricinae**

The moths are typically brown or fuscous with three transverse bands (fasciae) of darker colour (basal, median and sub-apical)of the forewings. Wingspan 11-29 mm. Many of the larvae are polyphagous, feeding on a wide variety of plants, usually in a tent or leaf-roll held together with silk. There are 94 British species, of which 55 have been found in Bedfordshire.

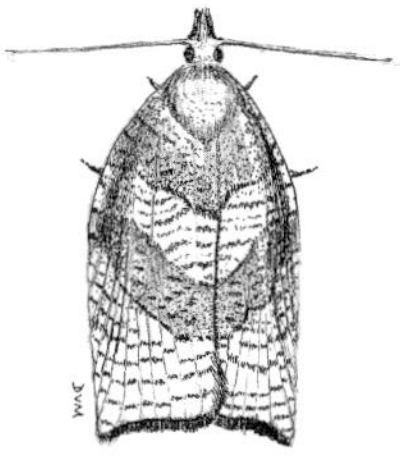

Pandemis corylana
(*x 2.5*)

Chequered Fruit-tree Tortrix *Pandemis corylana* (Fabricius) (969)

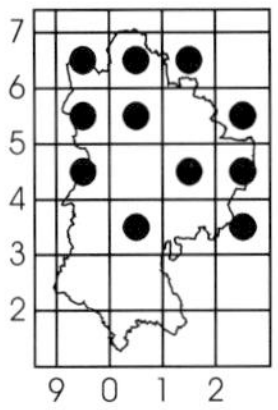

VCH: "Bedford, Luton".
Post VCH: Widespread and common.
Flight: July to September (weeks 28-39)*.
Larval Foodplants: Trees and shrubs.

Barred Fruit-tree Tortrix *Pandemis cerasana* (Hübner) (970)

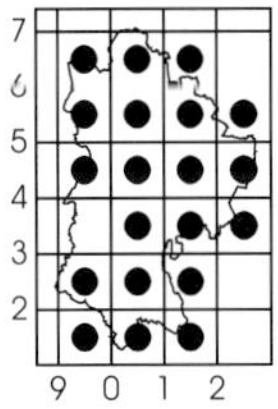

VCH: (as *Tortrix ribeana* Hb.) "Generally common".
Post VCH: Widespread and common.
Flight: June to August (weeks 24-34)*.
Larval Foodplants: Trees and shrubs.

***Pandemis cinnamomeana* (Treitschke) (971)**
Post VCH: Specimens have been confused with related species. Distribution records have been withdrawn pending identification of new specimens.

Dark Fruit-tree Tortrix *Pandemis heparana* ([Denis & Schiffermüller]) (972)

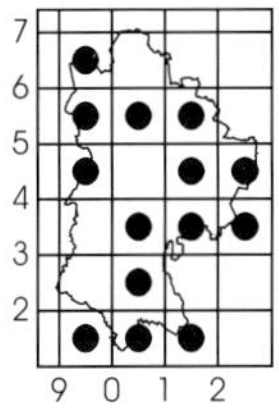

VCH: "Generally distributed".
Post VCH: Widespread and common.
Flight: June to September (weeks 26-37)*.
Larval Foodplants: Trees and shrubs.

***Argyrotaenia ljungiana* (Thunberg) (= *politana* (Haworth); *pulchellana* (Haworth)) (974)**

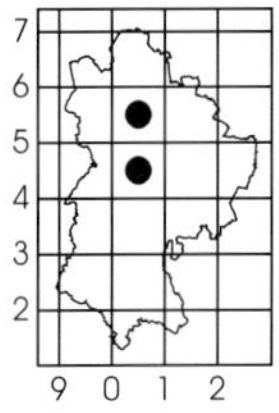

Post VCH: Local and uncommon: a colony appears to be established in an urban garden in Bedford, first recorded in 1994 by J.E.Childs. Specimens also received from a garden in Kempston in 1995 (H.Winter).
Flight: April to August (week 31)*.
Larval Foodplants: There appear to be two races, the common one on heather and the scarcer one, possibly a recent invader from the Continent, which is polyphagous and is extending its range in the south and east (A.M.Emmet pers. comm.).

For key to moth maps see page 3.

Fruit-tree Tortrix *Archips podana* (Scopoli) (977)
VCH: "Generally distributed".
Post VCH: Widespread and common.
Flight: June to September (weeks 24-33, 35, 37)*.
Larval Foodplants: Trees and shrubs.

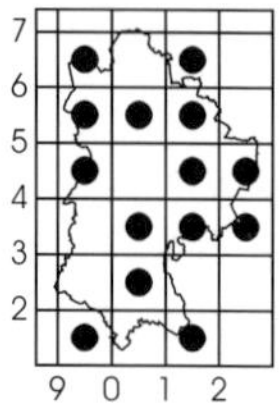

Brown Oak Tortrix *Archips crataegana* (Hübner) (979)
Post VCH: Locally common.
Flight: June to August (weeks 24-29)*.
Larval Foodplants: Trees and shrubs.

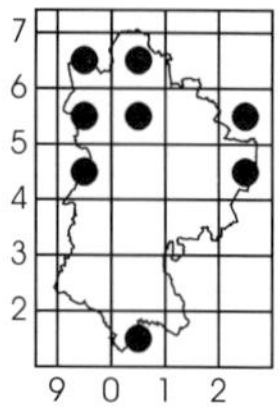

Variegated Golden Tortrix *Archips xylosteana* (Linnaeus) (980)
VCH: "Generally distributed".
Post VCH: Widespread and common.
Flight: June to August (weeks 25-33)*.
Larval Foodplants: Trees and shrubs.

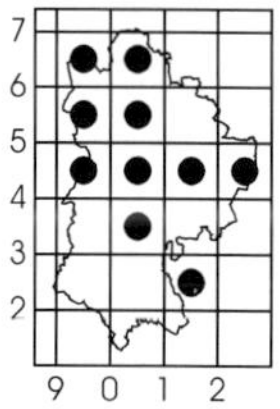

Rose Tortrix *Archips rosana* (Linnaeus) (981)
VCH: "Abundant everywhere".
Post VCH: Local and uncommon: Sharnbrook and in the RIS trap at Cockayne Hatley.
Flight: July (weeks 27, 28)* to September.
Larval Foodplants: Trees and shrubs.

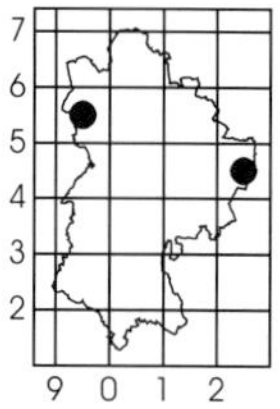

***Choristoneura diversana* (Hübner) (982)**
VCH: "Recorded at Luton by the late Mr. J.A.Saunders".
Post VCH: Local and uncommon: Bushmead and in the RIS trap at Cockayne Hatley.
Flight: June, July (week 28)*.
Larval Foodplants: Trees, shrubs and herbaceous plants.

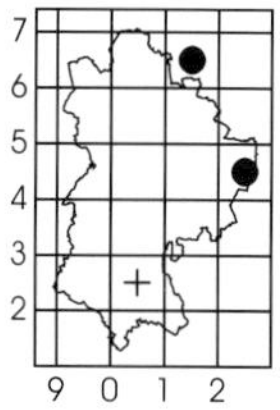

***Choristoneura hebenstreitella* (Müller) (983)**
VCH: (as *Tortrix sorbiana* Hb.) "Bedford, Luton".
Post VCH: Local and uncommon: King's Wood (Heath and Reach), West Wood and Stotfold.
Flight: June, July (weeks 24-28)*.
Larval Foodplants: Hazel* and other trees and shrubs.

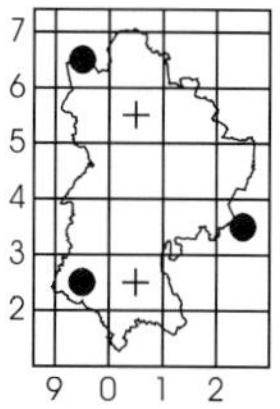

Carnation Tortrix *Cacoecimorpha pronubana* (Hübner) (985)
Post VCH: Widespread and common. (Plate 98)
Flight: April to October (weeks 15, 24-26, 32-37, 41)*.
Larval Foodplants: Trees, shrubs and herbaceous plants.

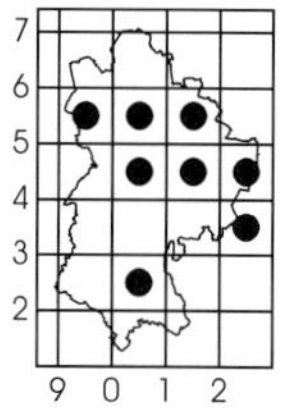

For details of standard weeks see page 6.

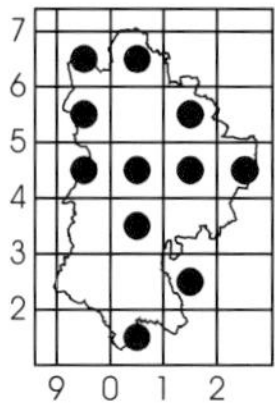

***Syndemis musculana musculana* (Hübner) (986)**
VCH: "Generally distributed".
Post VCH: Widespread and common.
Flight: May to July (weeks 18-25)*.
Larval Foodplants: Trees, shrubs and herbaceous plants.

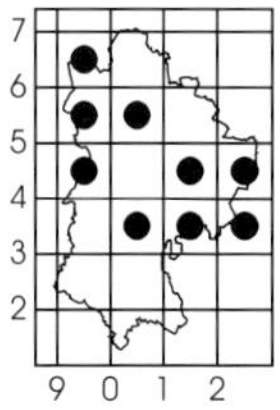

***Ptycholomoides aeriferanus* (Herrich-Schäffer) (987)**
Post VCH: Widespread and fairly common.
Flight: June to September (weeks 28-30)*.
Larval Foodplants: Larches.

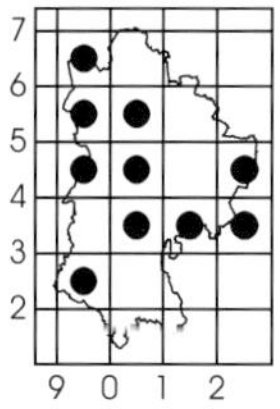

Timothy Tortrix *Aphelia paleana* (Hübner) (989)
Post VCH: Locally common.
Flight: June to August (weeks 24-34)*.
Larval Foodplants: Grasses and herbaceous plants.

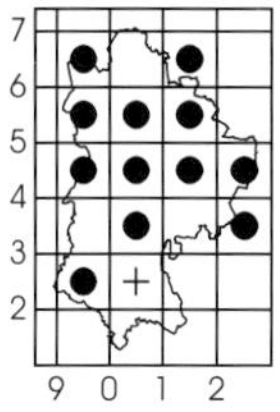

Straw-coloured or Cyclamen Tortrix *Clepsis spectrana* (Treitschke) (993)
VCH: (as *Tortrix costana* Schiff.) "Luton".
Post VCH: Widespread and common.
Flight: May to September (weeks 24-37)*.
Larval Foodplants: Willowherbs, meadowsweet, *Potentilla* spp. and many plants of damp places.

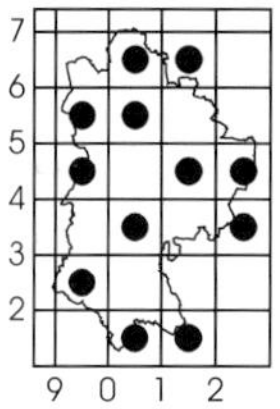

***Clepsis consimilana* (Hübner) (994)**
VCH: (as *Tortrix unifasciana* Dup.) "Generally common".
Post VCH: Widespread and common.
Flight: June to September (weeks 24-34)*.
Larval Foodplants: Privets and many other shrubs.

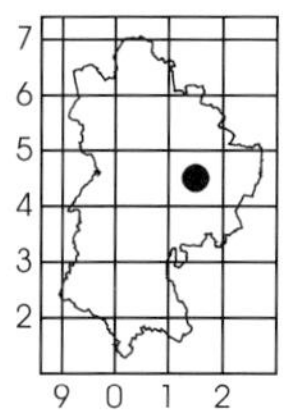

***Epiphyas postvittana* (Walker) (998)**
Post VCH: This species, native to Australia, was first found in Britain in Cornwall in 1936. By 1967 it had spread east to Hampshire and since then has been extending its range northwards. Recorded from Biggleswade in 1994 by R.C.Revels and Haynes in 1996 by J.E.Childs.
Flight: Continuous brooded.
Larval Foodplants: Garden plants.

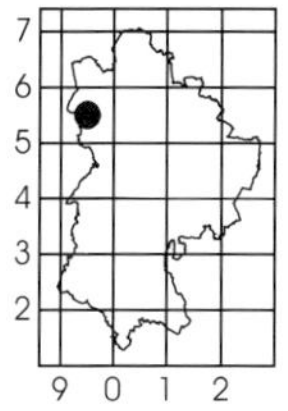

Summer Fruit Tortrix *Adoxophyes orana* (Fischer von Röslerstamm) (999)
Post VCH: A single record from Sharnbrook on 21 August 1983.
Flight: June to September (week 34)*.
Larval Foodplants: Fruit trees and other trees.

For key to moth maps see page 3.

***Ptycholoma lecheana* (Linnaeus) (1000)**
VCH: "Generally distributed".
Post VCH: Widespread and common.
Flight: June, July (weeks 24-29)*.
Larval Foodplants: Trees and shrubs.

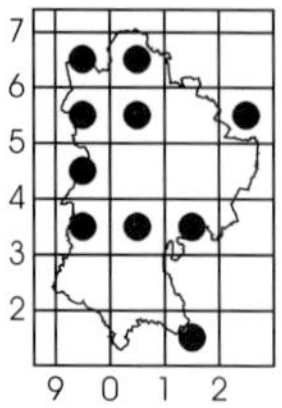

***Lozotaeniodes formosanus* (Geyer) (1001)**
Post VCH: Locally common.
Flight: June to August (weeks 27-34)*.
Larval Foodplant: Scots pine.

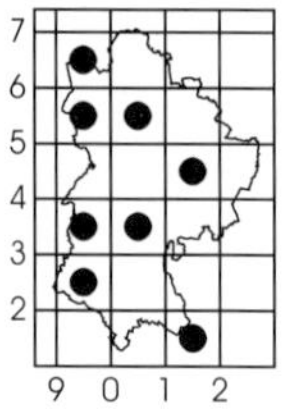

***Lozotaenia forsterana* (Fabricius) (1002)**
VCH: "Generally distributed".
Post VCH: Widespread and fairly common.
Flight: June, July (weeks 26-29)*.
Larval Foodplants: Polyphagous.

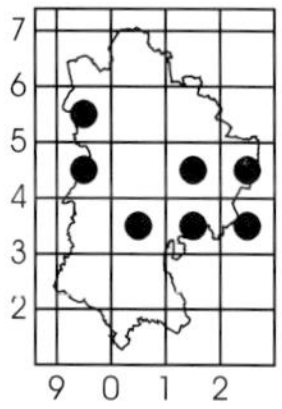

***Epagoge grotiana* (Fabricius) (1006)**
VCH: "Bedford".
Post VCH: Local and uncommon: Sandy and in the RIS trap at Cockayne Hatley.
Flight: June, July (week 28)*.
Larval Foodplants: Oaks, hawthorns and brambles.

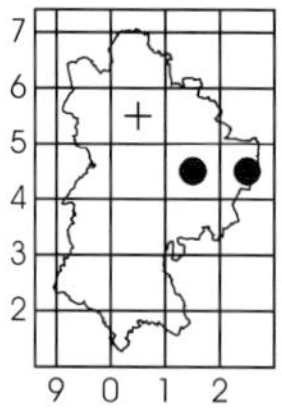

***Ditula angustiorana* (Haworth) (1010)**
VCH: "Generally common among privet and fruit trees".
Post VCH: Widespread and common.
Flight: June to August (weeks 24-32)*, September (week 37)*.
Larval Foodplants: Honeysuckle* and other shrubs and trees.

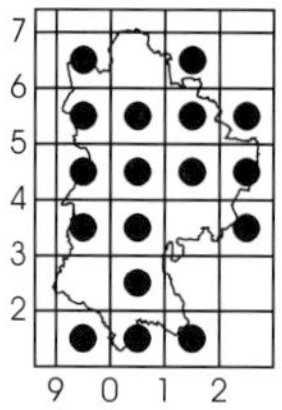

***Pseudargyrotoza conwagana* (Fabricius) (1011)**
VCH: "Bedford, Luton, among ash".
Post VCH: Widespread and common.
Flight: May to September (weeks 21-30, 34)*.
Larval Foodplants: Ash and privets.

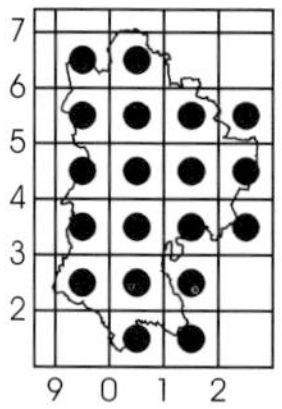

***Eulia ministrana* (Linnaeus) (1015)**
VCH: "Luton".
Post VCH: Locally common: Cranfield, Sharnbrook, West Wood, Studham, Coppice Wood and Potton Wood.
Flight: May, June (weeks 18-24)*.
Larval Foodplants: Trees and shrubs.

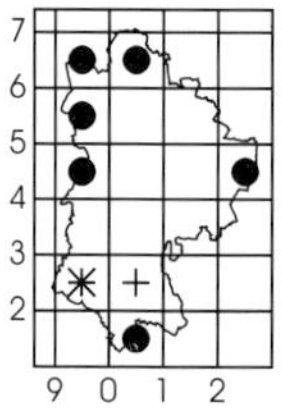

For details of standard weeks see page 6.

Cnephasia longana **(Haworth) (1016)**
Post VCH: Locally common: Cranfield, Thurleigh Cutting, Henlow, Little Staughton and in the RIS trap at Cockayne Hatley.
Flight: June to August (weeks 26-35)*.
Larval Foodplants: Oxeye daisy* and other herbaceous plants.

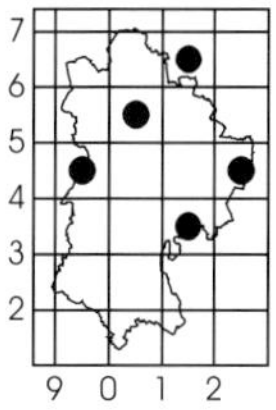

Cnephasia communana **(Herrich-Schäffer) (1018)**
VCH: "Bedford".
Post VCH: No recent record.
Flight: May to July.
Larval Foodplants: Herbaceous plants.

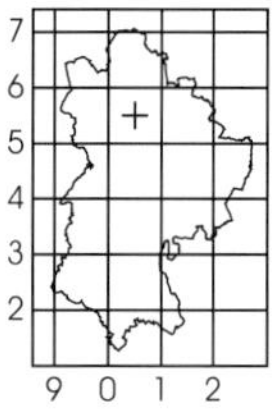

Grey Tortrix *Cnephasia stephensiana stephensiana* (Doubleday) (1020)
VCH: (as *Sciaphila chrysantheana* Dup.) "Bedford".
Post VCH: Widespread and common.
Flight: June to August (weeks 26-33)*.
Larval Foodplants: Docks* and other herbaceous plants.

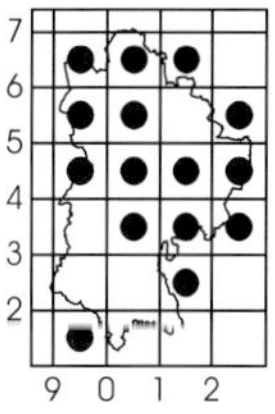

Flax Tortrix *Cnephasia asseclana* ([Denis & Schiffermüller]) (1021)
VCH: (as *Sciaphila virgaureana* Tr.) "Abundant everywhere".
Post VCH: Widespread and common.
Flight: June to August (weeks 25-32)*.
Larval Foodplants: Docks* and other herbaceous plants.

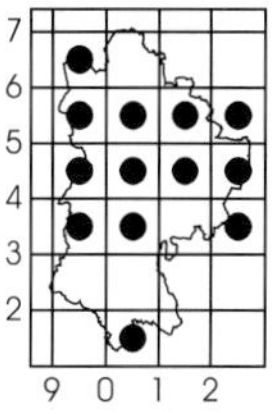

Cnephasia pasiuana **(Hübner) (1022)**
VCH: "Bedford".
Post VCH: Local and uncommon: Sharnbrook, Putnoe Wood and in the RIS trap at Cockayne Hatley.
Flight: June to August (weeks 28-32)*.
Larval Foodplants: Buttercups and Compositae.

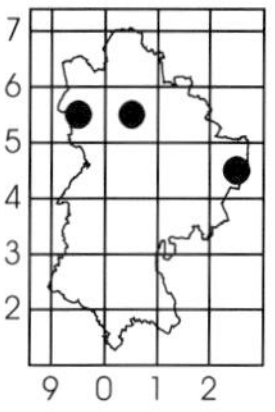

Light Grey Tortrix *Cnephasia incertana* (Treitschke) (1024)
VCH: (as *Sciaphila subjectana* Gn.) "Abundant everywhere".
Post VCH: Widespread and common.
Flight: June, July (weeks 24-30)*.
Larval Foodplants: Polyphagous on a wide range of plants.

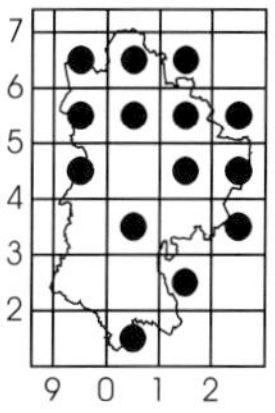

Tortricodes alternella **([Denis & Schiffermüller]) (1025)**
VCH: (as *Tortricodes hyemana* Hb.) "Bedford, Luton; among oak".
Post VCH: Widespread and common.
Flight: February, March (weeks 8-12)*.
Larval Foodplants: Oaks, hornbeam, birches, hazel, hawthorns, blackthorn and limes.

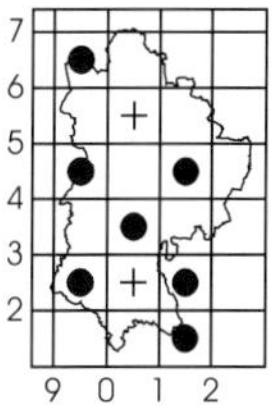

For key to moth maps see page 3.

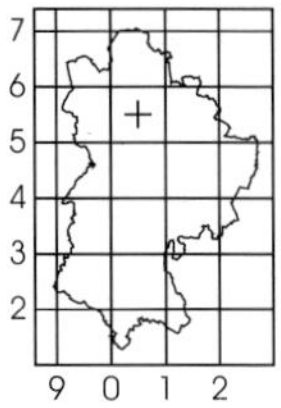

***Neosphaloptera nubilana* (Hübner) (1027)**
VCH: "Bedford, among hawthorn".
Post VCH: No recent record.
Flight: June, July.
Larval Foodplants: Hawthorns, *Prunus* spp., apple.

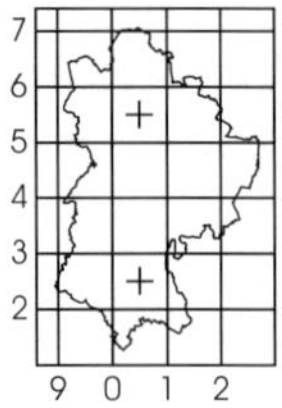

***Eana osseana* (Scopoli) (1029)**
VCH: "Bedford, Luton".
Post VCH: No recent record.
Flight: July, August.
Larval Foodplants: Polyphagous on herbaceous plants.

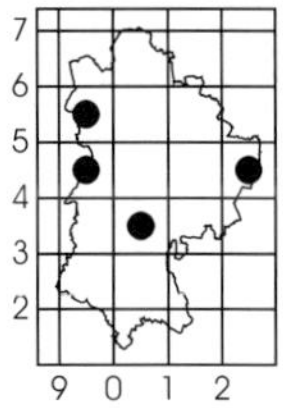

***Eana incanana* (Stephens) (1030)**
Post VCH: Local and uncommon: Marston Thrift, Maulden Wood, Sharnbrook and in the RIS trap at Cockayne Hatley.
Flight: June, July (weeks 26-29)*.
Larval Foodplants: Bluebell and oxeye daisy.

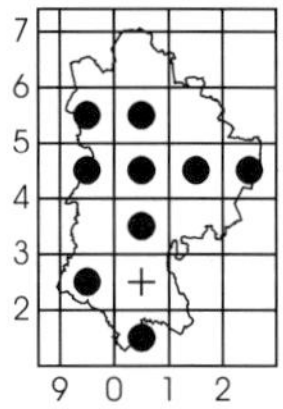

***Aleimma loeflingiana* (Linnaeus) (1032)**
VCH: "Luton, about oaks".
Post VCH: Widespread and fairly common.
Flight: June to August (weeks 26-30)*.
Larval Foodplants: Oaks, hornbeam and maples.

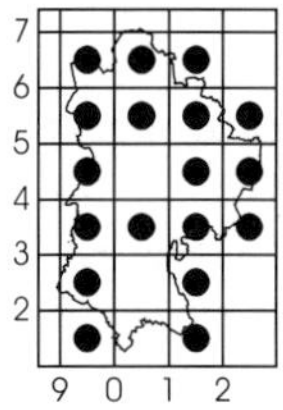

Green Oak Tortrix *Tortrix viridana* (Linnaeus) (1033) (Plate 45)
Pre VCH: "Small Green Oak Moth" Clapham Park Wood, 15 July 1799 (Abbot, MS1).
VCH: "Abundant among oaks".
Post VCH: Widespread and common. The larvae defoliate considerable areas of oak in some years.
Flight: June to August (weeks 24-31)*.
Larval Foodplants: Oaks*.

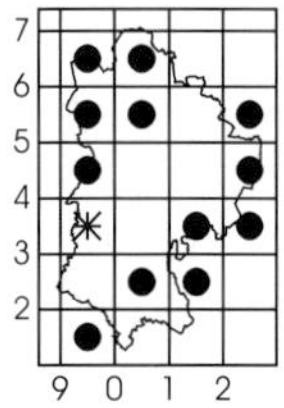

***Acleris bergmanniana* (Linnaeus) (1035)**
VCH: "Abundant everywhere among rose".
Post VCH: Widespread and common.
Flight: June to August (weeks 24-30)*.
Larval Foodplants: Roses.

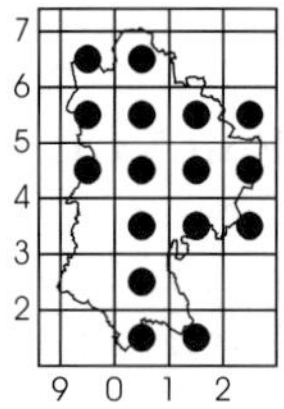

***Acleris forsskaleana* (Linnaeus) (1036)**
VCH: "Luton, among maple".
Post VCH: Widespread and common.
Flight: July to September (weeks 27-36)*.
Larval Foodplants: Field maple and sycamore.

For details of standard weeks see page 6.

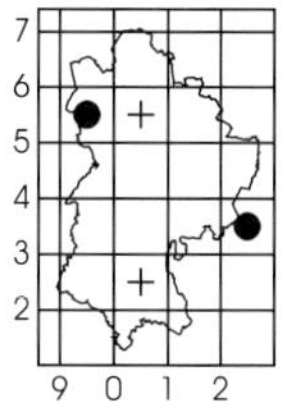

Acleris holmiana **(Linnaeus) (1037)**
VCH: "Luton, Bedford".
Post VCH: Local and uncommon: Sharnbrook and Stotfold.
Flight: July (week 29)*, August.
Larval Foodplants: Rosaceous trees and shrubs.

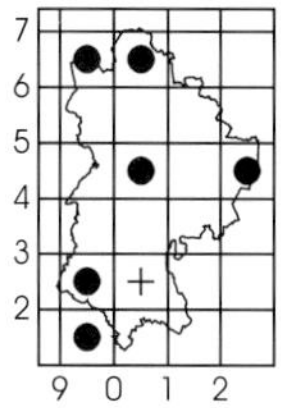

Acleris laterana **(Fabricius) (1038)**
VCH: (as *Peronea comparana* Hb.) "Luton".
Post VCH: Locally common.
Flight: August to October (weeks 31-37)*.
Larval Foodplants: Trees and shrubs.

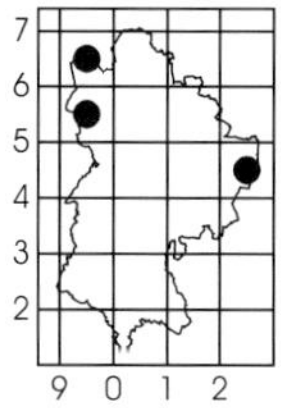

Strawberry Tortrix *Acleris comariana* (Lienig & Zeller) (1039)
Post VCH: Local and uncommon: Sharnbrook, West Wood and in the RIS trap at Cockayne Hatley.
Flight: June to November (weeks 32-35)*.
Larval Foodplants: Marsh cinquefoil and wild strawberry.

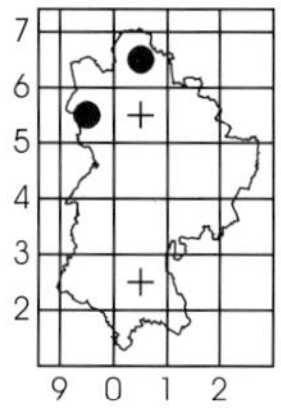

Acleris sparsana **([Denis & Schiffermüller]) (1041)**
Pre VCH: (as *Tortrix fagana*) noted by J.C.Dale in Clapham Park Wood on 31 May 1820.
VCH: (as *Peronea sponsana* Fab.) "Luton, among beech".
Post VCH: Local and uncommon: Felmersham Nature Reserve and Coppice Wood.
Flight: August (weeks 31, 32)* to May.
Larval Foodplants: Beech, hornbeam, sycamore and field maple.

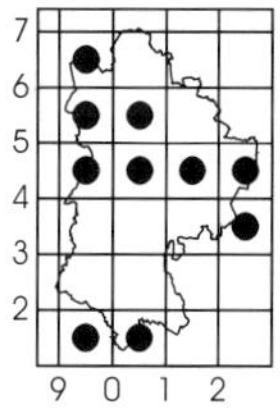

Rhomboid Tortrix *Acleris rhombana* ([Denis & Schiffermüller]) (1042)
VCH: (as *Teras contaminana* Hb.) "Common in every hawthorn hedge".
Post VCH: Widespread and common.
Flight: August to November (weeks 31-45)*.
Larval Foodplants: Rosaceous trees and shrubs.

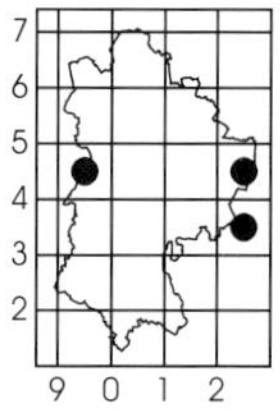

Acleris aspersana **(Hübner) (1043)**
Post VCH: Local and uncommon: Cranfield, Stotfold and in the RIS trap at Cockayne Hatley.
Flight: July, August (weeks 28-32)*.
Larval Foodplants: Herbaceous plants, field maple, brambles and sallows.

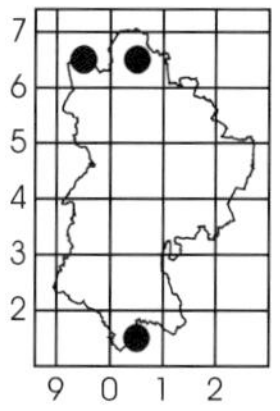

Acleris ferrugana **([Denis & Schiffermüller]) (1044)**
Post VCH: Local and uncommon: West Wood, Studham and Coppice Wood.
Flight: July (week 28)*, September to April (weeks 9, 10)*.
Larval Foodplants: Oaks and sallow.

For key to moth maps see page 3.

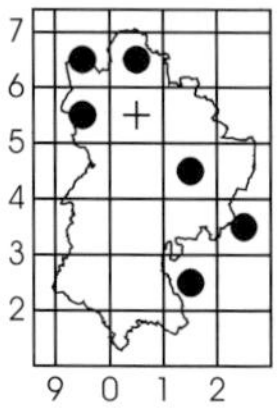

Acleris notana **(Donovan) (1045)**
VCH: (as *Peronea ferrugana* Tr.) "Bedford, in woods".
Post VCH: Widespread and fairly common.
Flight: July (weeks 28, 30)*, September to May (weeks 42, 48, 8-10)*.
Larval Foodplants: Birches and alder.

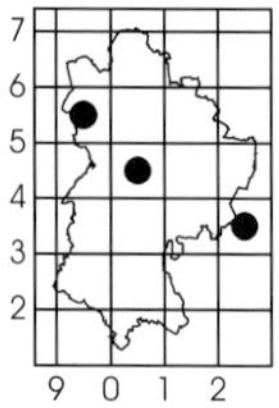

Acleris schalleriana **(Linnaeus) (1047)**
Post VCH: Local and uncommon: Sharnbrook, King's Wood (Houghton Conquest) and Stotfold.
Flight: August to May (weeks 31-36)*.
Larval Foodplants: Wayfaring-tree and guelder-rose.

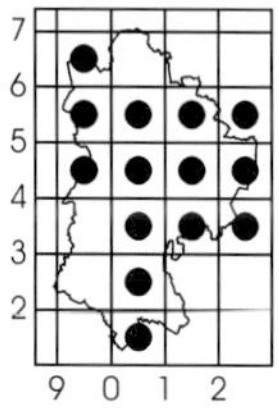

Garden Rose Tortrix *Acleris variegana* ([Denis & Schiffermüller]) (1048)
VCH: "Generally common".
Post VCH: Widespread and common.
Flight: July to November (weeks 29-45)*.
Larval Foodplants: Trees and shrubs.

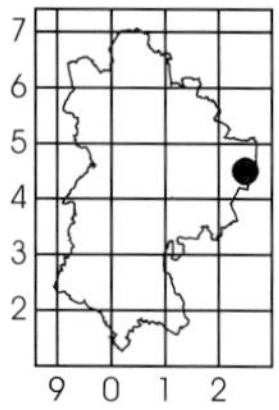

Acleris boscana **(Fabricius) (1050)**
Post VCH: A single record from the RIS trap at Cockayne Hatley in July 1992.
Flight: June, July*, September to April.
Larval Foodplants: Elms.

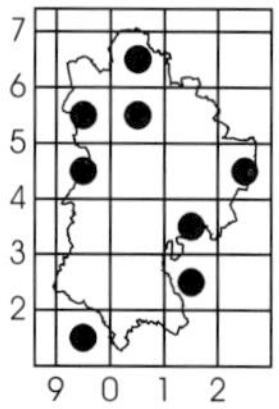

Acleris hastiana **(Linnaeus) (1053)**
Post VCH: Widespread and common.
Flight: June, July (week 30)*, August to April (weeks 37, 38, 44, 48, 8)*.
Larval Foodplants: Sallows and possibly white poplar and blackthorn.

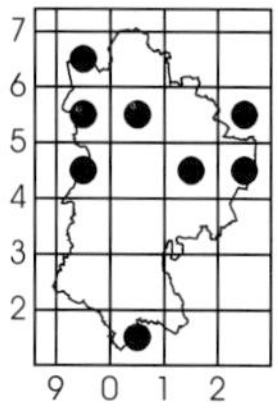

Acleris cristana **([Denis & Schiffermüller]) (1054)**
VCH: "Bedford".
Post VCH: Widespread but not common.
Flight: July to May (weeks 31, 37, 10, 16-18)*.
Larval Foodplants: Blackthorn, hawthorns, apple and common white-beam.

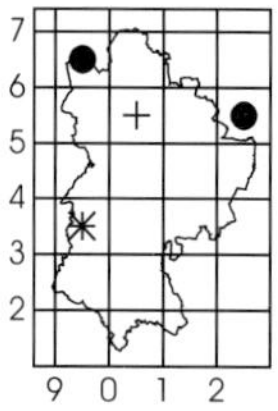

Acleris literana **(Linnaeus) (1061)**
VCH: "Bedford".
Post VCH: Local and uncommon: Aspley Heath (1946), West Wood and Potton Wood.
Flight: August to May (weeks 31, 45, 8, 9)*.
Larval Foodplants: Oaks.

For details of standard weeks see page 6.

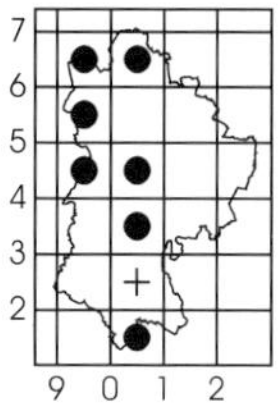

***Acleris emargana* (Fabricius) (1062)**
VCH: (as *Teras caudana* Fab.) "Luton".
Post VCH: Widespread but not common.
Flight: July to September (weeks 31-39)*.
Larval Foodplants: Sallows, poplars, birches, hazel and alder.

Subfamily: **Chlidanotinae**

A subfamily recently separated from the Tortricinae. Both British species occur in Bedfordshire. Wingspan 11-16 mm.

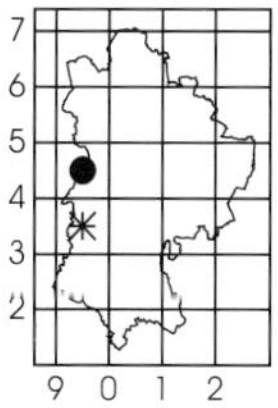

***Olindia schumacherana* (Fabricius) (= *ulmana* (Hübner)) (1013)**
Post VCH: Scarce: Aspley Heath on 26 June 1945 by S.H.Kershaw ("in water butt - 2 white spots on each f.w."), Marston Thrift, 19 July 1984, 2 and 18 July 1985.
Flight: June, July (weeks 27-29)*.
Larval Foodplants: Lesser celandine and occasionally other plants.

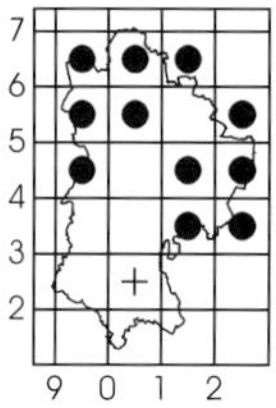

***Isotrias rectifasciana* (Haworth) (1014)**
VCH: (as *Sciaphila hybridana* Hb.) "Bedford, Luton".
Post VCH: Widespread and common.
Flight: May to July (weeks 21-29)*.
Larval Foodplants: Unknown.

For key to moth maps see page 3.

The Tortrices - Part 2

(Tortricidae: Olethreutinae)

D.V.Manning

Family: **Tortricidae**

Subfamily: **Olethreutinae**

The moths are similar to the Tortricinae, though mostly rather smaller and with the transverse bands on the forewings frequently not clearly marked. Often with a series of small lines (strigulae) on the leading (costal) edge of the forewing. A diagnostic circular patch of scales (the ocellus) is often present at the hind corner (tornus) of the wing. Wingspan 8-27 mm. Larval feeding varies, with some species being polyphagous. There are over 220 British species, of which 124 have been found in Bedfordshire.

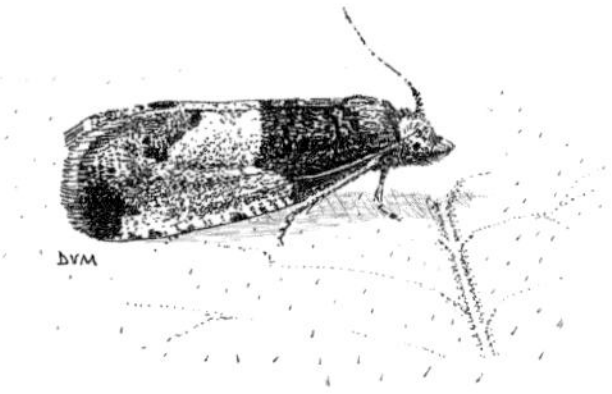

Spilonota ocellana
(*x 3*)

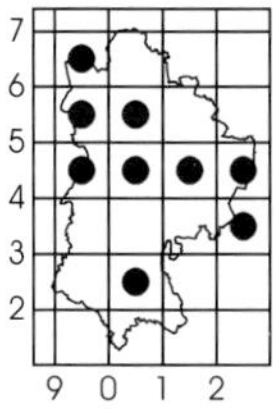

Celypha striana **([Denis & Schiffermüller]) (1063)**
VCH: "Bedford, Luton".
Post VCH: Widespread and common.
Flight: June to September (weeks 23-39)*.
Larval Foodplants: Dandelions.

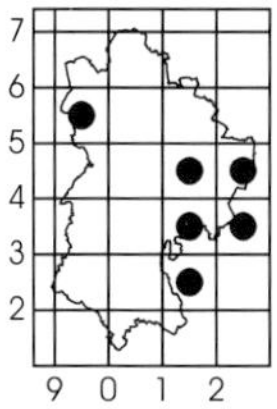

Celypha rosaceana **(Schläger) (1064)**
Post VCH: Widespread but not common: Sharnbrook, Pegsdon Hills, Clifton, Rowney Warren, Stotfold and in the RIS trap at Cockayne Hatley.
Flight: June to August (weeks 25-30, 34, 35)*.
Larval Foodplants: Sow-thistles and dandelions.

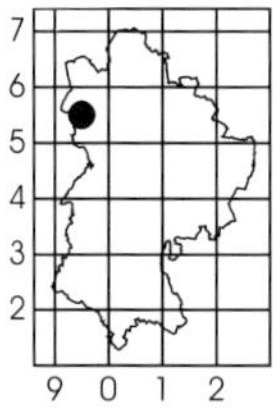

Celypha cespitana **(Hübner) (1067)**
Post VCH: Sharnbrook on 17 and 23 July 1983.
Flight: June to August (weeks 29, 30)*.
Larval Foodplants: Thymes and clovers.

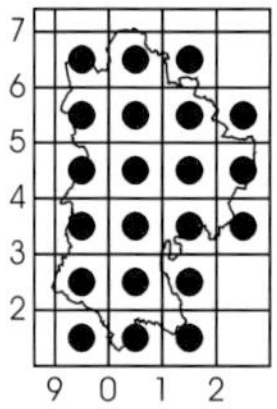

Dark Strawberry Tortrix *Olethreutes lacunana* ([Denis & Schiffermüller]) (1076)
VCH: "Everywhere common".
Post VCH: Widespread and common. recorded in all 10 km squares.
Flight: May to October (weeks 22-40)*.
Larval Foodplants: Great willowherb* and other herbaceous plants.

For details of standard weeks see page 6.

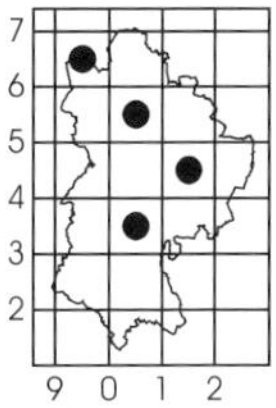

Olethreutes bifasciana **(Haworth) (1079)**
VCH: "Bedford".
Post VCH: Local and uncommon: West Wood, Maulden Wood, Bedford and Rowney Warren.
Flight: June, July (weeks 26-30)*.
Larval Foodplant: Scots pine.

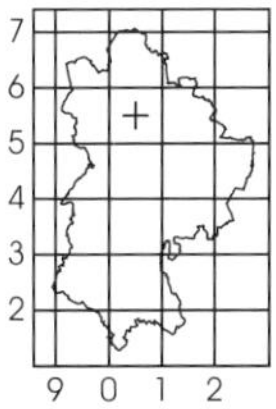

Olethreutes arcuella **(Clerck) (1080)**
VCH: (as *Roxana arcuana* Linn.) "Woods near Bedford".
Post VCH: No recent record.
Flight: May to August.
Larval Food: Leaf-litter.

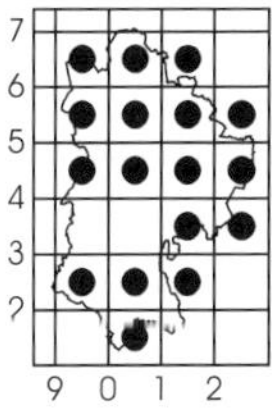

Plum Tortrix *Hedya pruniana* (Hübner) (1082)
VCH: "Generally abundant among sloe".
Post VCH: Widespread and common.
Flight: May to August (weeks 22-33)*.
Larval Foodplants: Blackthorn and plum. Also apple, pear, hawthorns and hazel.

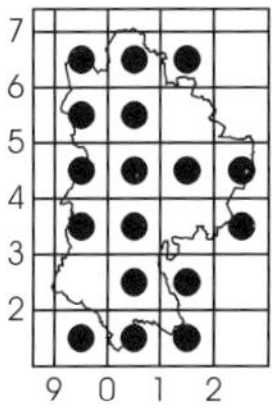

Marbled Orchard Tortrix *Hedya dimidioalba* (Retzius) (= *nubiferana* (Haworth)) (1083)
VCH: (as *Penthina variegana* Hb.) "everywhere common".
Post VCH: Widespread and common.
Flight: June to August (weeks 24-33)*.
Larval Foodplants: Hawthorns, blackthorn and other trees and shrubs.

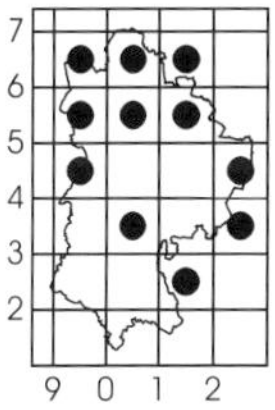

Hedya ochroleucana **(Frölich) (1084)**
Post VCH: Widespread and common.
Flight: June to August (weeks 23-33)*.
Larval Foodplants: Roses and apple.

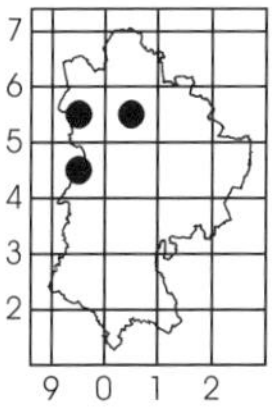

Hedya salicella **(Linnaeus) (1086)**
Post VCH: Local and uncommon: Cranfield, Sharnbrook and Clapham Park Wood.
Flight: June, July (weeks 28-30)*, August.
Larval Foodplants: White willow. Also other willows, sallows and poplars.

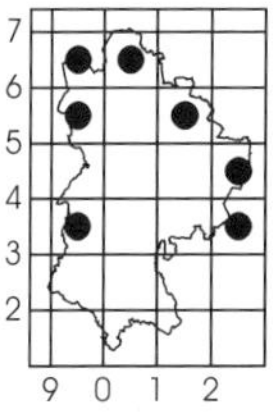

Orthotaenia undulana **([Denis & Schiffermüller]) (1087)**
Post VCH: Local and uncommon.
Flight: May to August (weeks 22-29, 33)*.
Larval Foodplants: Trees, shrubs and herbaceous plants.

For key to moth maps see page 3.

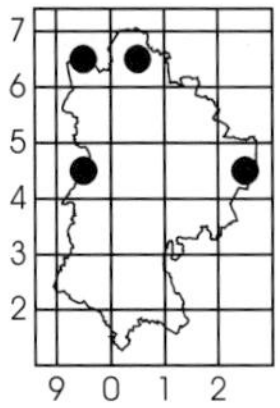

Pseudosciaphila branderiana **(Linnaeus) (1088)**
Post VCH: Local and uncommon: Marston Thrift, West Wood, Coppice Wood and in the RIS trap at Cockayne Hatley.
Flight: June to August (weeks 24-29)*.
Larval Foodplant: Aspen.

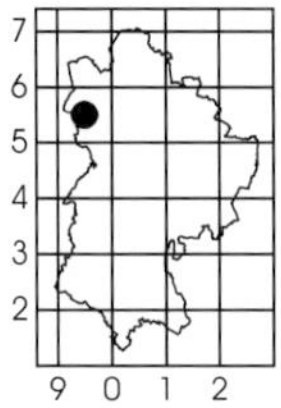

Apotomis lineana **([Denis & Schiffermüller]) (1091)**
Post VCH: A single record from Carlton on 14 July 1985 by G.Ping.
Flight: June, July (week 28)*, August.
Larval Foodplants: White willow and crack willow.

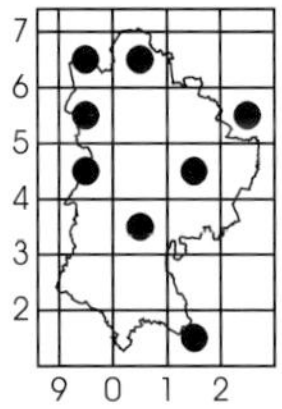

Apotomis turbidana **(Hübner) (1092)**
Post VCH: Locally common.
Flight: June to August (weeks 24-28, 32)*.
Larval Foodplants: Birches.

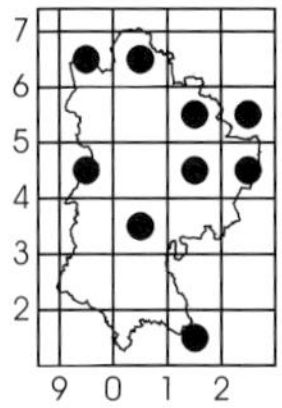

Apotomis betuletana **(Haworth) (1093)**
Post VCH: Locally common.
Flight: July to September (weeks 28-38)*.
Larval Foodplants: Birches.

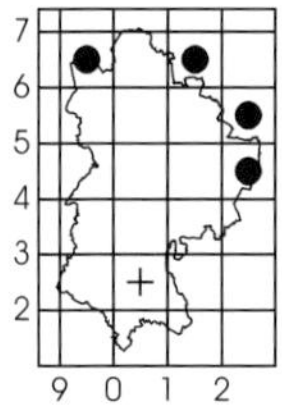

Apotomis capreana **(Hübner) (1094)**
VCH: "Luton, among sallow".
Post VCH: Local and uncommon: West Wood, Bushmead, in the RIS trap at Cockayne Hatley and Potton Wood.
Flight: June, July (weeks 27, 28)*, August.
Larval Foodplant: Sallow.

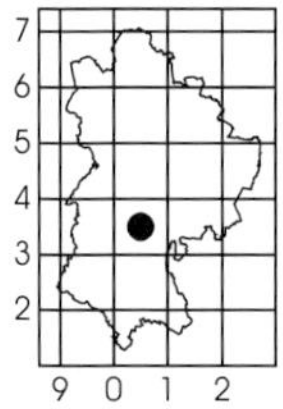

Apotomis sororculana **(Zetterstedt) (1095)**
Post VCH: A single record from Flitwick Moor on 11 June 1982 by T.S.Hollingworth.
Flight: May, June (week 24)*, July.
Larval Foodplants: Birches.

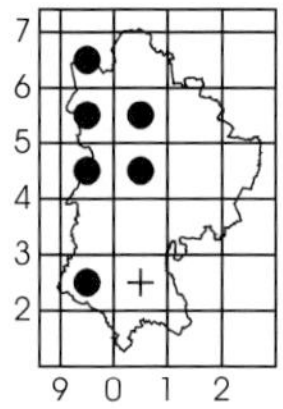

Endothenia gentianaeana **(Hübner) (1097)**
VCH: "Bedford, Luton; reared from heads of teazle".
Post VCH: Widespread and common.
Flight: June, July (weeks 26-30)*.
Larval Foodplant: Teasel*.

For details of standard weeks see page 6.

***Endothenia marginana* (Haworth) (1099)**
Post VCH: Local and uncommon: Sewell Cutting, Maulden Wood, Thurleigh Cutting and Stanford Wood.
Flight: May to August (weeks 24, 25, 31)★.
Larval Foodplants: Betony, hemp-nettles, yellow-rattle and teasel.

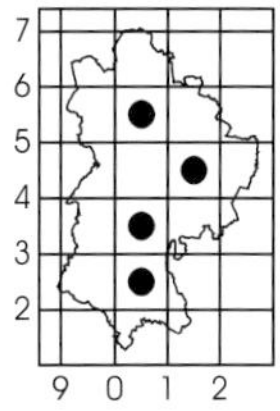

***Endothenia nigricostana* (Haworth) (1102)**
Post VCH: Scarce: Maulden Wood on 25 June 1983 and Riseley on 23 June 1985.
Flight: June (weeks 25, 26)★.
Larval Foodplant: Hedge woundwort.

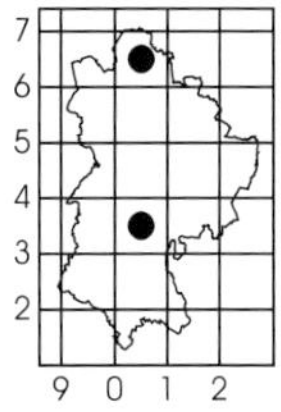

***Endothenia quadrimaculana* (Haworth) (1104)**
Post VCH: Local and uncommon: Biggleswade, Tempsford and in the RIS trap at Cockayne Hatley.
Flight: June to August (weeks 29, 30, 34)★.
Larval Foodplant: Marsh woundwort.

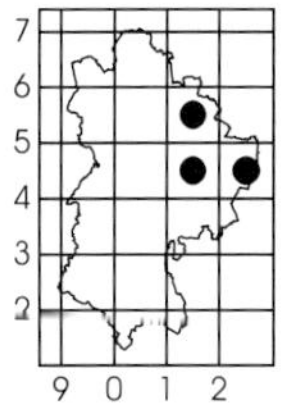

***Lobesia reliquana* (Hübner) (1106)**
VCH: "Bedford".
Post VCH: No recent record.
Flight: May, June.
Larval Foodplants: Oaks, blackthorn, birches.

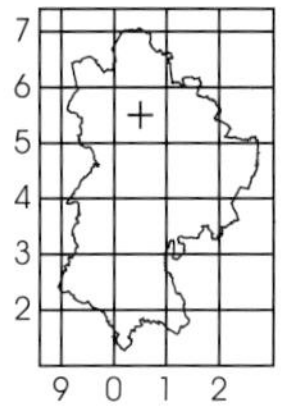

European Vine Moth *Lobesia botrana* ([Denis & Schiffermüller]) (1107)
Post VCH: This species was first recorded in Britain in 1976 at Enfield (Middlesex). The next record was one moth caught at MV light at West Wood on 21 August 1987 (illustrated by Wilson, 1989).
Flight: July, August (week 34)★.
Larval Foodplants: Shrubs and climbers. The species is a pest on grapevines in southern Europe.

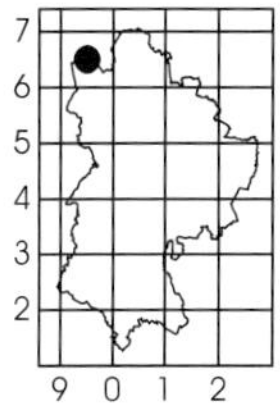

***Lobesia abscisana* (Doubleday) (1108)**
Post VCH: Locally common.
Flight: May, July, August (weeks 27-34)★.
Larval Foodplant: Creeping thistle.

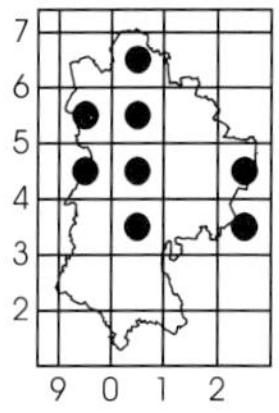

***Lobesia littoralis* (Humphreys & Westwood) (1109)**
Post VCH: Locally common: Sharnbrook, Bedford. This coastal species occurs inland in gardens where the foodplant is established.
Flight: June to September (weeks 24, 25, 33, 37)★.
Larval Foodplant: Thrift★.

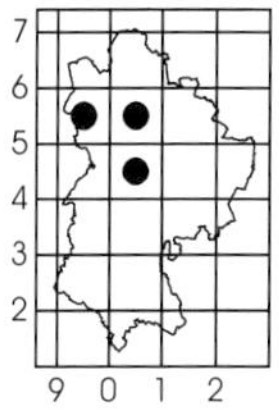

For key to moth maps see page 3.

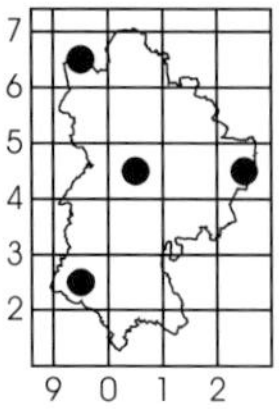

Bactra lancealana **(Hübner) (1111)**
VCH: "Everywhere among rushes".
Post VCH: Local and uncommon: King's Wood (Heath and Reach), West Wood, King's Wood (Houghton Conquest) and in the RIS trap at Cockayne Hatley.
Flight: May to October (weeks 21-24, 31-33)*.
Larval Foodplants: Compact rush and club-rushes.

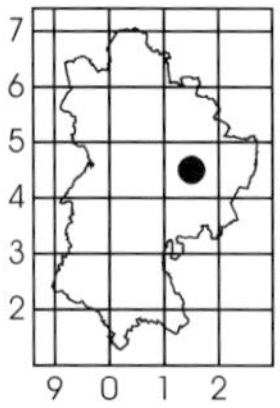

Eudemis profundana **([Denis & Schiffermüller]) (1113)**
Post VCH: A single record from Biggleswade in 1994 (date not recorded) by R.C.Revels.
Flight: July, August.
Larval Foodplants: Oaks.

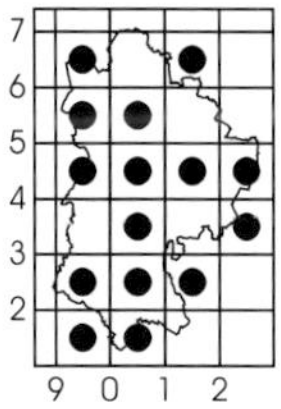

Ancylis achatana **([Denis & Schiffermüller]) (1115)**
VCH: "Bedford, among hawthorn".
Post VCH: Widespread and common.
Flight: June to August (weeks 24-31)*.
Larval Foodplants: Hawthorns and blackthorn.

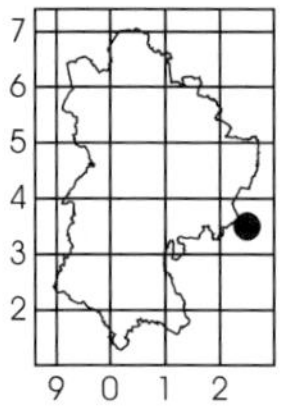

Ancylis comptana **(Frölich) (1116)**
Post VCH: A single record: Stotfold, 6 August 1986 by T.S.Hollingworth.
Flight: April to September (week 32)*.
Larval Foodplants: Salad burnet, *Potentilla* spp., thymes and wild strawberry.

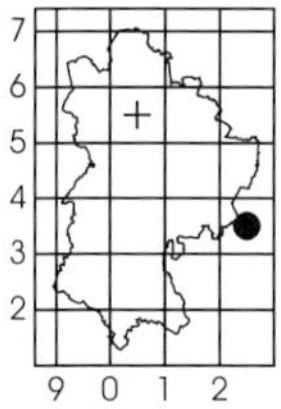

Ancylis unguicella **(Linnaeus) (1117)**
VCH: "Bedford, on heaths".
Post VCH: A single record from Stotfold, 10 July 1982 by T.S.Hollingworth.
Flight: May to July (week 28)*.
Larval Foodplant: Heather.

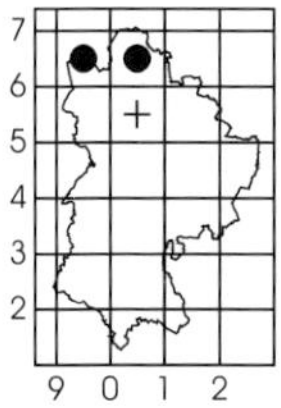

Ancylis geminana **(Donovan) (1119)**
VCH: (as *Phoxopteryx biarcuana* Steph.) "Recorded at Bedford by Mr. Sharpin".
Post VCH: Local and uncommon: West Wood and Worley's Wood.
Flight: May to August (weeks 22-27)*.
Larval Foodplants: Willows and sallows.

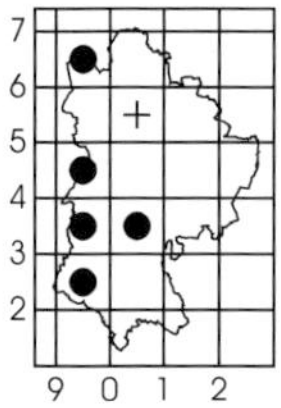

Ancylis mitterbacheriana **([Denis & Schiffermüller]) (1120)**
VCH: "Bedford, among oaks".
Post VCH: Widespread and fairly common: Hanger Wood, King's Wood (Heath and Reach), Salford, West Wood and Maulden Wood.
Flight: May to August (weeks 24-26, 32)*.
Larval Foodplants: Oaks and beech.

For details of standard weeks see page 6.

Ancylis laetana **(Fabricius) (1123)**
Post VCH: Local and uncommon: Marston Thrift, West Wood, Maulden Wood.
Flight: May, June (weeks 23-25)★.
Larval Foodplant: Aspen★.

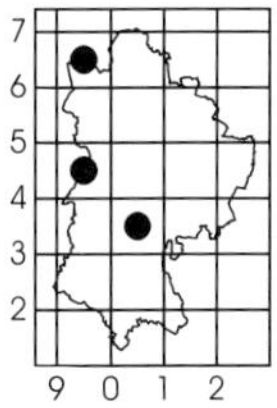

Ancylis badiana **([Denis & Schiffermüller]) (1126)**
VCH: (as *Phoxopteryx lundana* Fab.) "Among clover everywhere".
Post VCH: Widespread and common.
Flight: April to June (weeks 20-25)★, July, August (weeks 31-33)★.
Larval Foodplants: Vetches and clovers.

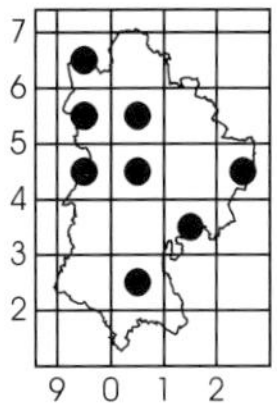

Ancylis myrtillana **(Treitschke) (1128)**
Post VCH: Old Wavendon Heath, larvae in "pods" on leaves of bilberry, October 1984.
Flight: May to July.
Larval Foodplant: Bilberry★.

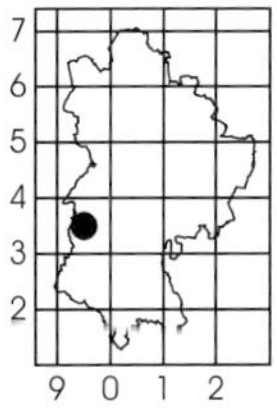

Epinotia pygmaeana **(Hübner) (1130)**
VCH: "Bedford district, among fir".
Post VCH: No recent record.
Flight: April to June.
Larval Foodplants: Spruces, silver fir.

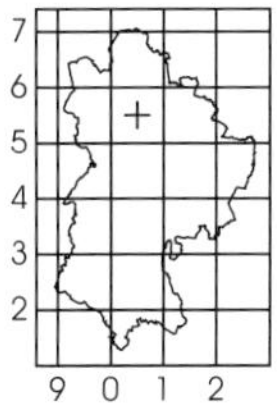

Epinotia subocellana **(Donovan) (1132)**
Post VCH: Local and uncommon: Sharnbrook, Worley's Wood and Coppice Wood.
Flight: May to July (weeks 18, 22-25)★.
Larval Foodplants: Sallows★.

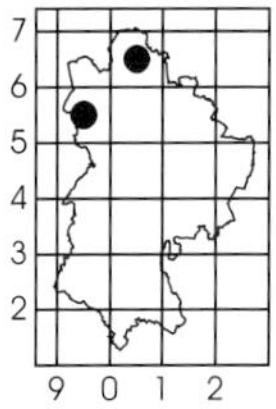

Epinotia bilunana **(Haworth) (1133)**
Post VCH: Locally common: Sharnbrook, Flitwick Moor, Rowney Warren and Sutton Fen.
Flight: June to August (weeks 25-28, 35)★.
Larval Foodplants: Birches.

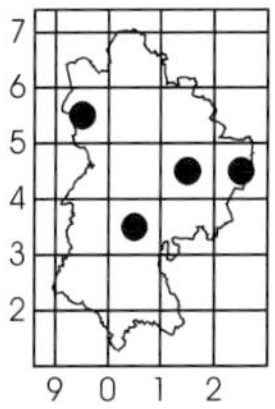

Epinotia ramella **(Linnaeus) (1134)**
VCH: "Bedford".
Post VCH: Locally common: West Wood, Flitwick Moor, Bedford, Rowney Warren and Potton Wood.
Flight: July to September (weeks 28-36)★.
Larval Foodplants: Birches.

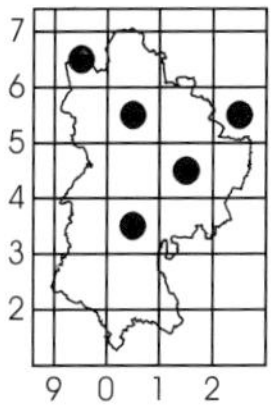

For key to moth maps see page 3.

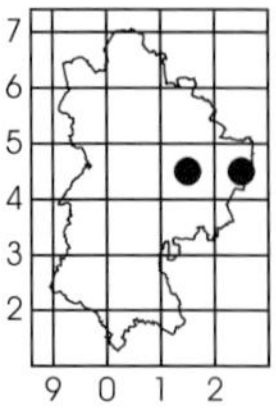

Epinotia demarniana **(Fischer von Röslerstamm) (1135)**
Post VCH: Scarce: Rowney Warren and Sutton Fen.
Flight: June, July (weeks 25-28)*.
Larval Foodplants: Birches, alder and sallow.

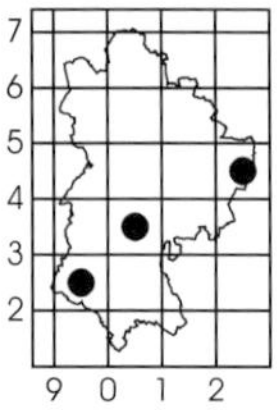

Epinotia immundana **(Fischer von Röslerstamm) (1136)**
Post VCH: Local and uncommon: King's Wood (Heath and Reach), Flitwick Moor and Sutton Fen.
Flight: April to June (weeks 20, 21)*, August, September.
Larval Foodplants: Alder and birches.

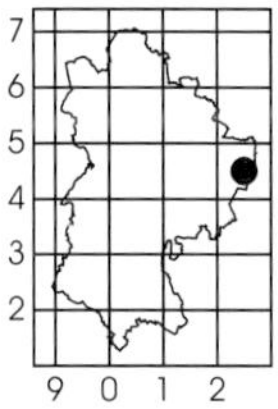

Epinotia tetraquetrana **(Haworth) (1137)**
Post VCH: A single record from Sutton Fen, 21 May 1982 by T.S.Hollingworth.
Flight: April to June (week 21)*.
Larval Foodplants: Alder and birches.

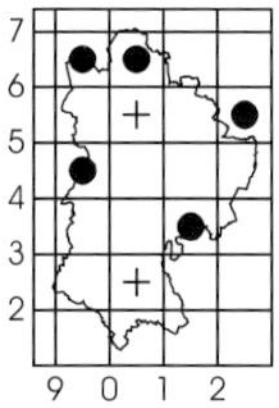

Epinotia nisella **(Clerck) (1138)**
VCH: "Bedford, Luton".
Post VCH: Locally common: Marston Thrift, West Wood, Worley's Wood, Henlow and Potton Wood.
Flight: July to September (weeks 28-37)*.
Larval Foodplants: Sallows and poplars.

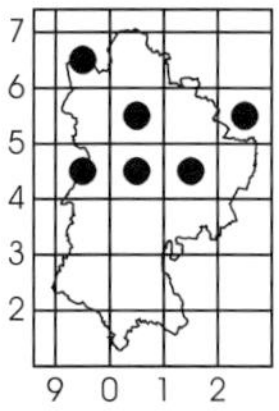

Nut Bud Moth *Epinotia tenerana* ([Denis & Schiffermüller]) (1139)
VCH: (as *Grapholitha penkleriana* Schiff.) "Generally common among alder".
Post VCH: Locally common.
Flight: July to October (weeks 27-29, 34-37)*.
Larval Foodplants: Hazel and alder.

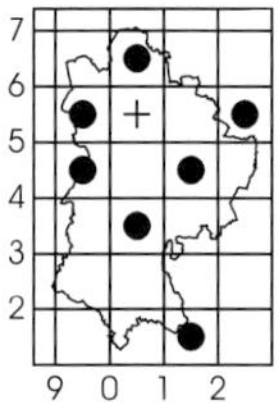

Epinotia tedella **(Clerck) (1142)**
VCH: (as *Coccyx taedella* Linn.) "Bedford district, among spruce fir".
Post VCH: Widespread and common.
Flight: May to July (weeks 18-28)*.
Larval Foodplants: Norway spruce and sitka spruce.

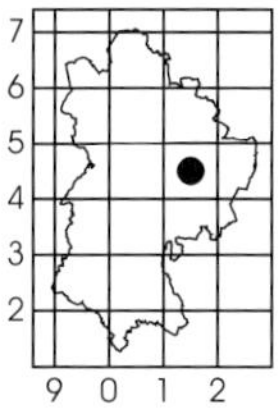

Epinotia signatana **(Douglas) (1144)**
Post VCH: A single record from Cople Pits, 13 June 1988 by W.J.Champkin.
Flight: June, (week 24)*, July.
Larval Foodplants: *Prunus* spp. and crab-apple.

For details of standard weeks see page 6.

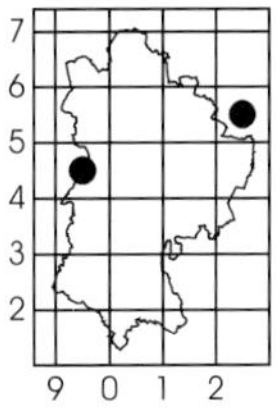

***Epinotia nanana* (Treitschke) (1145)**
Post VCH: Scarce: Marston Thrift and Potton Wood.
Flight: June to August (weeks 24, 27)*.
Larval Foodplants: Norway spruce and sitka spruce.

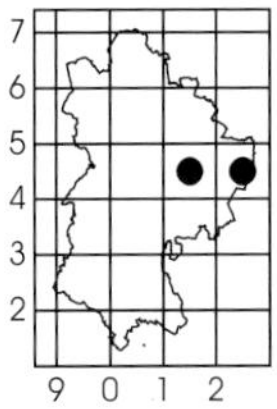

***Epinotia rubiginosana* (Herrich-Schäffer) (1146)**
Post VCH: Scarce: Stanford Wood and in the RIS trap at Cockayne Hatley.
Flight: May to July (weeks 26, 27)*.
Larval Foodplant: Scots pine.

Willow Tortrix *Epinotia cruciana* (Linnaeus) (1147)
VCH: "Generally common among sallow".
Post VCH: No recent record.
Flight: June to August
Larval Foodplants: Sallows and willows.

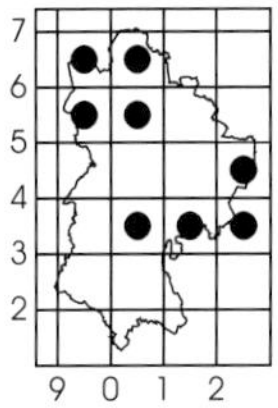

***Epinotia abbreviana* (Fabricius) (1150)**
VCH: (as *Grapholitha trimaculana* Don.) "Generally common among elm".
Post VCH: Widespread and fairly common.
Flight: June to August (weeks 24-30)*.
Larval Foodplants: Elms*.

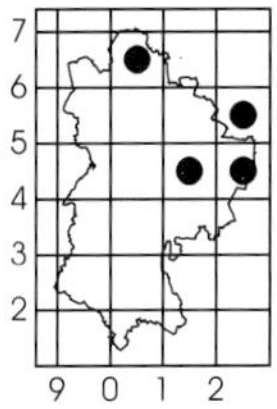

***Epinotia trigonella* (Linnaeus) (= *stroemiana* (Fabricius)) (1151)**
Post VCH: Local and uncommon: Coppice Wood, Rowney Warren, Potton Wood and in the RIS trap at Cockayne Hatley.
Flight: August, September (weeks 35, 36)*.
Larval Foodplants: Birches.

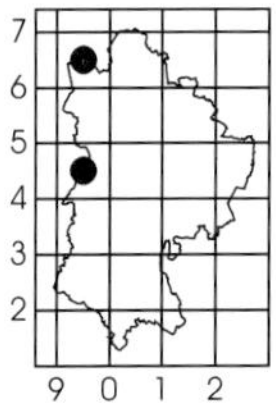

***Epinotia maculana* (Fabricius) (= *ophthalmicana* (Hübner)) (1152)**
Post VCH: Local and uncommon: Marston Thrift and West Wood.
Flight: August to October (weeks 39, 43)*.
Larval Foodplant: Aspen.

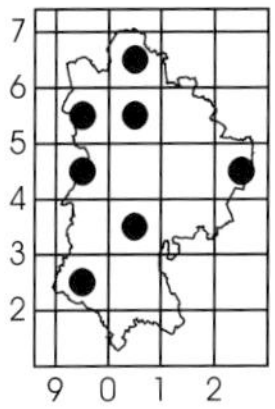

***Epinotia brunnichana* (Linnaeus) (1155)**
Post VCH: Widespread and common.
Flight: July to September (weeks 27-33)*.
Larval Foodplants: Birches*, hazel, sallows and willows.

For key to moth maps see page 3.

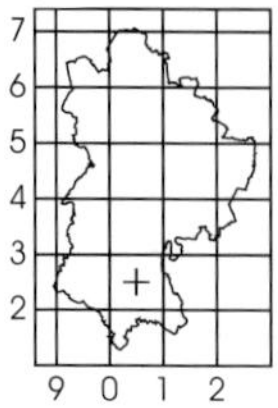

***Epinotia solandriana* (Linnaeus) (1156)**
VCH: "Luton, in hedges".
Post VCH: No recent record.
Flight: July, August.
Larval Foodplants: Birches, hazel, sallow.

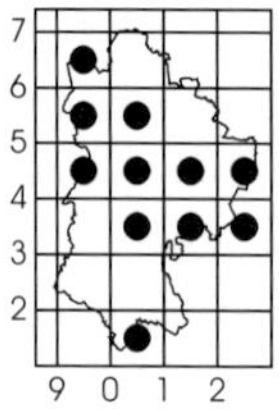

Holly Tortrix *Rhopobota naevana* (Hübner) (1159)
VCH: "Generally common among holly and fruit trees".
Post VCH: Widespread and common.
Flight: June to September (weeks 26-34)*.
Larval Foodplants: Holly, blackthorn and other trees and shrubs.

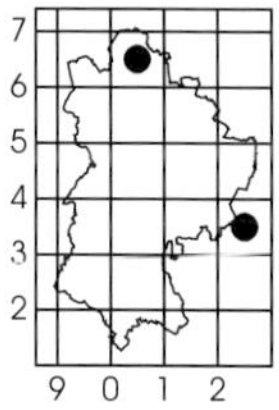

***Zeiraphera ratzeburgiana* (Ratzeburg) (1163)**
Post VCH: Local and uncommon: Worley's Wood and Stotfold.
Flight: July, August (weeks 29, 32)*.
Larval Foodplants: Spruces.

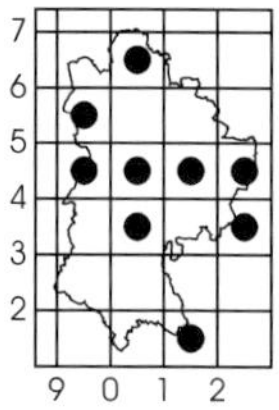

***Zeiraphera isertana* (Fabricius) (1165)**
VCH: (as *Poedisca corticana* Schiff.) "Generally common among oak".
Post VCH: Widespread and common.
Flight: July to September (weeks 26-37)*.
Larval Foodplants: Oaks.

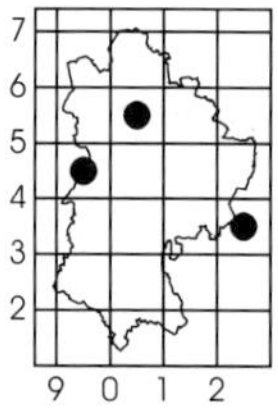

Larch Tortrix *Zeiraphera diniana* (Guenée) (1166)
Post VCH: Local and uncommon: Cranfield, Bedford and Stotfold.
Flight: July, August (weeks 31, 32)*.
Larval Foodplants: Sitka spruce, larches and pines.

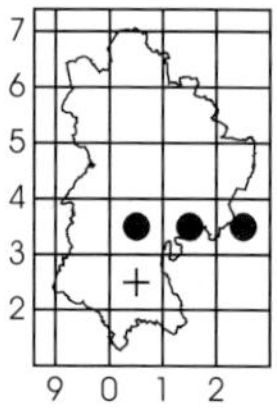

***Gypsonoma aceriana* (Duponchel) (1167)**
VCH: "Luton, on poplars".
Post VCH: Locally common: Flitwick Moor, Henlow and Stotfold.
Flight: July, August (weeks 27, 31)*.
Larval Foodplants: Poplars.

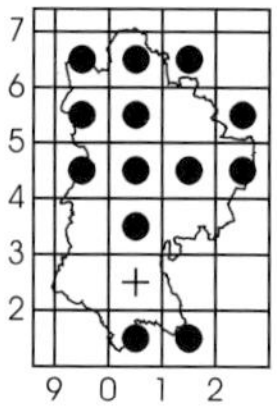

***Gypsonoma dealbana* (Frölich) (1169)**
VCH: "Bedford, Luton".
Post VCH: Widespread and common.
Flight: June to August (weeks 26-32)*.
Larval Foodplants: Hawthorns, oaks, poplars, hazel, sallow*, crack willow*.

For details of standard weeks see page 6.

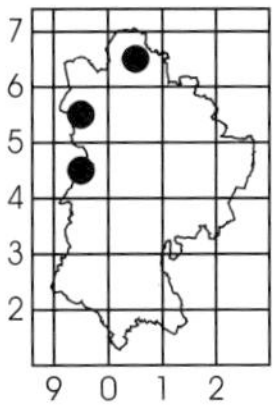

Gypsonoma oppressana **(Treitschke) (1170)**
Post VCH: Scarce: Cranfield, Sharnbrook and Coppice Wood.
Flight: June, July (weeks 24, 29)*.
Larval Foodplants: Black poplar and white poplar.

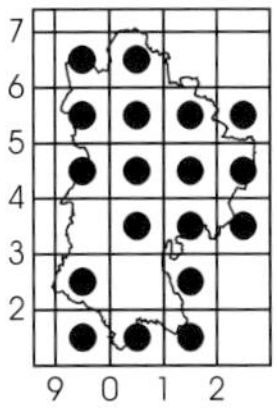

Epiblema cynosbatella **(Linnaeus) (1174)**
VCH: (as *Pardia tripunctana* Schiff.) "Generally common among wild rose".
Post VCH: Widespread and common.
Flight: May to July (weeks 22-29)*.
Larval Foodplants: Roses and brambles.

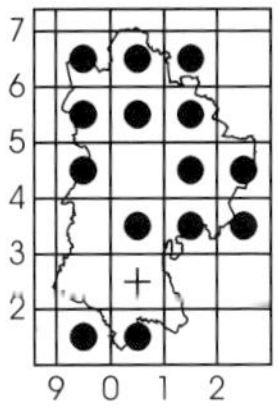

Bramble Shoot Moth *Epiblema uddmanniana* (Linnaeus) (1175)
VCH: "Bedford, Luton; among bramble".
Post VCH: Widespread and common.
Flight: June to August (weeks 24-34)*.
Larval Foodplants: Brambles.

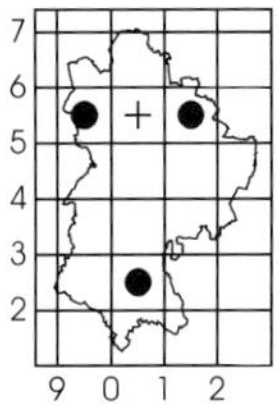

Epiblema trimaculana **(Haworth) (1176)**
VCH: (as *Spilonota suffusana* Koll.) "Bedford, Luton, about hawthorn".
Post VCH: Local and uncommon: Sharnbrook, Sharpenhoe and Waterloo Thorns.
Flight: June to August (week 29)*.
Larval Foodplants: Hawthorns.

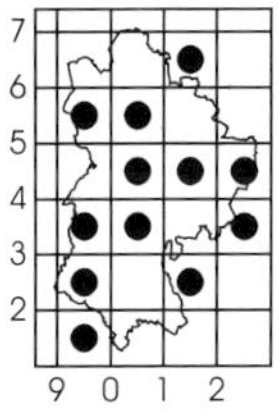

Epiblema rosaecolana **(Doubleday) (1177)**
VCH: "Bedford, among roses in gardens".
Post VCH: Widespread and common.
Flight: June to August (weeks 26-31)*.
Larval Foodplants: Roses*.

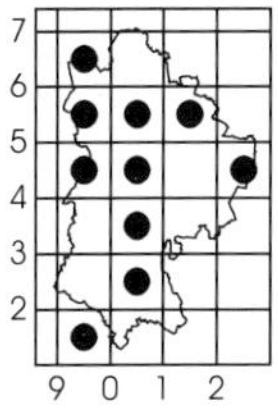

Epiblema roborana **([Denis & Schiffermüller]) (1178)**
VCH: "Generally common among wild rose".
Post VCH: Widespread and common.
Flight: June to August (weeks 26-33)*.
Larval Foodplants: Roses.

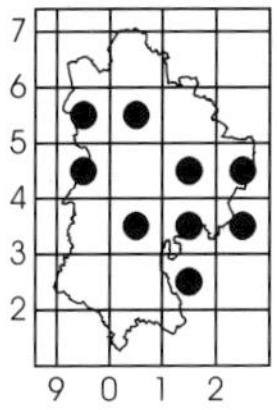

Epiblema foenella **(Linnaeus) (1183)**
Post VCH: Widespread and common.
Flight: July, August (weeks 28-32)*.
Larval Foodplant: Mugwort.

For key to moth maps see page 3.

Epiblema scutulana **([Denis & Schiffermüller]) (=** ***pflugiana*** **(Haworth)) (1184)**
VCH: (as *Halonota cirsiana* Zell.) "Luton".
Post VCH: Widespread and common.
Flight: May to July (weeks 20-29)*.
Larval Foodplants: Thistles.

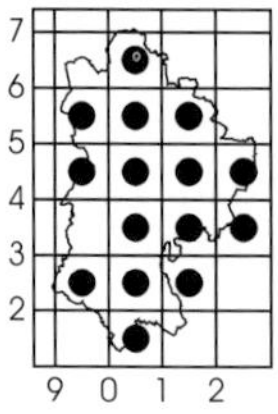

Epiblema cirsiana **(Zeller)) ((1184a)**
See 1184 above. These two species are considered by some authorities to be conspecific. The Bedfordshire records have not been kept separate.

Epiblema sticticana **(Fabricius) (=*****farfarae*** **Fletcher) (1186)**
VCH:(as *Halonota brunnichiana* Schiff.) "Luton, among colt's-foot".
Post VCH: Local and uncommon: Sewell Cutting, Cople Pits and Pegsdon Hills.
Flight: May to July (weeks 24-29)*.
Larval Foodplant: Colt's-foot.

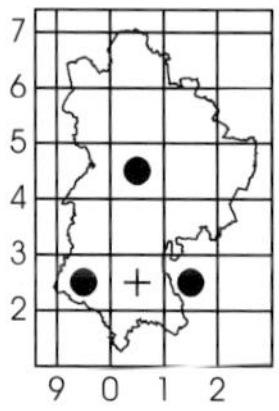

Epiblema costipunctana **(Haworth) (=** ***trigeminana*** **(Stephens)) (1187)**
Post VCH: Widespread and fairly common.
Flight: May to August (weeks 21-25, 28-32)*.
Larval Foodplant: Common ragwort.

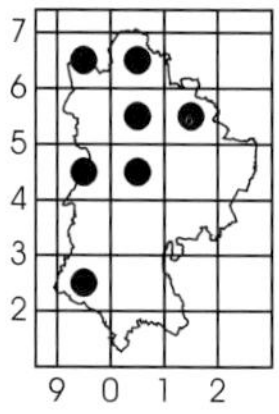

Eucosma conterminana **(Herrich-Schäffer) (1192)**
Post VCH: Local and uncommon: Biggleswade, Stotfold and in the RIS trap at Cockayne Hatley.
Flight: July*, August (week 32)*.
Larval Foodplant: Lettuce, including cultivated varieties.

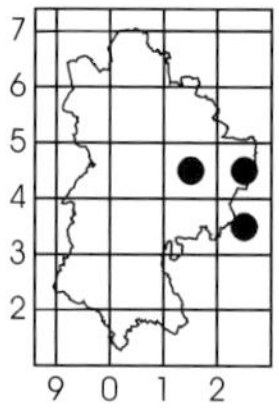

Eucosma aemulana **(Schläger) (=** ***latiorana*** **(Herrich-Schäffer)) (1194)**
Post VCH: Scarce: Cranfield, 30 June and 13 July 1982.
Flight: June to August (weeks 26, 28)*.
Larval Foodplant: Goldenrod.

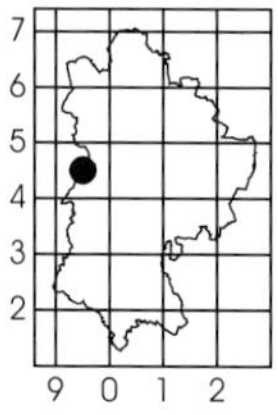

Eucosma campoliliana **([Denis & Schiffermüller]) (1197)**
VCH: (as *Grapholitha nigromaculana* Haw.) "Luton".
Post VCH: Widespread and fairly common.
Flight: June to August (weeks 23-31)*.
Larval Foodplant: Common ragwort.

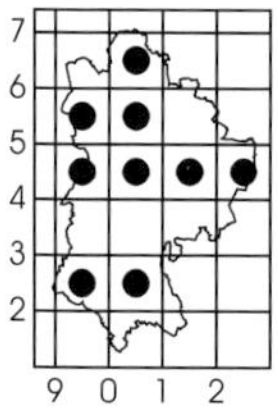

For details of standard weeks see page 6.

Plate 1

1. **Galley Hill** near Luton (page 31), a site typical of the chalk downland in the south of Bedfordshire. Much work has been done to clear encroaching scrub and re-introduce grazing to maintain the rich flora. Butterflies, such as Chalkhill Blue, are most abundant in small areas where the top-soil is thin, particularly on abandoned golf-course features.

Some butterflies found on chalk downland in Bedfordshire:

Plate 2

Plate 3

Plate 4

2. The **Chalkhill Blue** (page 234) depends on horseshoe vetch, its only larval foodplant. The pale blue males and brown females nectar on dwarf and carline thistles. (x 0.6)

3. EXTINCT! The **Adonis Blue** (page 235) is an example of the 14 species of butterfly that have been lost from the County. It requires short warm turf to survive. In the 1950s, sheep grazing ceased, the rabbits were killed by myxomatosis, and the grass on the Downs grew longer. The Adonis Blue died out. (x 1)

4. The **Small Blue** (page 231) forms scattered colonies where its larval foodplant, kidney vetch, grows. (x 1.3)

Plates are not all to the same scale. See captions for magnifications.

Some butterflies and moths found on chalk downland in Bedfordshire:

Plate 5

Plate 6

Plate 7

5. The **Green Hairstreak** (page 226) is difficult to spot as it perches on hawthorn or crab apple bushes. It never rests with open wings to show the brown upperside. (x1.1)
6. The **Duke of Burgundy** (page 238) lays its eggs on cowslip leaves growing in longer grass and favours clearings among bushes. (x 1.1)
7. The **Dark Green Fritillary** (page 249) is not often seen but hopefully numbers may recover as management encourages an increase in the violets on which the larvae feed. (x 0.9)

Plate 8

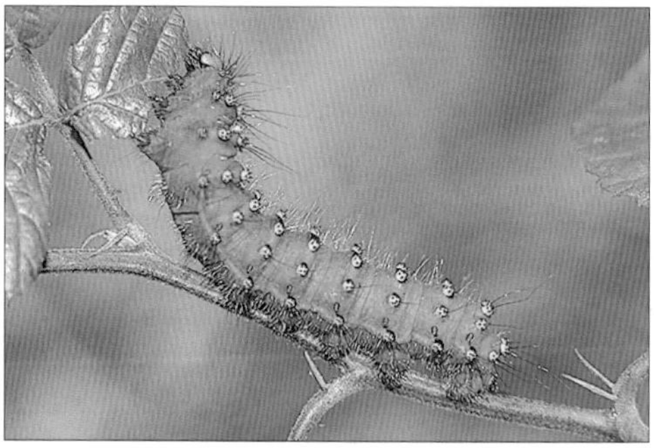

Plate 9

8. **Emperor Moth** (page 262) – the male (x 1) flies rapidly in the spring sunshine searching for the larger grey females. The larva (**9**) feeds on brambles, hawthorn and other plants. (x 0.75)

Plate 10

Plate 11

Plate 12

10. **Cistus Forester** (page 98) – a day-flying moth, sadly less often seen than formerly. (x 2)
11. **Narrow-bordered Five-spot Burnet** (page 99) – flies in the sunshine and nectars on flowers such as common knapweed. Its papery cocoons are usually attached to grass stems. (x 0.7)
12. **Burnet Companion** (page 367) – easily mistaken for Duke of Burgundy at a casual glance. (x1.4)

Plates are not all to the same scale. See captions for magnifications.

Some moths found on chalk downland in Bedfordshire:

Plate 13

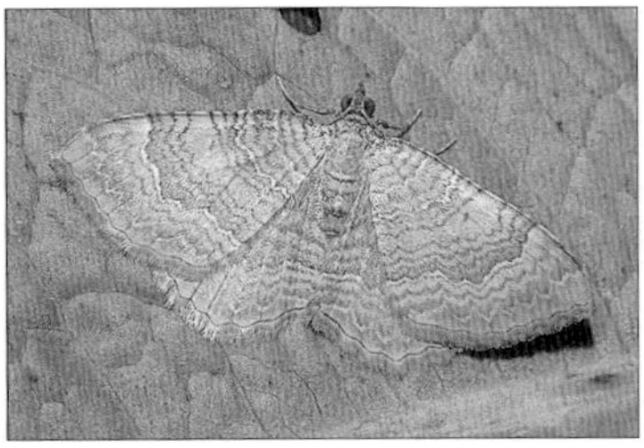

Plate 14

Plate 15

13. **Mother Shipton** (page 367) can look like a Grizzled Skipper as it flies in the sunshine. (x 1)
14. **Yellow Shell** (page 277) – a night-flying species often disturbed in the day-time. (x1.5)
15. ***Pyrausta aurata.*** (page 199) This colourful moth flies by day around marjoram. (x 2.3)

Plate 16

Plate 17

Plate 18

16. ***Metzneria metzneriella*** (page 149) emerges in spring from last years' heads of knapweed. (x 2.3)
17. ***Catoptria pinella*** (page 195) – one of the species of grass moth that fly up at every step through the grass in high summer. (x 2.5)
18. ***Dipleurina lacustrata*** (page 197) comes to light on the Downs and in many other habitats. The larvae feed on mosses. (x 2.3)

Plate 19

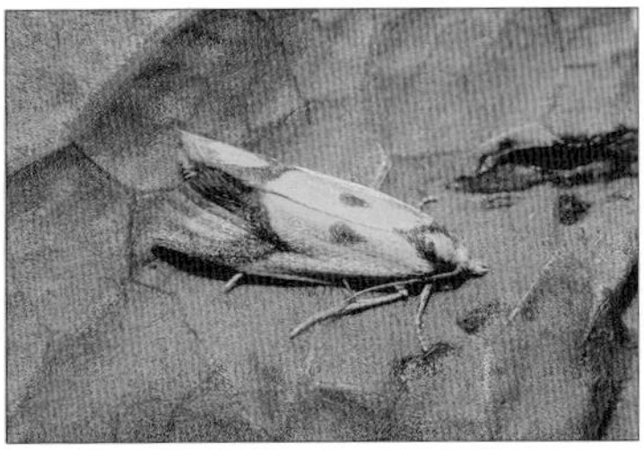

Plate 20

Plate 21

19. ***Elachista rufocinerea*** (page 140) – a tiny moth whose larvae feed in grasses. (x 5.2)
20. The larvae of ***Agapeta zoegana*** (page 162) feed in roots of knapweed and scabious. (x 2.8)
21. ***Monopis weaverella*** (page 102) can be found on the Downs and in other habitats. The larvae feed in animal carcases and dung. (x 2.9)

Plates are not all to the same scale. See captions for magnifications.

Plate 22

22. **Marston Thrift** (page 46), a mixed woodland in the Marston Vale, habitat for White Admiral and three species of hairstreak. Rides are being cleared and clearings created to improve the habitat for wildlife.

Some butterflies found in deciduous woods in Bedfordshire:

Plate 23

Plate 24

23. The **White Admiral** (page 239) needs sunny rides with bramble flowers and other nectar sources, and shaded honeysuckle on which to lay its eggs. (x 1)

24. In flight the **Comma** (page 246) can look like a fritillary but when settled its jagged outline is unmistakable. Mainly a woodland butterfly but often seen on ripe fruit and garden flowers in the autumn. (x 0.5)

Plates are not all to the same scale. See captions for magnifications.

Some butterflies and moths found in deciduous woods in Bedfordshire:

Plate 25

Plate 26

Plate 27

25. **Purple Hairstreak** (page 227) flies high around the oaks on which it lays its eggs. (x 1)
26. The elusive **Black Hairstreak** (page 229) flits around blackthorn, its larval foodplant. (x 1)
27. **White-letter Hairstreak** (page 228) flies around elms but also comes to flowers. (x 1.1)

Morning, late afternoon and early evening are often the best times to watch hairstreaks.

Plate 28

Plate 29

Plate 30

28. **Wood White** (page 219) – this delicate butterfly is currently one of the most scarce and vulnerable in Bedfordshire. (x 1)
29. **Green-veined White** (page 224) is widespread in woodland and other habitats. (x1)
30. **Speckled Wood** (page 253) – the butterfly of shady woodland where the males compete for spots of sunlight. (x 0.8)

Plate 31

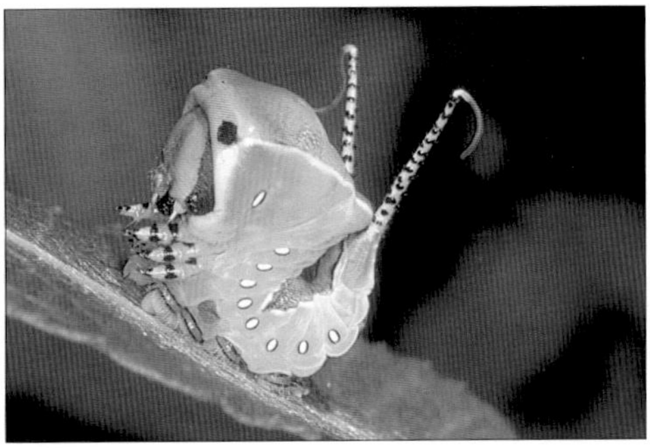

Plate 32

31. The **Puss Moth** (page 314) (x 0.9) sometimes comes to light. Its formidable larva (**32**), seen here in defensive posture (x 1), can be found on sallows and poplars.

Plates are not all to the same scale. See captions for magnifications.

Some moths found in deciduous woods in Bedfordshire:

Plate 33

Plate 34

Plate 35

33. **Merveille du Jour** (page 343) – beautifully camouflaged when at rest on lichen-covered bark. Its larvae rest by day in crevices in the trunks of oak trees. (x 1.3)
34. **Peach Blossom** (page 264) – a colourful woodland moth. The larvae feed on brambles. (x 1.4)
35. **Oak Hook-tip** (page 263) – the moths come commonly to light among oak trees on which the larvae feed. (x 1.1)

Plate 36

Plate 37

Plate 38

36. **Blotched Emerald** (page 267) – a local species in oak woodland in Bedfordshire. (x 1)
37. **Maiden's Blush** (page 269) – an uncommon species found mainly in woods along the Greensand Ridge. (x 1.3)
38. **Green Silver Lines** (page 363) – this beautiful but elusive moth occurs in many woods. (x 1.4)

Plate 39

Plate 40

Plate 41

39. The **Grey Dagger** (page 349) moth is indistinguishable from the Dark Dagger but the larvae are quite different. (x 1.2)
40. The **Black Arches** (page 319) sometimes comes to light in large numbers in oak woods. (x 1)
41. **Small Magpie** (page 201) – not confined to woods but seen around nettles. (x 1)

Plates are not all to the same scale. See captions for magnifications.

Some moths found in deciduous woods in Bedfordshire:

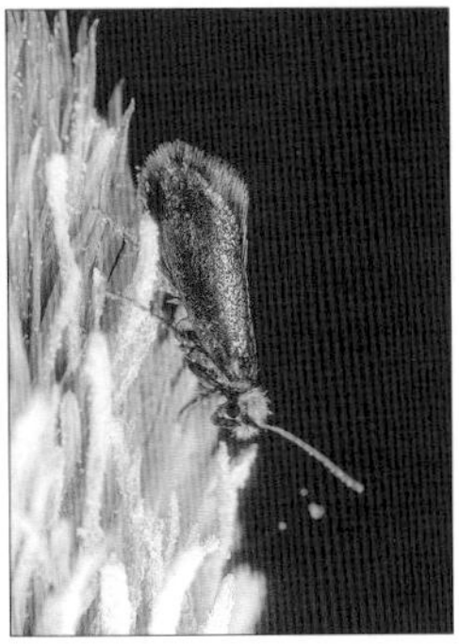

Plate 42

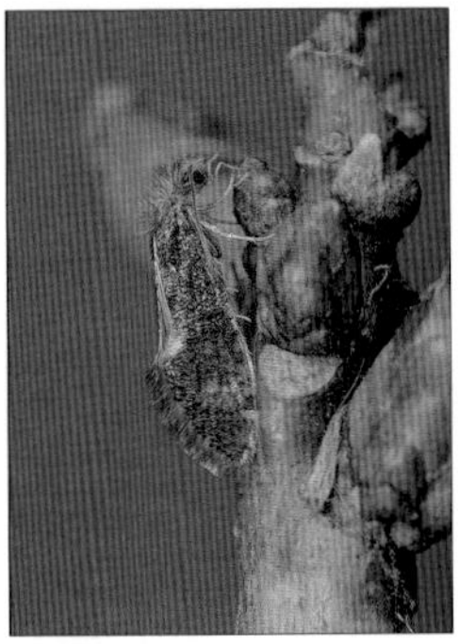

Plate 43

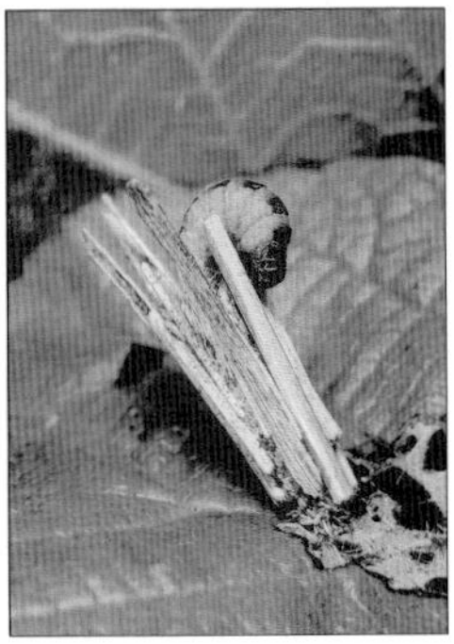

Plate 44

42. ***Micropteryx calthella*** (page 79) – often seen feeding on pollen on pendulous sedge. (x 4)
43. ***Eriocrania subpurpurella*** (page 80) – gold and purple moths which fly round oaks in spring. The larvae make blotch mines in the leaves. (x 2.8)
44. ***Psyche casta*** (page 100) – the wingless female never leaves its larval case. (x 2.3)

Plate 45

Plate 46

Plate 47

45. Larvae of **Green Oak Tortrix** (page 170) can strip the oak trees bare. (x 1.5)
46. ***Anthophila fabriciana*** (page 119) – a very common little moth seen running jerkily over leaves and flying in woodland rides and hedgerows. (x 3.5)
47. ***Caloptilia robustella*** (page 107) – the moths in the family Gracillariidae rest in this very characteristic position. (x 5)

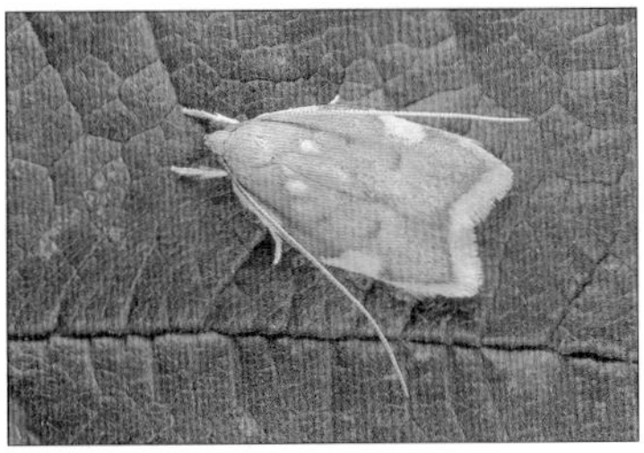

Plate 48

Plate 49

Plate 50

48. ***Carcina quercana*** (page 143) – larvae of this colourful moth feed on a range of trees. (x 2.3)
49. ***Blastodacna hellerella*** (page 160) – a common moth; the larvae feed on hawthorns. (x 4)
50. Leaf-mine of ***Stigmella tityrella*** (page 88) on beech. The area round the mine has remained green after the leaf fell. Leaf-mines are easy to find among fallen leaves in the autumn. (x 0.7)

Plates are not all to the same scale. See captions for magnifications.

Plate 51

51. **New Wavendon Heath** (page 42), conifer and birch woodland on the Greensand Ridge. Although Bedfordshire has no butterflies characteristic of heathland, the conifer and birch woodlands and remnants of heath along the Greensand Ridge support an important moth fauna.

Some moths found in coniferous and birch woods and on heathland in Bedfordshire:

Plate 52

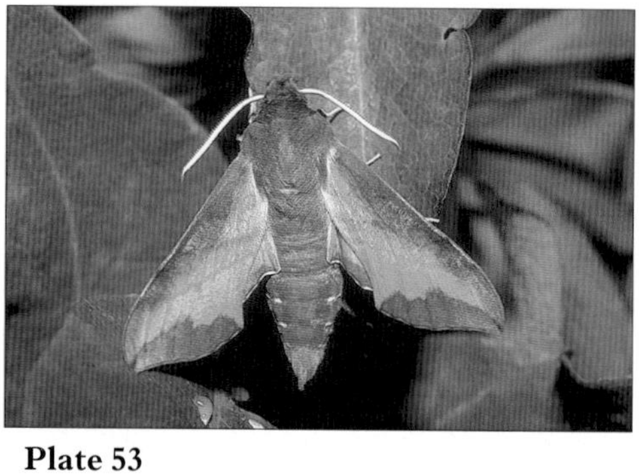

Plate 53

52. **Pine Hawk-moth** (page 311) – neither the larva (**52**) (x 0.6) nor the grey moth (drawing on page 42) are often seen, though the latter will come to light.
53. **Small Elephant Hawk-moth** (page 313) – the larvae of this colourful moth feed on bedstraws which grow in grassy areas on the Greensand Ridge as well as on the chalk downs. (x 1.1)

Plates are not all to the same scale. See captions for magnifications.

Some moths found in coniferous and birch woods and on heathland in Bedfordshire:

Plate 54

Plate 55

Plate 56

54. The **Rosy Footman** (page 320) sometimes arrives at light in numbers at heathy sites. (x 1.4)
55. The **Streak** (page 294) comes to light in areas where broom, its larval foodplant, grows. (x 1.2)
56. **Pine Beauty** (page 337). (x 1.4)

Plate 57

Plate 58

Plate 59

57. **Tawny Barred Angle** (page 298). (x 1.4)
58. ***Dioryctria abietella*** (page 205). (x 1.4)
59. ***Batrachedra pinicolella*** (page 158). (x 5)

The larvae of the four previous species feed on Scots pine.

Plate 60

Plate 61

Plate 62

60. ***Argyresthia pruniella*** (page 123) – the moths in the genus ***Argyresthia*** rest in this characteristic head-down position. (x 5)
61. The larvae of ***Batia lunaris*** (page 142) are found under dead bark. (x 6)
62. ***Cydia succedana*** (page 189) – this little moth often swarms around gorse bushes on sites such as Cooper's Hill. (x 2.8)

Plates are not all to the same scale. See captions for magnifications.

Plate 63

63. **Ashwell Green Lane** (page 54).

Corridor sites - green lanes, road verges, railway embankments and hedgerows are important both as habitats in themselves and as corridors linking other fragmented habitats. Green lanes, such as the one above, are often very rich in Lepidoptera.

Some butterflies of lanes, road verges and hedgerows in Bedfordshire:

Plate 64

Plate 65

64. **Brimstone** (page 222) (male x 1) – often the first butterfly to appear in spring. The paler females range widely looking for buckthorn bushes on which to lay their eggs.

65. **Orange Tip** (page 225) – another spring butterfly. The males are often seen flying along road verges. (x 1.1)

Plates are not all to the same scale. See captions for magnifications.

Some butterflies and moths of lanes, road verges and hedgerows in Bedfordshire:

Plate 66

Plate 67

Plate 68

66. **Small Skipper** (page 213) (left) and **Essex Skipper** (page 214) (right) – note the difference in the antennae. (x 1.4)
Large Skipper (page 215) male (**67**), female (**68**) – likes more sheltered areas of grass than the two previous species. (x 1)

Plate 69

Plate 70

Plate 71

69. **Brown Argus** (female) (page 233) – a species which has spread widely in recent years. (x 0.8)
70. **Wall Brown** (page 254) – a species of verges and hedgerows. Sometimes mistaken for a fritillary but its flitting flight is characteristic. (x 0.8)
71. **Gatekeeper** or **Hedge Brown** (page 256) – as its name implies, very much a hedgerow species. Large numbers can be seen on bramble flowers. (x 1)

Plate 72

Plate 73

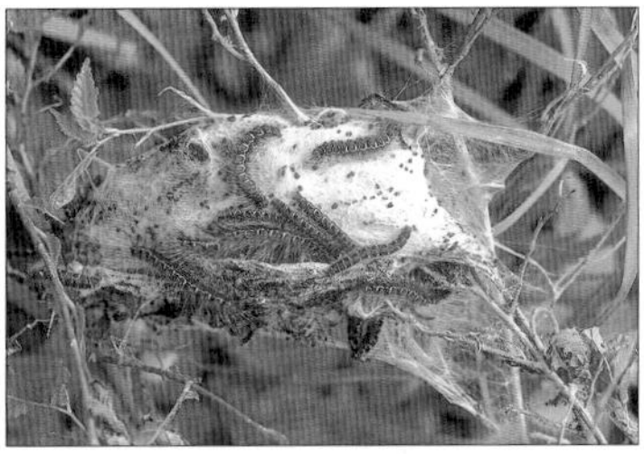

Plate 74

Ghost Moth (page 81) – the dancing flight of the male (**72**) (x 1.3) at dusk may help to attract the larger female (**73**) (x 1).
74. The larvae of the scarce **Small Eggar** (page 259) live communally in webs in hedgerow bushes.

Plates are not all to the same scale. See captions for magnifications.

Some moths of lanes, road verges and hedgerows in Bedfordshire:

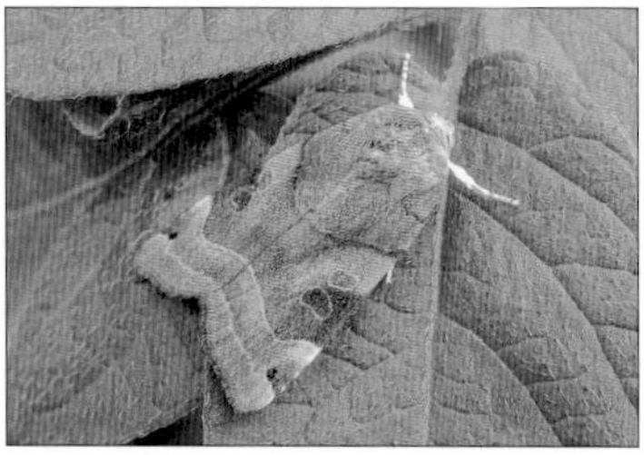

Plate 75

Plate 76

Plate 77

75. **Broad-bordered Yellow Underwing** (page 328) – the most attractively marked, though not the commonest, of the Yellow Underwing moths. (x 1)

76. **Herald** (page 368) – its larvae can be found on hedgerow sallows. The moth over-winters in sheds, caves and ice houses. (x 1.2)

77. ***Adela reaumurella*** (page 95) – the males with long antennae swarm in the sunshine around bushes in the spring and early summer. (x 1)

Plate 78

Plate 79

Plate 80

The larvae of the **Small Ermine** moths live communally in webs and can strip a hedge of leaves (**78** is the adult of *Yponomeuta cagnagella* (page 124) (x 2.6) and **79** is a larval web of *Y. padella* (page 123)).

80. ***Endotrichia flammealis*** (page 204) – a colourful and variable moth. Its larvae feed on a variety of herbaceous plants. (x 2.8)

Plate 81

Plate 82

Plate 83

The larvae of each species of *Coleophora* make characteristic cases, usually of leaf-fragments, in which they live. Plate **81** shows the case of ***Coleophora paripennella*** (x 2.5) (page 136) and the adult moth is at **82** (x 4).

83. These are characteristic leaf-mines of ***Coleophora gryphipennella*** (page 130) on rose (x 1). The mine extends only as far as the larva can reach through the hole without leaving its case.

Plates are not all to the same scale. See captions for magnifications.

Plate 84

84. Gardens: Small Tortoiseshell butterflies (page 243) on *Sedum*.
Garden flowers provide valuable nectar sources for butterflies and moths. The wide variety of plants grown in gardens also provide larval foodplants for many species. Some larvae cause enough damage to be pests.

Some garden butterflies.

Plate 85

Plate 86

85. **Peacock** (left) (page 245) is a common resident species which over-winters as an adult butterfly. **Red Admiral** (right) (page 242) is an immigrant species that may occasionally over-winter here. It is a common sight on late summer flowers and over-ripe fruit. (x 0.3)

86. **Holly Blue** female (page 237) – the only blue butterfly that regularly visits gardens (x 1). Numbers fluctuate widely with years of plenty and years when none are seen.

Plates are not all to the same scale. See captions for magnifications.

Some garden butterflies and moths:

Plate 87

Plate 88

87. **Large White** (page 223) – female (x 0.9). The male has no black dots on the forewings.
88. Brussels sprouts damaged by **Large** and **Small White** (page 223) caterpillars.

Plate 89

Plate 90

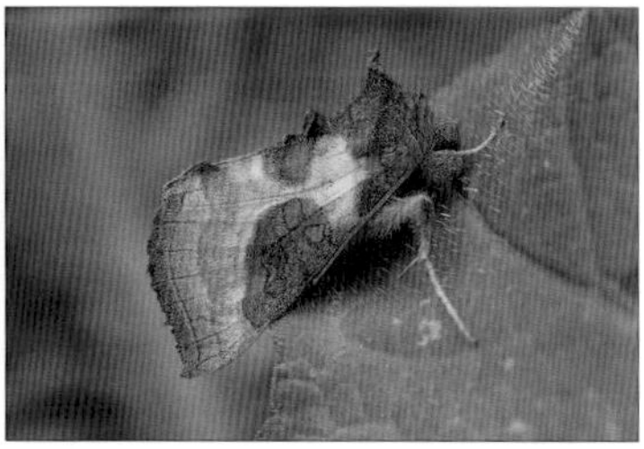

Plate 91

89. **Currant Clearwing** (page 117) – its larvae tunnel in the stems of currant and gooseberry bushes. Fortunately for the gardener it is not common. (x 1.5)
90. **Magpie** (page 297) – the larvae of this common moth also feed on currant and gooseberry bushes, but on the leaves. (x 1.3)
91. **Burnished Brass** (page 365) – comes to light in gardens. The larvae feed on nettles and other plants. (x 1.3)

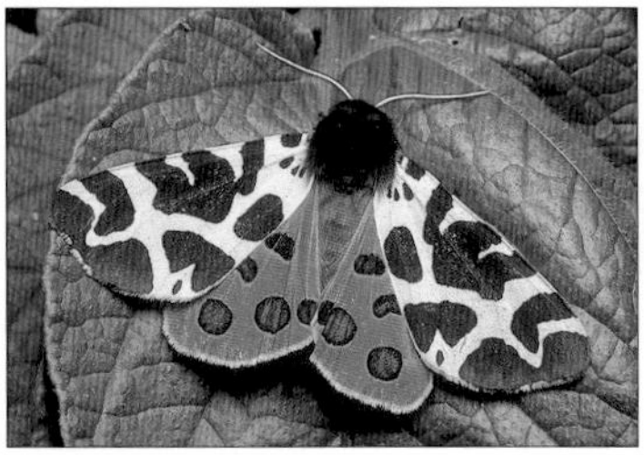

Plate 92

Plate 93

Plate 94

92. **Garden Tiger** (page 322) – its large hairy larvae can be seen in early summer. (x 0.6)
93. **Angleshades** (page 353) – a splendid example of camouflage. Its larvae sometimes damage plants in greenhouses. (x 0.8)
94. **Humming-bird Hawk-moth** (page 312) – an immigrant species which may be seen hovering over flowers, usually in late summer. (x 0.5)

Plates are not all to the same scale. See captions for magnifications.

Some garden and house moths:

Plate 95

Plate 96

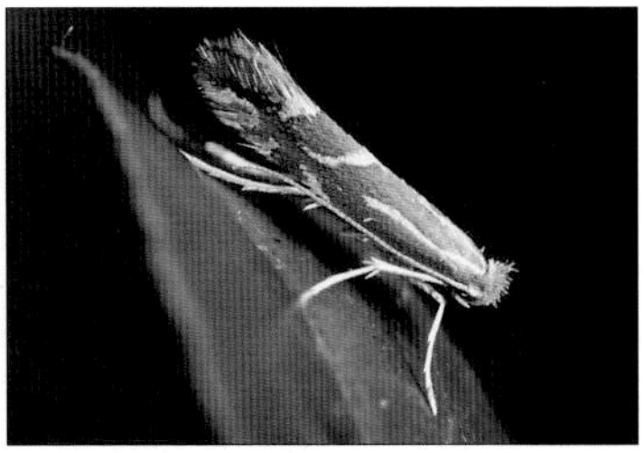
Plate 97

95. **Codling Moth** (page 190) – the larva is the one in 'maggoty' apples. (x 2.4)
96. **Twenty-plume Moth** (page 193) – with its divided wings, this is a remarkable moth. It over-winters as an adult and sometimes comes into houses. (x 3)
97. **Firethorn Leaf-miner** (page 111) – a recent arrival in Bedfordshire; the larvae of this tiny moth mine the leaves of *Pyracantha* bushes. (x 7)

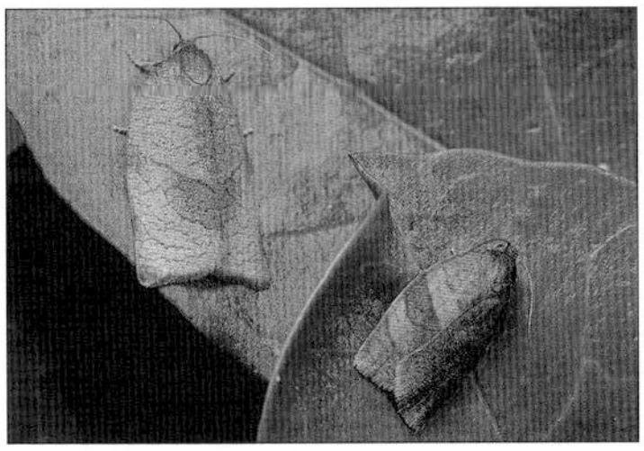
Plate 98

Plate 99

Plate 100

98. **Carnation Tortrix** (page 166) – female on left. The larvae feed on privet and other plants. (x2)
99. **Juniper Webber** (page 157) – the larvae sometimes damage juniper bushes. (x 2)
100. **White Plume Moth** (page 210) – plume moths have divided 'feathery' wings. (x 1.3)

Plate 101

Plate 102

Plate 103

101. **Water Veneer** (page 198) – comes to light in gardens some distance from the nearest pond where the larvae feed submerged on water plants. (x 3.5)
102. **Bee Moth** (page 204) – its larvae live in the nests of bumble-bees and wasps feeding on debris and on the comb and brood. (x 2.3)
103. The larvae of the **White-shouldered House-moth** (page 143) live in birds' nests but are also quite at home eating stored dried food in the kitchen. (x 4.4)

Plates are not all to the same scale. See captions for magnifications.

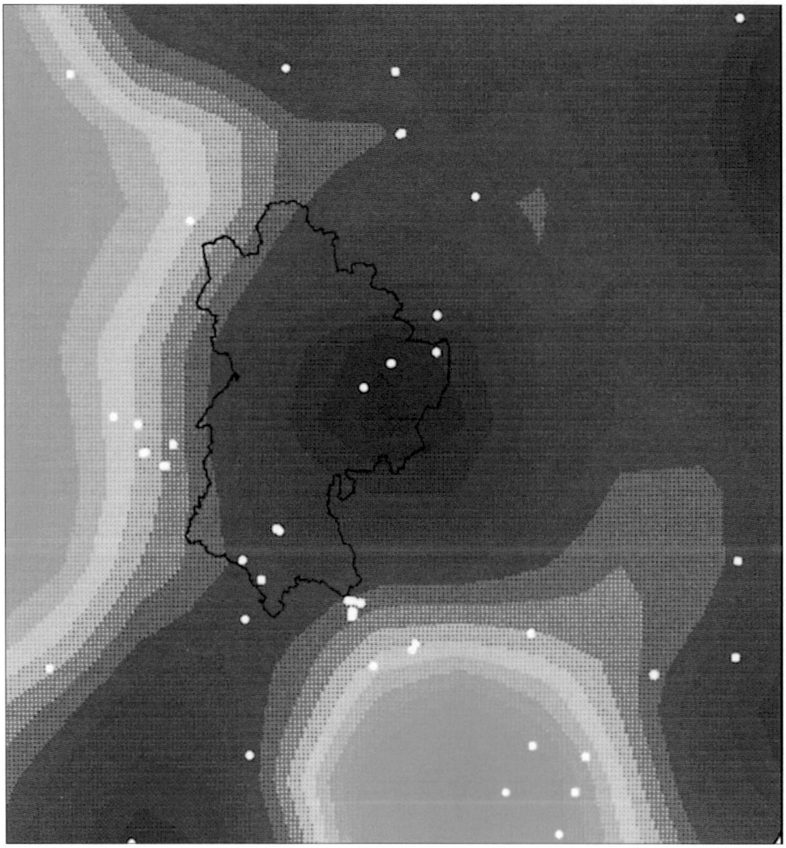

Plate 104

104. **Map of moth diversity** (log-series α – see pages 76-78), interpolated from the data of the Rothamsted Insect Survey's national light-trap network, showing Bedfordshire and surrounding areas.

Dark brown = high diversity.
Yellow and green = low diversity.
White circles = light-traps (further sites are present outside the map boundaries).

Contours in areas without good trap coverage should be interpreted with caution.

Bedfordshire appears to fall into an area of relatively high diversity with the light-traps on the Greensand (Sandy and Old Warden) producing notably high values. The low diversity associated with London urbanisation can be seen to the south-east of the county with another low diversity area to the west.

***Eucosma pauperana* (Duponchel) (1198)**
Post VCH: A single record from the RIS trap at Cockayne Hatley, April 1993.
Flight: April*, May.
Larval Foodplant: Dog-rose.

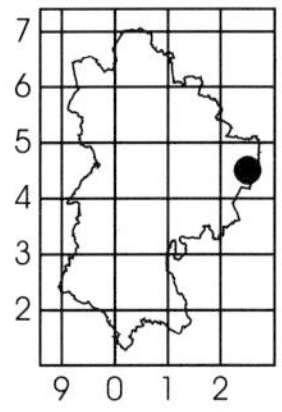

***Eucosma pupillana* (Clerck) (1199)**
Post VCH: A single record from Biggleswade, 1 August 1995, by R.C.Revels.
Flight: July, August (week 31)*.
Larval Foodplant: Wormwood.

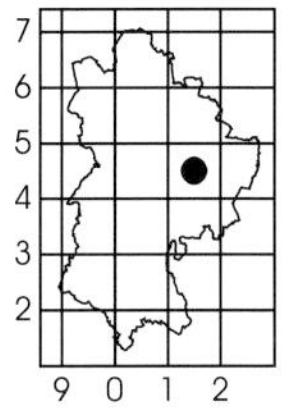

***Eucosma hohenwartiana* ([Denis & Schiffermüller]) (1200)**
VCH: (as *Catoptria scopoliana* Haw.) "Luton,among black knapweed".
Post VCH: Widespread and common. Records include the form *E. fulvana* (Stephens).
Flight: June to August (weeks 25-33)*.
Larval Foodplants: Knapweeds and saw-wort.

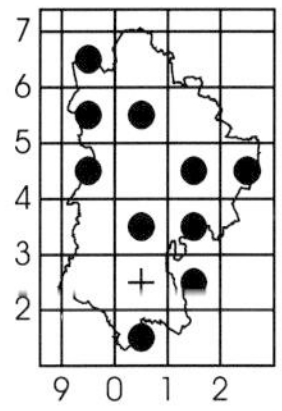

***Eucosma fulvana* (Stephens)) ((1200a)**
See 1200 above. Possibly only a form of the preceding species. Records have not been separated. This form was noted from the RIS trap at Cockayne Hatley on 14 July 1979.

***Eucosma cana* (Haworth) (1201)**
Post VCH: Widespread and common.
Flight: June to August (weeks 24-33)*.
Larval Foodplants: Thistles.

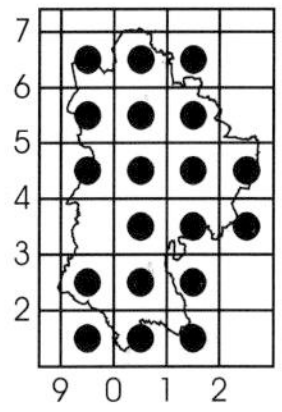

***Eucosma obumbratana* (Lienig & Zeller) (= *expallidana* auctt.) (1202)**
Post VCH: Local and uncommon: Cranfield, Sharnbrook, Maulden Wood, Stotfold and in the RIS trap at Cockayne Hatley.
Flight: July, August (weeks 27-35)*.
Larval Foodplant: Perennial sow-thistle.

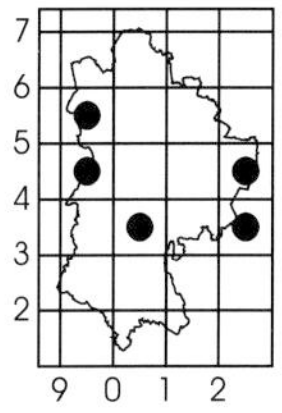

Bud Moth *Spilonota ocellana* ([Denis & Schiffermüller]) (1205)
VCH: "Bedford".
Post VCH: Widespread and common. (Drawing on page 174)
Flight: June to September (weeks 26-36)*.
Larval Foodplants: Trees and shrubs.

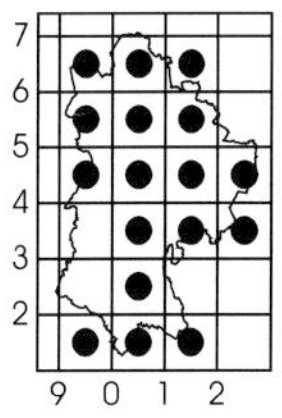

***Spilonota laricana* (Heinemann)) ((1205a)**
See 1205 above. Possibly only a form of the preceding species. Records have not been separated.

For key to moth maps see page 3.

Pine Leaf-mining Moth *Clavigesta purdeyi* (Durrant) (1207)
Post VCH: Local and uncommon: Sharnbrook, Bedford and Rowney Warren.
Flight: July to September (weeks 30, 36)*.
Larval Foodplant: Scots pine.

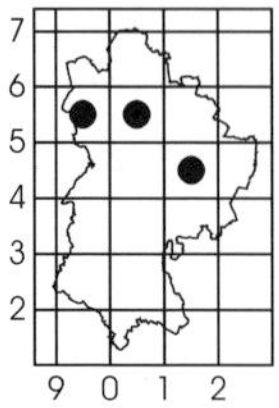

Pine Bud Moth *Blastesthia turionella* (Linnaeus) (1209)
Post VCH: A single record from the RIS trap at Cockayne Hatley in June 1989.
Flight: May, June*.
Larval Foodplant: Scots pine.

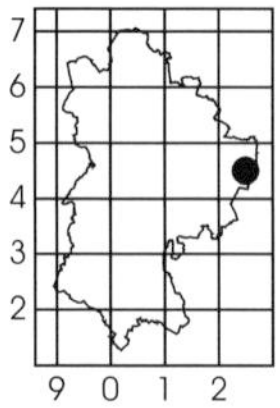

Pine Shoot Moth *Rhyacionia buoliana* ([Denis & Schiffermüller]) (1210)
VCH: "Bedford, among fir".
Post VCH: Locally common: Old Wavendon Heath, Cranfield, Sharnbrook, Bedford and Stotfold.
Flight: June to August (weeks 26-32)*.
Larval Foodplant: Scots pine.

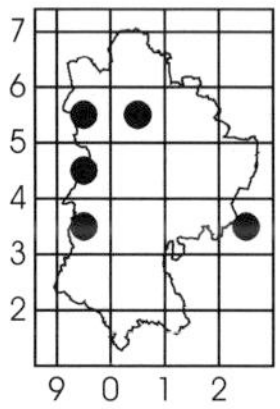

***Rhyacionia pinicolana* (Doubleday) (1211)**
Post VCH: Scarce: West Wood on 15 July 1989 and Biggleswade, 1994.
Flight: July (week 28)*, August.
Larval Foodplant: Scots pine.

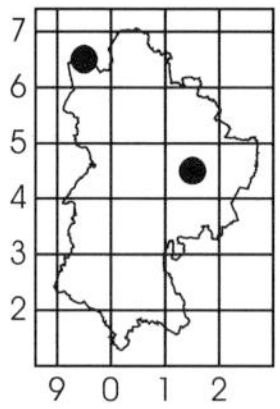

Spotted Shoot Moth *Rhyacionia pinivorana* (Lienig & Zeller) (1212)
VCH: "Bedford, among fir".
Post VCH: Local and uncommon: Sharnbrook, Maulden Wood and Rowney Warren.
Flight: May to July (weeks 25-28)*.
Larval Foodplant: Scots pine.

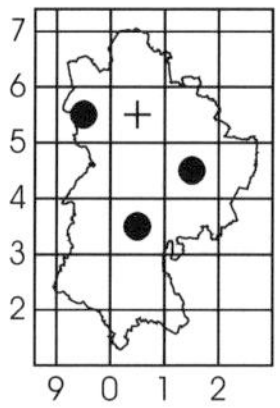

Cherry-bark Tortrix *Enarmonia formosana* (Scopoli) (1216)
Post VCH: Local and uncommon: Sharnbrook, Dedmansey Wood and Bedford.
Flight: June, July (week 27)*.
Larval Foodplants: Apple, wild* and ornamental cherries and other rosaceous trees. The larvae tunnel in the bark, especially in galled or cankered areas.

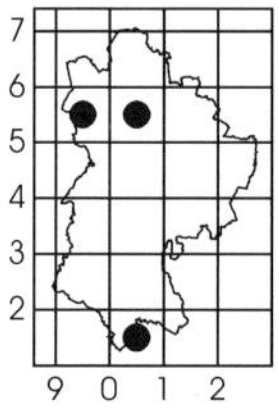

***Lathronympha strigana* (Fabricius) (1219)**
VCH: (as *Catoptria hypericana* Hb.) "Luton, among St. John's wort".
Post VCH: Widespread and common.
Flight: May to September (weeks 21-37)*.
Larval Foodplants: St John's-worts and common bird's-foot-trefoil.

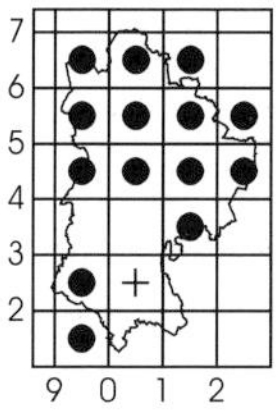

For details of standard weeks see page 6.

Strophedra weirana **(Douglas) (1221)**
Post VCH: Local and uncommon: Charle Wood, Sharnbrook and Stotfold.
Flight: May, June.
Larval Foodplant: Beech*.

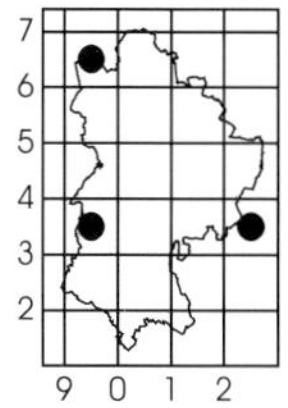

Strophedra nitidana **(Fabricius) (1222)**
Post VCH: Local and uncommon: West Wood.
Flight: May to July (weeks 26, 27)*.
Larval Foodplants: Oaks.

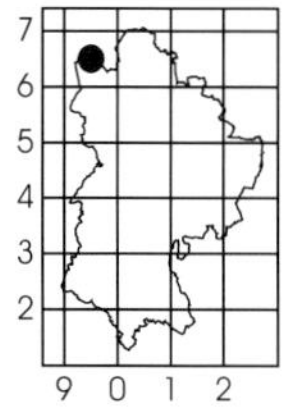

Pammene splendidulana **(Guenée) (1223)**
VCH: "Luton, among oak".
Post VCH: A single record from West Wood on 5 June 1993.
Flight: April to June (week 23)*.
Larval Foodplants: Oaks.

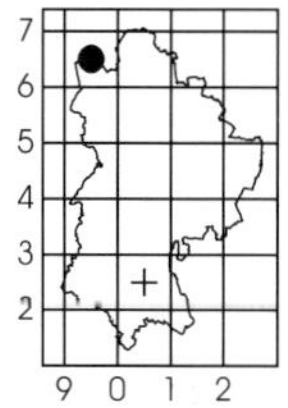

Pammene obscurana **(Stephens) (1225)**
Post VCH: A single record from Coppice Wood on 29 May 1987.
Flight: May (week 22)*, June.
Larval Foodplants: Birches.

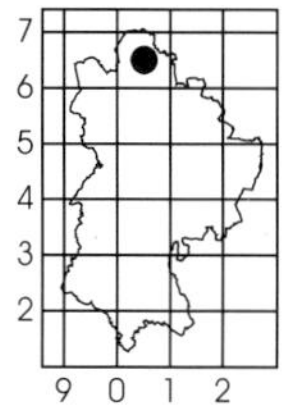

Pammene inquilina **(Fletcher) (1227)**
VCH: (as *Hemimene fimbriana* Steph.) "Bedford, among oak".
Post VCH: No recent record.
Flight: March to May.
Larval Foodplants: Oaks.

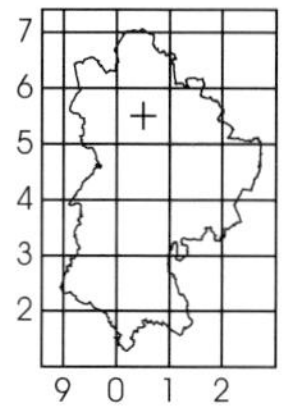

Pammene argyrana **(Hübner) (1228)**
VCH: "Luton, on oak trunks".
Post VCH: Locally common: Sharnbrook, Priestley Plantation and Coppice Wood.
Flight: April, May (week 18)*.
Larval Foodplants: Oaks.

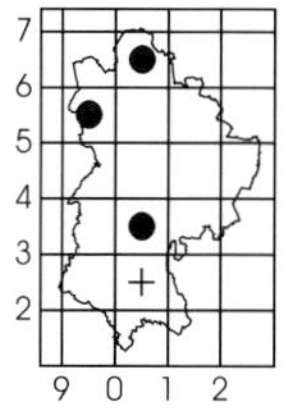

Pammene aurantiana **(Staudinger) (1233)**
Post VCH: A single record from Putnoe Wood on 16 June 1976 (det. J.D.Bradley).
Flight: June (week 24)* to August.
Larval Foodplant: Sycamore.

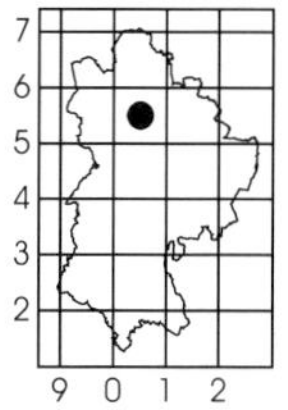

For key to moth maps see page 3.

Pammene regiana **(Zeller) (1234)**
VCH: "Bedford, Luton; on sycamore trunks".
Post VCH: Local and uncommon: Cranfield and Maulden Wood.
Flight: May to August (weeks 28, 31)*.
Larval Foodplants: Sycamore and Norway maple.

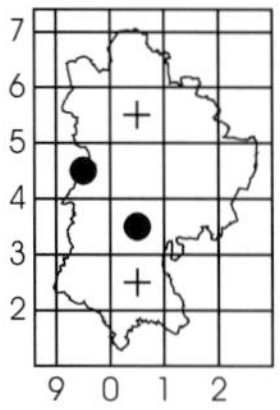

Pammene fasciana **(Linnaeus) (1236)**
Post VCH: Local and uncommon: Sharnbrook, Coppice Wood and in the RIS trap at Cockayne Hatley.
Flight: May to July (weeks 18, 28)*.
Larval Foodplants: Oaks and sweet chestnut.

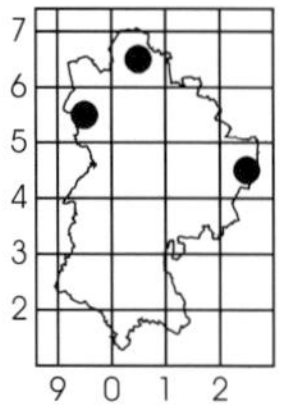

Fruitlet Mining Tortrix *Pammene rhediella* (Clerck) (1239)
VCH: "Luton, among hawthorn".
Post VCH: Local and uncommon: Odell Great Wood, Studham, Putnoe Wood and Stotfold.
Flight: May, June (weeks 20-22)*.
Larval Foodplants: Hawthorns and other shrubs.

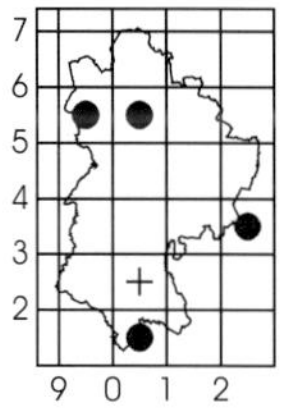

Cydia compositella **(Fabricius) (1241)**
VCH: "Bedford, Luton; among clover".
Post VCH: Widespread and common.
Flight: May to July (weeks 22-29)*, August.
Larval Foodplants: Clovers and common bird's-foot-trefoil.

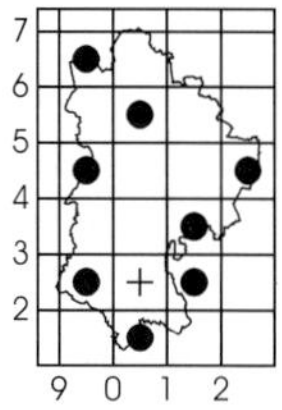

Cydia internana **(Guenée) (1242)**
Post VCH: A single record from Carlton in 1983 by G.Ping.
Flight: April to June.
Larval Foodplant: Gorse.

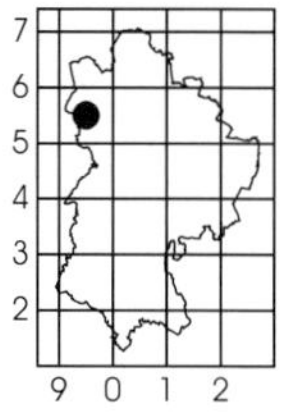

Cydia janthinana **(Duponchel) (1245)**
VCH: "Bedford, about hawthorn".
Post VCH: Widespread and common.
Flight: July (weeks 28, 29)*, August.
Larval Foodplants: Hawthorns.

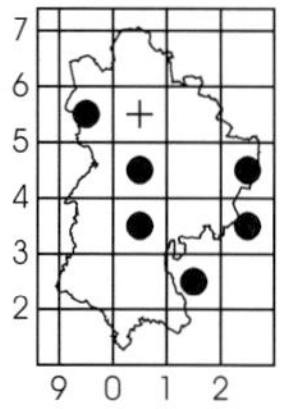

Cydia tenebrosana **(Duponchel) (1246)**
Post VCH: A single record of larvae from Maulden Wood on 14 October 1984 by A.M.Emmet.
Flight: June, July.
Larval Foodplants: Roses*.

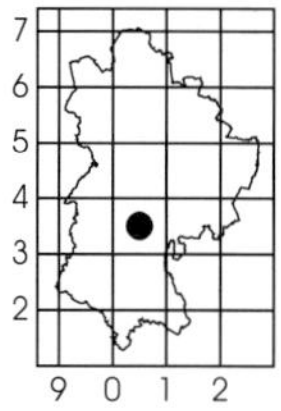

For details of standard weeks see page 6.

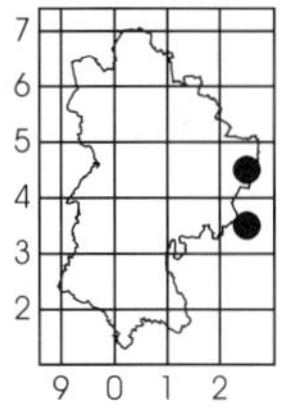

Plum Fruit Moth *Cydia funebrana* (Treitschke) (1247)
Post VCH: Scarce: Stotfold, 1986 (larvae on wild plum) and in the RIS trap at Cockayne Hatley, July 1993.
Flight: June, July*, August.
Larval Foodplants: Blackthorn and plum*.

Oriental Fruit Moth *Cydia molesta* (Busck) (1248)
Post VCH: A single record from Sharnbrook where a moth was found in a house on 26 November 1983.
Flight: March to July, November (week 48)*.
Larval Foodplants: Larvae found in imported peach and apricot fruit.

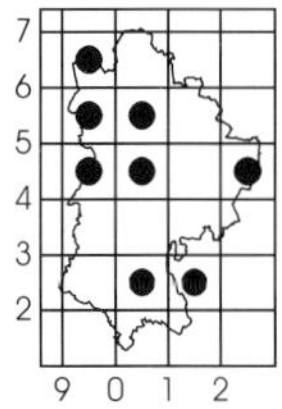

***Cydia jungiella* (Clerck) (1251)**
Post VCH: Widespread and common.
Flight: April to June (weeks 17-23)*.
Larval Foodplants: Bitter-vetch and bush vetch.

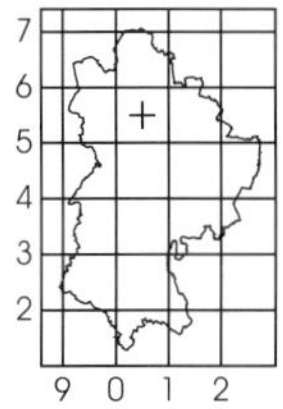

***Cydia strobilella* (Linnaeus) (1254)**
VCH: "Bedford, among spruce fir".
Post VCH: No recent record.
Flight: May.
Larval Foodplants: Spruces.

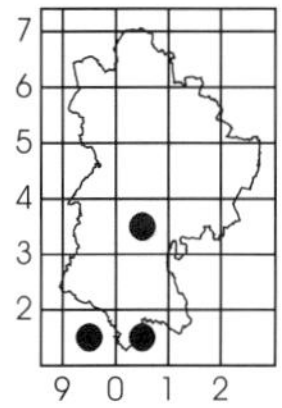

***Cydia succedana* ([Denis & Schiffermüller]) (1255)** (Plate 62)
VCH: (as *Catoptria ulicetana* Haw.) "Everywhere abundant among furze".
Post VCH: Locally common: Whipsnade Wild Animal Park, Studham Common and Cooper's Hill.
Flight: May, June (weeks 18-24)*, July to September.
Larval Foodplants: Gorse, *Genista* spp., broom and bird's-foot-trefoils.

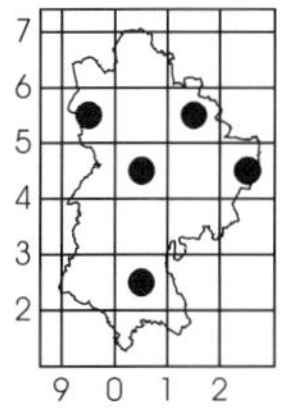

Pea Moth *Cydia nigricana* (Fabricius) (1257)
Post VCH: Locally common: Sharnbrook, Dunstable, Cople Pits, Great Barford and in the RIS trap at Cockayne Hatley.
Flight: May to July (weeks 24-29)*.
Larval Foodplants: Vetches, and a pest on cultivated pea*.

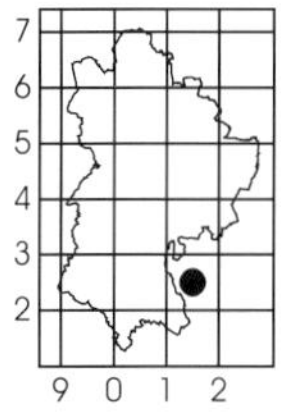

***Cydia fagiglandana* (Zeller) (1259)**
Post VCH: A single record from Pegsdon Hills on 21 July 1986 by T.S.Hollingworth.
Flight: June to August (week 28)*.
Larval Foodplant: Beech.

For key to moth maps see page 3.

Cydia splendana **(Hübner) (1260)**
VCH: "Bedford, among oak".
Post VCH: Widespread and common.
Flight: July to September (weeks 30-37)★.
Larval Foodplants: Oaks and sweet chestnut★.

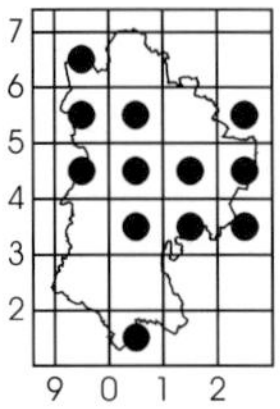

Codling Moth ***Cydia pomonella*** **(Linnaeus) (1261)** (Plate 95)
VCH: (as *Carpocapsa pomonana* Linn.) "Everywhere among apple trees".
Post VCH: Widespread and common.
Flight: May to September (weeks 21-36)★.
Larval Foodplants: Apple★, peach★, pear, plum and other fruits.

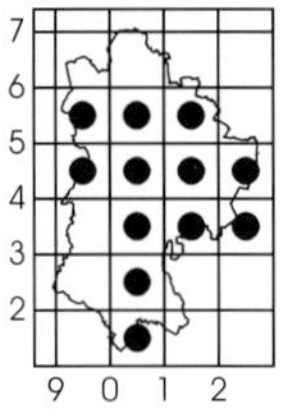

Cydia pactolana **(Zeller) (1266)**
Post VCH: One specimen tapped from Norway spruce in Worley's Wood on 22 June 1986 (illustrated by Wilson, 1989). This species was first recorded in Britain in 1965 from Hampshire, with other records since from Surrey and Berkshire.
Flight: June (week 25)★, July.
Larval Foodplants: Norway spruce and larches.

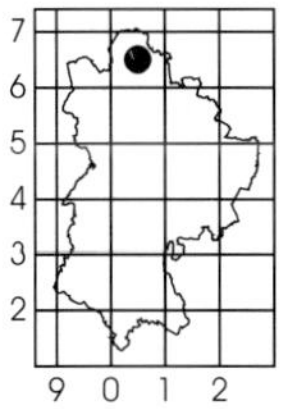

Cydia coniferana **(Ratzeburg) (1268)**
Post VCH: Bred in May 1995 from a larva collected in autumn 1994 at Heath and Reach by C.R.B.Baker.
Flight: May to August.
Larval Foodplant: Scots pine.

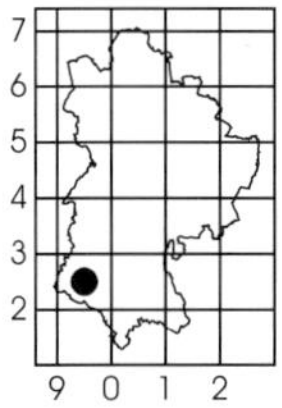

Cydia aurana **(Fabricius) (1272)**
VCH: "Luton".
Post VCH: Widespread and common.
Flight: June, July (weeks 23-28)★.
Larval Foodplant: Hogweed.

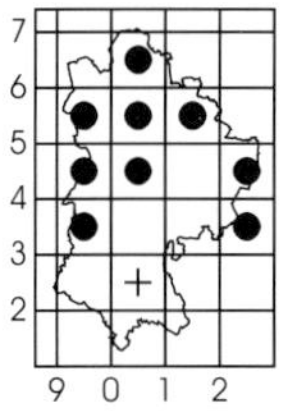

Dichrorampha petiverella **(Linnaeus) (1273)**
VCH: "Generally common".
Post VCH: Widespread and common.
Flight: June to August (weeks 24-31)★.
Larval Foodplants: Yarrow and dandelions.

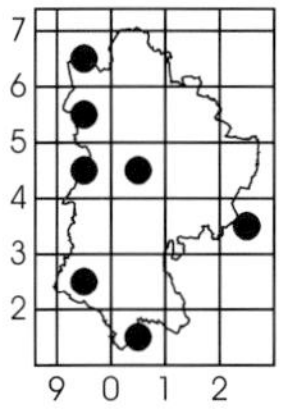

Dichrorampha alpinana **(Treitschke) (1274)**
Post VCH: Locally common: Sewell Cutting, Thurleigh Cutting, Old Warden Tunnel and in the RIS trap at Cockayne Hatley.
Flight: June to August (weeks 23-29)★.
Larval Foodplant: Oxeye daisy.

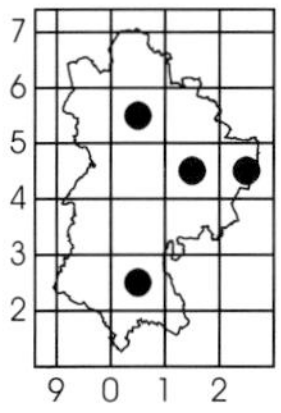

For details of standard weeks see page 6.

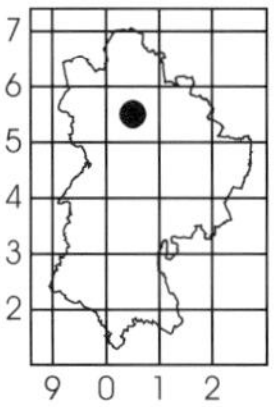

Dichrorampha flavidorsana **(Knaggs) (1275)**
Post VCH: A single record from Bedford on garden tansy, 21 July 1988, by W.J.Champkin.
Flight: July (week 29)*, August.
Larval Foodplant: Tansy.

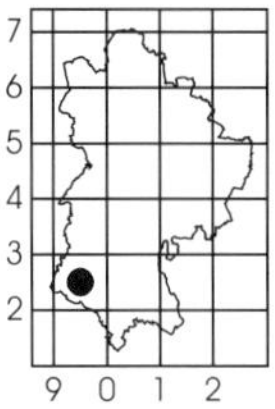

Dichrorampha plumbagana **(Treitschke) (1276)**
Post VCH: Sewell Cutting on 4 June 1985 and 18 June 1987.
Flight: June (weeks 22, 25)*, July.
Larval Foodplant: Yarrow.

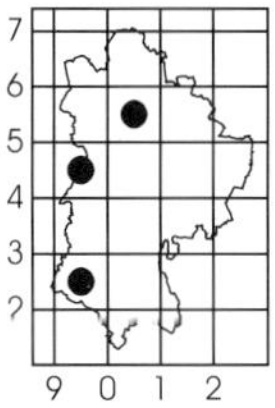

Dichrorampha sequana **(Hübner) (1278)**
Post VCH: Local and uncommon: Sewell Cutting, Marston Thrift and Thurleigh Cutting.
Flight: June (weeks 23-26)*.
Larval Foodplants: Yarrow and tansy.

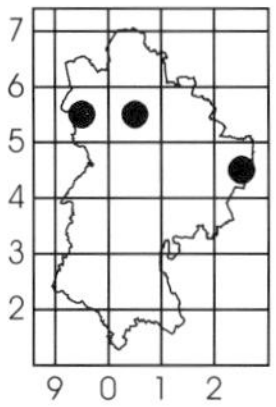

Dichrorampha acuminatana **(Lienig & Zeller) (1279)**
Post VCH: Local and uncommon: Sharnbrook, Thurleigh Cutting and in the RIS trap at Cockayne Hatley.
Flight: May (week 20)*, June, July to September (weeks 29-36)*.
Larval Foodplants: Oxeye daisy and tansy.

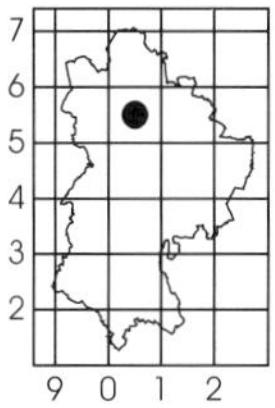

Dichrorampha consortana **Stephens (1280)**
Post VCH: Two records from Thurleigh Cutting, 6 July 1985 and 24 May 1990 (a very early date -specimen dissected).
Flight: May, July (weeks 21, 27)*, August.
Larval Foodplant: Oxeye daisy.

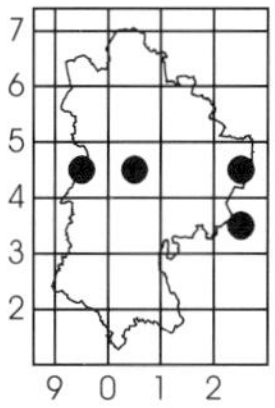

Dichrorampha simpliciana **(Haworth) (1281)**
Post VCH: Local and uncommon: Marston Thrift, Cople Pits, Stotfold and in the RIS trap at Cockayne Hatley.
Flight: June to September (weeks 27-31, 36)*.
Larval Foodplant: Mugwort.

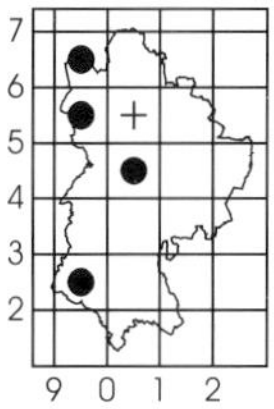

Dichrorampha gueneeana **Obraztsov (1284)**
VCH: (as *D. politana* Schiff.) "Bedford, among yarrow".
Post VCH: Local and uncommon: Sewell Cutting, Sharnbrook, Podington Airfield and Cople Pits.
Flight: June to August (weeks 23, 27-31)*.
Larval Foodplants: Yarrow and tansy.

For key to moth maps see page 3.

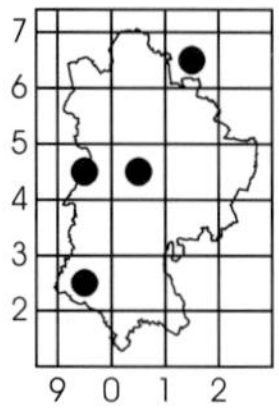

***Dichrorampha plumbana* (Scopoli) (1285)**
Post VCH: Local and uncommon: Sewell Cutting, Marston Thrift, Cople Pits and Little Staughton.
Flight: May, June (weeks 23-25)*.
Larval Foodplants: Oxeye daisy and yarrow.

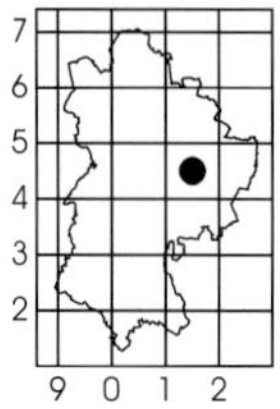

***Dichrorampha sedatana* (Busck) (1286)**
Post VCH: A colony appears to be established in a garden in Biggleswade, reported in 1996 by R.C.Revels.
Flight: May to July.
Larval Foodplant: Tansy.

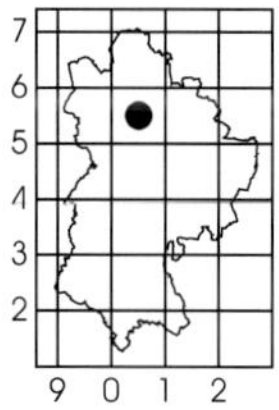

***Dichrorampha aeratana* (Pierce & Metcalfe) (1287)**
Post VCH: A single record from Thurleigh Cutting on 7 June 1992.
Flight: May, June (week 23)*, July.
Larval Foodplant: Oxeye daisy.

For details of standard weeks see page 6.

Pyrales and Plumes

(Alucitidae, Pyralidae and Pterophoridae)

D.V.Manning

Family: **Alucitidae**

There is only one British species, which has each wing divided into six lobes. Wingspan about 14 mm.

Twenty-plume Moth or Many-plumed Moth *Alucita hexadactyla* (Linnaeus) (1288)
VCH: (as *Orneodes polydactyla* Hb.) "Bedford, Luton".
Post VCH: Widespread and common. (Plate 96)
Flight: August to July (weeks 41-43, 13-32)*.
Larval Foodplant: Honeysuckle.

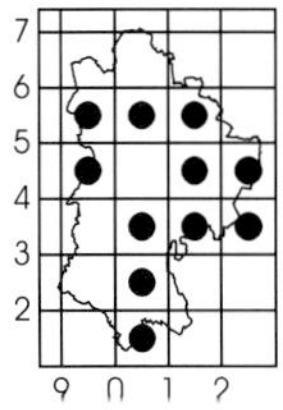

Family: **Pyralidae**

There are about 200 British species, of which 94 have been found in Bedfordshire.

Subfamily: **Crambinae The grass moths.**

These are probably the most commonly seen of the smaller moths as many are readily disturbed from long grass in the daytime. They rest with their wings held close to the body. The forewings are narrow and usually straw-coloured with pale or white longitudinal lines. Wingspan 12-34 mm. The larvae feed on grasses or on mosses.

***Chilo phragmitella* (Hübner) (1290)**
Post VCH: A single record from Henlow, 10 August 1986, by T.S.Hollingworth.
Flight: June to August (week 32)*.
Larval Foodplants: Common reed and reed sweet-grass.

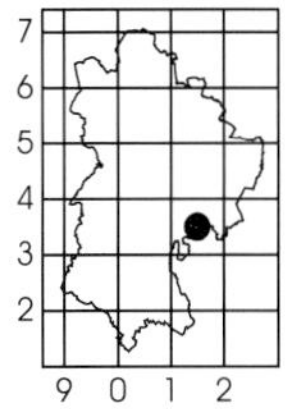

***Calamotropha paludella* (Hübner) (1292)**
Post VCH: Local and uncommon: Cranfield, Flitwick Moor, Priory Country Park, Bedford and The Lodge, Sandy.
Flight: June to August (weeks 24, 29-33)*.
Larval Foodplant: Bulrush.

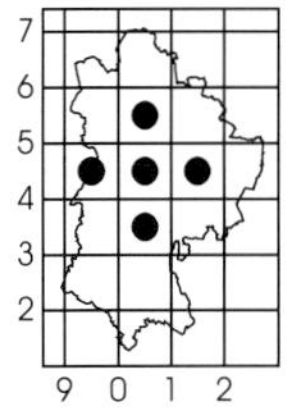

***Chrysoteuchia culmella* (Linnaeus) (= *hortuella* (Hübner)) (1293)**
VCH: (as *Crambus hortuellus* Hb.) "Everywhere among grass".
Post VCH: Widespread and common.
Flight: June to September (weeks 22-37)*.
Larval Foodplants: Grasses.

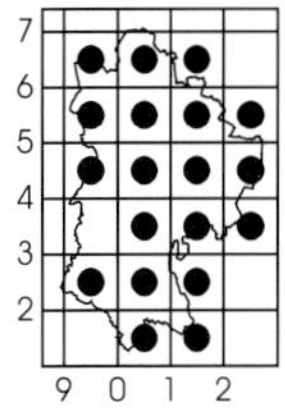

For key to moth maps see page 3.

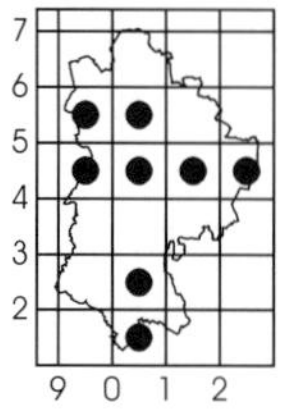

***Crambus pascuella* (Linnaeus) (1294)**
Post VCH: Widespread but uncommon: Cranfield, Sharnbrook, Studham, Luton, Cople Pits, Thurleigh Cutting, Biggleswade and in the RIS trap at Cockayne Hatley.
Flight: June to August (weeks 25-32)*.
Larval Foodplants: Grasses.

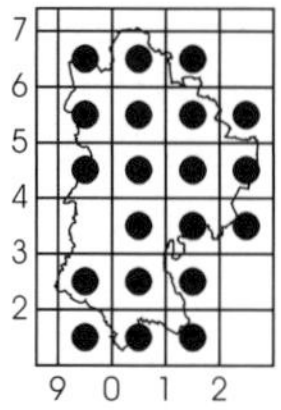

***Crambus lathoniellus* (Zincken) (= *nemorella* auctt.) (1301)**
VCH: (as *Crambus pratellus* Linn.) "Everywhere abundant among grass".
Post VCH: Widespread and common.
Flight: May to August (weeks 21-31)*.
Larval Foodplants: Grasses.

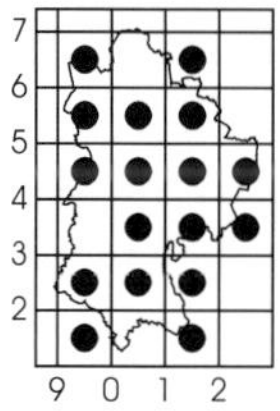

***Crambus perlella* (Scopoli) (1302)**
VCH: "Bedford".
Post VCH: Widespread and common.
Flight: June to August (weeks 24-34)*.
Larval Foodplants: Grasses.

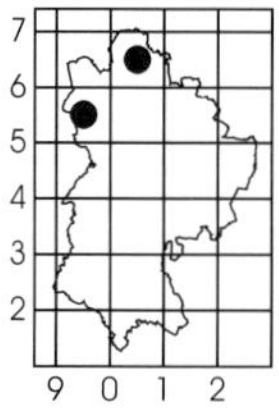

***Agriphila selasella* (Hübner) (1303)**
Post VCH: Local and uncommon: Sharnbrook and Coppice Wood.
Flight: July, August (weeks 30-33)*.
Larval Foodplants: Grasses.

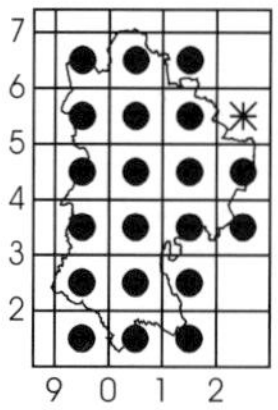

***Agriphila straminella* ([Denis & Schiffermüller]) (= *culmella* auctt.) (1304)**
VCH: (as *Crambus culmellus* Linn.) "Everywhere abundant among grass".
Post VCH: Widespread and common.
Flight: July to September (weeks 28-38)*.
Larval Foodplants: Grasses.

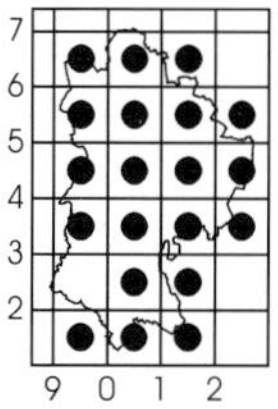

***Agriphila tristella* ([Denis & Schiffermüller]) (1305)**
VCH: "Common everywhere among grass".
Post VCH: Widespread and common.
Flight: July to September (weeks 27-39)*.
Larval Foodplants: Grasses.

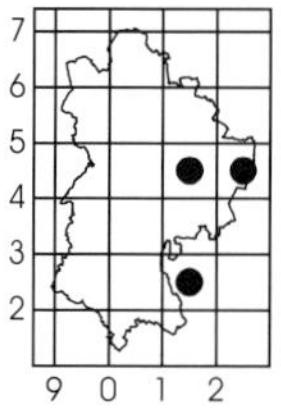

***Agriphila inquinatella* ([Denis & Schiffermüller]) (1306)**
Post VCH: Local and uncommon: Pegsdon Hills, Sandy and in the RIS trap at Cockayne Hatley.
Flight: June, July (weeks 28-30)*, August, September.
Larval Foodplants: Grasses.

For details of standard weeks see page 6.

Agriphila latistria **(Haworth) (1307)**
Post VCH: A single record from Ampthill Park on 18 August 1994.
Flight: July, August (week 33)★, September.
Larval Foodplants: Grasses.

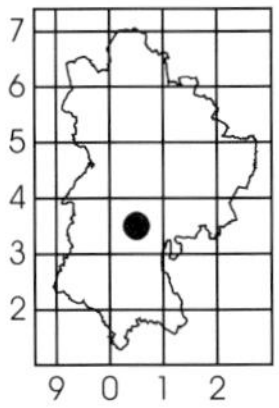

Agriphila geniculea **(Haworth) (1309)**
VCH: "Luton".
Post VCH: Widespread and common.
Flight: July to September (weeks 29-37)★, October.
Larval Foodplants: Grasses.

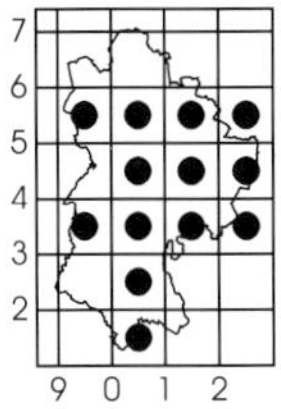

Catoptria pinella **(Linnaeus) (1313)** (Plate 17)
VCH: (as *Crambus pinetellus* Linn.) "Bedford, Luton".
Post VCH: Widespread and fairly common.
Flight: July, August (weeks 27-32)★.
Larval Foodplants: Grasses and sedges.

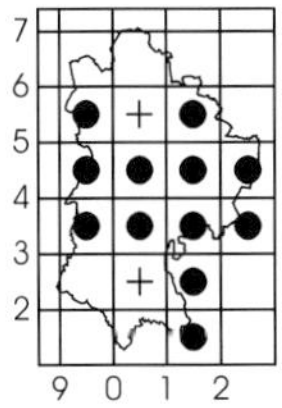

Catoptria falsella **([Denis & Schiffermüller]) (1316)**
Post VCH: Widespread and common.
Flight: June to August (weeks 26-35)★.
Larval Foodplants: Mosses on buildings.

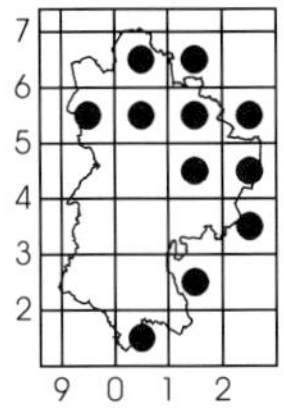

Thisanotia chrysonuchella **(Scopoli) (1321)**
Post VCH: Recorded at Barton by Dr. Gifford Nash (Foster, 1934).
Flight: May, June.
Larval Foodplants: Grasses.

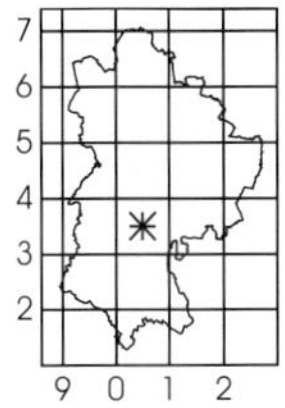

Pediasia contaminella **(Hübner) (1323)**
Post VCH: A single record from the RIS trap at Cockayne Hatley, 16-22 July 1994.
Flight: July (week 29)★, August.
Larval Foodplants: Grasses.

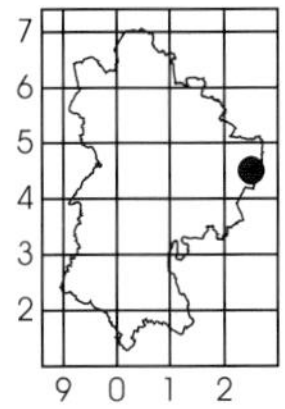

Subfamily: **Schoenobiinae**

The moths are similar in appearance to grass moths but have more sharply-pointed forewings. Wingspan 22-35 mm. The larvae feed on aquatic plants.

For key to moth maps see page 3.

***Donacaula forficella* (Thunberg) (1329)**

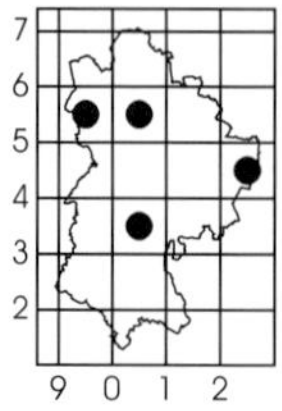

Post VCH: Local and uncommon: Sharnbrook, Flitwick Moor, Bedford and in the RIS trap at Cockayne Hatley.
Flight: June, July, August (weeks 29-31)*, September.
Larval Foodplants: Reed sweet-grass, common reed and sedges.

***Donacaula mucronellus* ([Denis & Schiffermüller]) (1330)**

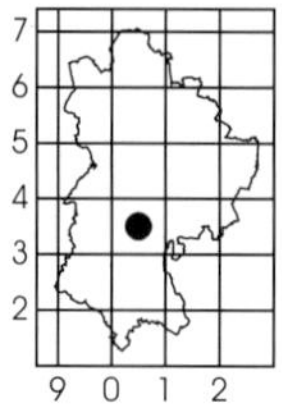

Post VCH: A single record from Flitwick Moor in 1982 by T.S.Hollingworth.
Flight: June (week 24)* to August.
Larval Foodplants: Reed sweet-grass and common reed.

Subfamily: **Scopariinae**

Most of the moths is this subfamily have greyish-patterned wings. Wingspan 16-27 mm. The larvae feed on mosses, lichens or roots of herbaceous plants.

***Scoparia subfusca* Haworth (= *cembrella* auctt.) (1332)**

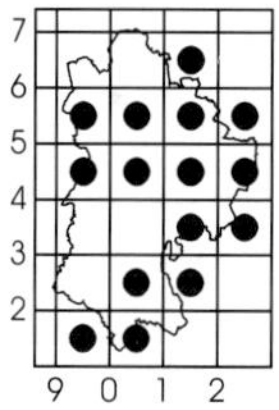

VCH: (as *S. cembrae* Haw.) "Luton".
Post VCH: Widespread and common.
Flight: June to August (weeks 25-35)*.
Larval Foodplants: Hawkweeds, oxtongues and colt's-foot.

***Scoparia pyralella* ([Denis & Schiffermüller]) (= *dubitalis* (Hübner)) (1333)**

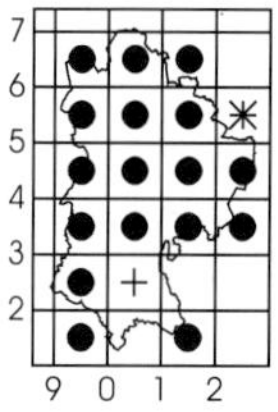

VCH: (as *S. dubitalis* Curt.) "Bedford, Luton".
Post VCH: Widespread and common.
Flight: June to August (weeks 23-33)*.
Larval Food: Decaying vegetable matter.

***Scoparia ambigualis* (Treitschke) (1334)**

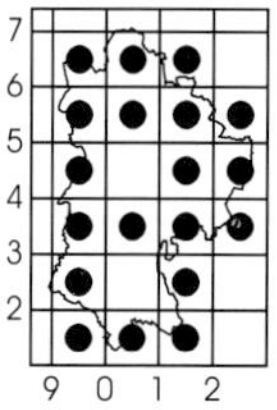

VCH: "Generally common on tree trunks".
Post VCH: Widespread and common.
Flight: May to September (weeks 20-36)*.
Larval Foodplants: Common valerian and probably on mosses.

***Scoparia basistrigalis* (Knaggs) (1334a)**

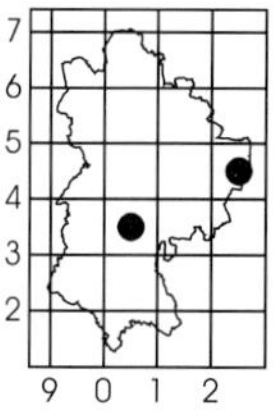

Post VCH: Scarce: Flitwick Moor, 11 July 1992 and in the RIS trap at Cockayne Hatley in the period 23 July to 5 August 1995.
Flight: July, August (weeks 28-31)*.
Larval Foodplants: Unknown.

For details of standard weeks see page 6.

***Scoparia ancipitella* (la Harpe) (= *ulmella* Knaggs) (1335)**
Post VCH: RIS trap at Cockayne Hatley, a single record in July 1994.
Flight: July (week 27)*, August.
Larval Foodplants: Unknown.

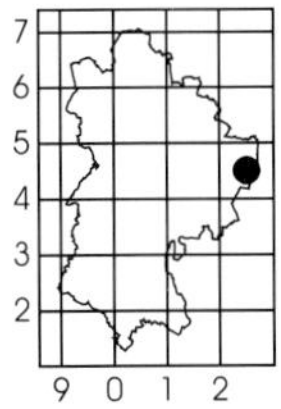

***Dipleurina lacustrata* (Panzer) (= *crataegella* (Hübner)) (1338)**
Post VCH: Widespread and common.
Flight: June to August (weeks 24-31)*.
Larval Foodplants: Mosses.

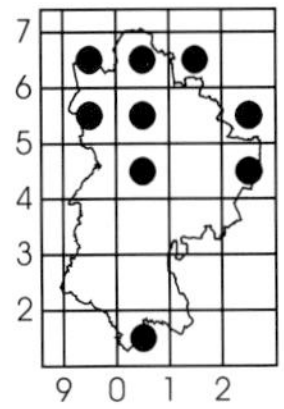

***Eudonia pallida* (Curtis) (1336)**
Post VCH: Scarce: Felmersham Nature Reserve.
Flight: June to August (weeks 28-31)*.
Larval Foodplants: Probably mosses and lichens.

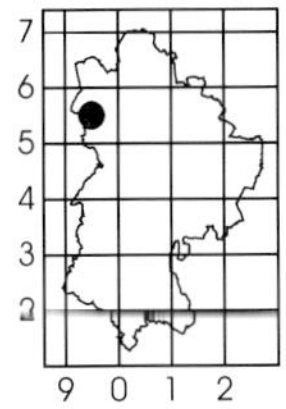

***Eudonia truncicolella* (Stainton) (1340)**
Post VCH: Local and uncommon: Sharnbrook, Old Warden Tunnel, Stotfold and in the RIS trap at Cockayne Hatley.
Flight: July, August (weeks 27-32)*, September.
Larval Foodplants: Mosses.

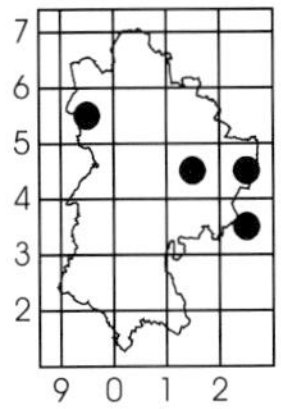

***Eudonia angustea* (Curtis) (1342)**
Post VCH: Local and uncommon: Aspley Heath (1945), Sharnbrook, Pavenham, Sandy, Stotfold and in the RIS trap at Cockayne Hatley.
Flight: June to October (weeks 26, 33-44)* and over-wintering.
Larval Foodplants: Mosses.

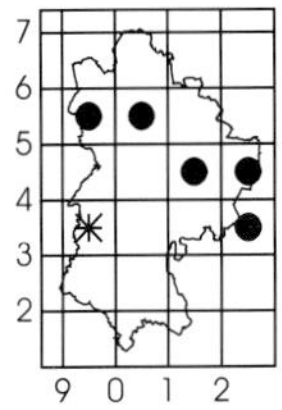

***Eudonia delunella* (Stainton)) (= *resinella* auctt.) ((1343)**
(Recorded at Sharnbrook (July 1976), but no subsequent record. This was probably a misidentification, and I await further specimens before confirming this species on the county list.)

***Eudonia mercurella* (Linnaeus) (1344)**
VCH: (as *Scoparia mercuralis* Linn.) "Bedford".
Post VCH: Widespread and common.
Flight: June to September (weeks 25-33, 36)*.
Larval Foodplants: Mosses.

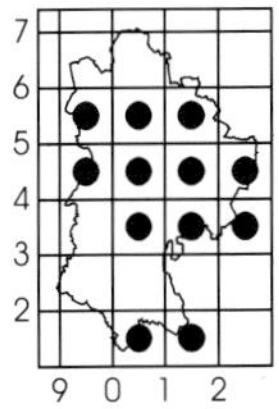

For key to moth maps see page 3.

Subfamily: **Nymphulinae China-mark moths.**

Beautiful China-mark (x 2)

The moths of several species in this subfamily are strikingly patterned with white and brown markings. They are very variable in size with wingspans ranging from 9 to 33 mm. The larvae feed submerged on aquatic plants.

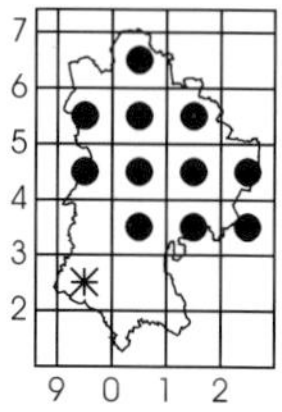

Brown China-mark *Elophila nymphaeata* (Linnaeus) (1345)
VCH: (as *Hydrocampa nymphaealis* Linn.) "Bedford, Luton; about water".
Post VCH: Widespread and common.
Flight: June to August (weeks 25-35)*.
Larval Foodplants: Aquatic plants.

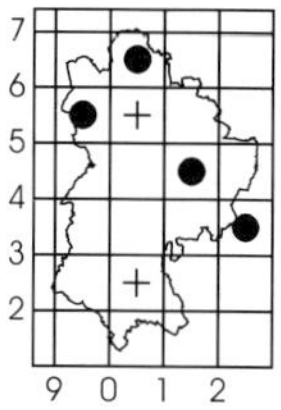

Beautiful China-mark *Nymphula stagnata* (Donovan) (1350)
VCH: (as *Hydrocampa stagnalis* Don.) "Bedford, Luton; about water".
Post VCH: Locally common: Felmersham Nature Reserve, Coppice Wood, Biggleswade and Stotfold.
Flight: July, August (weeks 26-31)*.
Larval Foodplants: Bur-reeds and yellow water-lily.

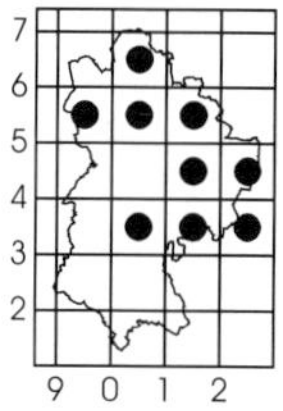

Ringed China-mark *Parapoynx stratiotata* (Linnaeus) (1348)
VCH: (as *P. stratiotalis* Linn.) "Bedford, about water-plants".
Post VCH: Widespread and common.
Flight: June to September (weeks 24-36)*.
Larval Foodplants: Aquatic plants.

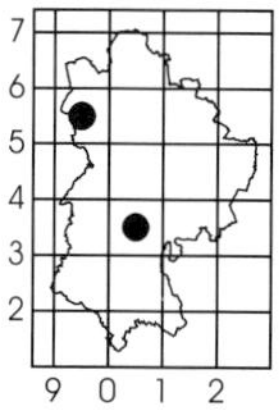

Small China-mark *Cataclysta lemnata* (Linnaeus) (1354)
VCH: (as *C. lemnalis* Linn.) "Bedford, about water-plants".
Post VCH: Local and uncommon: Felmersham Nature Reserve and Flitwick Moor.
Flight: June (weeks 23, 24)*. to August (weeks 31-33)*.
Larval Foodplants: Duckweeds.

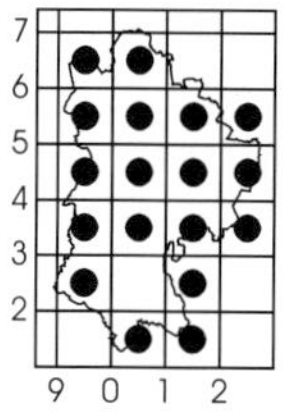

Water Veneer *Acentria ephemerella* ([Denis & Schiffermüller]) (= *nivea* (Olivier)) (1331) (Plate 101)
Post VCH: Widespread and common. Often seen flying low over water on summer evenings but comes to light in places far from standing water.
Flight: June to September (weeks 24-37)*.
Larval Foodplants: Aquatic plants.

For details of standard weeks see page 6.

Subfamily: **Evergestinae**

Moths whose forewings are pale straw-coloured with fine brown markings. Wingspan 24-31 mm. The larvae feed on Cruciferae.

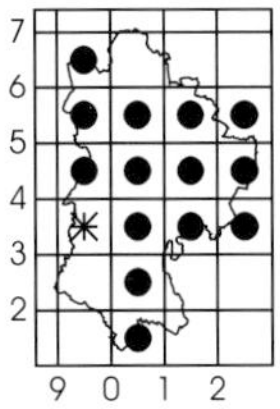

Garden Pebble *Evergestis forficalis* (Linnaeus) (1356)
VCH: "Frequent everywhere in gardens".
Post VCH: Widespread and common.
Flight: May to September (weeks 20-39)*, October.
Larval Foodplants: Brassicas*, especially cultivated varieties, radish and other crucifers. Sometimes becomes a pest.

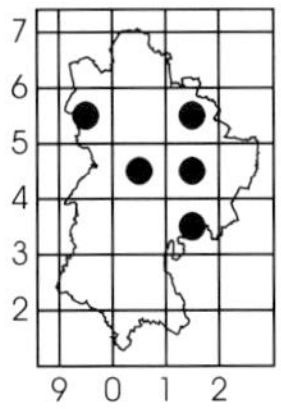

***Evergestis pallidata* (Hufnagel) (1358)**
Post VCH: Local and uncommon: Felmersham Nature Reserve, Cardington, Henlow, Biggleswade and Tempsford.
Flight: June to August (weeks 28-31)*.
Larval Foodplants: Winter-cress and other crucifers.

Subfamily: **Pyraustinae**

A large subfamily. The moths have a wide varity of colours, patterns and size. Wingspan 14-37 mm. The larvae mostly feed in spun leaves of herbaceous plants.

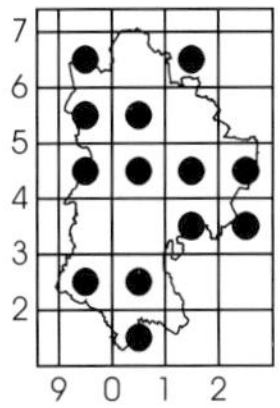

***Pyrausta aurata* (Scopoli) (1361)** (Plate 15)
Post VCH: Widespread and common.
Flight: May to September (weeks 21, 22, 25-36)*.
Larval Foodplants: Cat-mint, marjoram and mints*.

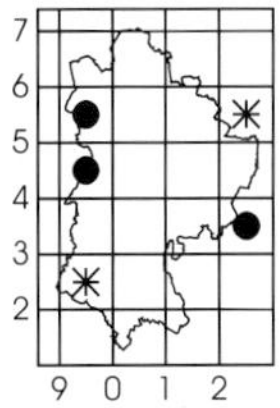

***Pyrausta purpuralis* (Linnaeus) (1362)**
Post VCH: Local and uncommon: Aspley Heath (1949), Marston Thrift, Sharnbrook, Stotfold and White Wood (1957).
Flight: May to August (weeks 23, 28-31)*.
Larval Foodplants: Corn mint and wild thyme.

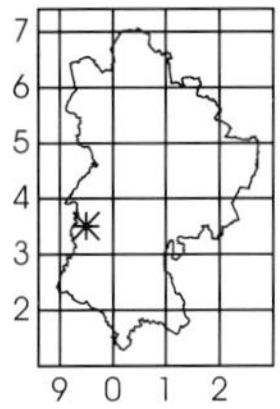

***Pyrausta ostrinalis* (Hübner) (1363)**
Post VCH: A single record from "Mills Field", Woburn Sands on 1 August 1949 by S.H.Kershaw. No voucher specimen has been seen.
Flight: May to August .
Larval Foodplants: Not known.

For key to moth maps see page 3.

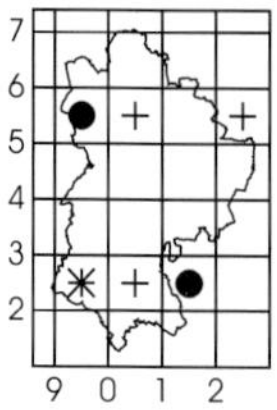

Pyrausta cespitalis **([Denis & Schiffermüller]) (1365)**
Pre VCH: Noted on "Common nr White Wood, Gamlingay" by J.C.Dale on 17 July 1819 (Dale, MS2). This site may have been just over the county boundary in Cambridgeshire.
VCH: "Bedford, Luton".
Post VCH: Scarce: Totternhoe on 8 April 1945 by S.H.Kershaw, Sharnbrook on 29 July 1978 and Pegsdon Hills on 14 July 1995.
Flight: May to August (weeks 28, 30)*.
Larval Foodplants: Plantains.

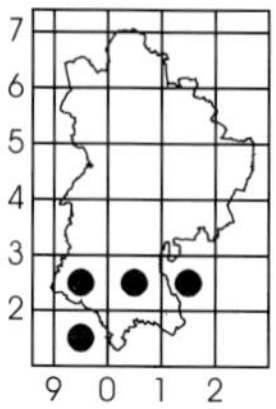

Pyrausta nigrata **(Scopoli) (1366)**
Post VCH: Locally common: Bison Hill, Sewell, Barton Hills and Pegsdon Hills.
Flight: May to August (week 28)*.
Larval Foodplants: Marjoram, wild thyme, corn mint and woodruff.

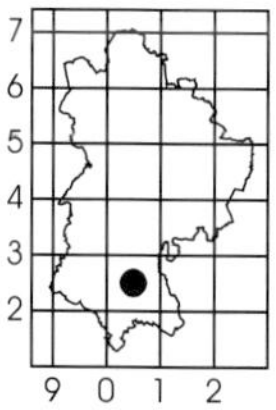

Pyrausta cingulata **(Linnaeus) (1367)**
Post VCH: TL02, location not known, 1971.
Flight: May to August.
Larval Foodplant: Wild thyme.

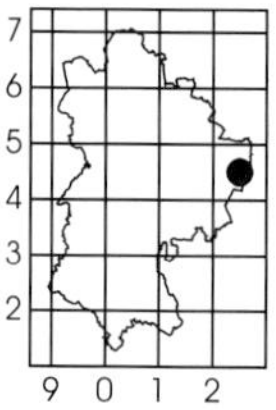

Margaritia sticticalis **(Linnaeus) (1368)**
Post VCH: Nationally scarce, but appeared in large numbers during 1995. A single record from the RIS trap at Cockayne Hatley on 31 July 1995 by I.P.Woiwod. (This corrects the record in Woiwod & Manning, 1996).
Flight: June to August (week 31)*.
Larval Foodplants: Mugwort, field wormwood.

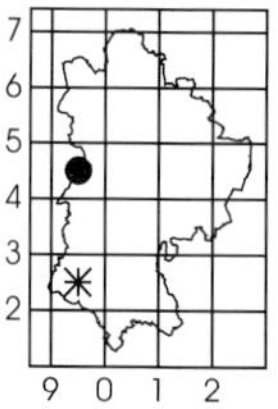

Sitochroa palealis **([Denis & Schiffermüller]) (1370)**
Post VCH: Two records only: Totternhoe on 25 July 1945 by S.H.Kershaw, Marston Thrift on 25 July 1985 by T.S.Hollingworth.
Flight: June, July (week 30)*.
Larval Foodplants: Wild carrot, parsnip, hogweed and fennel.

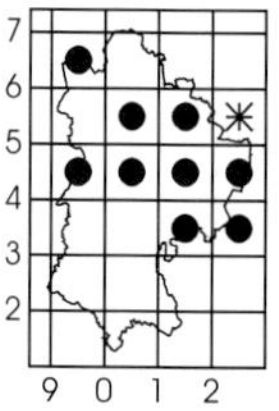

Sitochroa verticalis **(Linnaeus) (1371)**
Post VCH: Locally common.
Flight: June to August (weeks 23-32)*.
Larval Foodplants: Creeping thistle, wood sage, broom, oraches, docks and perennial wall-rocket.

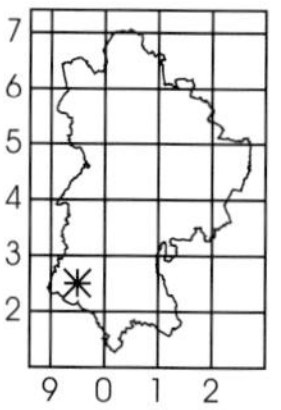

Microstega hyalinalis **(Hübner) (1374)**
Post VCH: A single record from Totternhoe on 17 June 1947 by S.H.Kershaw. No voucher specimen has been seen.
Flight: June and July.
Larval Foodplants: Common knapweed and occasionally great mullein.

For details of standard weeks see page 6.

European Corn Borer *Ostrinia nubilalis* (Hübner) (1375)

Post VCH: Local and uncommon: Old fish-ponds at Newnham Priory, where a number of specimens were netted between 17 June 1974 and 9 July 1974. The site was subsequently destroyed by over-use by motor-cyclists using it as a dirt-track. A few specimens were obtained in Bedford, about 1 km from the site at Newnham Priory in August 1974. Also found in White Wood on 29-30 June 1957, Tempsford on 3 July 1993, Biggleswade in 1994, and in the RIS trap at Cockayne Hatley on 1 August 1995 (Woiwod and Manning, 1996).
Flight: May to August (weeks 24-31)*.
Larval Foodplant: Mugwort.

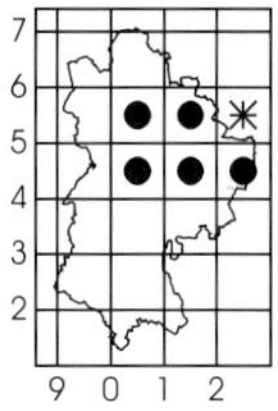

Small Magpie *Eurrhypara hortulata* (Linnaeus) (1376) (Plate 41)
VCH: (as *Botys urticalis* Linn.) "Everywhere among nettles".
Post VCH: Widespread and common.
Flight: May to August (weeks 22-33)*.
Larval Foodplants: Nettles, also black horehound, white horehound, woundworts, mints and field bindweed.

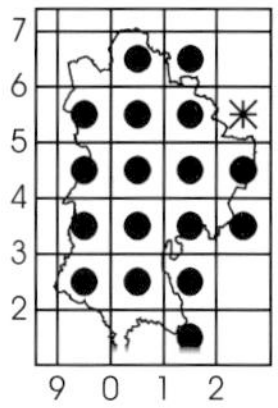

***Perinephela lancealis* ([Denis & Schiffermüller]) (1377)**
Post VCH: A single record from Aspley Heath on 14 July 1989 by V.W. Arnold.
Flight: June to August (week 28)*.
Larval Foodplants: Hemp-agrimony, wood sage, woundworts and rag-worts.

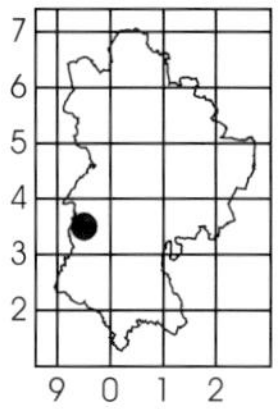

***Phlyctaenia coronata* (Hufnagel) (1378)**
VCH: (as *Ebulea sambucalis* Schiff.) "Bedford, Luton; probably everywhere".
Post VCH: Widespread and common.
Flight: June to August (weeks 25-33)*.
Larval Foodplants: Elder, *Viburnum* spp., lilac and privets.

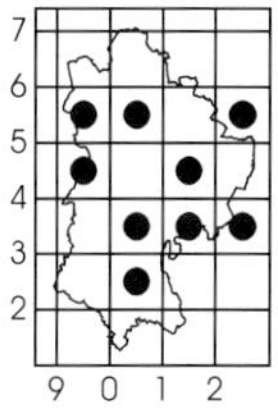

***Phlyctaenia perlucidalis* (Hübner) (1380)**
Post VCH: RIS trap at Cockayne Hatley, 11 July 1990, 2-8 July 1994 and between 25 June and 15 July 1995.
Flight: June, July (weeks 26-28)*.
Larval Foodplants: Thistles.

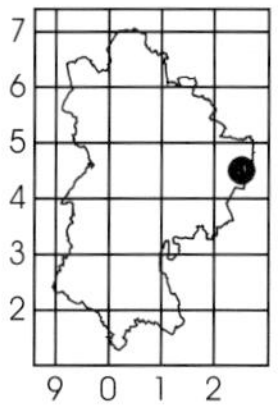

***Ebulea crocealis* (Hübner) (1385)**

VCH: "Bedford, among fleabane".
Post VCH: Scarce: Felmersham Nature Reserve on 12 July 1981 and Cople Pits on 21 August 1988.
Flight: July (week 28)*, August (week 34)*.
Larval Foodplant: Common fleabane.

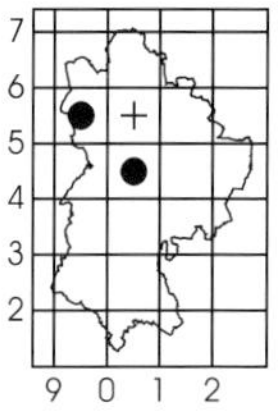

For key to moth maps see page 3.

Opsibotys fuscalis **([Denis & Schiffermüller]) (1386)**
Post VCH: A single record from Clifton on 23 July 1989 by A.R.Outen.
Flight: June, July (week 30)*.
Larval Foodplants: Yellow-rattle, goldenrod and louseworts.

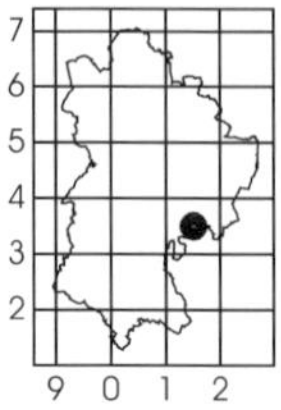

Udea lutealis **(Hübner) (=** ***elutalis*** **auctt.) (1388)**
VCH: "Luton, among thistles".
Post VCH: Widespread and common.
Flight: July to September (weeks 28-35)*.
Larval Foodplants: Herbaceous plants.

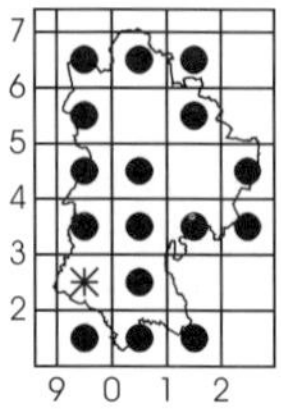

Udea prunalis **([Denis & Schiffermüller]) (=** ***nivealis*** **(Fabricius)) (1390)**
VCH: "Generally common in hedges".
Post VCH: Widespread and common.
Flight: June to August (weeks 25-32)*.
Larval Foodplants: Polyphagous on herbaceous plants, shrubs and trees.

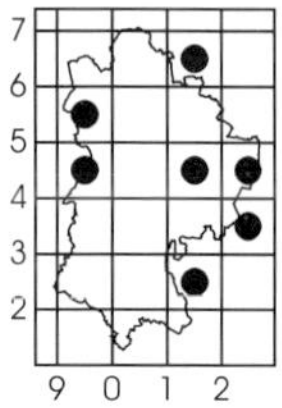

Udea olivalis **([Denis & Schiffermüller]) (1392)**
VCH: "Generally common in hedges".
Post VCH: Widespread and common.
Flight: June to August (weeks 23-31)*.
Larval Foodplants: Labiates and other herbaceous plants and shrubs.

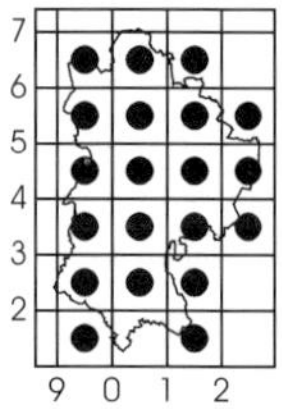

Udea ferrugalis **(Hübner) (1395)**
VCH: "Luton, in hedges".
Post VCH: Normally an uncommon immigrant to Bedfordshire: Sandy, Stotfold and in the RIS trap at Cockayne Hatley where it was very common in 1996.
Flight: Any month (week 38)*.
Larval Foodplants: Herbaceous plants.

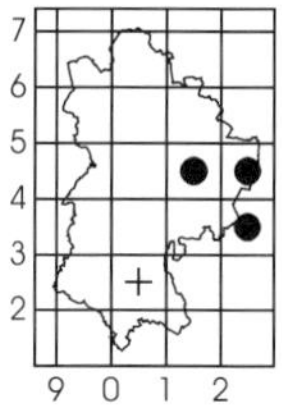

Rush Veneer ***Nomophila noctuella*** **([Denis & Schiffermüller]) (1398)**
VCH: (as *N. hybridalis* Hb.) "Generally common".
Post VCH: A widespread and fairly common immigrant. Record numbers appeared in the RIS trap at Cockayne Hatley in 1996.
Flight: May to September (weeks 23, 32-41)*.
Larval Foodplants: Clovers and knotgrass.

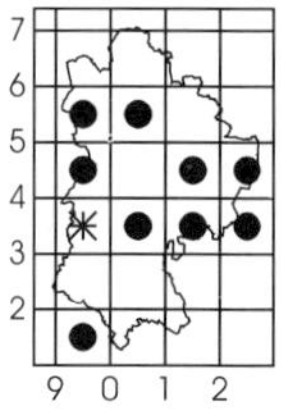

Diasemiopsis ramburialis **(Duponchel) (1403)**
Post VCH: A scarce immigrant, recorded once only, from the RIS trap at Cockayne Hatley in 1976.
Flight: June to October.
Larval Foodplants: Not known.

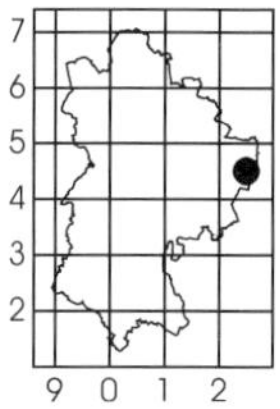

For details of standard weeks see page 6.

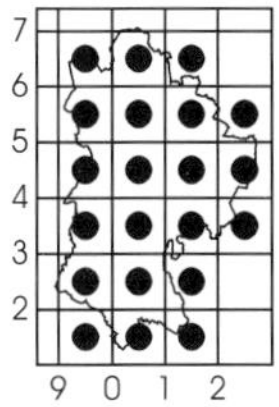

Mother of Pearl *Pleuroptya ruralis* (Scopoli) (1405)
VCH: "Generally distributed among nettles".
Post VCH: Widespread and common.
Flight: June to September (weeks 24, 27-37)⋆.
Larval Foodplants: Nettles⋆. Also goosefoots, oraches, meadowsweet and hop.

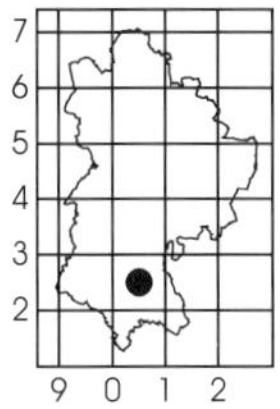

***Sceliodes laisalis* (Walker) (1412)**
Post VCH: An African species recorded in Britain on four occasions, either an immigrant or as larvae feeding on imported tomatoes. Luton, 30 July 1983 (Webb, 1984d).

Subfamily: **Pyralinae**

The moths are variable in colour and size, some being strongly patterned and others more sombre. Wingspan 18-40 mm. Larvae often on refuse or stored products.

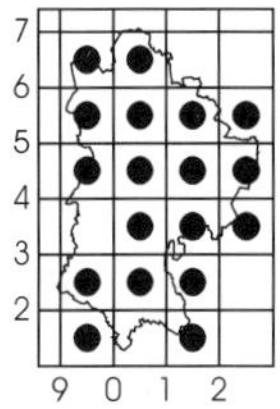

Gold Triangle *Hypsopygia costalis* (Fabricius) (1413)
VCH: "Bedford".
Post VCH: Widespread and common.
Flight: April to November (weeks 20-37, 42)⋆.
Larval Food: Hay (clover and grass) and in squirrel's dreys. Probably also in thatch and in dead leaves.

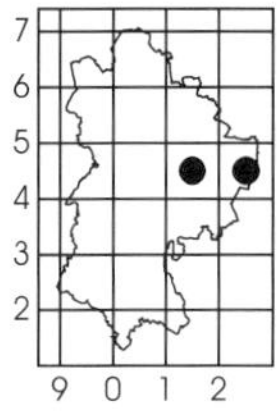

***Synaphe punctalis* (Fabricius) (1414)**
Post VCH: Local and uncommon: The Lodge, Sandy and in the RIS trap at Cockayne Hatley.
Flight: June to August (weeks 28, 30)⋆.
Larval Foodplants: Mosses.

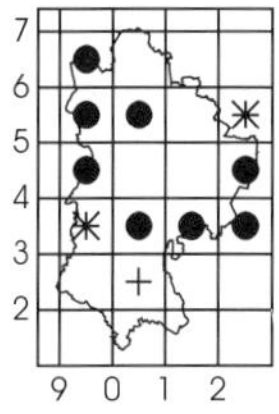

***Orthopygia glaucinalis* (Linnaeus) (1415)**
VCH: "Luton".
Post VCH: Widespread and fairly common.
Flight: July, August (weeks 27-35)⋆.
Larval Food: Dead and decaying vegetable matter.

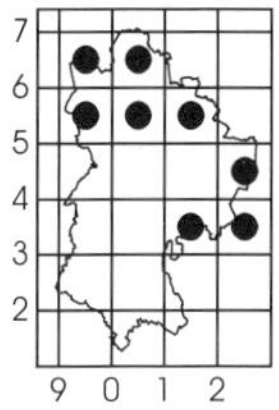

Meal Moth *Pyralis farinalis* (Linnaeus) (1417)
VCH: "Generally common in houses and corn stores".
Post VCH: Widespread and common.
Flight: June to August (weeks 26-33)⋆, September.
Larval Food: Stored cereals, and on cereal products⋆.

For key to moth maps see page 3.

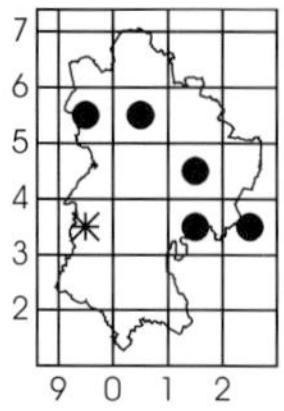

Large Tabby *Aglossa pinguinalis* (Linnaeus) (1421)
VCH: "Generally common about stables".
Post VCH: Widespread and fairly common: Aspley Heath (1946), Sharnbrook, Bedford, Sandy, Tempsford and Stotfold.
Flight: June, July (weeks 27-31)*, August.
Larval Food: Chaff and refuse where animal feeds are stored.

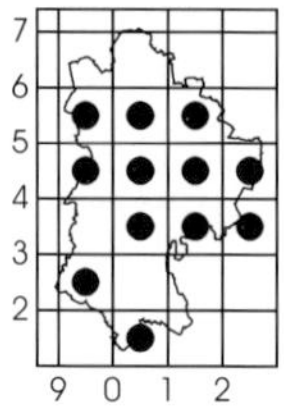

***Endotricha flammealis* ([Denis & Schiffermüller]) (1424)** (Plate 80)
Post VCH: Widespread and common.
Flight: June, July to September (weeks 27-32, 36)*.
Larval Foodplants: Greater bird's-foot-trefoil, and probably other plants; later on leaf-litter.

Subfamily: **Galleriinae** **The Wax and Bee Moths**

A group of rather dull-coloured moths (wingspan 15-41 mm) whose larvae mostly live in the nests of bees or wasps.

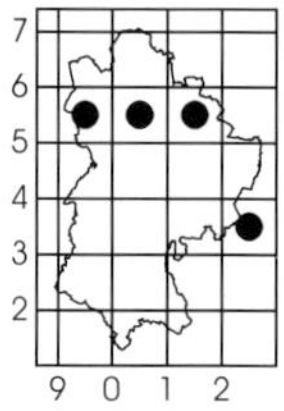

Wax Moth *Galleria mellonella* (Linnaeus) (1425)
Post VCH: Local and uncommon: Sharnbrook, Bedford, Tempsford and Stotfold.
Flight: July to October (weeks 33, 34)*.
Larval Food: Wax comb in bee-hives.

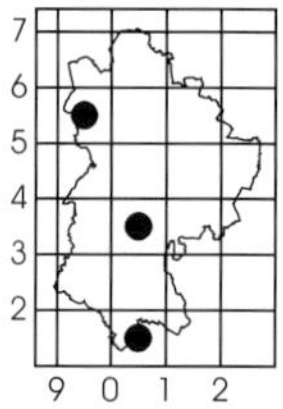

Lesser Wax Moth *Achroia grisella* (Fabricius) (1426)
Post VCH: Local and uncommon: Sharnbrook on 14 July 1992, Studham on 21 August 1995 and Flitwick Moor on 26 July 1992.
Flight: June to October (weeks 28-30)*.
Larval Food: Wax comb in bee-hives.

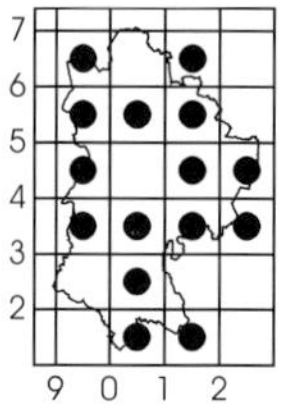

Bee Moth *Aphomia sociella* (Linnaeus) (1428)
VCH: "Bedford, Luton".
Post VCH: Widespread and common.
Flight: May (week 18)*, June to August (weeks 23-33)*.
Larval Food: Comb in nests of wasps, dead mammals and faeces.

Subfamily: **Phycitinae**

A large subfamily of moths with elongate forewings, variable in size, some with strongly patterned forewings. Wingspan 18-29 mm. Larval habits varied.

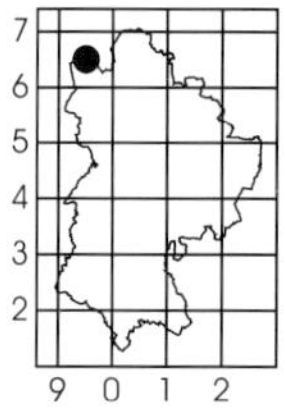

***Cryptoblabes bistriga* (Haworth) (1433)**
Post VCH: Local and uncommon: West Wood.
Flight: June, July (weeks 23-28)*.
Larval Foodplants: Oaks.

For details of standard weeks see page 6.

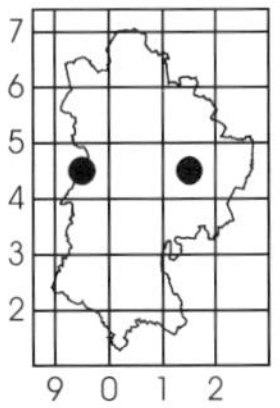

Pyla fusca **(Haworth) (1451)**
Post VCH: Scarce: Cranfield in 1984 and Biggleswade in 1994.
Flight: June to August.
Larval Foodplants: Heather and bilberry.

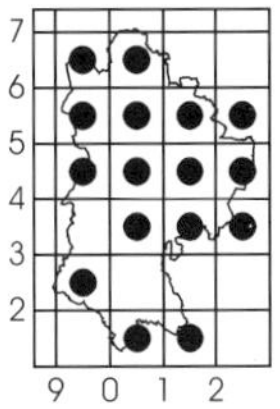

Phycita roborella **([Denis & Schiffermüller]) (1452)**
VCH: (as *Nephopteryx spissicella* Fab.) "Bedford".
Post VCH: Widespread and common.
Flight: June to September (weeks 26-35)*.
Larval Foodplants: Oaks. Also pear and apple.

Pempelia palumbella **([Denis & Schiffermüller]) (1442)**
Post VCH: A specimen with incomplete data label (1964/1965) was identified by the author in a local collection made by R.Passley.
Flight: July, August.
Larval Foodplants: Heather, milkworts and wild thyme.

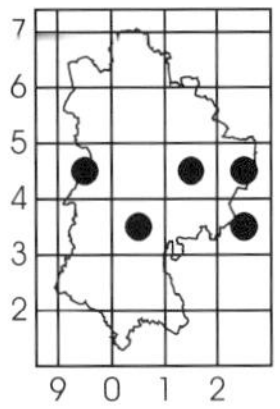

Pempelia formosa **(Haworth) (1445)**
Post VCH: Local and uncommon: Marston Thrift, Maulden Wood, Biggleswade, Stotfold and in the RIS trap at Cockayne Hatley.
Flight: June, July (weeks 30, 31)*.
Larval Foodplants: Elms.

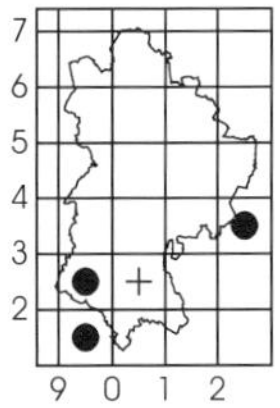

Hypochalcia ahenella **([Denis & Schiffermüller]) (1457)**
VCH: "Taken at 'light' at Luton".
Post VCH: Local and uncommon: Bison Hill, Sewell and Stotfold.
Flight: May, June (weeks 22-25)* to August.
Larval Foodplants: Unknown.

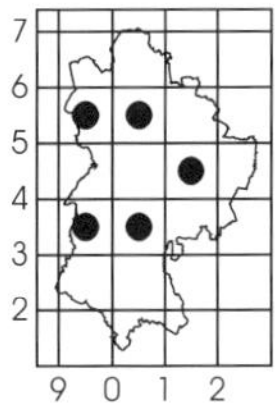

Dioryctria abietella **([Denis & Schiffermüller]) (1454)** Plate 58
Post VCH: Local and uncommon: Aspley Heath, Sharnbrook, Maulden Wood, Bedford and Rowney Warren.
Flight: July, August (weeks 28-31)*.
Larval Foodplants: Scots pine and Norway spruce.

Dioryctria schuetzeella **Fuchs (1454a)**
Post VCH: A single record from the RIS trap at Cockayne Hatley on 26 July 1996.
Flight: July and August (week 30)*.
Larval Foodplant: Norway spruce.

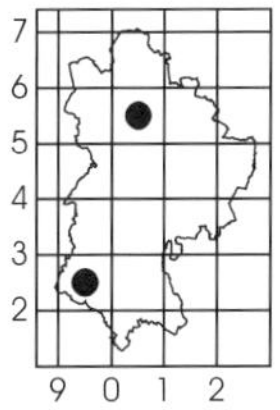

Dioryctria mutatella **Fuchs (1455)**
Post VCH: Scarce: King's Wood (Heath and Reach) on 13 August 1987 and Bedford in 1994.
Flight: July to September (week 33)*.
Larval Foodplant: Scots pine.

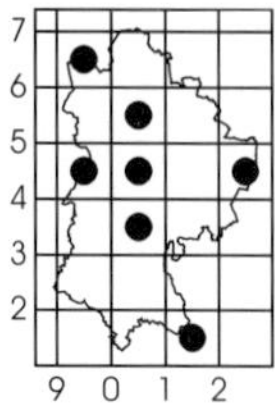

***Acrobasis repandana* (Fabricius) (1436)**
VCH: (as *Rhodophaea tumidella* Zk.) "Bedford".
Post VCH: Locally common: Marston Thrift, West Wood, Maulden Wood, King's Wood (Houghton Conquest) Bedford, Luton Hoo and in the RIS trap at Cockayne Hatley.
Flight: June to August (weeks 25-34)*.
Larval Foodplants: Oaks.

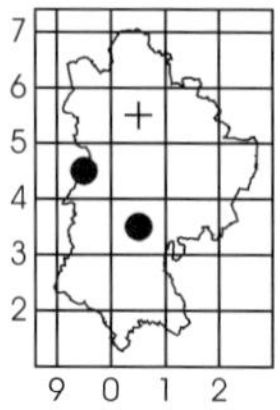

***Acrobasis consociella* (Hübner) (1437)**
VCH: "Bedford".
Post VCH: Scarce: Cranfield and Maulden Wood.
Flight: July (week 27)*, August.
Larval Foodplants: Oaks.

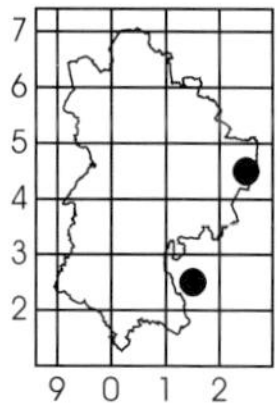

***Numonia suavella* (Zincken) (1438)**
Post VCH: Found only twice: at Pegsdon Hills on 14 July 1995 during a meeting of the Bedfordshire Natural History Society and in the RIS trap at Cockayne Hatley (6 - 12 August 1995).
Flight: July, August (weeks 28, 32)*.
Larval Foodplants: Blackthorn, hawthorns and rowan.

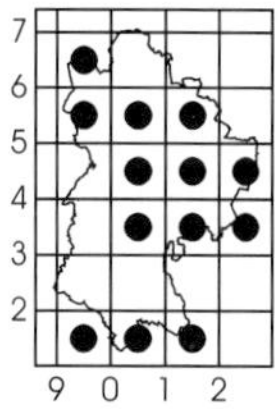

***Numonia advenella* (Zincken) (1439)**
Post VCH: Widespread and common.
Flight: July, August (weeks 28-35)*.
Larval Foodplants: Hawthorns and rowan.

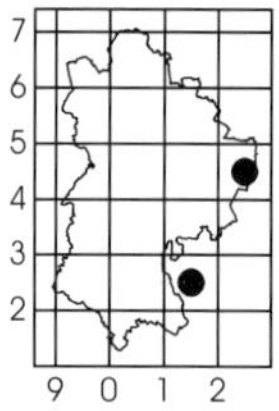

***Numonia marmorea* (Haworth) (1440)**
Post VCH: Scarce: Pegsdon Hills on 14 July 1995 and Potton Wood on 13 August 1985.
Flight: July, August (weeks 28, 33)*.
Larval Foodplants: blackthorn, hawthorns and *Sorbus* spp.

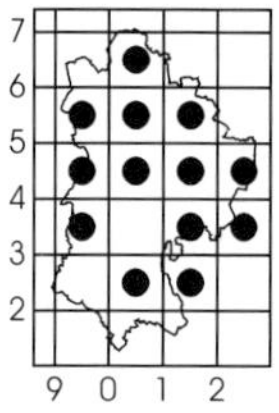

***Myelois cribrella* (Hübner) (1458)**
Post VCH: Widespread and common.
Flight: June to August (weeks 22-33)*.
Larval Foodplants: Woolly thistle, spear thistle and greater burdock.

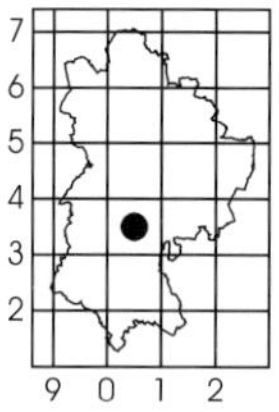

***Assara terebrella* (Zincken) (1461)**
Post VCH: A single record from Maulden Wood on 23 July 1985 by T.S.Hollingworth.
Flight: June to August (week 30)*.
Larval Foodplant: Norway spruce.

For details of standard weeks see page 6.

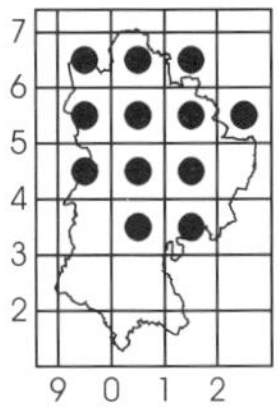

***Euzophera pinguis* (Haworth) (1470)**
Post VCH: Widespread and common.
Flight: July to September (weeks 27-34, 37)★.
Larval Foodplant: Ash.

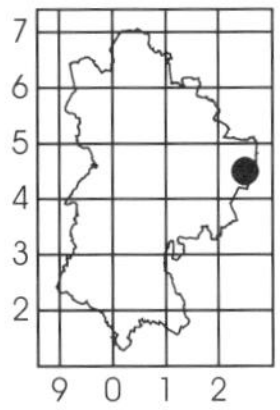

***Ancylosis oblitella* (Zeller) (1467)**
Post VCH: A scarce immigrant. Found in the RIS trap at Cockayne Hatley in 1976, a year when the species was widely recorded in Britain.
Flight: May, July, August.
Larval Foodplants: Goosefoots.

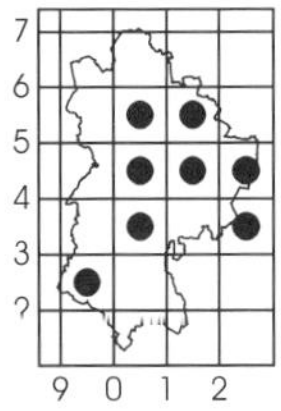

***Homoeosoma sinuella* (Fabricius) (1481)**
Post VCH: Locally common.
Flight: June to August (weeks 23-32)★.
Larval Foodplant: Ribwort plantain.

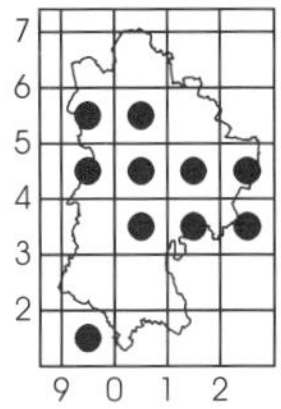

***Phycitodes binaevella* (Hübner) (1483)**
Post VCH: Widespread and common.
Flight: June to August (weeks 26-33)★.
Larval Foodplant: Spear thistle.

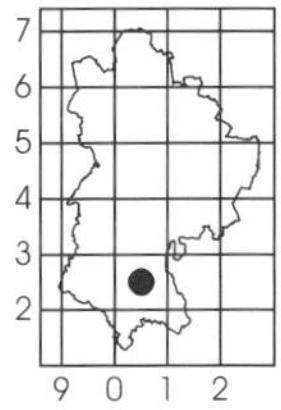

***Phycitodes saxicola* (Vaughan) (1484)**
Post VCH: One specimen has been confirmed, by dissection, from the RIS trap at Houghton Regis on 17 August 1985 (Riley, 1986). This species is widespread in coastal locations.
Flight: June, August (week 33)★.
Larval Foodplants: Chamomiles and other Compositae.

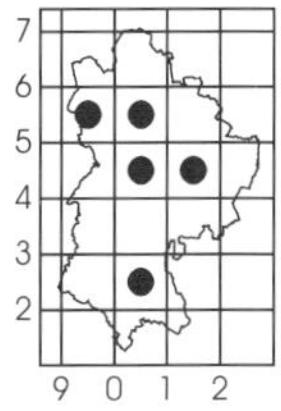

Indian Meal Moth *Plodia interpunctella* (Hübner) (1479)
Post VCH: Locally common: Sharnbrook, Dunstable (Riley, 1991a), Bedford and The Lodge, Sandy.
Flight: Continuous brooded (weeks 1-7, 43)★.
Larval Food: Stored cereals and other stored food products. All records are from pet shops and houses where grain and seeds are stored for bird-seed★ and pet food★.

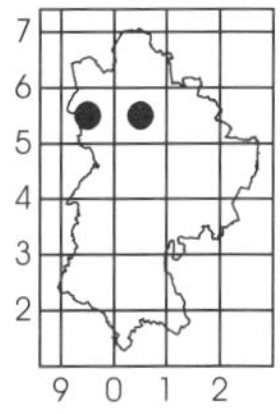

Cacao Moth *Ephestia elutella* (Hübner) (1473)
VCH: "Bedford".
Post VCH: Local and uncommon: Sharnbrook and Bedford
Flight: June to October (weeks 26, 29)★.
Larval Food: Stored food products.

For key to moth maps see page 3.

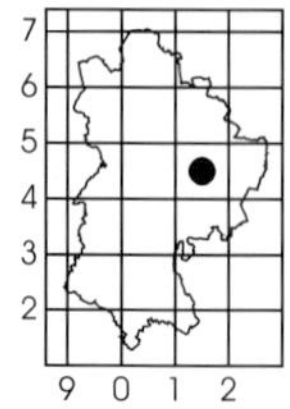

Ephestia parasitella **Staudinger ssp.** ***unicolorella*** **Staudinger (1474)**
Post VCH: A single record from Biggleswade in 1994 by R.C.Revels.
Flight: June to September.
Larval Food: Dried vegetable matter.

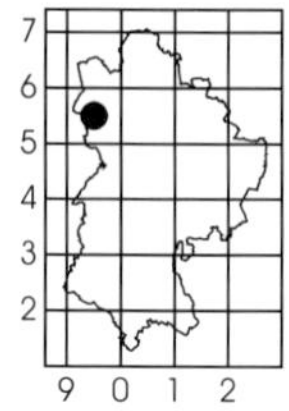

Mediterranean Flour Moth ***Ephestia kuehniella*** **(Zeller) (1475)**
Post VCH: A single record from Sharnbrook on 14 August 1978.
Flight: Continuous brooded (weeks 33, 41)*.
Larval Food: Flour*, and other stored food products.

Family: **Pterophoridae The Plume Moths.**

Most plume moths have their forewings divided into two lobes and the hindwings into three lobes. Wingspans 12-27 mm. In two species in the genus *Agdistis* the wings are not divided into lobes but neither of these species has been found in Bedfordshire. There are 38 British species, of which 18 have been found in Bedfordshire.

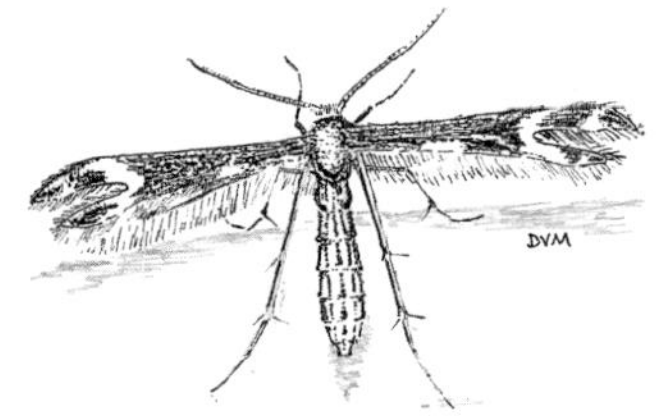

Marasmarcha lunaedactyla
(*x 2*)

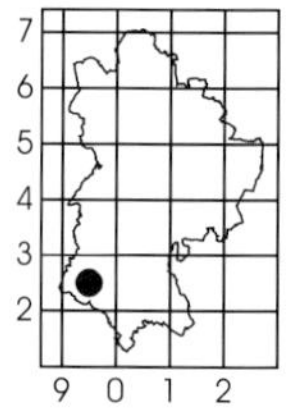

Oxyptilus parvidactylus **(Haworth) (1490)**
Post VCH: A single record from Sewell Cutting on 18 June 1987.
Flight: June (week 25)* to August.
Larval Foodplant: Mouse-ear hawkweed.

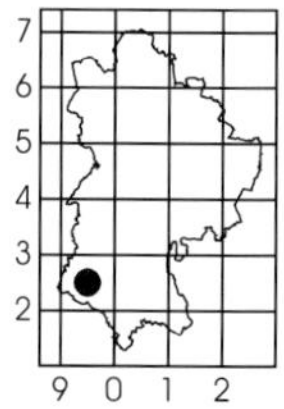

Marasmarcha lunaedactyla **(Haworth) (1495)**
Post VCH: A single record from Totternhoe Knolls on 11 July 1986 by A.R.Outen.
Flight: July (week 28)*.
Larval Foodplants: Common and spiny rest-harrow.

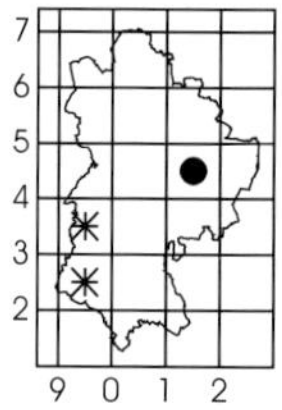

Amblyptilia acanthadactyla **(Hübner) (1497)**
Post VCH: Three records only: Totternhoe on 18 July 1947 and Aspley Heath on 14 September 1946, both by S.H.Kershaw and Sandy on 10 July 1995 by I.K.Dawson.
Flight: July (week 28)*, August to May.
Larval Foodplants: Herbaceous plants.

For details of standard weeks see page 6.

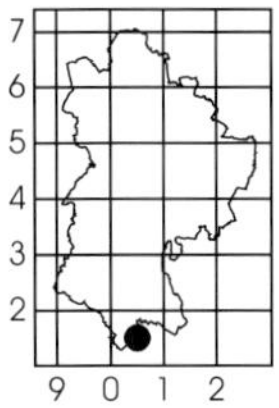

Amblyptilia punctidactyla **(Haworth) (=** ***cosmodactyla*** **(Hübner)) (1498)**
Post VCH: A single record from Studham on 17 July 1995 by C.R.B.Baker.
Flight: July (week 29)*, September to May.
Larval Foodplants: Herbaceous plants.

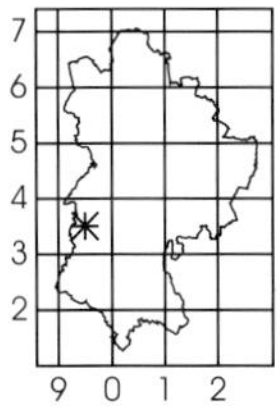

Platyptilia calodactyla **([Denis & Schiffermüller]) (1500)**
Post VCH: Recorded by S.H.Kershaw from Aspley Heath on 23 June 1936 (as *zettersteddi*) and on 4 June 1950 (as *taeniadactylus*). No specimen has been seen.
Flight: June and July.
Larval Foodplant: Goldenrod.

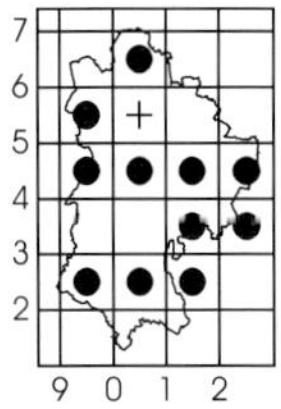

Platyptilia gonodactyla **([Denis & Schiffermüller]) (1501)**
VCH: "Bedford, among coltsfoot".
Post VCH: Widespread and common.
Flight: May, June (weeks 20-25)*, August, September (weeks 32-37)*.
Larval Foodplant: Colt's-foot.

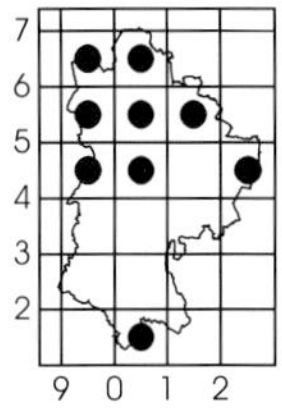

Platyptilia pallidactyla **(Haworth) (1504)**
Post VCH: Widespread and common.
Flight: June to August (weeks 27-31)*.
Larval Foodplants: Yarrow and sneezewort.

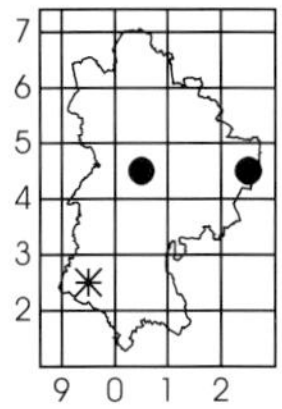

Stenoptilia zophodactylus **(Duponchel) (1507)**
Post VCH: Local and uncommon: Totternhoe on 19 June 1946 by S.H. Kershaw, Stewartby Country Park on 21 July 1993 and in the RIS trap at Cockayne Hatley on 27 August - 2 September 1994.
Flight: July to September (weeks 29, 35)*.
Larval Foodplant: Common centaury.

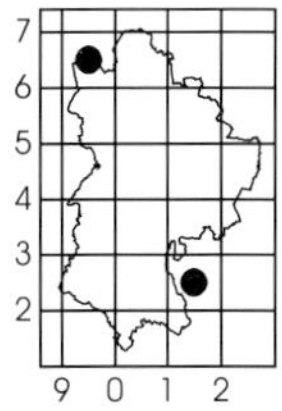

Stenoptilia bipunctidactyla **(Scopoli) (1508)**
Post VCH: Local and uncommon: West Wood and Pegsdon Hills.
Flight: May, June, July to October (weeks 28, 33)*.
Larval Foodplants: Field scabious, small scabious and devils'-bit scabious.

Note: This species is under review; current research suggests that the three foodplants listed here may each support a separate species in a closely-related complex. Bedfordshire specimens cannot yet be reliably separated (Agassiz, 1987; 1988).

For key to moth maps see page 3.

***Stenoptilia pterodactyla* (Linnaeus) (1509)**
VCH: "Bedford, Luton".
Post VCH: Widespread and common.
Flight: June to August (weeks 25-33)*.
Larval Foodplant: Germander speedwell*.

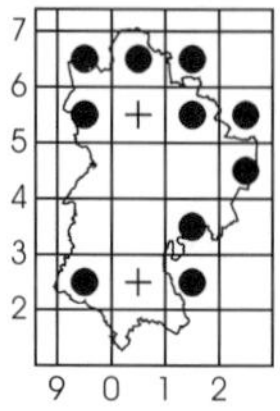

***Pterophorus tridactyla* (Linnaeus) (1510)**
Post VCH: Local and uncommon: Pegsdon Hills.
Flight: June (week 25)* to August.
Larval Foodplant: Wild thyme.

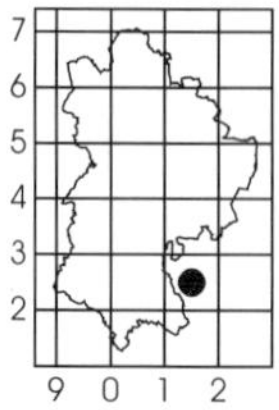

***Pterophorus baliodactylus* Zeller (1512)**
Post VCH: recorded at Barton by W.G.Nash (Foster, 1934).
Flight: July, August.
Larval Foodplant: Marjoram.

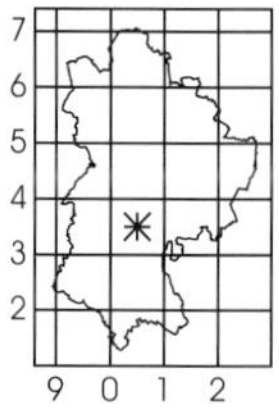

White Plume Moth *Pterophorus pentadactyla* (Linnaeus) (1513)
VCH: "Bedford, Luton, Woburn".
Post VCH: Widespread and common. (Plate 100)
Flight: June to August (weeks 25-33)*.
Larval Foodplants: Bindweeds.

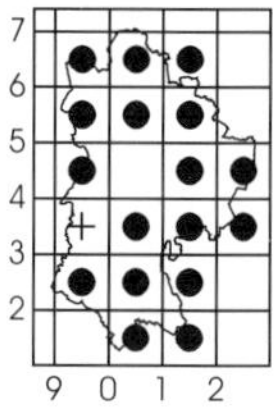

***Pterophorus galactodactyla* ([Denis & Schiffermüller]) (1514)**
Pre VCH: recorded at Clapham Park Wood, 1 June 1820, by J.C.Dale (MS3), "3 larvas on large Burrdock leaves on ye underside of *Alucita Galactodactyla*". Not found in Bedfordshire since then.
Flight: June, July.
Larval Foodplant: Greater burdock.

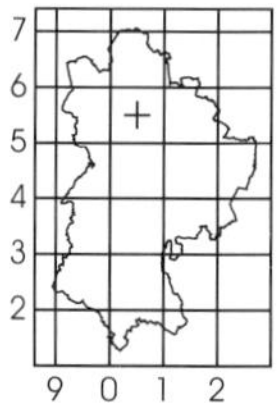

***Adaina microdactyla* (Hübner) (1517)**
Post VCH: A single record from the RIS trap at Cockayne Hatley in August 1989.
Flight: May, June, August*.
Larval Foodplant: Hemp-agrimony.

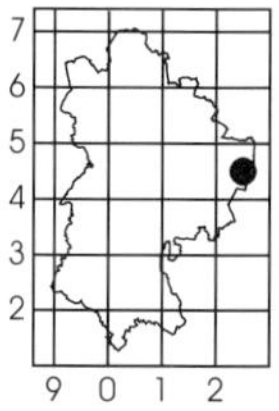

***Leioptilus carphodactyla* (Hübner) (1519)**
Post VCH: A single record from the RIS trap at Cockayne Hatley in the week 6 - 12 August 1995.
Flight: June, August (week 32)* and September.
Larval Foodplants: Ploughman's-spikenard and carline thistle.

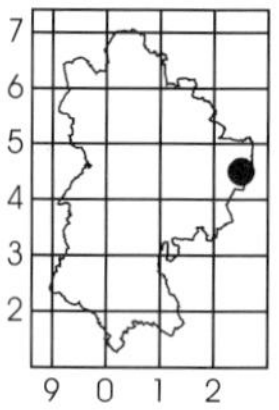

For details of standard weeks see page 6.

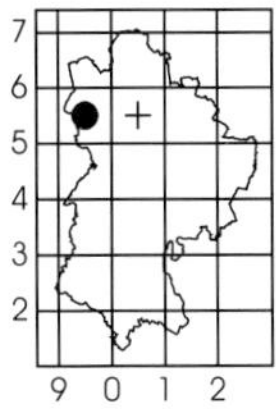

Oidaematophorus lithodactyla **(Treitschke) (1523)**
VCH: "Bedford, among fleabane".
Post VCH: A single record at Sharnbrook on 22 September 1973.
Flight: July to September (week 38)*.
Larval Foodplant: Common fleabane.

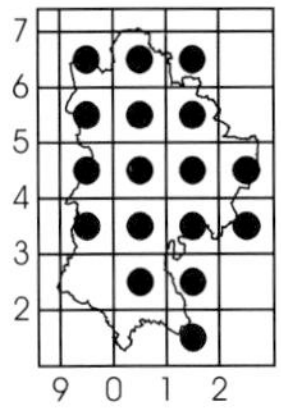

Emmelina monodactyla **(Linnaeus) (1524)**
VCH: "Luton, probably everywhere".
Post VCH: Widespread and common.
Flight: Most months (weeks 9-20, 25-48).
Larval Foodplants: Bindweeds.

For key to moth maps see page 3.

Butterflies

(Hesperiidae to Nymphalidae: Danainae)

C.R.B.Baker

Family: **Hesperiidae The Skippers**

The 'skippers', small butterflies known for their darting flight which is often so quick that they seem to vanish against the background of their habitats. The adults use all six legs when perching and have wider heads in proportion to the rest of the body than other butterflies with the bases of the antennae widely separated. The skippers are regarded as the most primitive and moth-like of the butterflies.

Subfamily: **Hesperiinae**

These are skippers with mainly orange or orange and brown wing colours. Apart from the Chequered Skipper, the males have a prominent black line of 'scent' scales on each forewing. Wingspans 25-36 mm. They have only one generation a year (univoltine). Some species overwinter as eggs and others as larvae. The eggs have little if any surface structure. The larvae feed within silken tubes or tents made from drawing the edges of grass leaves together with silk. Out of the six species resident in Britain, three breed in Bedfordshire and another two have done so in the past.

Large Skipper

Chequered Skipper *Carterocephalus palaemon* (Pallas) (1525)

Pre VCH: The Chequered Skipper was first reported in Britain by Charles Abbot. His notebook (MS1) records "Clapham Wood Copiose May 8th 1798" and also "June 8th 1799 Clapham Park Wood". Although it has been published elsewhere, his report to the Linnean Society, dated August 12th 1798, is worth repeating here. It suggests that initially he was not believed and gives a fascinating description of the habits of the newly-found butterfly, *Papilio Paniscus*:

> "I here beg leave to offer a few Remarks on the actions and manners of a Butterfly, which the Aurelian's Company (formerly established in London) passed over in silence, but which I have too high an opinion of our present institution to suppose that the members of the Linnaean Society will disregard – The times when this Papilio is most easily taken are May and June when the *lucina* is out, though it's term of existence must be longer, as I have taken several of them in good Condition a full fortnight after the Burgundy has disappeared –They should be sought for from seven to nine o'clock in the morning, indeed I have observed them playing in pairs just after sunrise, or at least as soon as the morning Fog has evaporated – It's flight is extremely short, and the insect is far from being timid, for should the maladroitness of the Aurelian suffer him to escape after capture, he may be easily traced among the herbage by a vigilant Eye and retaken – They fly near the ground and delight to settle on the blades of very long Grass, or the various species of the *Carex* tribe – The Larva or Chrysalis I do not profess to know –".

For details of standard weeks see page 6.

Unfortunately none of Abbot's specimens appear to have survived but J.C.Dale's notes (Dale, MS2) record the receipt of specimens from Clapham Park Wood when he bought Abbot's collection. The entry is annotated in pencil in what would appear to be the same hand: "when Dr Abbot took this first he was disbelieved till he took several". W.Bucklow, who sold Abbot's collection to Dale, wrote to Dale on 20 June 1821 that he could not find the Chequered Skipper. This "despite visiting Clapham Park every day" though he had obtained one from Lady Tavistock's collection. Writing again in 1823, he said he had looked for Chequered Skipper during the last two seasons and found none.

Abbot is also reported as finding the Chequered Skipper in White Wood, near Gamlingay in 1802 (South, 1906) and this is recorded in J.C.Dale's notes. According to Barrett (1893) it was there from 1803 to 1842 "when it disappeared from the district". Fryer (1938) mentioned M.Lee against the 1842 record. Abbot's notebook also contains a pencil entry after the record from Clapham Park Wood "& nr Luton Beds". The note was probably added by J.C.Dale as his notebooks contain the comments "Stephens says his specimens were taken in Bedfordshire .... [illegible] within 30 miles of London" with "nr Luton" added and "nr Luton Bedfordshire May 1 1826 Mr Henderson". (No reference to the latter could be found in Joseph Henderson's letters to Dale and it seems surprising that Henderson who lived in Milton, near Peterborough, would have collected near Luton). Lucas (1855) recorded it as "common" in the neighbourhood of Luton but no record of a locality has yet been found. No specimens from Bedfordshire have been located in collections. The date when the Chequered Skipper was last seen in Bedfordshire is not known.

VCH: "Recorded by the late Professor Westwood at Clapham Park Woods and near Luton". There is nothing to indicate whether these were personal observations by Westwood or merely repetition of earlier records.

Post VCH: Not recorded. The Chequered Skipper was present not far away in Northamptonshire but declined rapidly in the early 1970s and was last seen in England in 1979 (Ravenscroft, 1995) though populations remain in Scotland. In 1995 the first steps were taken to reintroduce this delightful butterfly into England (Warren, 1995) and we can but hope that it will return to many of its former haunts.

Small Skipper *Thymelicus sylvestris* (Poda) (1526) (Plate 66)

Pre VCH: Charles Abbot (MS1) recorded finding the Small Skipper (as *Linea*) on 20 July 1799. He gave no locality but it was probably in one of his favourite haunts near Bedford. J.C.Dale (MS2) found it on 17 July 1819 near White Wood. Lucas (1855) reported it as "common in lanes" in the neighbourhood of Luton and E.A.S.Hatton (1898) found it outside some woods about 2 miles from Bedford.

VCH: as *Hesperia linea* Fab. "Bedford, Luton; in marshy places".

Post VCH: Other than R.Palmer's note that it was abundant on Barton Hills in 1923, there is little information on the status of this species between the VCH and West's assessment in 1949 as "Very common

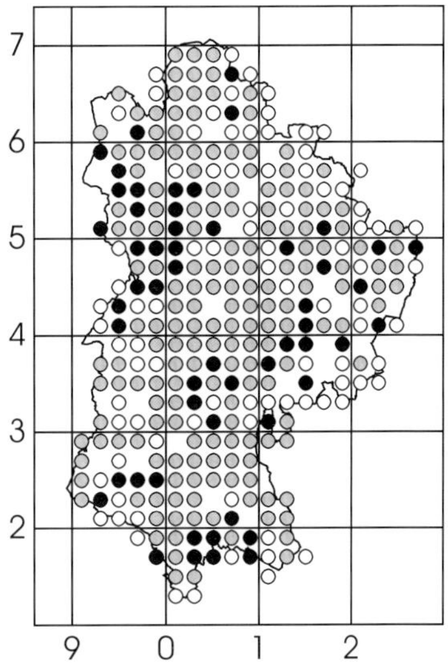

For key to butterfly maps see page 3.

throughout the county". Kershaw (1954) recorded it as common in King's Wood, Heath and Reach.

Specimens in collections: "Bedfordshire" 1918 & 1922 W.G.Nash (Oxford County Museum); Putnoe 1913, Ampthill 1946 (Buckinghamshire County Museum).

Currently widespread and common on road verges and in open grassy spaces throughout the County. In some sites the Small Skipper is less abundant than the Essex Skipper. Recorded since 1977 in 319 tetrads.
Flight: June to August (weeks 25 to 34, peak 29 to 31)*.
Larval Foodplants: Mainly Yorkshire-fog* but also timothy and false brome.

Essex Skipper *Thymelicus lineola* (Ochsenheimer) (1527) (Plate 66)
Pre VCH: E.A.S.Hatton (1898) found this species near Bedford along with the Small Skipper. This was probably the report noted by South (1906).
VCH: "This species, of recent discovery as British, has been found by Dr. Nash and Rev. O. W. Harries in woods and lanes near Bedford".
Post VCH: Nash (1918) reported the Essex Skipper as common and widely distributed from Kimbolton to Biggleswade and Shefford. R.M.Craske recalled finding it in Putnoe Lane, Bedford in the 1920s but not in other areas around Bedford at that time. It was evidently present in the Aspley Heath area in the 1930s and at Ampthill, Putnoe, Renhold and Willington in the 1940s (West, 1949).

Specimens in collections: Aspley Heath 1938 (Humphrey-Kershaw); Ampthill 1944 & 1948 (Hopkins-Alexander).

Currently widespread in open grassy areas but appears to be less so than the Small Skipper, though this may be in part due to confusion between the two species. In some sites in 1994 and 1995, particularly in the north of the County, it was much the more abundant species. Recorded from 227 tetrads, of which 129 are new records since 1990. The latter may reflect an improvement in observers' ability to recognise the Essex Skipper rather than a real increase in its distribution.

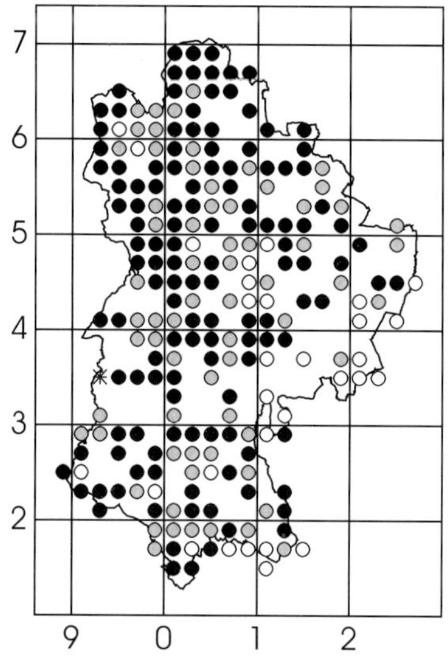

Flight: July to August (weeks 28 to 33, peak 30 to 31)*.
Larval Foodplants: Cock's-foot, creeping soft-grass and other grasses.

Silver-spotted Skipper *Hesperia comma* (Linnaeus) (1529) (Drawing on page 31)
Pre VCH: T.Orlebar Marsh (MS1) recorded *Comma* from Clapham and Biddenham in 1798 but he was almost certainly referring to the Large Skipper. (Moses Harris (1775) had used *comma* as the scientific name for the Large Skipper. Abbot (MS1) followed this practice but used the Chequered Hog Butterfly as the common name making it clear that he was not referring to the Silver-spotted Skipper which he apparently did not find.) A.H.Foster (1937) cited S.Tuke for the occurrence of this species at Pegsdon Firs from 1867-1880.
VCH: Not recorded.

For details of standard weeks see page 6.

Post VCH: The Silver-spotted Skipper occurred throughout the first half of this century along the chalk downs from Dunstable Downs, Warden Hill and Barton Hills to Pegsdon Hills and Knocking Hoe (Anon 1915, Bowden 1947 & 1965, Foster 1934). Foster (1916) noted it as "in limited spots" and it was likely to have been most abundant on the hottest, most closely grazed slopes. This species requires just these conditions to survive and it declined as grazing on the hills became less economic. It had probably gone from Dunstable Downs by the 1930s as R.M.Craske visited the site annually during the flight period and did not see any.

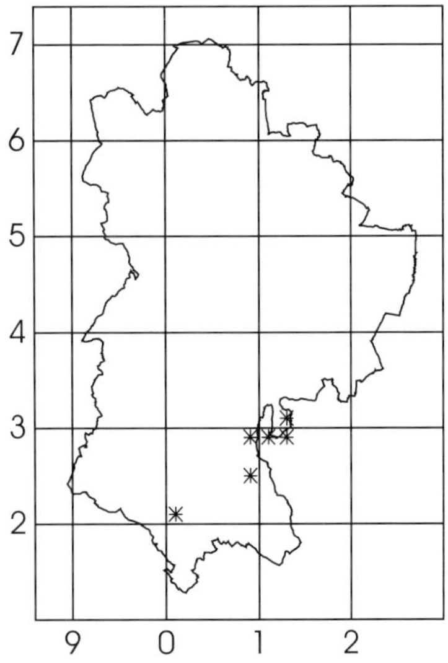

Pegsdon Hills seems to have been a favoured locality, especially in Barn Hole in the 1940s (Birdsall, 1988). It was still present there around 1950 (West, 1950) but was finally lost in the following few years when the rabbit populations crashed during the outbreak of myxomatosis. There was less disturbance of the ground to produce the small clumps of sheep's-fescue adjacent to bare soil that are preferred for egg-laying. The grass quickly grew longer than the critical height of 1-5 cm and the early stages of the Silver-spotted Skipper could not survive the cooler conditions at the surface of the ground. A single record from Bison Hill in 1983 was eventually agreed to have been an unusually marked Large Skipper.

Specimens in collections: "Dunstable 22.8.1916 A.E.Gibbs" (Natural History Museum); Pegsdon 1944 and 1951(Humphrey-Kershaw).

Large Skipper *Ochlodes venata* (Bremer and Grey) ssp. *faunus* (Turati) (1531)
(Plates 67 and 68 and drawing on page 212)

Pre VCH: In his notebook (MS1), Abbot noted "*Comma* – Chequered Hog Butterfly" as "far from rare 1797". Elsewhere he mentioned finding "*Papilio sylvanus* – Large Skipper" at Clapham Wood on 28 May 1798 and on 24 June 1799 in Clapham Park. J.C.Dale (MS3) found it on 19 June 1818 in Clapham Park Wood and also recorded this species probably from the same area on 1 June 1820. Lucas (1855) wrote that it was "not scarce" in the neighbourhood of Luton.

VCH: "Generally common".

Post VCH: The Large Skipper was recorded by West (1949) as "a very plentiful insect of woodland and woodland margins, and which is also locally common in the chalk bottoms." Kershaw (1954) reported it as common in King's Wood, Heath and Reach, otherwise little is known of its status before 1977 apart from a record from Whipsnade in 1950.

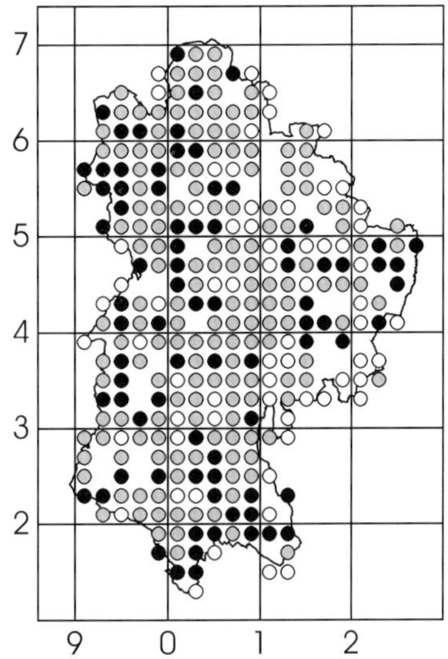

For key to butterfly maps see page 3.

Specimens in collections: Whipsnade 1950 (Hopkins-Alexander); "Bedfordshire" 1918 W.G.Nash (Oxford County Museum).

Widespread and common in recent years, the Large Skipper has been recorded since 1977 in 305 tetrads. The highest number seen on one transect walk was 63 on Whipsnade Downs in 1995. Found in grassy areas, but generally in greatest numbers in green lanes, woodland rides and other places rather more sheltered than those preferred by the Small and Essex Skippers.
Flight: From the end of May to the end of August (weeks 22 to 35, peak 25 to 28)* but may be much shortened in hot weather.
Larval Foodplants: Cock's-foot and possibly other wide-leaved grasses.

Subfamily: **Pyrginae**

The two species in this subfamily differ from the other British skippers in being greyish-brown or black and white in colour. Wingspans 23-34 mm. The Dingy Skipper in particular is easily mistaken for a day-flying moth and its resting position is different from all other butterflies found in Britain. Usually they have only one generation a year although in hot summers a few individuals may emerge in the late summer. The Dingy Skipper passes the winter in the larval stage but the Grizzled Skipper does so as a pupa. The egg shells differ from those of other skippers in being patterned with small ribs similar to those found in many other butterfly species in Britain. The larvae feed on herbaceous plants, not grasses. Both the British species occur in Bedfordshire.

Dingy Skipper

Grizzled Skipper

Dingy Skipper ***Erynnis tages tages*** **(Linnaeus) (1532)**
Pre VCH: Recorded by Charles Abbot (MS1) in Clapham Wood on 10 May 1798 and on 3 June 1799 in Hanger Wood. J.C.Dale (MS3) mentions finding this species on 1 June 1820 probably in the area of Clapham Park Wood where he recorded other insects on that day. "Scarce" on hills in the neighbourhood of Luton was the assessment of Lucas (1855).
VCH: "Bedford, Luton; on hillsides and railway banks".
Post VCH: W.G.Nash reported the Dingy Skipper from Barton Hills at the beginning of the century (Tutt, 1905-9). R.M.Craske recalled not seeing it near Bedford in the 1920s. S.R.Bowden (1965) found it at Knocking Hoe in 1917-21 and abundantly there in 1943. He reported it as "common all over Pegsdon" in 1921. Later records were from Aspley

For details of standard weeks see page 6.

Heath, Totternhoe, Kensworth and King's Wood, Heath and Reach where Kershaw (1954) found it to be common. West described it in 1949 as having "a patchy distribution but is common locally" and listed it as found at Totternhoe, Dedmansey Wood, Ravensden, Stevington, Bromham, Dean, Shillington, Barton and Flitwick. There was a small colony at Souldrop Tunnel in the mid 1960s.

Specimens in collections: Barton 1916 W.G.Nash (Oxford County Museum); Dunstable Downs 1931 (Graveley-Edwards); Aspley Heath 1944 and Totternhoe 1944 and 1948 (Humphrey-Kershaw) ; Kensworth 1929 and Skimpot 1927 (Luton Museum).

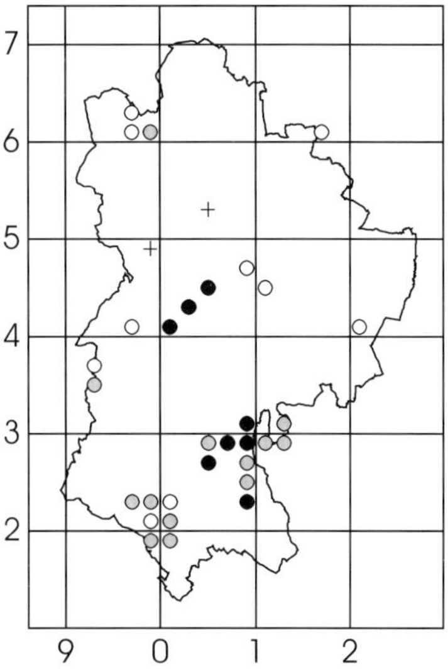

In recent years the Dingy Skipper has become local and uncommon with rarely more than 5 individual sightings being recorded on transect walks. Recorded since 1977 in only 31 tetrads. Found on open spaces, mostly on chalk downland from Whipsnade Downs east to Pegsdon Hills and in quarry sites such as Sewell and Totternhoe, but also on railway embankments such as Sharnbrook Summit where 15 were seen in 1979. Off the chalk and limestone, colonies have been found in the clay pits of the Marston Vale and on rough ground in the Elstow Storage Depot site. Occasionally individuals are seen in more wooded localities such as Aspley Woods and Marston Thrift.

Flight: April to mid June (weeks 17 to 25, peak 21 to 22)★. Occasional second-generation butterflies have been seen in July and August.

Larval Foodplants: Common bird's-foot-trefoil★, greater bird's-foot-trefoil and horseshoe vetch.

Grizzled Skipper *Pyrgus malvae* (Linnaeus) (1534) (Drawing on page 216)

Pre VCH: In Charles Abbot's notebook (MS1) there are entries for Clapham Wood on 8 and 10 May 1798 and for Hanger Wood on 3 June 1799. J.C.Dale (MS3) also recorded the Grizzled Skipper on 1 June 1820, probably in the area of Clapham Park Wood where he found the Dingy Skipper that day as well as other insects. Lucas (1855) found it to be "common" in the neighbourhood of Luton.

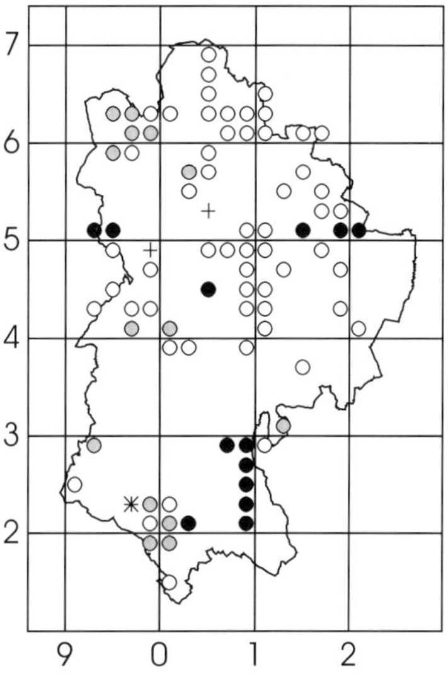

VCH: "Bedford, Luton, Potton".

Post VCH: W.G.Nash's report (cited by Tutt, 1905-9) of Grizzled Skipper from Twin Wood is the only one from the early years of the century. Bowden (1965) found it on Deacon Hill in 1921 and on Knocking Hoe in 1917-21, "abundant" there in 1943. By 1949 West could write "It is commonest on the chalk but is generally well distributed". Kershaw (1954) reported it as common in King's Wood, Heath and Reach. Other records from the 1940s and 1950s

For key to butterfly maps see page 3.

were from Aspley Heath, Totternhoe, Whipsnade and in 1965 at Cople Pit.

Specimens in collections: "Bedfordshire" 1923 W.G.Nash (Oxford County Museum); Aspley Heath 1955, King's Wood, Heath and Reach 1952 and Totternhoe 1946 (Humphrey-Kershaw); Dunstable Downs 1945 (G.F.B.Prior); Whipsnade 1951 (Hopkins-Alexander); Barton 1925 & 1936, Bedford 1922, Odell 1931(Tebbs); Kensworth 1929 (Luton Museum).

In 1976 there were reports from Dunstable Downs and in 1979 ten were seen at the opposite end of the County at Sharnbrook Summit. In 1978 one was found on a disused allotment in central Bedford. Like the Dingy Skipper, colonies have been found in the clay pits of the Marston Vale and on rough ground in Elstow Storage Depot. Occasional butterflies have been seen in more wooded sites such as West Wood and Marston Thrift.

In recent years the Grizzled Skipper has been local and uncommon. Recorded since 1977 in 83 tetrads but in only 26 since 1990. This suggests a serious decline paralleling that recorded nationally. Usually seen in ones or twos, though 14 were seen on a transect walk on Dunstable Downs in 1993 and R.C.Revels saw 20-30 at Waterloo Thorns in June 1996.
Flight: April to early July (weeks 18 to 27, peak 20 to 23)*. Occasional second-generation butterflies have been seen in late July and August.
Larval Foodplants: Wild strawberry, creeping cinquefoil*, silverweed, tormentil, agrimony and brambles.

Family: **Papilionidae**

The 'swallowtails' are among the largest (wingspans 76-96 mm) and most strikingly patterned butterflies in Britain. With their prominent markings and long 'tails' on the hindwings, they are readily recognisable. There are no records of swallowtails forming breeding colonies in Bedfordshire and only early and uncertain records of their occurrence in the County.

The Swallowtail *Papilio machaon* Linnaeus (1539)

Pre VCH: There is a postscript to Charles Abbot's manuscript report to the Linnean Society dated 12 August 1798 (on the Chequered Skipper and other finds) in which he recorded seeing the Swallowtail on two occasions that year. He caught one at Clapham Park Wood but "it being his first season, thro' awkwardness, suffered it to escape out of his net." In the same document he reported that in June (or July overwritten) 1798 he was given a larva by a lady who found it in a patch of carrots in a garden in Bedford. An entry in his notebook (MS1) reads:

"Caterpillar of the *Machaon* taken nearly full fed last week in June 1798 began to spin July 16. Chrysalised 20th. remained in Chrysalis all the winter. appeared in the fly state Aug. 10. 1799."

Against the entry is written, in a different hand, "Windlesham, Surrey ?". This was repeated without the question mark at several places in J.C.Dale's notebooks and has continued to be repeated in the literature, including Collins (1995). However, elsewhere in Abbot's notebook under *Papilio machaon* there is the entry "chrysalised at Windlesham July 20th 1798". It seems likely that Abbot took the larva that he had been given in Bedford with him on his excursion to Surrey and that it pupated there. Whether he found a second larva at Windlesham is not clear. J.C.Dale did not record acquiring a specimen with Abbot's collection.
Post VCH: The only known records during this century have been of escapes from captivity.

For details of standard weeks see page 6.

Scarce Swallowtail *Iphiclides podalirius* (Scopoli) (1540)

Pre VCH: Said to have been taken by Charles Abbot in or near Clapham Park Wood in May 1803 (Haworth, 1803). He is also said to have reported seeing Scarce Swallowtail on two or three occasions before he caught one. J.C.Dale (MS2) recorded the specimen amongst those he acquired from Abbot so the one in the Dale collection side-labelled "Bedford May 1803" is probably the same specimen. According to Walker (1907) the label under the specimen in J.C.Dale's handwriting reads "Clapham Park wood, May 1803? nr. Bedford. Dr Abbot? Mus. Dr. Abbot". Whether this was a genuine wild individual is uncertain, but Dale (1833) considered it "undoubtedly British" and R.S.Wilkinson (1982) in his review of the early records of the Scarce Swallowtail was inclined to give Abbot the benefit of the doubt. J.C.Dale (1833 and MS3) wrote of seeing one from his coach near Eltisley in Cambridgeshire on 9 July 1818 so it seems possible that the occasional individual was flying in England during the early part of the 19th century. (See also pages 12-13) No more recent records are known.

Family: **Pieridae Whites and Yellows**

The 'whites' are one of the best known or, in the case of two species, notorious groups of butterflies. All six legs are used when perching and walking. The eggs are characteristically tall and conical or spindle- shaped with slight external ribbing. The larvae feed exposed on their foodplants and in some species, such as the Large White, are gregarious. The pupae are attached to the substrate, usually a stem of a plant, by a silk girdle.

Subfamily: **Dismorphiinae**

The Wood White is the only representative in Britain of this predominantly New World group. Although the white colour of the wings appears similar to that of other species in the Pieridae, the pigments are chemically different. Wingspan around 42 mm. Its larvae feed on legumes.

Wood White

Wood White *Leptidea sinapis sinapis* (Linnaeus) (1541) (Plate 28)

Pre VCH: Recorded by Abbot (MS1) from "Clapham Wood" on 13 August 1798 and from Twin Woods on 24 June 1799. J.C.Dale (MS5) gave White Wood as a locality but the date is not clear.

VCH: Not listed.

Post VCH: Nothing is known of the status of this species, which flies weakly along woodland rides, during much of this century, though H.Nicholls was reported (Anon, 1915) as saying in 1915 that "it has disappeared from most of its old haunts & feared may become extinct". No Bedfordshire specimens have been found in collections but it was known from Odell Great Wood in the 1940s. West commented in 1949 that it was "very rare indeed and in need of the greatest protection that can be given to it".

For key to butterfly maps see page 3.

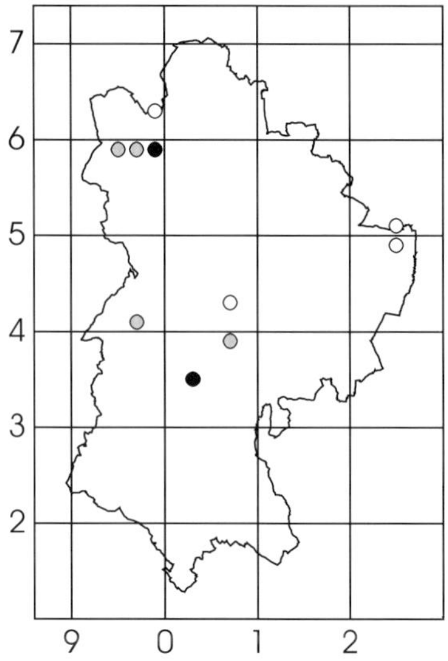

Currently very local and uncommon. Recorded since 1977 in only 10 tetrads. Found in Wilstead Wood in 1978, West Wood and Odell Great Wood in 1979. It was reported from Maulden Woods in 1975 and was still present in 1989 and 1990. No reports were received from 1991 to 1994 but the Wood White was seen there again in 1995.It was seen in Marston Thrift around 1983 and six were seen there in June 1996. Two sightings were made in 1993 and 1994 in Felmersham Nature Reserve, an unusual habitat for this species. Despite their apparently feeble flight, it is possible that these were strays from Odell Great Wood where Wood Whites were flying at the time. Sawford (1987) mentioned two being seen at Knocking Hoe in 1977 and wondered about their origin. There were also sightings in Potton Wood in 1985 and in Flitwick Wood in 1994 but these occasional finds seem more likely to be releases of captive stock rather than butterflies which have dispersed naturally. The Wood White prefers broad sunny rides or clearings where its foodplants are abundant and can disappear if such sites become overgrown.

Flight: May to July (weeks 18 to 29, with most seen in 23 to 25)*. The later sightings may represent a second generation.

Larval Foodplants: Meadow vetchling*, tufted vetch*, other vetches and common bird's-foot-trefoil.

Subfamily: **Coliadinae**

The wing colour in this subfamily is yellow or orange-yellow with a black or orange spot in the centre of each wing. Wingspans 50-74 mm. The three species of Clouded Yellow have black borders to the wings. The Brimstone is unusual in this family in over-wintering as an adult and in feeding as a larva on shrubs. It is the only species resident in Britain and Bedfordshire. The other three species are immigrants whose larvae feed on legumes.

Brimstone

Pale Clouded Yellow *Colias hyale* (Linnaeus) (1543)

Berger's Clouded Yellow *Colias alfacariensis* Berger (1544)

Records of the "Pale Clouded Yellow" do not distinguish these two species and the few specimens surviving in collections have not been dissected. The two species are therefore put together here but one would expect Berger's Clouded Yellow to be found on the chalk downs where its foodplant, horseshoe vetch, grows. Records from sites away from the chalk are more likely to refer to the Pale Clouded Yellow.

For details of standard weeks see page 6.

Pre VCH: In the Natural History Notebooks (MS1) of T.Orlebar Marsh there is a reference to *hyale* at Clapham and Biddenham in 1798.
VCH: "Bedford, Woburn; plentiful in 1900 and 1901".
Post VCH: Found by S.H.Kershaw at Sharpenhoe on 3 days in August 1933 and by R.E.R.Sanderson there in September 1934. W.G.Nash (1934) also found 10 in 1934 in lucerne fields around Bedford. West (1949) reported it as found near Woodcraft Wood, Stevington in 1940 and "odd specimens" in 1947. D.Rands saw a "Pale Clouded Yellow" in the Marston Vale in 1983. G.Herbert saw a larva with markings similar to those of Berger's Clouded Yellow on horseshoe vetch on Whipsnade Downs in 1992 but the identification was not confirmed.

Specimens in collections: Sharpenhoe 1934 (Humphrey-Kershaw); Wilden 1933 (Tebbs).

Flight: Immigrants may appear as early as April but this species is most often seen from July to September.
Larval Foodplants: Pale Clouded Yellow – lucerne and clovers; Berger's Clouded Yellow – horseshoe vetch.

Clouded Yellow *Colias croceus* (Geoffroy) (1545)

Pre VCH: Abbot's notebook (MS1) contains the entry against *Edusa* "this rare insect taken in tolerable plenty about Clapham August and September 1797". It seems likely that the *Papilio Palaeno* that he reported to the Linnean Society on 12 August 1798 as taken "about the middle of August 1797 in the County of Bedford" was the white form of the female Clouded Yellow, var. *helice*.

F.O.Morris (1895) mentioned several at Bushmead Priory though the date is not clear, probably in the mid-1800s. H.W.Tomlinson (1892) reported that "*C. edusa* was very abundant in a field in the middle of the village of Clapham at the beginning and middle of August" in 1892. It was also seen in that year on the Great Barford to Blunham road and at Bromham, Turvey, near Harlington and at Milton. E.R.Williams noted "14 males & only 2 females taken round Bedford in September 1894. Males very numerous & many more could have been captured." (Mitchell, 1990).

VCH: as *C. edusa* Linn. "Bedford, Potton; abundant in the year 1900".
Post VCH: This colourful immigrant species can appear almost anywhere in the County. Usually only one or two individuals are seen in a year but occasionally it is common as in 1947 (West, 1949) and 1983. Some eight individuals were seen in 1994 and around 35 to date in 1996. The white form of the female, var. *helice*, has rarely occurred in the County but was seen in 1921, 1933, 1947, 1959 and 1996.

Specimens in collections: Ampthill 1949 (Hopkins-Alexander).

Flight: Any time between April and September. In 1943 West found one flying at Thurleigh as late as 2 November.
Larval Foodplants: Clovers and lucerne.

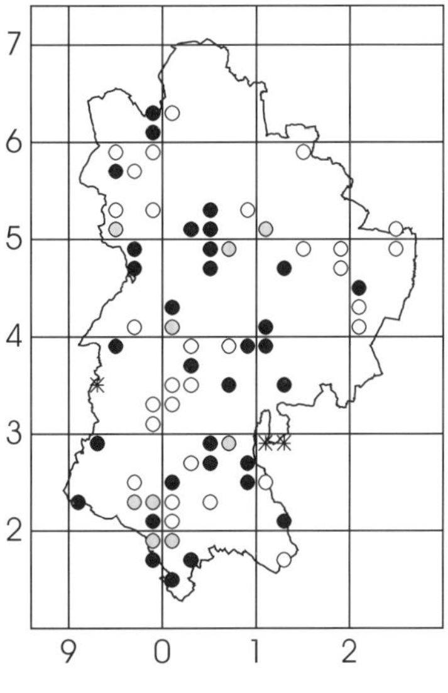

For key to butterfly maps see page 3.

Brimstone ***Gonepteryx rhamni rhamni*** **(Linnaeus) (1546)**
(Plate 64 and drawing on page 220)
Pre VCH: T.Orlebar Marsh (MS1) recorded the Brimstone from Clapham and Biddenham in 1798. Charles Abbot (MS1) recorded finding it as "common August & September 1797" and also on 23 February 1799 but gave no locality. "Common in the spring and autumn" in the neighbourhood of Luton wrote Lucas in 1855. Reported as seen in the Everton area on 3 January 1835 (Anon, 1891) and from Bedford by Hasted in 1890.
VCH: "Bedford, Luton, Potton; frequent in clover fields".

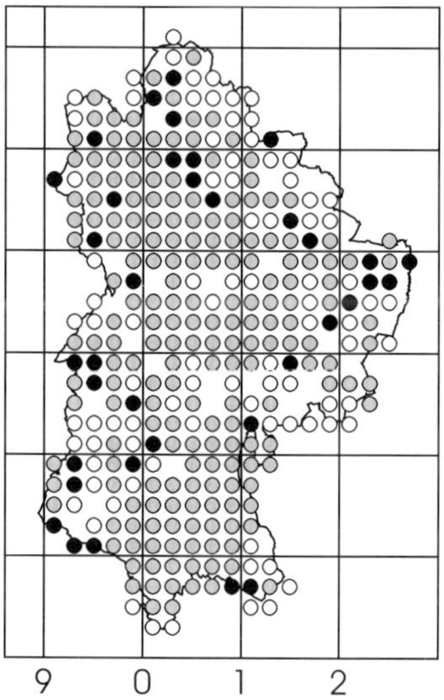

Post VCH: In 1949 West reported the Brimstone as having a "fairly even distribution throughout the county" though Kershaw (1954) rated it as uncommon in King's Wood, Heath and Reach.

Currently widespread, the Brimstone has been recorded since 1977 in 318 tetrads but is rarely encountered in large numbers. Thus it would be unusual for more than 15 individuals to be seen on a transect walk, though 48 were counted on one walk on Whipsnade Downs in August 1993. Numerous eggs can often be found under the leaves of buckthorn bushes in early summer. Hibernating individuals are rarely seen though in February 1985 one was found in a cultivated *Berberis* plant in Dunstable. It was seen to remain in the same position during a period of heavy snowfall but disappeared during subsequent warmer weather.
Flight: Often the first species seen in the spring. In Bromham in 1995 a male was seen flying on 15 January and again on 3 March flying over snow-covered ground. Seen on transects in every week from the beginning of April to the end of September (weeks 14 to 39, peaks 18 to 21 and 30 to 34)*. Elsewhere, individuals have been seen on mild days through most of the autumn and winter.
Larval Foodplants: Buckthorn* and alder buckthorn*.

Subfamily: **Pierinae**

The ground colour of the wings is white with black markings. Wingspans 40-70 mm. There is usually more than one generation in the annual life cycle and the winter is spent in the pupal stage. The larvae of most species in this group feed on crucifers. All the four species that breed in Britain also do so in Bedfordshire, one is extinct and one is a rare immigrant.

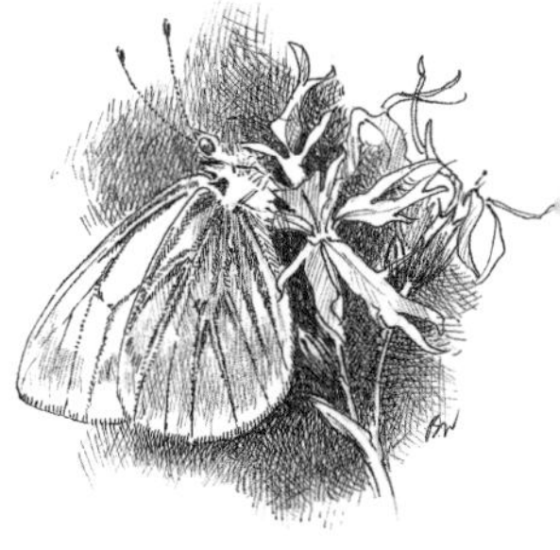

Green-veined White

For details of standard weeks see page 6.

Black-veined White *Aporia crataegi* (Linnaeus) (1548)
Pre VCH: In his notebook (MS1), Charles Abbot made the following entry: "11 larvae of *Papilio crataegi* found in a web in Clapham between Woods May 27th 1799". The notes record that he bred out 5 between 15 and 22 July. He also recorded another sighting on "June 29th 1799 Clapham Pasture South". In 1915 H.Nicholls (Anon, 1915) referred to Abbot taking it at Oakley and near Thurleigh but the source of this information is not known.
VCH: "Reported by Mr. H.Studman to have formerly occurred near Woburn".
Post VCH: Extinct in Britain by about 1922. Occasional sightings, such as one in Priory Park in 1996, are almost certainly of individuals released from captivity.

Large White *Pieris brassicae* (Linnaeus) (1549) (Plate 87)
Pre VCH: "Seen every where in fine weather" was Abbot's comment (MS1). Lucas (1855) wrote "everywhere abundant" in the neighbourhood of Luton.
VCH: "Abundant everywhere".
Post VCH: The Large White is a species whose status has probably changed little over the years though always subject to large changes in abundance from year to year. Currently widespread and usually common, spectacularly so in 1992 when as many as 817 were counted on a single walk. The large numbers apparently resulted from larvae feeding on spring oil-seed rape which was planted widely that year, possibly supplemented later by immigration from the Continent. The larvae can cause considerable damage to brassica crops in farms and gardens as well as to garden nasturtiums (Plate 88). Recorded since 1977 in 363 tetrads.

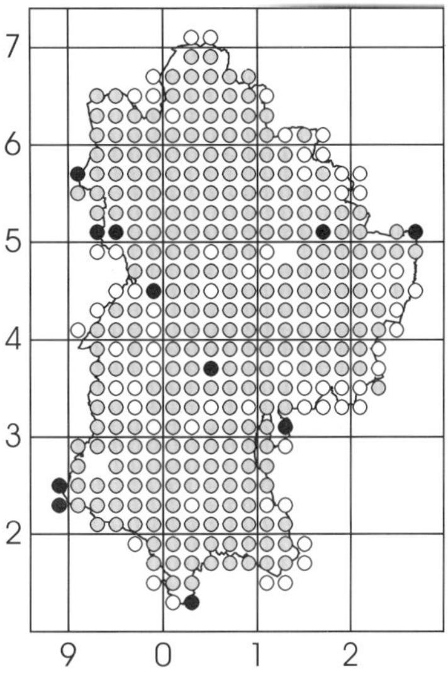

Specimens in collections: Bedford, Pegsdon and Putnoe 1931-1936 (Tebbs).

Flight: April to October in two broods (weeks 17 to 41, peaks 20 to 24 and larger from 28 to 35)*.
Larval Foodplants: Cabbage*, Brussels sprouts*, oil-seed rape* and other members of the cabbage family, wild mignonette and nasturtium.

Small White *Pieris rapae* (Linnaeus) (1550)
Pre VCH: Charles Abbot (MS1) recorded it as "seen very often Autumn 1797" and also on 22 May 1799 but gave no locality. Lucas noted it in 1855 as "everywhere abundant" in the neighbourhood of Luton.
VCH: "Abundant everywhere".

Post VCH: Like the previous species, the Small White is widespread and common in most years, indeed found almost anywhere with larvae damaging cabbages and other brassicas (Plate 88). Recorded since 1977 in 364 tetrads with up to 85 seen on one transect walk.

Specimens in collections: "Bedford District" 1917 (Oxford County Museum); Dunstable Downs 1932 (G.F.B.Prior); Bedford, Pegsdon and Putnoe 1927-1937 (Tebbs).

Flight: April to October in two broods (weeks 15 to 41, peaks 21 to 24 and 29 to 36)★.
Larval Foodplants: Cabbage★, Brussels sprouts★ and other members of the cabbage family, wild mignonette★, nasturtium and aubretia★.

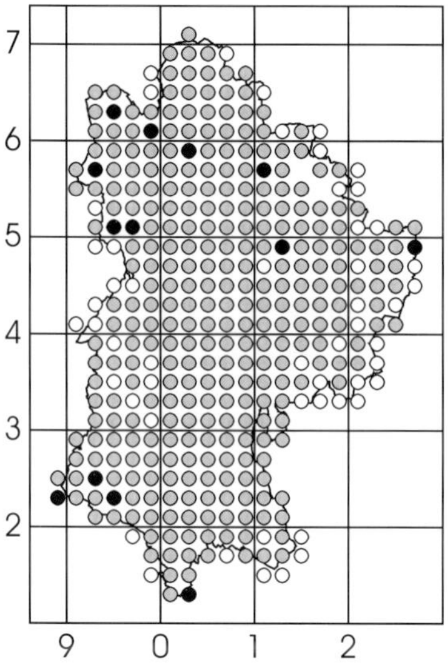

Green-veined White *Pieris napi* (Linnaeus) ssp. *sabellicae* (Stephens) (1551)

(Plate 29 and drawing on page 222)

Pre VCH: Noted by Abbot (MS1) as "Pastures – common August 1797" and also found on 23 May 1799, presumably in the neighbourhood of Bedford. Listed by Lucas (1855) as "everywhere abundant" in the neighbourhood of Luton.
VCH: "Abundant everywhere".
Post VCH: Widespread (recorded since 1977 in 343 tetrads) but less commonly seen than the two previous species, transect sightings rarely exceeding 30 individuals on one walk. Prefers more sheltered and damper places such as woodland rides, damp meadows and ditch edges.

Specimens in collections: Barton, Bedford, Odell, Putnoe and Wilden 1931-1937 (Tebbs).

Flight: April to September in two broods (weeks 16 to 39, peaks 21 to 24 and 29 to 33)★.
Larval Foodplants: Garlic mustard★, horse-radish★ and other crucifers.

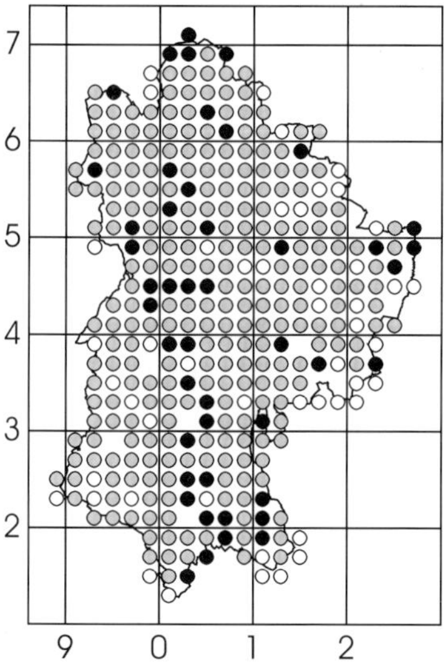

Bath White *Pontia daplidice* (Linnaeus) (1552)

Pre VCH: A.H.Haworth (1803) reported Abbot's find of a faded Bath White in White Wood, near Gamlingay in June of that year. There is a specimen set as an underside in the Dale collection and side-labelled "1803 Gamlingay". According to Walker (1907) the label under the specimen in J.C.Dale's handwriting reads "Mus. Dr. Abbot, White Wood, Gamlingay, Camb. June 1803, Dr Abbot ". Whether this is the same specimen or a mislabelling is not clear as C.W.Dale (1890) said that his father J.C.Dale gave the original

For details of standard weeks see page 6.

to the national collection in 1846. Fryer (1938) also noted this specimen as in the British Museum but D.Carter (pers. comm. 1995) said that it is not now in the collections in the Natural History Museum.(See also pages 12-13). There have been no further records in the County.

Orange Tip *Anthocharis cardamines* (Linnaeus) ssp. *britannica* (Verity) (1553) (Plate 65)

Pre VCH: Charles Abbot recorded in his notebook (MS1) that he found Orange Tip on 24 and 25 April 1798 and on 3 June 1799 but, as for many other species, gave no locality. J.C.Dale (MS3) noted seeing it on 18 June 1818 near Bedford. Living near Everton, Emily Shore noted in her diary on 16 May 1835 "Orange-tip abounds" (Anon, 1891). Lucas wrote in 1855 that it was "very common in May and June" in the neighbourhood of Luton. Hasted recorded seeing it in Bedford in 1890.

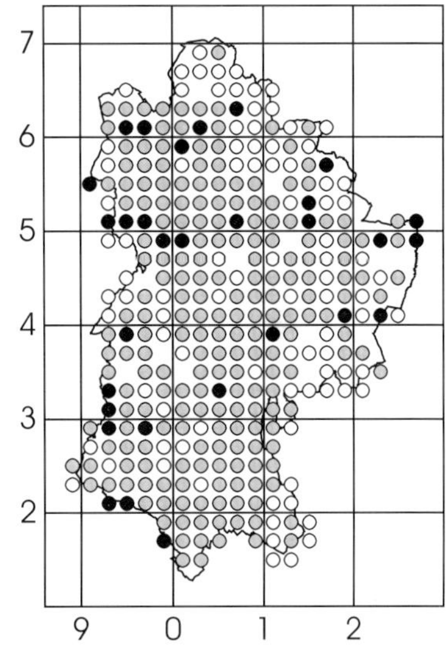

VCH: "Generally distributed".

Post VCH. West (1949) recorded the Orange Tip as "plentiful throughout the county" but Kershaw rated it as scarce in King's Wood, Heath and Reach in 1954. W.J.Champkin (1975) wrote of a "wonderful season" in 1974.

Specimens in collections: Dunstable Downs 1941 (G.F.B. Prior); Barton, Odell and Putnoe 1931-1934 (Tebbs).

Widespread – recorded since 1977 in 327 tetrads. Males are most commonly seen on roadside verges but usually as single individuals well spaced from one another.

Flight: On the wing from early April in warm springs and in cold weather (as in 1994) individuals can still be seen at the beginning of July (weeks 15 to 25, peak 18 to 22)*.

Larval Foodplants: Garlic mustard*, hedge mustard, cuckooflower*, charlock*, honesty*, horse-radish*, oil-seed rape* and dame's-violet*. Eggs can be found easily on garlic mustard.

Family: **Lycaenidae**

The 'hairstreaks', 'coppers', 'blues' and 'metalmarks' are at first sight a diverse assemblage of species to be collected together in one family. Except in the latter group, all six legs are used when perching and walking. The brilliant iridescent colours, green, purple, orange and blue are interference colours produced not by pigments but by the structure of the scales. The eggs are hemispherical with complicated shell structure in some species.

For key to butterfly maps see page 3.

Subfamily: **Theclinae** **The Hairstreaks**

White-letter Hairstreak

The 'hairstreaks' are secretive butterflies, often difficult to find and therefore greatly under-recorded. Their life cycle has only one generation per year. All, except the Green Hairstreak, overwinter in the egg stage. The larvae feed mainly on shrubs and trees. Five species occur in Britain of which four breed in Bedfordshire. The fifth is probably extinct in the County. Wingspans 25-36 mm.

Green Hairstreak *Callophrys rubi* (Linnaeus) (1555) (Plate 5)
Pre VCH: Reported from Clapham Wood on 22 May 1798 and 6 June 1799 by Abbot (MS1). Lucas (1855) noted it as "occasionally taken" in the neighbourhood of Luton.
VCH: Not listed.
Post VCH: H.Nicholls was quoted (Anon, 1915) as finding Green Hairstreak at Sandy around 1915. S.R.Bowden recorded it on Deacon Hill in 1921 and on Knocking Hoe in 1917-21 and 1943 (Bowden, 1965). R.M.Craske recalled it as common on the west side of Sharpenhoe Clappers in the period 1918-28 and again in 1953. It was still present there in 1995. A.H.Foster (1934) reported it as "fairly common on Pegsdon and Barton Hills". According to West (1949) it was a "common, but secretive species" recorded from Stevington, Barton, Totternhoe, Clapham, Dedmansey Wood and Pegsdon. Blackie (1950b) found it at Totternhoe in that year. Kershaw (1954) reported it as common in King's Wood, Heath and Reach in 1954 but there has been only one recent record, from an adjacent area. It probably occurs elsewhere on the Greensand Ridge but is easily overlooked. R.C.Revels found one near Biggleswade in 1961.

Colonies were reported from Bison Hill, Old Warden Tunnel and Sharnbrook Summit in 1979, Stewartby Lakes in 1989 and the Elstow Storage Depot site in 1993 to 1995.

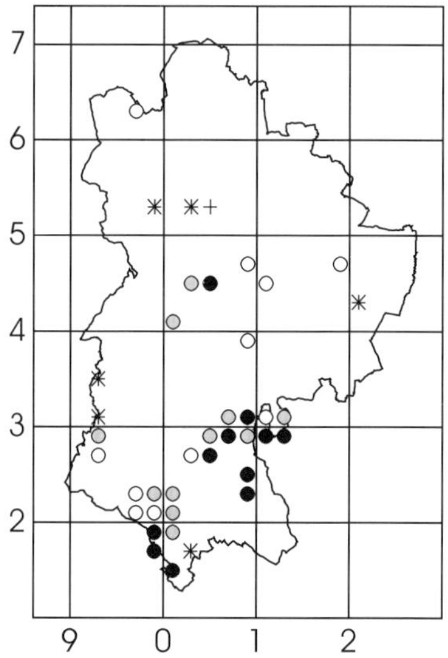

Specimens in collections: "Bedfordshire" 1919 W.G.Nash (Oxford County Museum); Whipsnade 1945 & 1948 (Buckinghamshire County Museum); Barton 1934-1938 (Tebbs).

Currently the Green Hairstreak is best described as local, living along woodland edges and among downland scrub. Recorded since 1977 in only 33 tetrads, mostly along the chalk downs. It remains secretive and difficult to locate and as with all the other Hairstreaks is probably under-recorded, especially off the chalk. However once a favoured perching place has been found several may be seen on the same bush. One small wild apple tree on Whipsnade Downs yielded 26 on one occasion in 1993 and over 100 were reported from the same area on 31 May 1994.
Flight: April to June (weeks 15 to 26, peak 18 to 21)*.

For details of standard weeks see page 6.

Larval Foodplants: Common rock-rose*, common bird's-foot-trefoil, gorse, broom and several other plants.

Brown Hairstreak *Thecla betulae* (Linnaeus) (1556)

Pre VCH: Abbot (MS1) found the Brown Hairstreak in Clapham Park on 8 September 1797 and on 13 August 1798. He also found it in Sheerhatch Wood on 7 September 1799.

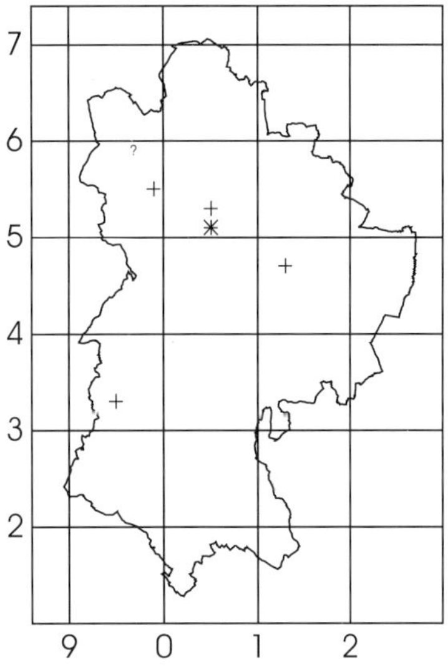

VCH: "Reported near Woburn by Mr. H.Studman".

Post VCH: H.Nicholls mentioned in 1915 that it was found "once only between Stevington and Pav-en-ham" (Anon, 1915). A single male was found by B.B.West in Bedford Cemetery on 3 August 1944. Larvae were reported by West (1949) as found in Odell by J.H.Payne between 1943 and 1948 but this report is now thought to be incorrect (JHP pers. comm. 1994). A.J.Martin commented in 1979 that "it still cannot be found in its old Bedfordshire haunts". Mention of "small numbers in south" in the 1940s in Nau *et al.*. (1987) would appear to be an error as the only record in the south of the County is a possible sighting by R.C.Revels in Whipsnade Wild Animal Park in the late 1980s. Releases in Odell Great Wood and an attempt to introduce Brown Hairstreak in the Maulden area in the 1970s do not seem to have been successful.

Flight: August and September.

Larval Foodplant: Blackthorn.

Purple Hairstreak *Quercusia quercus* (Linnaeus) (1557) (Plate 25)

Pre VCH: Charles Abbot (MS1) noted Purple Hairstreak on 10 August 1799 but gave no locality. J.C.Dale (MS3) found "larvas of *Thecla quercus*" on 1 June 1820; from the context it was in Clapham Park Wood. W.Greenwell-Lax (1878) found Purple Hairstreak near Stagsden and thought it unusual as it had not been seen for many years in the Bedford district.

VCH: "Generally about oaks in woods".

Post VCH: Tutt (1905-9) reported Purple Hairstreak from Bedford (quoting W.G.Nash), Potton (quoting W.Bond-Smith) and Luton (quoting Lucas). "Our commonest Hairstreak, though not often observed owing to the height at which it flies" wrote West (1949), listing Putnoe, Keysoe, Odell, Swineshead, Bolnhurst, Wootton, Houghton Conquest and Aspley Heath as localities. In 1954 S.H.Kershaw reported it as common in King's Wood, Heath and Reach. Prior to 1977 it was also reported from Hanger Wood (Goodson, 1966), Hardwick Spinney in 1953, Odell in 1974 and Maulden in 1976.

Specimens in collections: Putnoe 1922 and 1923 (Tebbs).

For key to butterfly maps see page 3.

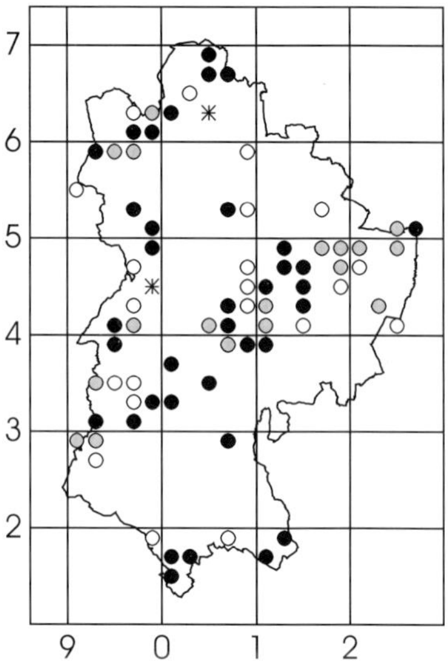

Although recorded since 1977 in 74 tetrads, the Purple Hairstreak is probably greatly under-recorded for the reason cited above. It gives the impression of being local and uncommon, occurring mainly in old oak woodland, but it is by no means confined to the larger woods. It is often most easily found by scanning the foliage of prominent ash trees growing amongst oaks but sometimes other trees, such as horse chestnut, are favoured. The butterflies seem to be more active morning and evening. In 1995 good numbers were flying up to 7.30 pm BST and small groups of 2 and 3 individuals could be seen chasing one another around the tree canopy. In hot weather they mostly walk around among the leaves, making only short flights and may descend to ground level. Occasionally individuals have been seen leaving woodland and flying out over adjacent fields. It is currently most readily seen in the larger woods, such as Chicksands Wood, King's Wood (Heath and Reach), Marston Thrift, Maulden Wood and Odell Great Wood, but populations probably exist in most woods in the County where oak is growing and also in many small copses.
Flight: Late June to the end of August (weeks 26 to 35, peak 29 to 31)★.
Larval Foodplants: Oaks★. Eggs have been found on oaks at several sites.

White-letter Hairstreak *Satyrium w-album* (Knoch) (1558)
(Plate 27 and drawing on page 226)
Pre VCH: J.C.Dale's notebooks contain references to Abbot finding this species although Abbot himself (MS1) did not record it. Dale (MS2) noted receiving specimens from Abbot's collection. The specific name given is "*pruni*" in the earlier notebooks but the Black Hairstreak had not been discovered in Britain at that time.
VCH: "Bedford and Woburn about wych elm".
Post VCH: According to Tutt (1905-9), W.G.Nash found this species in Clapham. R.M.Craske recalled finding White-letter Hairstreak in Roxton Spinney in the 1920s and it was present in Great Barford in 1926. S.H.Kershaw saw it in Aspley Heath in 1937. Recorded in the 1940s from Clapham Park, Clophill, Odell, Pulloxhill, Shefford and from the area between Pavenham and Felmersham (West, 1949). It continued to be reported from Pavenham in 1952, 1959 and 1960. It was also found at Hinwick and Pictshill in 1952 and in Felmersham, Stevington and Sheerhatch Wood in 1959. R.Palmer in his diary for 7 July 1943 noted it as "abundant in lane between Pulloxhill and Barton". Kershaw (1954) reported that larvae were common in King's Wood, Heath and Reach.

R.C.Revels recalled an explosion in numbers in the east of the County during 1956-57 when this butterfly occurred in numbers wherever elms were common in hedgerows and spinneys. In late June and July it seemed that almost all the hedgerows in that area contained colonies. The adults were seen flying round the trees and feeding on thistle, bramble and mayweed flowers. By 1959, the numbers had dropped and only "favoured" elms, particularly wych elm, supported colonies.

Specimens in collections: Great Barford 1926 (Tebbs).

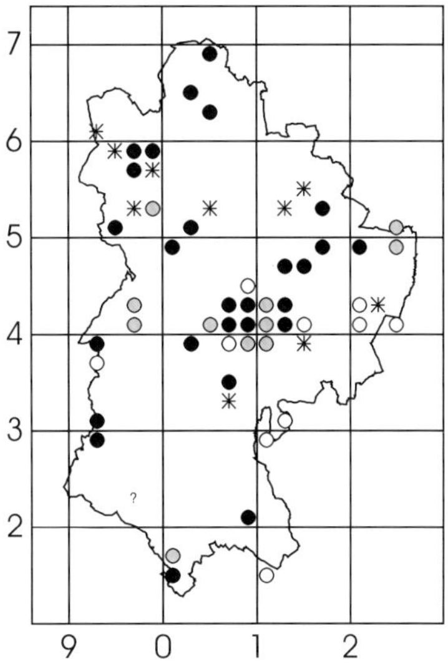

Some colonies of White-letter Hairstreak were lost following the outbreak of elm disease in the 1970s and changes in the management of some woodland habitats. It was found in Maulden Wood in 1976 and in Marston Thrift in 1951 and 1976 and was still present on the latter site in 1994. B.Fensome found it in Heath Wood near Whipsnade from 1977 to 1979 but since then it had not been seen in the area until one was noticed in 1995 in a garden near Whipsnade Wild Animal Park and another in Studham in 1996.

One of its main strongholds is currently Chicksands Wood where it was first reported in 1988. It has been recorded from 45 tetrads since 1977 and from the number of sites reported during the 1990s it seems to be widespread in the County. These include Ampthill Park, Barton Hills, Box End, Bromham Lake Nature Reserve, Clophill, College Wood, Coppice Wood, Cranfield, several around Haynes, Home Wood, Houghton Conquest, King's Wood (Heath and Reach), Potton, Sandy, Sheerhatch Wood, Tempsford, Turvey, Upper Dean and Wilstead Wood. Because it lives in very local colonies it is probably under-recorded. However in favourable seasons, large numbers may be seen. Over 50 individuals were seen on 19 July 1993 in Chicksands Wood.

Flight: Late June to August (weeks 26 to 33, peak 28 to 30)★.

Larval Foodplants: Wych elm★ and other elms.

Black Hairstreak *Satyrium pruni* (Linnaeus) (1559) (Plate 26)

VCH: "Found near Bedford by Dr. Nash".

Post VCH: Tutt (1905-9) quoted W.G.Nash as finding it in Putnoe Lane. Found in Keysoepark Wood by B.B. and K.E.West on 13 June 1944 (West, 1949, 1961) and seen there regularly until the early 1970s. The colony was thought to have disappeared with the clearance of parts of the wood and replanting with conifers. However, J.E.Thomas (1975) stated that breeding colonies survived the clearances and that the wood was being managed voluntarily by the owners to encourage the species. He also suggested that both Putnoe Wood and Keysoepark Wood supported colonies for at least 30 years and probably for 150 years. The last written record of sightings in Keysoepark Wood was in 1971. Although there are a few sheltered and sunny blackthorn bushes in the wood, most of it is no longer suitable for Black Hairstreak (see page 51) but it is just possible that a small population may still survive there.

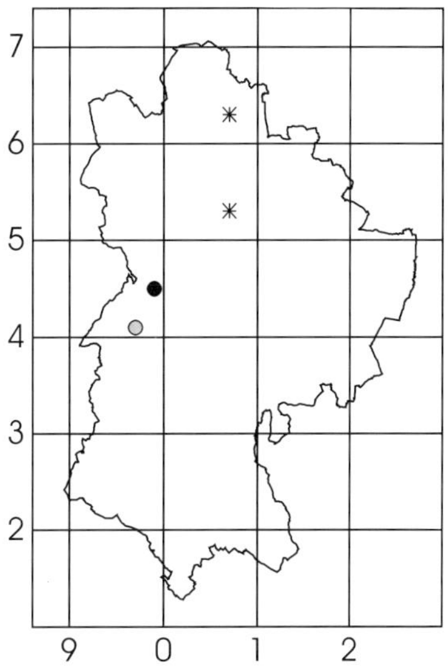

Specimens in collections: Keysoepark Wood 1940s (B.B.West collection).

For key to butterfly maps see page 3.

A colony was discovered in Marston Thrift in 1984 by A.Tomczynski and L.Carman. During the late 1980s good numbers were seen well distributed in the wood but in recent years the colony appeared to have become small and localised and therefore very vulnerable (see also pages 46-47). However, in 1996 it was seen again in other parts of the wood. In 1995 one individual was seen in Wootton Wood, 3 km north-east of Marston Thrift. Given the sedentary nature of the Black Hairstreak, there is hope that this may represent a separate colony. With the low numbers present in recent years, it is possible that it may linger undetected in other woods in north Bedfordshire.

Some of the records in Nau *et al.* (1987) and also some mapped in Emmet and Heath (1989) have not been traced and must be regarded as not confirmed.

Flight: Late June and early July (weeks 25 to 28)*.

Larval Foodplants: Blackthorn* and wild plum.

Subfamily: **Lycaeninae The Coppers**

The 'coppers' may be single or double brooded, overwintering as larvae which feed on *Rumex* species. The Small Copper (wingspan 26-34 mm) is the only species breeding in Bedfordshire.

Small Copper *Lycaena phlaeas* (Linnaeus) ssp. *eleus* (Fabricius) (1561) (Cover)

Pre VCH: T.Orlebar Marsh (MS1) recorded Small Copper from Clapham and Biddenham in 1798 and Abbot (MS1) noted it on 20 June 1799 but gave no locality. "Not scarce" in the neighbourhood of Luton according to Lucas (1855).

VCH: "Generally distributed".

Post VCH: Tutt (1905-9) quoted W.G.Nash as finding it in Bedford and Hill for its presence in Sandy. Bowden (1965) found it on Knocking Hoe in 1917-21. "Locally common" in the 1940s according to West (1949). S.H.Kershaw noted it regularly in a field near Woburn Sands with over 100 seen on 23 September 1947. Reported as scarce in the early 1970s but more common in 1975, 1984 and 1989. R.C.Revels saw over 300 in a field near Sandy in the late 1980s.

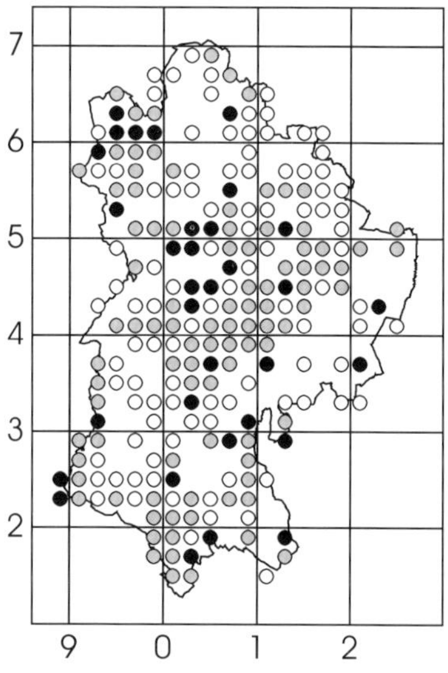

Specimens in collections: "Bedfordshire" 1918 W.G.Nash (Oxford County Museum); Luton 1918 (Turner); Dunstable Downs 1937, 1939 (G.F.B.Prior); Aspley Heath 1947 (Humphrey-Kershaw); Totternhoe Knolls 1952 (Graveley-Edwards); Barton 1925, Great Barford 1922, Pegsdon 1936, Putnoe 1922-35 and Wilden 1933 (Tebbs).

Currently remains local, though recorded since 1977 in 226 tetrads, but not often common. Found, usually in small numbers, along woodland rides and clearings and also on downland and rough grass sites such as Whipsnade Downs, Studham Common and Wavendon Heath. On sandy soils it is more common in wetter summers as the main foodplant, sheep's sorrel, soon wilts and dies in hot dry weather.

Flight: May to October (weeks 21 to 41, peaks 21 to 24 and 30 to 34)*.

For details of standard weeks see page 6.

Larval Foodplants: Sheep's sorrel*, common sorrel and broad-leaved dock*.

Large Copper *Lycaena dispar dispar* (Haworth) (1562)
Pre VCH: There is an entry against *dispar* in Charles Abbot's notebook (MS1) in another hand, possibly that of J.C.Dale, "Tempsford, Beds in letter from Drury to Mr Walcott". This record is also mentioned in Dale's notebooks. The original letter, if it still exists, has not been located.

Subfamily: **Polyommatinae The Blues**

The 'blues' may go through one or more generations per year and most species overwinter as larvae. The larvae feed mainly on herbaceous legumes. One exception is the Holly Blue whose larvae feed on the buds and fruits of woody plants. The larvae of several species have more or less complex associations with ants. Of the eight species that currently breed as native races in Britain, five breed in Bedfordshire. The record of one species is uncertain and two species are extinct in the County. One species is an occasional immigrant. Wingspans 18-34 mm.

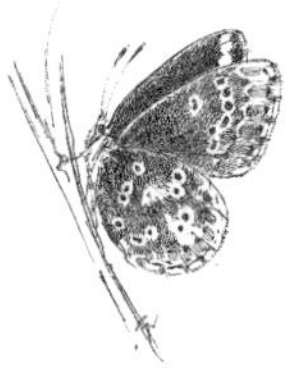

Brown Argus

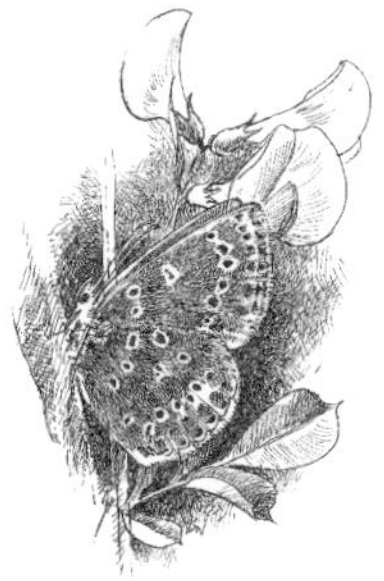

Common Blue

Long-tailed Blue *Lampides boeticus* (Linnaeus) (1567)
Post VCH: There are two specimens in the Hitchin Museum labelled "Sharpenhoe, Beds. June 1974" collected by S.Woodhall. No more details are known. These specimens are in a worn condition which would appear to rule against the release of bred individuals. However, the date is unusually early for this rare immigrant which is seen most often in August and September.

Small Blue *Cupido minimus* (Fuessly) (1569) (Plate 4)
Pre VCH: J.C.Dale on a manuscript list (MS4) of British Lepidoptera made a note "I do not know why Samouelle & Co call this species the Bedford Blue. Dr Abbott MSS mention only Windlesham Heath Where he took it." This is not correct because Abbot (MS1) also recorded finding *Alsus* on 23 July 1799 but gave no locality. (The entry "Windlesham Heath July 16th" is in Abbot's notebook after "*Alsus* – Small Blue Lewin" but is entered in what may be a different hand. The year was probably in 1798 when we know from other entries that he was in Surrey on that date.)

The textbooks state repeatedly that the Small Blue was first found in Bedfordshire and for a time was known as the Bedford Blue. However the original record has not been located.

For key to butterfly maps see page 3.

Lewin (1795), who first reported this species in Britain, called it the Small Blue and made no mention of Bedfordshire.

VCH: as *Polyommatus alsus* Schiff. "Hills and railway banks around Bedford and Luton".

Post VCH: According to W.G.Nash (as quoted by Tutt) the Small Blue was locally common on Barton Hills in the early years of the century. Bowden (1965) saw it on Deacon Hill and Knocking Hoe in 1917-21 and A.H.Foster (1934) recorded it from Barton and Warden Hills. West (1949) reported that this species needed "protection within the County as it is very local in distribution." He listed it as found in the 1940s at Totternhoe, Dunstable Downs and Barton and it was also known from Sewell and Sharpenhoe at that time. Blackie (1950b) found it at Totternhoe in that year.

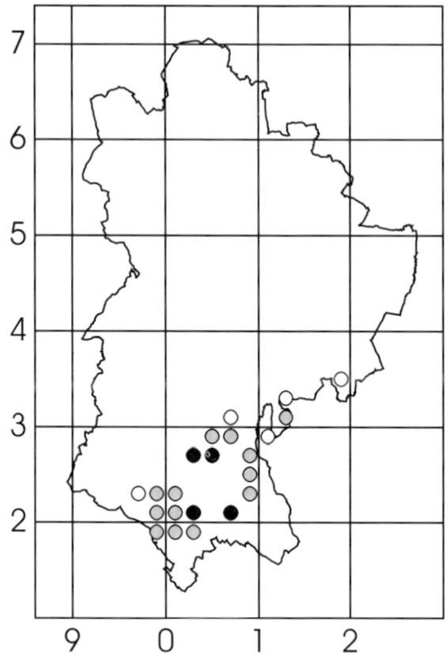

Specimens in collections: Dunstable Downs 1932-36 (G.F.B.Prior), 1941 (Graveley-Edwards), 1969 (Buckinghamshire Museum); Hexton 1942 (Buckinghamshire Museum); Pegsdon 1946 (R.S.Ferry collection); Sewell 1944 and 1945, Sharpenhoe 1944 and 1953 (Humphrey-Kershaw); Totternhoe Knolls 1948 (Graveley-Edwards); Luton 1931 (Tebbs); Sharpenhoe 1926 (Luton Museum).

The Small Blue exists in local colonies where its foodplant occurs on chalk downland, such as Whipsnade Downs and Dunstable Downs, Blow's Downs, Bradgers Hill, Galley Hill, Warden Hill and Sharpenhoe. Quarry sites, such as Sewell Cutting and Totternhoe Quarries, are especially important as kidney vetch is an early coloniser of bare chalk. Recorded since 1977 in only 22 tetrads. In favourable seasons strong colonies may reach more than 50 individuals, as on a quarry face near Totternhoe in 1994.

Flight: May to August (weeks 21 to 32, a first peak in weeks 25 to 28 and in some years a smaller peak in late July and August, weeks 30 to 32)*.

Larval Foodplant: Kidney vetch*.

Silver-studded Blue *Plebejus argus argus* (Linnaeus) (1571)

Pre VCH: In several of J.C.Dale's manuscripts (*e.g.* MS3 & MS4) there are entries against *Lycaena argus* on the Common or Heath near White Wood, Gamlingay where he found it on 17 July 1819. Sometimes the Reverend L.Jenyns' name is added alongside this record and the VCH for Cambridgeshire (Fryer, 1938) has the entry "Gamlingay in the time of Jenyns" against *P. argus.*

Gamlingay Heath is just over the County boundary in Cambridgeshire so these records make Abbot's notebook (MS1) entry "*Argus* June 29th" 1799 (no locality given) just possible. The Common Blue was also given the Latin name *argus* at that time but is clearly distinguished in Dale's notes. At one point in his notebook, against a 1797 record, Abbot used *argus* as the Latin name for the Blue Argus Butterfly, *i.e.* the Common Blue, but in the list containing the 1799 record he listed *icarus* separately from *argus* so perhaps he was by then aware of the difference. T.Orlebar Marsh (MS1) recorded *argus* from Clapham and Biddenham in 1798 but we do not know whether his identification was reliable or whether,

For details of standard weeks see page 6.

as is more likely, he was referring to the Common Blue. No further records have been found.

Brown Argus *Aricia agestis* ([Denis and Schiffermüller]) (1572)
(Plate 69 and drawing on page 231)
Pre VCH: Charles Abbot's notebook (MS1) lists "*Idas* June 27th 1799" but with no locality. *Lycaena idas* is an old synonym for *Aricia agestis*. Described by Lucas (1855) to have been "scarce" in the neighbourhood of Luton.
VCH: "Bedford, on hillsides".
Post VCH: Said by A.H.Foster (1917) to be "very common" on Pegsdon Hills and S.R.Bowden (1965) saw it on Knocking Hoe in 1917-21. R.Palmer (MS1) recorded it as "abundant" on Barton Hills in 1923. West (1949) reported it as "common especially on the chalk". S.H.Kershaw saw it in King's Wood (Heath and Reach) in 1956.

Specimens in collections: "Bedfordshire" 1918 W.G.Nash (Oxford County Museum); Dunstable Downs 1932 (Graveley-Edwards), 1933-46 (G.F.B.Prior); Barton 1943 and Sharpenhoe 1930 and 1944 (Humphrey-Kershaw); Barton 1936-41, Pegsdon 1933-34 and Putnoe 1935 (Tebbs).

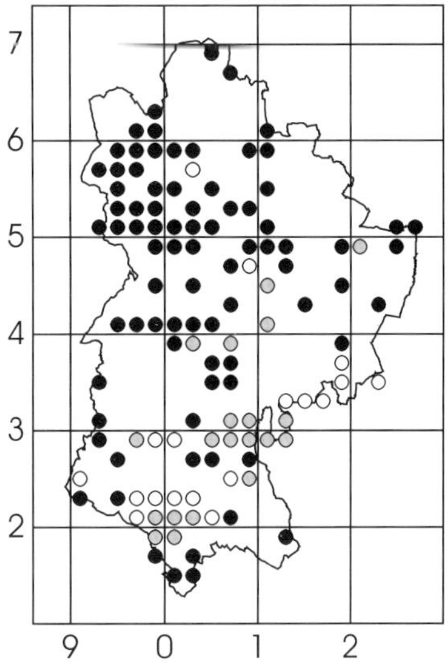

At present the Brown Argus is local but common, especially so in 1994 to 1996. Recorded since 1977 in 119 tetrads, of which 81 are new records in the 1990s. Over 30 individuals were seen on some transect walks and 60 on one occasion on Barton Hills in 1991. Until the last few years it was found mainly on chalk downland sites, such as Barton Hills and Whipsnade and Dunstable Downs but in 1994-95 a great expansion in range resulted in some 50 new sites being recorded on the Greensand Ridge as well as in green lanes, road verges and woodland rides on the clays. These sites included Bletsoe, Bolnhurst, Bromham Lake, Centenary Wood, Colmworth, Felmersham Nature Reserve, Hill Rise (Bedford), Holcot Wood, King's Wood (Heath and Reach), Marston Thrift, Odell Great Wood, Potton Wood, Renhold, Sheerhatch Wood, Studham Common, Warden Warren, Wavendon Heath, West Wood, Willington, Wootton Meadow and Yelnow New Wood. Although the Brown Argus is not always easy to distinguish from the brown form of the female Common Blue (note the difference in the spots underneath the forewings on page 231), it is not likely that this expansion in range is merely an artefact of previous under-recording. Similar changes in range have been reported from adjacent counties. One suggested cause is the increased availability of foodplants on 'set-aside' land. Numbers remained high at some sites in 1996 and R.C.Revels reported seeing well over 1000 at the land-fill site near Cople on 28 July.
Flight: May to early October in two broods (weeks 20 to 40, peaks 21 to 25 and 31 to 36)*. In hot weather, as in 1995, there is a distinct gap between the broods. In other years, individuals may be seen in most weeks through the flight period.
Larval Foodplants: Common rock-rose*, common stork's-bill, cut-leaved crane's-bill*, dove's-foot crane's-bill* and meadow crane's-bill*. In 1996 a female was seen showing egg-laying behaviour on herb-Robert but no eggs have so far been found on this plant.

For key to butterfly maps see page 3.

Common Blue *Polyommatus icarus icarus* (Rottemburg) (1574)
(Drawing on page 231)
Pre VCH: Abbot (MS1) noted this species as "common 1797" and also seen on 15 June 1799 without indicating where. (See also under Silver-studded Blue above). Lucas (1855) listed it as "very common" in the neighbourhood of Luton.
VCH: "Generally common".
Post VCH: Recorded by Bowden (1965) from Knocking Hoe in 1917-21 and 1943. In the 1940s "of very wide distribution, and locally abundant" wrote West (1949).

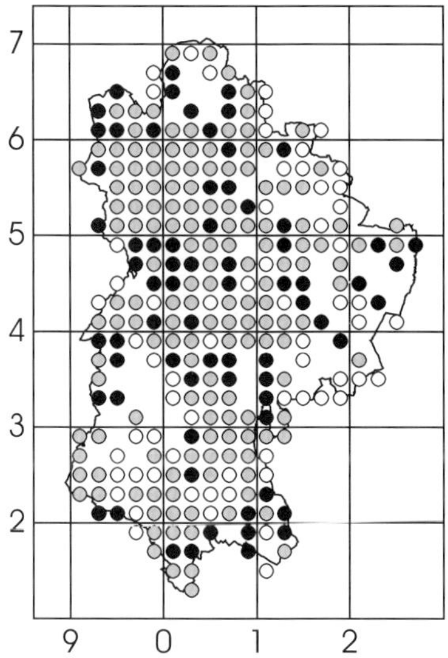

Specimens in collections: Dunstable 1916 (Liverpool Museum); Pegsdon 1935 and Totternhoe 1939 (Humphrey-Kershaw); Barton Hills 1941 and Dunstable Downs 1940 (Graveley-Edwards); Dunstable Downs 1934-40 and Totternhoe Knolls 1946-51 (G.F.B.Prior); Pegsdon 1936 and Putnoe 1927-35 (Tebbs)

The Common Blue remains widespread and often common on road verges and in rough fields and open areas. Recorded since 1977 in 286 tetrads with up to 76 seen on a single transect walk and occasional reports of 100s as in the north-west of the County in 1993.

Flight: May to September in two broods (weeks 20 to 39, peaks 22 to 26 and 31 to 36)*.
Larval Foodplants: Common bird's-foot-trefoil*, black medick*, hop trefoil*, restharrows and clovers.

Chalkhill Blue *Lysandra coridon* (Poda) (1575) (Plate 2)
Pre VCH: Charles Abbot (MS1) recorded finding the Chalkhill Blue at "Ravensbury Castle on the Chalk Hills near Barton" where he took 17 on 8 August 1799. J.C.Dale (MS2) recorded obtaining this species from Abbot's collection. Lucas (1855) reported it as "common" on Warden Hill, Luton.
VCH: "On chalk hillsides near Bedford".
Post VCH: H.Nicholls (Anon, 1915) is quoted as finding it at Barton Cutting around 1915. It is clear from the many specimens seen in collections that the Chalkhill Blue was present and probably abundant on most of the chalk hillsides between Whipsnade Downs and Pegsdon Hills during the first half of this century. Bowden (1965) knew in on Knocking Hoe in 1917-21. A.H.Foster (1917) reported it as "very abundant" on Pegsdon Hills and again (1934) as "in profusion" there. R.Palmer (MS1) found it abundant on Barton Hills in 1923. West (1949) described it as "confined solely to the chalk in the south of the County and there locally common", listing Totternhoe, Barton, Knocking Hoe and Blow's Downs as sites. It is clear that on many sites the Chalkhill Blue was present in much greater numbers than have been seen since the 1950s when the advent of myxomatosis changed the character of the downland vegetation. R.M.Craske described seeing thousands of individuals at the base of Dunstable Downs around Pascomb Pit between the wars. However, it is doubtful if the numbers in Bedfordshire ever reached the levels of those on Therfield Heath, the 'mecca' for collectors in the years before about 1930. (L.H.Newman (1954) gave a graphic

description of collecting on the Heath.) West (1954) remarked on the great numbers at Pegsdon but in 1957 was decrying the "disastrous spoliation of the Pegsdon habitat" and in 1962 was unable to find any there. This is confirmed by an entry in S.H.Kershaw's notebook stating that he saw none there on 9 September 1961 when it was flying at Sharpenhoe. He commented "cattle all over the breeding ground". Fortunately the Chalkhill Blue has survived at Pegsdon or recolonised this site and could be seen there in the 1990s.

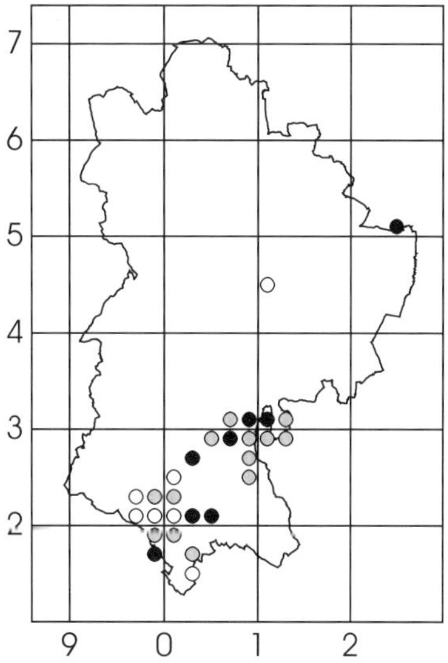

Specimens in collections include: Sharpenhoe between 1929 and 1941, Sewell 1936 (R.E.R.Sanderson, Natural History Museum); Barton 1918 (W.G.Nash in P.N.Crow); Dunstable 1950 (S.C.Fraser); Dunstable Downs 1928, 1940 (Graveley-Edwards), 1932-59 (G.F.B.Prior), 1949 (G.H.B.Oliver, Buckinghamshire Museum), 1976-77 (R.S.Ferry collection); Sharpenhoe 1924 to 1930 (Luton Museum), 1939 (Fryer) and 1944 (Humphrey-Kershaw); Pegsdon 1918 (W.G.Nash in P.N. Crow's collection), 1929 to 1931 (Tebbs) and 1951 and 1957 (Humphrey-Kershaw); Totternhoe Knolls 1947, 1956, 1966 (Graveley-Edwards), Whipsnade 1922 (Fryer).

This attractive butterfly remains local, confined to open chalkland on the Chiltern Hills but, excluding strays, has been recorded since 1977 in only 24 tetrads. Numbers of Chalkhill Blues seen on transect walks have reached 153, far short of estimates in earlier decades. However, during the 1990s considerable efforts have been made to improve management of sites such as Whipsnade Downs, Dunstable Downs, Pegsdon Hills and Sharpenhoe Clappers and it is to be hoped that this will allow populations to return to their former levels. The males are prone to wander away from their colonies and odd individuals have been seen in Studham and Potton Wood.

Flight: July to September (weeks 26 to 39, peak 29 to 34)*.

Larval Foodplant: Horseshoe vetch*.

Adonis Blue *Lysandra bellargus* (Rottemburg) (1576) (Plate 3)

VCH: "On chalk hillsides near Bedford".

Post VCH: W.G.Nash was quoted by A.H.Foster as finding 4 specimens at Barton in 1903 and by Tutt (1905-9) as reporting Adonis Blue to be rare there. Curiously Frohawk (1924) gave Bedfordshire as a locality for Adonis Blue but not for Chalkhill Blue. Foster (1917) recorded the Adonis Blue as very rare on Pegsdon Hills and in 1934 wrote that this species "has been seen rarely on Pegsdon Hills ..... but not for many years". S.H.Kershaw's notebooks record 12 visits to Pegsdon during late August and September in the 1930s but do not mention finding Adonis Blue there. B.Sawford (1987) noted reports of "thousands in both broods near Hexton and Pegsdon from 1943 to 1946" probably referring to S.R.Bowden's (1965) description of "many hundreds on Knocking Hoe" on 13 June 1943 and again on 28 May 1944 "*bellargus* was present in thousands, nearly all male". G.B.Oliver (1949) wrote that he "found *bellargus* well established on any suitable ground stretching from Aldbury to the Barton Hills in Bedfordshire".

P.Taylor recalled finding this species at Totternhoe and Markham Hills in the early 1940s. West (1949) listed Totternhoe, Sharpenhoe, Sundon, Dunstable and Barton as localities.

For key to butterfly maps see page 3.

He recalled it as being all over Totternhoe Knolls in the 1940s and had found it up the hill from Moleskin to Sharpenhoe Clappers. Entries in S.H.Kershaw's diaries show that he continued to see it at Totternhoe until 1951. R.Palmer recorded in his diaries that it was "on the wing in fair numbers" on 13 June 1943 at Barton Hills. West (1954b) noted that it was still present "in the long valley behind Barton church" in 1953 and W.J.Champkin understood it to be still present there in 1956. Bowden (1954) commented on its decline on the "hills west of Hitchin" and wrote "a few years back the invading *bellargus* here vastly outnumbered the long-established *coridon* which had been in eclipse". The last one recorded was that taken at Pegsdon by R.S.Ferry on 15 June 1959.

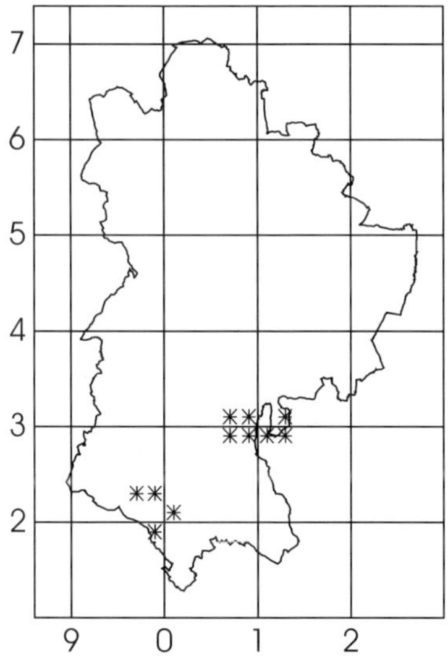

Specimens in collections: Pegsdon 13 June 1943 (S.R. & K.R. Bowden North Herts Museum) and 15 June 1959 (R.S.Ferry); The Knolls, Totternhoe 1943-44 (G.F.B.Prior, Humphrey-Kershaw, B.B.West); Sharpenhoe 1942 and 1944 (Humphrey-Kershaw). Specimens are also in the Hopkins-Alexander labelled "Whipsnade G.E.Tite" dated 1948 and 1950. The Gravely-Edwards collection contains specimens from Dunstable Downs 1940-42, Barton Hills 1941 and Totternhoe Knolls 1944. Specimens from Streatley (1942) and Sharpenhoe (1943) are in W.J.D.Eberlie's collection in Ontario, Canada.

Although from the VCH entry and Nash's record it would appear that the Adonis Blue was a long-term resident in the County, understanding of its status is unusually complicated by possible artificial introductions. According to Newman (1954) G.B.Oliver successfully introduced it to the Princes Risborough area. Bowden (1949b) said that the stock came from Folkestone in Kent. Stock from the Princes Risborough site was subsequently released in the 1940s at Totternhoe and Sharpenhoe by R.E.R.Sanderson (S.W.Humphrey pers. comm.). Whether this species was present in these areas and on the Dunstable and Whipsnade Downs before that time is not known but the fact that we have not found any earlier specimens or reports suggests that it may not have been there. Some were rumoured to have been released on Totternhoe Knolls in the 1970s but did not survive.
Flight: In two broods in May-June and August-September.
Larval Foodplant: Horseshoe vetch.

Mazarine Blue *Cyaniris semiargus* (Rottemburg) (1578)
Pre VCH: Whether the Mazarine Blue was ever found in Bedfordshire is very doubtful. Around Charles Abbot's time, the specific name *arion* was variously used for both the Large Blue and the Mazarine Blue. In 1797 Donovan gave the names *arion* and Mazarine Blue to a butterfly which he illustrated but the picture is clearly of a Large Blue. Abbot's notebook (MS1) entries, made in 1798 and 1799 at the start of his interest in Lepidoptera, suggest that he was following Donovan's (1797) lead but he gave specimens of *arion* from Bedfordshire to A.H.Haworth who appears to have been satisfied with their identification as Large Blue (Haworth, 1803). Although most authors seem to have accepted that Abbot was referring to the Large Blue when he used the name *arion*, R.F.Bretherton (1951) appears to have reached the opposite conclusion. In his 1951 paper he quoted *verbatim* the VCH entry for the Large Blue as a record of the Mazarine Blue in Bedfordshire. J.C.Dale clearly distin-

guished the two species when in 1819 he recorded (MS3) finding *arion* at Mouse's Pasture near Bromham on 14 July and *Lycaena Cymon* (annotated *acis*, both early synonyms for *semiargus*) just over the county boundary at Gamlingay on 16 July. Dale would have been familiar with both species and his accuracy was well respected. It seems therefore that there is no definite record of the Mazarine Blue in Bedfordshire from the 18th or early 19th centuries and none has been reported since.

Holly Blue *Celastrina argiolus* (Linnaeus) ssp. *britanna* (Verity) (1580)
(Plate 86 and drawing on page 56)
Pre VCH: In Abbot's notebook (MS1) against *argiolus* there is an entry in another hand, possibly J.C.Dale's, "It does not appear that Dr Abbot ever took this species or even had it".
VCH: "Bedford".
Post VCH: Tutt (1905-9) gave Bedford as a locality quoting Sharpin. West (1949) noted it as "very common throughout the county, especially in suburban areas".

Specimens in collections: "Bedfordshire" 1918, 1919 & 1925 W.G.Nash; "Bedford District" no date or collector (Oxford County Museum).

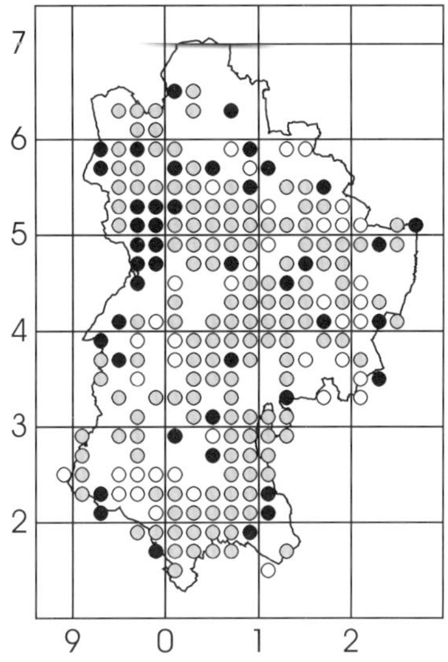

Recorded since 1977 in 220 tetrads, but population densities are extremely variable with large numbers occurring for one or two years followed by a crash with few if any being seen in the intervening years until numbers rise again to another peak. High numbers have been recorded in Bedfordshire in 1916 (Nash,1916), 1924 (R.M.Craske pers. comm.), 1934-36, 1946-51, 1958-60, 1971-72, 1978, 1984-85 and 1990-1 but this list is not complete. In Bedfordshire, R.C.Revels (1994) has investigated the role of the ichneumonid *Listrodromus nycthemerus*, a parasitoid specific to the Holly Blue. He found an increase in the percentage parasitism in larvae collected in the field. In the autumn of 1990 7.7% of larvae were parasitised but by the spring of 1992 this figure had risen to 99%. No larvae could be found in the autumn of 1992. Adults were extremely scarce during 1993 (only 6 sites) and 1994 (5 sites) but numbers were starting to rise again in 1995 (19 sites). The Holly Blue was again seen commonly in the spring and summer of 1996.
Flight: In two broods in April-June and July-September (weeks 14 to 38, peaks 22 to 26 and 30 to 35)*.
Larval Foodplants: Flowers of holly*, dogwood*, Pyracantha* and Cotoneaster*in spring and ivy* in late summer and autumn. Egg-laying has also been observed in spring on the terminal leaves of buddleia but no evidence of larval feeding was seen.

Large Blue *Maculinea arion* (Linnaeus) ssp. *eutyphron* (Fruhstorfer) (1581)
Pre VCH: The records of the Large Blue in Bedfordshire are among the more important in Charles Abbot's notebook (MS1). He recorded finding it "between Woods. June 28th 1798. Several at Mouse's Pasture Bromham". Also "July 5th 1799 between Hanger Wood

For key to butterfly maps see page 3.

& Asties" (*i.e.* Astey Wood). J.C.Dale's papers (MS2) record receiving specimens from Abbot's collection and there are also several entries recording his finding of this species on 14 July 1819, a "female *Lycaena arion* a bad one" at "Mouses Pasture, Bromham, 3 miles from Bedford not far from Lord Tavistocks who has 2 from Dr Abbot" (Dale, MS3). The Bedfordshire specimens, if indeed they survive, cannot be identified in the Dale collection. A side label "n Bedford" is misplaced alongside a specimen of *Maculinea alcon* which has Haworth's label underneath it and allegedly originated in Buckinghamshire. The entry in the Curtis diaries against *alcon* support this. For *arion* the entry is "heathy places, commons & pastures ... nr Bedford" and refers to J.C.Dale's 1819 specimen but there is no evidence that any of the specimens in the Curtis collection is from Bedfordshire. "Last seen June 1820" (Guppy, MS – source unknown). Spooner (1963) thought that the Large Blue had disappeared from Bedfordshire by 1830. (See also discussion of the identity of this species in Bedfordshire on pages 236-237).

VCH: "Haworth in 1803 says: 'Taken in Bedfordshire and sent to me by my friend Dr. Abbot'; Professor Westwood (1849) adds that it was taken in 'Mouse's pasture' near Bedford and that Mr. J. C.Dale took it there again in 1819; further that it was taken on commons near Bromham".

Post VCH: Not recorded. See pages 34-35 for the recent fate of Mouse's Pasture.

Subfamily: **Riodininae** **The Metalmarks**

The Duke of Burgundy is the only representative in Britain of a mainly tropical subfamily. Many taxonomists regard the metalmarks as a separate family. Although the immature stages resemble those of the other lycaenid species, the adults are somewhat different. In particular, the males use only two pairs of legs, foreshadowing the families that follow. Wingspan 27-30 mm.

Duke of Burgundy

Duke of Burgundy *Hamearis lucina* (Linnaeus) (1582) (Plate 6)

Pre VCH: Abbot (MS1) noted "Seen in Clapham Wood May 8th 1798" and also "*lucina* June 8th 1799". J.C.Dale (MS3) recorded finding this species on 1 June 1820 probably in the area of Clapham Park Wood where he recorded other insects that day. Stainton (1857) gives Clapham Park Wood as a locality but does not indicate where the record came from. "Clapham Park Woods Bedford seen by H.W.Finlinson", (Mitchell, 1990). This would have been in the 1890s.

Post VCH: B.B.West did not mention this species in his 1949 review but ten years later reported its "discovery" on Dunstable Downs by V.H.Chambers in 1957. At that time he had not found any colonies elsewhere in the County and speculated as to its origin. We therefore do not know whether the present colonies were introduced or are native to the area. It is possible that they may have spread naturally from a local source with adjacent woodland, such as Ivinghoe Beacon as much of the chalk downs would have been unsuitable when covered with close-grazed turf and devoid of scrub.

Specimens in collections: Dunstable (bred) 1957 (G.F.B.Prior).

Currently the Duke of Burgundy is one of the rarer species in the County, recorded since 1977 in only 8 tetrads. It is one of the species that has benefited from the longer grass and scrub invasion of the downs as the females prefer sheltered cowslips for egg-laying and the males use the scrub for perching. It forms very local colonies confined to clearings in the scrub on the chalk downlands and in abandoned quarries which provide shelter for its host plant and an abundance of perching sites. Although as many as 40 individuals were said to have been counted on a walk on Dunstable Downs and Whipsnade Downs in 1992 and also in Totternhoe Quarry, less than 10 would be more normal. Also recorded at Noon Hill, Pegsdon in 1985 and 1992. A single sighting on Warden Hill in 1994 has not been repeated to date.

Flight: May and June (weeks 18 to 24, peak 20 and 21)*.

Larval Foodplants: Cowslip* and primrose.

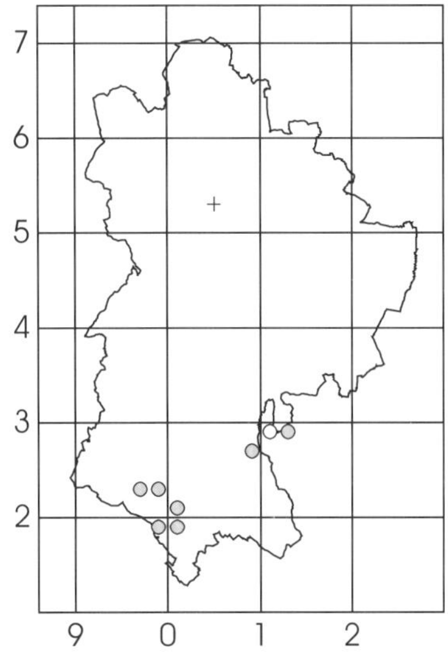

Family: **Nymphalidae**

This family contains a miscellany of species which some taxonomists would split into several smaller families. It includes the White Admiral, Purple Emperor, nymphalines (Red Admiral, Peacock etc.), fritillaries and browns. Throughout the family the adults use only two pairs of legs for perching and walking. The front pair are mainly sensory in function. The pupae of most, though not all, species hang suspended by the tail end and many, especially among the Nymphalinae and Argynninae, are strikingly marked with brilliant metallic areas. It is to these pupae that the name 'chrysalis' is properly applied.

Subfamily: **Limenitinae**

The single British species, the White Admiral, occurs in Bedfordshire. Wingspan 52-64 mm. Its larva is spiny and the pupa ornate with projections on the head and back.

White Admiral *Ladoga camilla* (Linnaeus) (1584) (Plate 23)

Pre VCH: J.C.Dale's manuscript notes (MS2) of specimens acquired from Charles Abbot include two males and one female "*prope Bedfordiam*". The White Admiral is not recorded in Abbot's notebook (MS1) and one can only assume that he took these specimens at a later date and recorded them else-

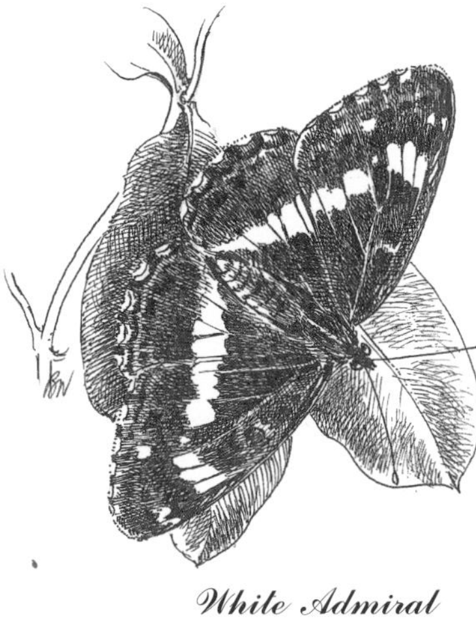

White Admiral

For key to butterfly maps see page 3.

where, perhaps in one of the manuscripts not yet found. Lucas (1855) noted that "one specimen has been taken" in the neighbourhood of Luton.

Post VCH: West (1949) wrote: "This insect, like the Comma, has only returned to the eastern counties since the period 1920-30, and it is now well represented in Bedfordshire, especially in the north. Putnoe, Odell, Swineshead, Potton, Worley's Wood, Melchbourne, Haynes. Abundant at Flitwick Moor, 1947. None seen 1948." Kershaw (1956) described finding aberrations of the White Admiral in an unnamed wood on the Buckinghamshire border. His note-books and his unpublished report in 1955 confirmed this as King's Wood, Heath and Reach. S.W.Humphrey and J.B.Barnwell were present at the time. The presence of the aberrations suggests the existence of a strong population. Although in 1954 he wrote that it was "widespread, never common"in the wood, he noted seeing 50 on 23 July 1956. The colony in Putnoe Wood was still thriving in 1958 but has not been reported there since then.

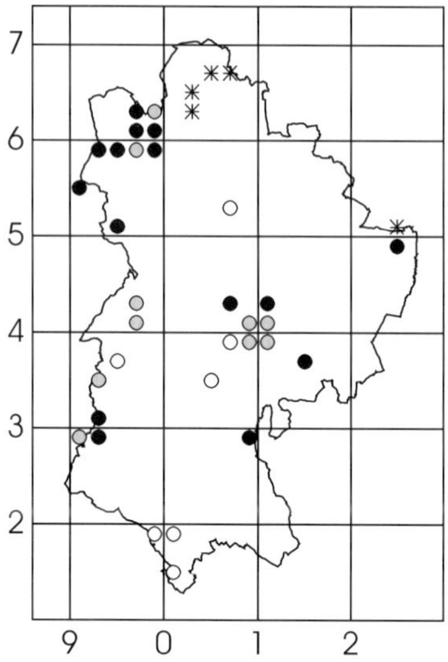

Specimens in collections: King's Wood, Heath and Reach (Humphrey-Kershaw, J.B.Barnwell).

The White Admiral is currently local, mostly in old woodland but some sites, such as Chicksands Wood, are predominantly conifer plantations. Its main focus through the 1980s appears to have been West Wood where it was recorded in 1972 and subsequently in every year since 1982. In addition to Chicksands Wood which appears to have been colonised (or recolonised) in 1989, this species has been found in recent years in its old haunts in King's Wood, Heath and Reach and also in Wilstead Wood and Marston Thrift. It has been found in Odell Great Wood and in several other woods in the north-west of the County. It was seen again in Flitwick Moor in 1986 but does not appear to have persisted there. The females require shaded honeysuckle for egg-laying, a point which needs to be remembered in woodland management. In favourable years individuals may wander far from their breeding colonies and single butterflies have been seen around Dunstable Downs, Barton Hills and other sites in the south of the county. The dots on the map in squares SP91, TL01 and TL02 represent some of these casual sightings. Excluding these strays, it has been recorded since 1977 in 27 tetrads. Only rarely have as many as 10 individuals been seen in one day at any one site, though more than 20 were seen on separate visits to King's Wood, Heath and Reach in August 1996.

Flight: Late June to August (weeks 25 to 34, peak 28 to 30)*.

Larval Foodplant: Honeysuckle*.

Subfamily: **Apaturinae**

The one British species, the Purple Emperor, is probably extinct in Bedfordshire despite sporadic records. Although larger (wingspan 70-92 mm) the adult bears a superficial resemblance to the White Admiral, but the larva is quite different being slug-like in shape, cryptically coloured and without prominent spines.

For details of standard weeks see page 6.

Purple Emperor *Apatura iris* (Linnaeus) (1585)

Pre VCH: Charles Abbot's notebook (MS1) contains extensive notes on the Purple Emperor which are worth quoting in full:

> "*Papilio Nymphalis Iris* Purple Emperor. Thirty at least seen at Clapham P. Wood on the 10th of August 1799 soaring very high. 12th one took his station on an oak tree to the left of the Putnoe Gate for an hour. I could not take him the poles of the net being too short. 13th one settled on a low hazel bush and another on a high oak but missed both. 14th saw thirteen flies. 15th staid [*sic*] at home on account of a very boisterous wind. 16th Saw one which settled as before on a low hazel bush but lost him after two efforts." (in pencil after this "Bad management"). "Never saw any more after the 16th."

Following this written in pencil in a less tidy hand, presumably J.C.Dale's:

> "Robt Barnes of the Bedford Militia told me that he helped Dr Abbot beat some larvae – that he bred them & I had 4 from his cab. (female) of which I gave to Mr Stephens. Therefore after the year 1800 Mr Barnes went with me to C. P. Wood &c & Mr Bucklow of Swan Inn Bedford."

J.C.Dale (MS2) recorded obtaining one male and one female from Abbot's collection but these specimens no longer exist. T.Orlebar Marsh notes (MS1) include a reference to Abbot finding the Purple Emperor in King's Wood, Houghton Conquest in 1800.

Stainton (1857) gives Clapham Park Wood as a locality but it is not clear whether he was merely repeating previous records. The North Herts Museum contains a specimen from Southill in 1894.

VCH: "Recorded at Clapham Park Woods by Professor Westwood (1849) on the authority of the Rev. W.T.Bree".

Post VCH: H.Nicholls was reported in 1915 as commenting that Bedfordshire was "once a noted county for Purple Emperor, now rather rare" (Anon, 1915). A manuscript of a butterfly report read by A.H.Foster to the Letchworth Naturalists Society in around 1916 notes that the Purple Emperor "has been taken in the woods near Southill" but gives no further information. Foster (1937) mentions its occurrence in Southill and Warden Woods "fifty years ago". Although West (1948) wrote that "it certainly occurs in such north Bedfordshire woods as Worley's, Swineshead and Halsey", he subsequently (1949) indicated that he had seen no records since the 1900s. Kershaw (1954) writing of King's Wood, Heath and Reach said "Not seen for some years" but did not note the source of any earlier records.

There have only been three modern sightings of this magnificent butterfly. These were on 11 July 1984 in Marston Thrift, in 1987 in Redding's Wood, Ampthill and on 19 July 1995 in King's Wood, Heath and Reach. There has been much speculation on the origin of these individuals, whether they had been released or were wanderers from one of the colonies in Buckinghamshire or Northamptonshire. One can only hope that with improvements in the management of some woods, Bedfordshire will once again become "a noted county" for the Purple Emperor.

Flight: July and August.

Larval Foodplants: Sallow, sometimes grey sallow and crack willow.

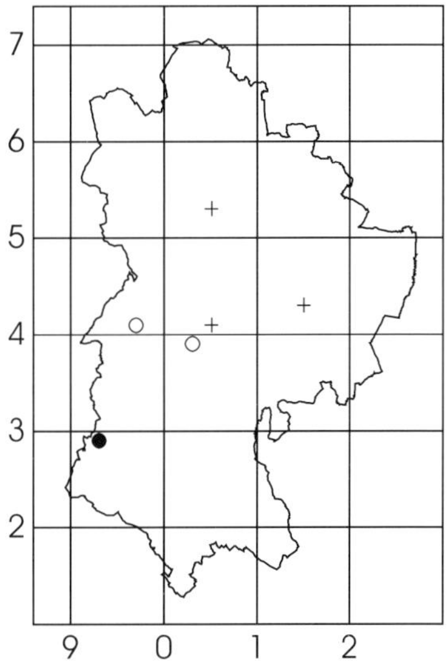

For key to butterfly maps see page 3.

Subfamily: **Nymphalinae**

The wing-patterns of the species in this subfamily are very variable and wingspans range from 45 to 88 mm. The larvae are spiny and those of two resident species, the Peacock and Small Tortoiseshell, are strongly gregarious until the last instar. The three resident British species all occur in Bedfordshire. One is extinct, two are annual immigrants and one a rare immigrant.

Red Admiral

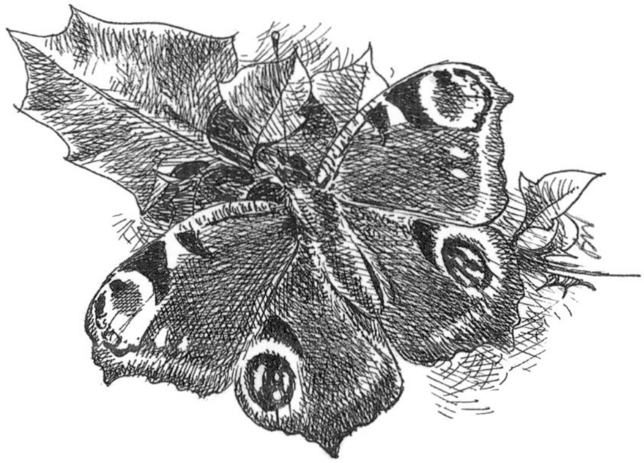

Peacock

Red Admiral ***Vanessa atalanta*** **(Linnaeus) (1590)** (Plate 85)

Pre VCH: T.Orlebar Marsh (MS1) recorded the Red Admiral at Clapham and Biddenham in 1798. Abbot (MS1) noted "3 or 4 specimens seen September 1797" and also finding it on 8 July 1799 but gave no locality. Reported as "common" in the neighbourhood of Luton by Lucas (1855).

VCH: "Generally distributed".

Post VCH: West (1949) commented that this species is "an immigrant which reaches and breeds in Bedfordshire in numbers, during a normal season, and abundantly in such summers as 1947".

The Red Admiral has been recorded since 1977 in 293 tetrads and continues to appear each year, though usually seen singly until the autumn when larger numbers appear on the late flowers and rotting fruit. There are no definite records of Red Admiral overwintering in the County. The butterflies probably do not normally survive the winter but some of the very early sightings, *e.g.* 2 February 1990 and 29 February 1996 may have been of overwintered individuals.

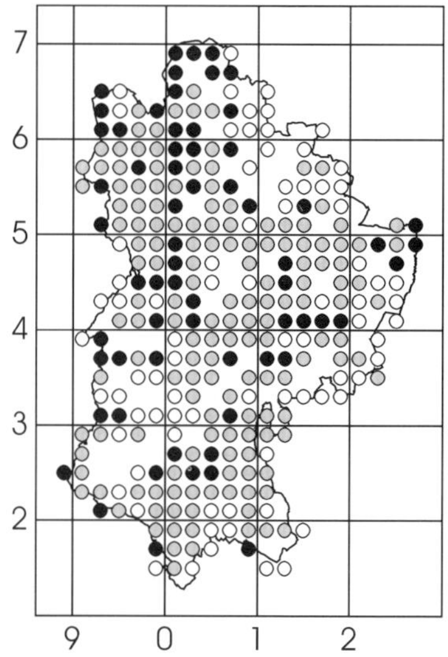

Flight: From spring onwards. Has been seen on the transects in almost every week from April to the end of September (weeks 14 to 39, peaks 28 to 31 and 36 to 39)* with sightings elsewhere between March and late November.

For details of standard weeks see page 6.

Larval Foodplants: Nettles*.

Painted Lady *Cynthia cardui* (Linnaeus) (1591)

Pre VCH: Abbot (MS1) noted "3 taken in August 1797" and also finding the Painted Lady on 24 September 1799 but once again gave no locality. Listed by Lucas (1855) as "common" in the neighbourhood of Luton.

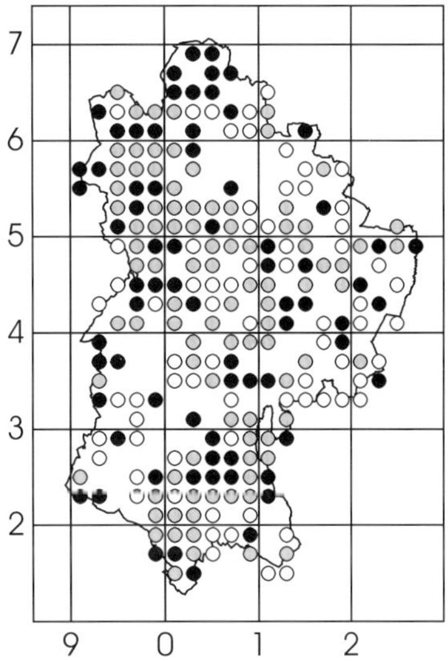

VCH: "Generally distributed".

Post VCH: Another immigrant species, common in some years but rarely seen in more than ones or twos. At the end of May and early June 1996 there was a large influx, part of a massive countrywide immigration during a period of warm weather accompanied by southerly winds. Individuals were seen at many places in the County and 45 were counted in Sundon Quarry. In the subsequent generation, the butterflies were being counted in hundreds. Recorded since 1977 in 237 tetrads though in 1996 they were probably present in every tetrad. Although West (1949) suggested that the Painted Lady may survive the winter "under mild conditions", it is less long lived than the Red Admiral. Individuals seen early in the spring are most likely to be early arrivals from the Continent.

Specimens in collections: Dunstable 1933 (Turner); Totternhoe Knolls 1958 (Graveley-Edwards).

Flight: Mostly seen from June through to October (weeks 22 to 42)*. Occasionally early immigrants may arrive in March, as in 1952.

Larval Foodplants: Creeping thistle*, musk thistle*, spear thistle* and welted thistle* but may feed on nettles in captivity.

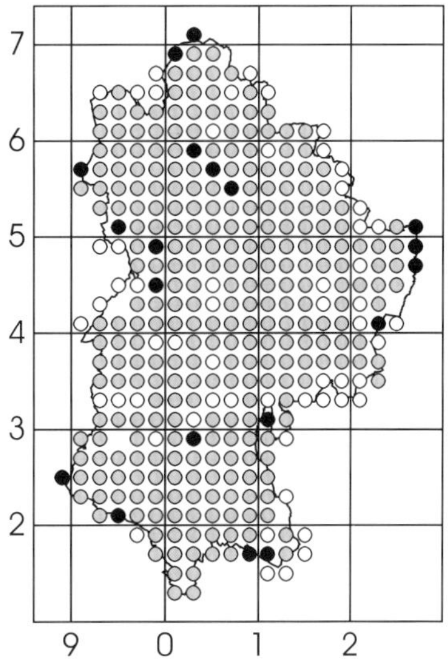

Small Tortoiseshell *Aglais urticae* (Linnaeus) (1593) (Plate 84)

Pre VCH: Abbot (MS1) recorded this species as "common in clover fields August 1797" and also noted it on 24 February 1799. "Everywhere abundant" in the neighbourhood of Luton reported Lucas (1855). Hasted noted it in Bedford in 1890.

VCH: "Abundant everywhere".

Post VCH: West in his 1949 review noted the Small Tortoiseshell as "of very wide distribution throughout the county".

Specimens in collections: Totternhoe Knolls 1955, 1964 (Graveley-Edwards).

The Small Tortoiseshell has been recorded since 1977 in 356 tetrads so it is widespread in the County and is

For key to butterfly maps see page 3.

usually common. However, annual numbers vary greatly probably due to severe predation and/or parasitism. Thus a population explosion was noted in 1987 but numbers were low in 1993 and 1994 rising again in 1995.
Flight: Hibernated Small Tortoiseshell butterflies are on the wing from early spring to late May (peak in weeks 15 to 19)⋆. There is usually a short interval in June when none are seen before the next generation of adults appear at the end of the month. Peak sightings are in July (weeks 27 to 30)⋆ with numbers declining in August and September as individuals go into hibernation in sheds, ice houses and hollow trees. Occasional individuals may be active on warm days as late as December. Those attempting to hibernate in houses rarely survive the warm dry atmosphere.
Larval Foodplants: Nettles⋆.

Large Tortoiseshell *Nymphalis polychloros* (Linnaeus) (1594)
(Drawing on page 20)
Pre VCH: Charles Abbot (MS1) recorded finding the Large Tortoiseshell on 10 April 1798 and 19 May 1799. He does not give the locality but presumably it was in the Bedford district. Lucas (1855) noted it as "not scarce" in the neighbourhood of Luton. E.R. Williams noted it in 1894-5 as "seen often around Bedford" (Mitchell, 1990). The North Herts Museum contains a specimen from Biggleswade in 1898.
VCH: "This fine butterfly seems to be well distributed over the county".
Post VCH: According to Bernard West, his father recalled being shown the Large Tortoiseshell in Chicksands Wood in the early years of the century. "Occasionally at Bromham 1934-39" (Guppy, MS). S.H.Kershaw noted seeing one on the Icknield Way near Hexton on 29 May 1935. West (1949) recorded reports from Bromham in 1943 and Everton in 1947 and J.B.Barnwell knew the Large Tortoiseshell from the Woburn Sands area in the 1940s. There was an invasion from mainland Europe in 1947 and the Large Tortoiseshell became common for about two years in Kent and adjoining counties before becoming scarce again. The only more recent reports are of one seen at The Lodge, Sandy in 1961 and another at Woburn in 1991. This butterfly is now regarded as extinct in Britain but it is often reared in captivity so individual sightings may be or escapes or deliberate releases.

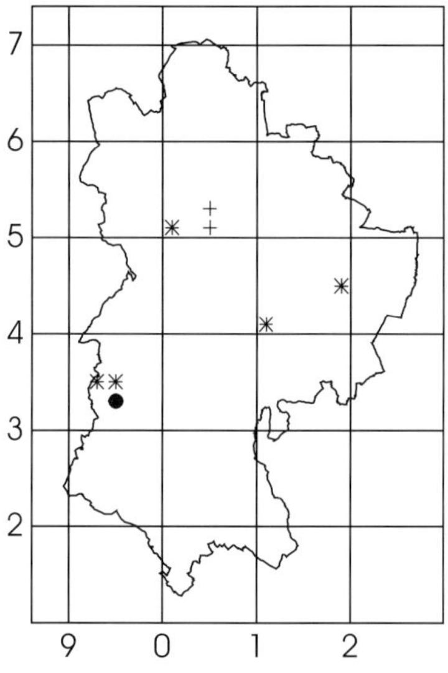

Specimens in collections: "Bedford District" No date or collector (Oxford County Museum).

For details of standard weeks see page 6.

Camberwell Beauty *Nymphalis antiopa* (Linnaeus) (1596)

(Drawing on title page)

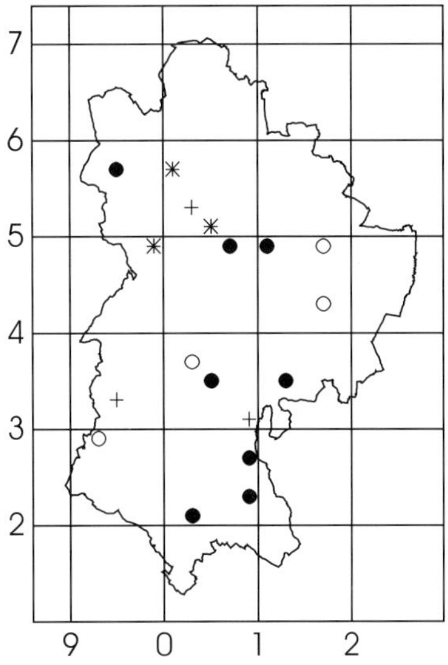

Pre VCH: F.O. Morris (1895) listed two at Clapham and one at Woburn in 1846. There is a specimen in Luton Museum labelled "Haynes Park, 1876". H.Nicholls was quoted as referring to one found at Hammer Hill by Mr Cole in about 1897 (Anon, 1915).

VCH: Not listed.

Post VCH: The Camberwell Beauty is a distinctive butterfly not likely to be confused with any other species. It is a rare immigrant which is not known to breed in Great Britain. Reported from Milton Ernest in 1932 (Hedges, 1932), Bromham Road, Bedford in 1947, Stagsden in 1952, Sandy in 1968 (French, 1973), Broom in 1976 – an invasion year (Chalmers-Hunt, 1976, 1977), Ampthill in 1979, Sandy in 1983 and Heath and Reach in 1984. The most sightings in one year were in August to October 1995 at Bedford, Cople, Dunstable, Harrold, Luton and Shillington, part of a considerable country-wide immigration (Bowles, 1996). An over-wintered individual was seen in Houghton Conquest on 21 April 1996. The latest record was from Flitton on 15 August 1996.

Peacock *Inachis io* (Linnaeus) (1597)

(Plate 85 and drawing on page 242)

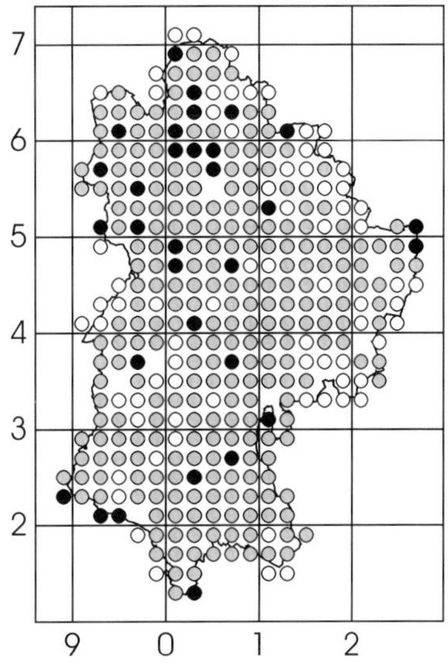

Pre VCH: Noted by Abbot (MS1) as "seen sparingly August 1797" and also on 10 May 1799. Described by Lucas (1855) as "very common in autumn" in the neighbourhood of Luton.

VCH: "Generally distributed".

Post VCH: Recorded by West (1949) as "very common throughout the county", the Peacock remains widespread (recorded since 1977 in 352 tetrads) and usually common though numbers may fluctuate from year to year. Overwintering adults have been noted each winter recently by groups recording bats roosting in ice houses and similar sites.

Flight: Individuals leave hibernation sites on warm days in early spring and are on the wing until late May (peak in weeks 15 to 18)*. The second brood appears from late July (peak weeks 30 to 33)* but most have gone into hibernation by the end of August though a few may appear into October.

Larval Foodplant: Common nettle*.

Comma *Polygonia c-album* (Linnaeus) (1598) (Plate 24)

Pre VCH: Although he noted it as "far from rare 1797", the Comma seems to have been a notable species to Charles Abbot as he took the trouble to record separately several finds during 1797-99: "one taken at Clapham Park Sep. 8th 1797"; "one Twin Woods Sep 28th"; "one Clapham Village Oct 3"; "3 Clapham Wood" and "1 in Corn Close" August 1798; also "May 27th 1799" (no locality) (MS1). Lucas (1855) listed it as "occasionally met with near woods" in the neighbourhood of Luton.

VCH: Not listed.

Post VCH: West (1949) wrote: "Since the 1920s when this insect began to spread from the west of England, it has become more and more common in the eastern counties. It occurs throughout Bedfordshire". H.A.N.Tebbs (1923) reported its arrival in Bedford in 1923. R.M.Craske saw it there in 1925 and W.G.Nash found it at Thurleigh in the same year. W.J.D.Eberlie (*in litt.* 1995) found a Comma in 1940 in Luton when it appears to have been still regarded as a rarity but R.Palmer (1942) wrote that "during the late summer and autumn of 1942 Comma butterflies have been reported as common in many parts of the district" and went on to say that in Flitwick they were more numerous than Red Admirals, Tortoiseshells and Peacocks.

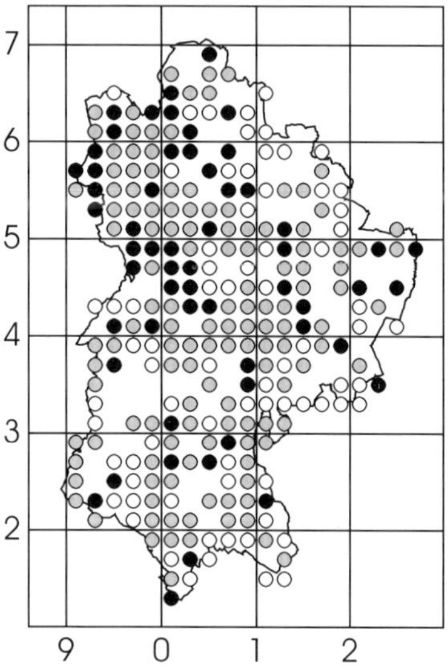

Specimens in collections: Bedford 1923-35 (Tebbs).

Currently the Comma is widely distributed and sometimes common though it is most often seen singly. Recorded since 1977 in 261 tetrads, it is usually found in woodland where it visits the flowers and over-ripe fruits of brambles, but it is also frequently seen in gardens on flowers and fallen fruit in late summer. Warm weather in spring, as in 1995, can lead to early egg-laying, with the result that a proportion of the next generation are of the paler *hutchinsonii* form. The adult butterflies overwinter, mostly in woods. The jagged outline of their wings makes them very difficult to see so they are rarely found in their hibernating sites, in contrast to the Peacock and Small Tortoiseshell which often hibernate in man-made structures.

Flight: Overwintered butterflies are flying from early spring through May and into June (weeks 14 to 24)*. The next generation is on the wing from July to September (weeks 27 to 43, peaks 29 to 30 and 38 to 39)*. Some may still be active into November and a few have been seen as late as December.

Larval Foodplants: Common nettle*, hop* and elms. In 1996 a female was seen egg-laying on ash* though it is not known if any larvae survived on this foodplant.

For details of standard weeks see page 6.

Subfamily: **Argynninae** **The Fritillaries**

Dark Green Fritillary

The first subfamily of 'fritillaries' is a fairly homogeneous group with orange and black wing patterns and spiny larvae which feed solitarily on various species of violet. Wingspans are more variable ranging from 35 to 80 mm. Of the five species that breed in Britain, only one is seen regularly in Bedfordshire. The others are extinct in the County.

Small Pearl-bordered Fritillary *Boloria selene selene* ([Denis & Schiffermüller]) (1600)
Pre VCH: Recorded by Charles Abbot (MS1) as *Euphrasia* (with "or *selene*" added in another hand) from Twin Woods on 24 June 1799.
VCH: "Common in woods about Woburn".
Post VCH: West (1949) had no recent records of this species in the County but it is recalled by J.B.Barnwell as occurring in King's Wood, Heath and Reach in the 1940s. Kershaw (1954) reported it as "rare – last seen 1952" there and confirmed its disappearance in his 1956 note. There have been no further records from anywhere in the County since then.

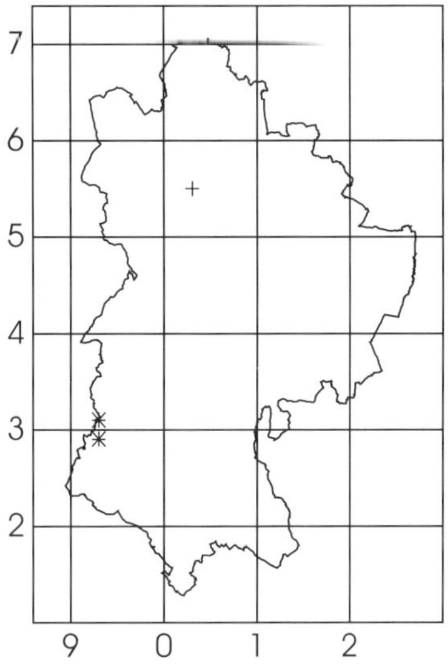

Pearl-bordered Fritillary *Boloria euphrosyne* (Linnaeus) (1601)
Pre VCH: Abbot's notebook (MS1) contains the entry: "7 specimens first taken in Clapham Wood May 8th 1798". Also "June 8th 1799" without qualification. J.C.Dale (MS2) recorded specimens from Abbot's collection. The *euphrosyne* series in the Dale collection contains a specimen with dark wing bases in poor condition side-labelled "nr Bedford" which may be an Abbot specimen. Listed as "scarce" in woody places in the neighbourhood of Luton by Lucas (1855).
VCH: "Bedford district, in woods".
Post VCH: A.W.Guppy (MS) noted it as "plentiful in Yelnow Plantation 1920-21". In his notebook, S.H.Kershaw recorded meeting West in 1945 and being told that Pearl-bordered Fritillary was swarming that year with 7 seen on one flower-head. The localities noted were Putnoe, Odell and Keysoe Woods. West (1948, 1949) wrote "this has a patchy distribution but is locally common" listing Odell Great Wood, Bromham until agricultural clearances

For key to butterfly maps see page 3.

in 1942-43, Heath and Reach and Dedmansey Wood. He recalled the Bromham record as more correctly being at "The Baulk" near Biddenham. At Heath and Reach he found it by the road to Stockgrove and in King's Wood. Kershaw (1953) noted that the Pearl-bordered Fritillary was less scarce in that year in the Aspley Heath area than for the previous three years. In 1954 he reported it as "very local" in King's Wood, Heath and Reach. However an entry in his notebook for 26 May 1954 records his seeing over 100 there. A peak seems to have been reached in 1955 when he saw some 200 in the wood on 15 June. J.B.Barnwell saw it there on 20 May 1956 and Kershaw noted a fair number on 2 June. His sighting of 6 or 7 in the wood on 28 May 1957 may well have been the last seen in the County.

Specimens in collections: King's Wood, Heath and Reach 1952-57 (Humphrey-Kershaw, J.B.Barnwell).

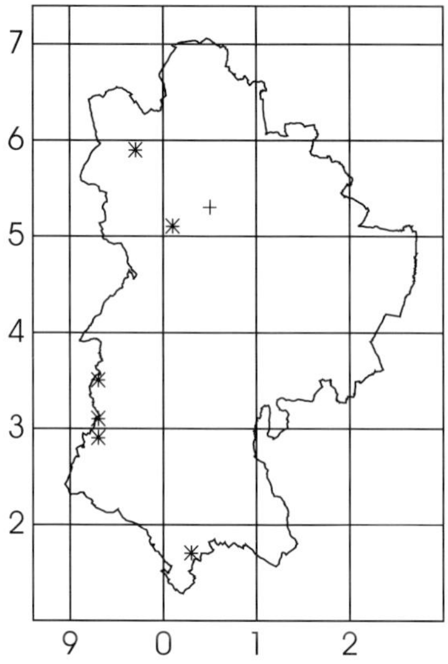

Queen of Spain Fritillary ***Argynnis lathonia*** **(Linnaeus) (1603)**

Pre VCH: A.H. Haworth (1803) reported Abbot's find of a Queen of Spain Fritillary in White Wood, near Gamlingay in June of that year. There is a specimen in the Dale collection and side-labelled "1803 Gamlingay". According to Walker (1907) the label under the specimen in J.C.Dale's handwriting reads "Mus. Dr. Abbot, White Wood, Gamlingay, Camb. June 1803, Dr Abbot". This could well be the same specimen. (See also pages 12-13). There are no later records.

High Brown Fritillary ***Argynnis adippe*** **([Denis & Schiffermüller]) ssp.** ***vulgoadippe*** **(Verity) (1606)**

Pre VCH: The Dale collection contains a specimen of the variety *cleodoxa*, which is side labelled "Bedford" and according to Walker (1907) is labelled "e mus Dr Abbot". Abbot's notebook (MS1) does not mention this species but J.C.Dale recorded finding it in Clapham Park Wood on 29 June 1826.

VCH: "Recorded near Bedford by Dr. Nash and near Woburn by Mr. McKay".

Post VCH: West (1949) gave Odell Great Wood (1943) and Clapham (1943) as localities for the High Brown Fritillary. The latter record was in Clapham Park in the open and he also recalled finding it in the 1940s between Bushmead and Staughton on a road-side verge. It may well have been more widespread in the County at that time. S.H.Kershaw reported it in 1954 as "common – local" in King's Wood, Heath and Reach but very scarce there in 1956. In his notebook he recorded seeing only small numbers, the last being

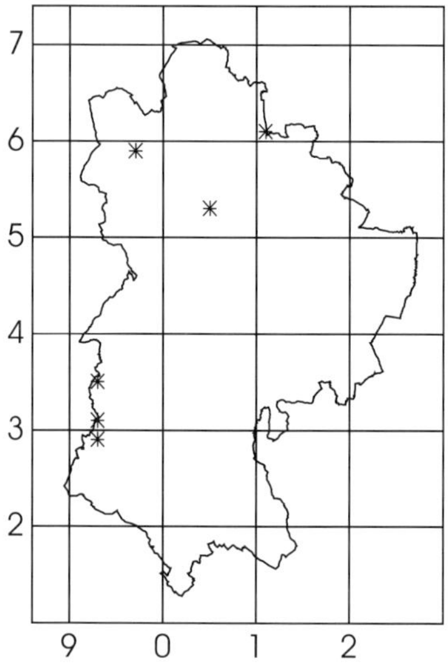

on 23 July 1956. No more recent records are known and the species is presumably extinct in the County as in so many parts of England.

Specimens in collections: King's Wood, Heath and Reach 1954-56 (Humphrey-Kershaw, J.B.Barnwell).

Dark Green Fritillary *Argynnis aglaja aglaja* (Linnaeus) (1607)
(Plate 7 and drawing on page 247)

Pre VCH: Abbot (MS1) noted finding this species on 27 June 1798 and 17 July 1799 with no locality given. J.C.Dale's manuscript catalogue (MS2) lists "(sub) Fine var. *Co Bedfordiense*. Dr C Abbott. Jul. *Dom*. Mr Bucklow *ex Mus*. Dr Abbott." The Dale collection contains an underside "Charlotta Sowerby var" and side-labelled "Bedford". According to Walker (1907) the label under the specimen in J.C.Dale's handwriting reads "Mus. Dr. Abbot". It may well be that referred to in the manuscript. It is similar in appearance to one figured by Frohawk (1938, page 61). Dale (1837a) mentions that Abbot caught three specimens of this variety and gave the other two to Haworth and Sowerby. There is also in the Dale collection an upperside with additional black areas side-labelled "nr Bedford".

Post VCH: In the first three decades of this century the Dark Green Fritillary was found in the Bedford district, Colesden, Wilden, Sundon and Sharpenhoe. A.W.Guppy (MS) noted it as "plentiful at Colesden 1918-21". West (1949) wrote: "This has its headquarters on the chalk in the southern end of the County and is there locally common. It occurs in small numbers elsewhere, Barton and Warden Hills, Putnoe Woods". He recalled finding it in Odell Great Wood in 1944, as common on the Downs in the 1940s and 50s and as being regularly seen at the northern end of Putnoe Lane before the expansion of Bedford. P.Taylor knew it from Markham Hills in the early 1940s and S.W.Humphrey found it frequently along the road past Houghton House, Ampthill in the 1930s and 1940s. Bowden recorded it from Deacon Hill in 1944 and described it as "very numerous" on Pegsdon Hills on 13 July 1947 (Bowden, 1947, 1965). S.H.Kershaw was able to find larvae at Sharpenhoe in the 1930s. He reported it in 1954 as "often common" in King's Wood, Heath and Reach but he noted that it had gone by 1956. It was recorded from Sharnbrook Summit in 1959 and 1960. These records give a picture of a wider distribution than now from which colonies have been lost because of destruction and degradation of their habitats.

Specimens in collections: "Bedfordshire" 1918 W.G.Nash, "Bedford District" 1913, Colesden 1921 (Oxford County Museum); Ampthill 1935 and 1944 (Humphrey-Kershaw); Sharpenhoe 1930 (Sanderson, Luton Museum), 1935 (Sanderson, Natural History Museum) and 1949 (Goodson, Hopkins-Alexander); Sundon 1936 (Sanderson, Natural History Museum); Wilden 1925, 1930 and 1934 (Tebbs); Barton Hills 1941 (Graveley-Edwards); Pegsdon 1943 (North Herts Museum); Sharnbrook Summit 1982 and 1984 (G.Ping).

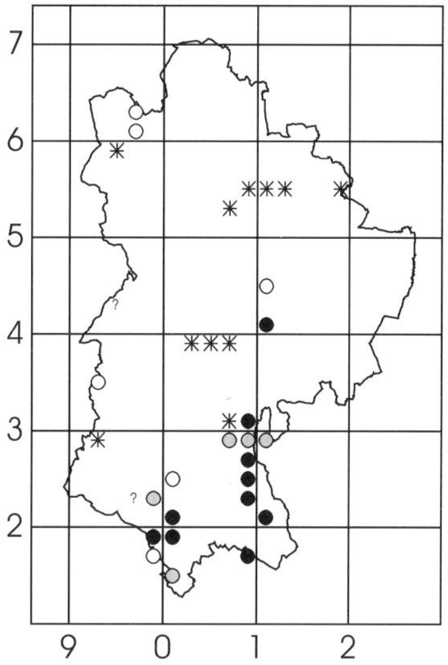

Currently, the Dark Green Fritillary is best described as local and rare in Bedfordshire. Reliably recorded since 1977 in only 21 tetrads. Most of the sightings have been on the chalk in the south of the County, on Whipsnade Downs, Dunstable Downs and Barton Hills with singles in 1976 in Sewell Quarry, 1983 in Whipsnade Wild Animal Park, 1994 at Someries Castle, 1995 in Totternhoe Quarry and 1996 at

For key to butterfly maps see page 3.

Sharpenhoe Clappers. The Dark Green Fritillary has also been seen sporadically on the Greensand Ridge south of Aspley Guise by J.B.Barnwell and was reported from Old Warden Tunnel in 1984 and Chicksands Wood in 1996. In the north of the County it has been seen on Sharnbrook Summit in 1979, 1982, 1984-86 but there are no more recent records from this area. Other possible but unconfirmed sightings have been made on Bradgers Hill, Luton in 1992 and 1993 and at Cranfield in 1994. Almost all the sightings in recent years have been of one or at the most two individuals and it is doubtful if they represent viable colonies. Although releases of bred specimens cannot be ruled out in all instances, it is just possible that the individuals seen are emigrants from a population breeding on an inaccessible site such as a railway embankment or from colonies further west on the Chilterns. The only known evidence of breeding was a mating pair seen in Studham in 1985 but none have been seen on that site recently. The only place where more than three individuals have been seen is Noon Hill, Pegsdon. "Many" were reported there in 1985 and up to 8 at one time in 1986. Hopefully the conservation efforts on the chalk downs will result in the growth of more foodplants and the recovery of this exciting species.
Flight: July and August (weeks 27 to 31)*.
Larval Foodplants: Hairy violet and common dog-violet.

Silver-washed Fritillary *Argynnis paphia* (Linnaeus) (1608)
Pre VCH: Abbot's notebook (MS1) refers to this species in "Clapham Wood " and also on another page "August 6th 1799" but with no locality given. J.C.Dale (MS3) saw it in Clapham Park Wood on 1 July 1818. Graham (1878) reported that it "used to abound some years ago in the neighbourhood of Colworth, and probably may be plentiful there still. Several I captured on the outskirts of Round Wood, and other parts there".
VCH: "Generally distributed in woods".
Post VCH: S.R.Bowden (1965) recorded the Silver-washed Fritillary as "fairly numerous" in 1917-21 in and around Tingley Field Plantation near Pegsdon. "Our commonest of the larger fritillaries, and well distributed, especially in the older oak woods" wrote West in 1949. In that paper and in discussion in 1994 he listed the following localities: Putnoe Wood, Keysoe, Odell Great Wood, Halsey Wood, West Wood, Worley's Wood, Swineshead Wood, Bolnhurst, Bushmead, Dedmansey Wood, Great Bramingham Wood, Streatley, Leet Wood, Wootton Wood, Potton Wood, Kempston Wood, Astey Wood, Ridgmont and Hinwick Dungee. R.Palmer's diary records "numerous Silver-washed fritillaries flying in Hatley and Potton Woods" on 3 August 1947. J.B.Barnwell recalled seeing it in abundance in the 1950s, including numbers of f. *valezina*. in Aspley Woods and King's Wood, Heath and Reach. In the latter site, S.H.Kershaw reported it in 1954 as "common – local" and he noted that it was only still about in numbers there in 1955 (Kershaw, 1954, 1955, 1956). In his notebooks he recorded seeing 200 on 23 July 1956 and this may have been the last occasion when this species was seen in any numbers in the County.

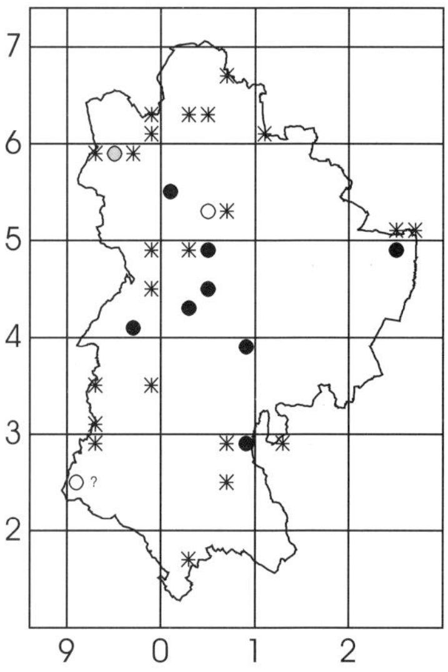

For details of standard weeks see page 6.

Specimens in collections: King's Wood, Heath and Reach (J.B.Barnwell, Humphrey-Kershaw) latter dated 1953, 1955 and 1956.

Sometime in the late 1950s numbers declined and this splendid butterfly is possibly extinct in the County. However, one was seen in Leighton Buzzard in 1976, one in Clapham Park Wood on 23 July 1989 and in 1992 one was photographed in Marston Thrift. In 1994 two, possibly three, were seen on Buddleia in a garden in Pavenham and another, a male, 10 days later in Elstow Storage Depot, again on Buddleia. Neither of the last two sites are adjacent to woodland. Releases of bred specimens have occurred, *e.g.* in Odell in 1984, and cannot be entirely ruled out in 1994 as both a male and a female were seen at Pavenham, but the dates, 17, 20 and 30 July are rather late in the season for bred specimens to emerge, particularly as the weather had been hot. In 1995 singles were seen: at Barton Hills on 9 July, in Coronation Pit on 16 July, in Potton Wood on 22 July and also in Yelden. In 1996 single individuals were seen in Bedford and Chicksands Wood. The dots on the map for the 1980s and 1990s represent these casual sightings.

Unidentified Large Fritillaries

During the last few decades there have been a number of sightings of large fritillaries which could not be identified to species. Some of the reports may have been due to confusion with Comma or Wall Brown but there are a few which are more definite, such as those from King's Wood, Heath and Reach, in 1980 and near Wavendon Heath in 1994.

Subfamily: **Melitaeinae More Fritillaries**

Although also called 'fritillaries' the wing patterns of this group are reticulated rather than composed of black marks on a plain background as in the previous group. Wingspans 30-50 mm. The larvae are gregarious in the earlier instars. Only one of the three British species has occurred in Bedfordshire this century but is now extinct.

Marsh Fritillary *Eurodryas aurinia aurinia* (Rottemburg) (1610)

Pre VCH: There are confusing entries in Charles Abbot's notebook (MS1), *viz* "*maturna* Heath Fritillary – *Captus* Clapham Pasture South *die maii* 24 1798". Morris (1895) gives *maturna* Esper as one of the specific names used for the Marsh Fritillary so it is not clear which species this entry refers to. The date is too early for Heath Fritillary but is within the flight period of Marsh Fritillary which seems likely to be what Abbot found. This is supported by another entry: "*Artemis* June 15th 1799" but with no locality given (*artemis* is another synonym for *aurinia*). He also records finding six larvae on 19 April at "Pickerings". Abbot also recorded plants from this site but J.G.Dony (1953) could not identify it. "Clapham Park Wood 1849" (Guppy, MS – source not given).

VCH: as *Melitaea artemis* Hb. "Clapham Park Woods; Prof. Westwood".

Post VCH: West (1949) reported the Marsh Fritillary as occurring at Heath and Reach in 1948. J.B.Barnwell also recalled it as present there, but Kershaw (1954) wrote that it was last seen in King's Wood in 1950. It was abundant at times on Totternhoe Knolls and on a damp field called the Litany to the north-east of the Knolls between 1942 and 1948 but West (1953) could not find it at the Litany in 1952. Blackie (1950b) searched for it in vain at Totternhoe in 1950 and the last time it was seen there was probably in 1953. The origin of the Totternhoe colony is unclear but notes with A.Bell's collection, said to have been made between 1910 and 1930, report "a flourishing colony estimated at several hundreds on rough

For key to butterfly maps see page 3.

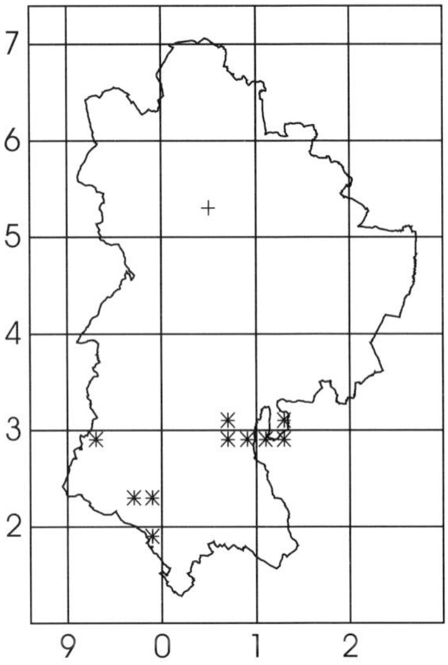

ground next to the undulating land to the right of the road entering the village." P.Taylor remembers seeing Marsh Fritillary at Maiden Bower and on Markham Hills in the early 1940s. R.E.R.Sanderson released stock at Sharpenhoe in the 1940s (S.W.Humphrey pers. comm.) and R.Palmer (MS2) recorded releasing six specimens on Barton Hills on 16 June 1947. In the Pegsdon Hills area, Birdsall (1988) described finding it in Barn Hole in the 1940s, Bowden (1965) found two on Knocking Hoe in 1944 and B.B.West recalled seeing it on Deacon Hill during 1952-53. At the western end of the chalk downs, it was found at Whipsnade in 1922 and 1948 and Bowden (1949a) reported that I.West found three specimens on Dunstable Downs in 1948.

Specimens in collections: Totternhoe: Graveley-Edwards (some 29 specimens 1945-46), Humphrey-Kershaw (1945-49), G.F.B.Prior (1939-46) and B.B.West, the last one being dated 1953. A specimen labelled "vi/22 Whipsnade" is in the Fryer collection and the Hopkins-Alexander contains a series of specimens taken there in 1948 by G.E.Tite.

It would appear from these records that there were a number of colonies of the Marsh Fritillary in the County, some possibly introduced or reinforced by introductions, but these all seem to have died out by the early 1950s. The growth of grass and scrub following myxomatosis may have contributed to the decline by shading the larval foodplant, devils'-bit scabious, and creating conditions too cool for larval development.

Glanville Fritillary *Melitaea cinxia* (Linnaeus) (1612)

Pre VCH: Three reports of Glanville Fritillary in Bedfordshire have been seen. Charles Abbot's notebook (MS1) contains an entry for 1799 "*cinxia* seen July 5th between Hanger & Astie's Wood". Since this was in the early days of his interest in Lepidoptera it seems likely that this was a misidentification but Rennie (1832) included Bedfordshire in his list of localities for this species. South (1906) quoted Stephens (1828) "in a wood near Bedford". More puzzling is the report from Lucas in 1855 "occasionally seen in gardens" in the neighbourhood of Luton. It is very doubtful if this species was ever established in Luton or elsewhere in Bedfordshire though there may have been occasional releases, either accidental or deliberate.

Heath Fritillary *Mellicta athalia* (Rottemburg) (1613)

Pre VCH: In Charles Abbot's notebook (MS1) there is an entry: "Small Pearl Border Likeness Harris *Dictynna* Fabricius Aspley Wood July 10 1800". These were both names in use for the Heath Fritillary at that time. J.C.Dale (MS2) recorded receiving specimens from this locality from Abbot's collection. Abbot in *Flora Bedfordiensis* (1798) recorded the larval foodplant of Heath Fritillary, common cow-wheat, as rare in Aspley Wood. It is a plant that has not been seen in the County for many years, though in 1954 S.H.Kershaw could still find a few in King's Wood, Heath and Reach, and speculated on the likelihood of Heath Fritillary having occurred there in the past. Westwood (1855) reported it as "abundant .... near Bedford". Its occurrence "near Bedford" is also mentioned by Morris (1895).

VCH: "Recorded in Aspley Woods, fifty years ago, by Westwood". Not found since.

Subfamily: **Satyrinae** **The Browns**

The 'browns' are a fairly homogeneous group in which the adults are mostly brown or orange in colour with prominent eye-spot markings on the wings. Wingspans 33 -60 mm. The exception is the Marbled White with its black and white chequer-board pattern. However, its grass-feeding larvae and other immature stages are typical of the rest of the browns.

Small Heath

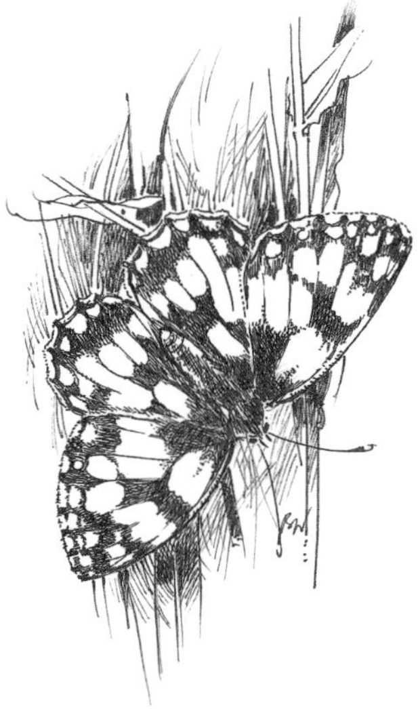

Marbled White

Speckled Wood ***Pararge aegeria*** **(Linnaeus) ssp.** ***tircis*** **(Godart) (1614)** (Plate 30)

Pre VCH: T.Orlebar Marsh (MS1) recorded the Speckled Wood from Clapham and Biddenham in 1798. Abbot (MS1) noted it as "Seen often. August 1797." and also "May 18th 1799". Lucas (1855) listed it as "common in woods and lanes" in the neighbourhood of Luton.

VCH: "Bedford, in lanes and wood borders".

Post VCH: R.M.Craske recalled this species as uncommon in the Bedford area in the 1920s. Bowden (1946) referring to the Letchworth district remarked that "After fifty years the Speckled Wood seems to be coming back." In 1947 he noted its presence at Pegsdon and also, as a new locality record, in Potton Wood and in 1948 he listed further 1947 records from P.Taylor in Warren Wood, Clophill and Studham and in 1948 at Sharpenhoe. West (1949) recorded its status at that time as "common throughout our woodlands, but becomes rarer towards the southern end of the County". A.W. Guppy (MS) noted it as "frequent at Bromham before 1949". Kershaw (1954) reported it as "common" in King's Wood, Heath and Reach. It was also reported as common in Hardwick Spinney in 1953. Sawford (1987) described the changes in the distribution of the Speckled Wood in Hertfordshire during this century and it is likely that a similar rise and fall in populations occurred in Bedfordshire. (See also pages 68-69)

Specimens in collections: Odell 1931-34 (Tebbs).

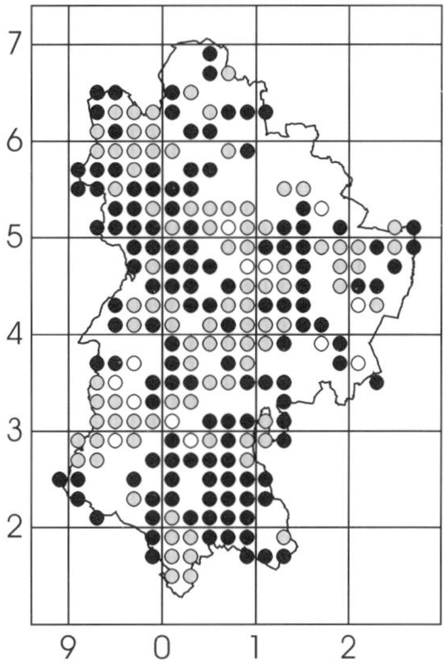

For key to butterfly maps see page 3.

Currently the Speckled Wood is a common insect in shaded areas both in woodland and in downland scrub. Recorded since 1977 in 235 tetrads of which 129 are new records since 1990. This appears to reflect a real expansion of its range in recent years rather than an increase in recording effort. The numbers observed on transect walks have also shown an increase, peaking in 1992 with 88 seen on one walk on Whipsnade Downs. Since then it has declined a little, particularly in 1995. It is another species that has benefited from the increasing amount of scrub on the downs.
Flight: Recorded in every week between April and mid October (weeks 16 to 42, peaks 18 to 20, 24 to 26 and with the highest numbers in 34 to 38)*.
Larval Foodplants: Cock's-foot and other grasses.

Wall Brown *Lasiommata megera* (Linnaeus) (1615) (Plate 70, drawing on page 54)

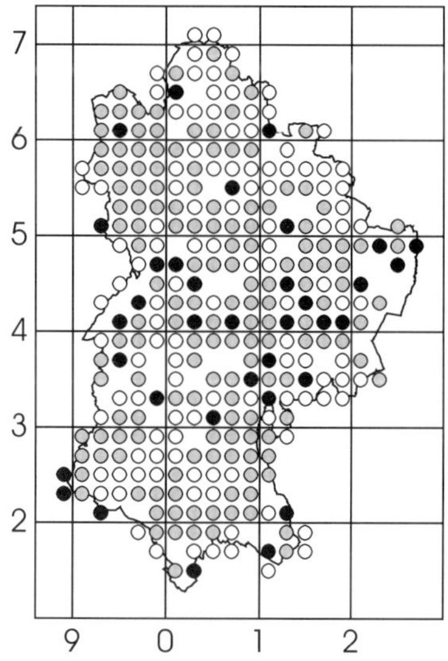

Pre VCH: T.Orlebar Marsh (MS1) recorded the Wall Brown (as *Maera*) from Clapham and Biddenham in 1798. Abbot (MS1) recorded it (again as *Maera*) as "seen often August 1797" and also (as *Megara*) on 10 June 1799 without any locality. Lucas (1855) listed it as "very common" in the neighbourhood of Luton.
VCH: as *Pararge megaera* Linn. "Generally distributed".
Post VCH: S.R.Bowden (1965) found it in the area of Knocking Hoe in 1917-21. "Very common throughout the County" noted West in 1949.

Specimens in collections: Barton 1941, Bedford 1923 and Putnoe 1922-33(Tebbs).

Currently widespread (recorded since 1977 in 305 tetrads) but usually seen in small numbers, rarely as many as 15 on one transect walk. The flight pattern of the Wall Brown is characteristic, flitting along paths and basking in open spaces but it is sometimes mistaken for a small fritillary.
Flight: May to October in two broods (weeks 18 to 42, peaks 21 to 24 and 32 to 34)*.
Larval Foodplants: Cock's-foot and other grasses.

Marbled White *Melanargia galathea* (Linnaeus) ssp. *serena* Verity (1620)
(Drawing on page 253)
Pre VCH: Charles Abbot (MS1) found Marbled White at Clapham Park on 16 June 1798 and also on 8 July 1799 but not necessarily at the same place. J.C.Dale (MS3) recorded it from Clapham Park Wood on 13 July 1819 and again the next day, probably at Mouse's Pasture. "Occasionally taken" in the neighbourhood of Luton (Lucas, 1855).
VCH: "On chalk hills near Bedford".
Post VCH: W.G.Nash was reported in 1915 to have seen a Marbled White in his garden in Bedford (Anon, 1915) and it occurred at the Wilderness, near Colesden in the late 1920s and early 1930s. A.W.Guppy (MS) noted it as "abundant at Colesden 1918-21, Riseley 1920,

For details of standard weeks see page 6.

Sharnbrook Summit and Forty Foot Lane 1921". West (1949) wrote: "This has a fairly general distribution. Cleete Hill ... Fields beyond Foster Hill till 1943, Oakley, Clapham, Bolnhurst, Putnoe, Keysoe, Riseley, West Wood, Knotting, Dean and Ridgmont". From this description it would seem that the stronghold of the Marbled White in the 1940s was in the north of the County and W.J.Champkin recalled that it was common north of Putnoe until the golf course was built. It was present in Pavenham around 1956 "in the fields and roadsides leading down to Stafford Bridge" (Anon, 1956). S.R.Bowden and R.M.Newland reported sightings from Deacon Hill, Pegsdon in 1947 (Bowden, 1947). Through the 1980s to date it has been found most frequently on the chalk in the south of the County. Occurrences in the north were only local but it has become more common there in recent years.

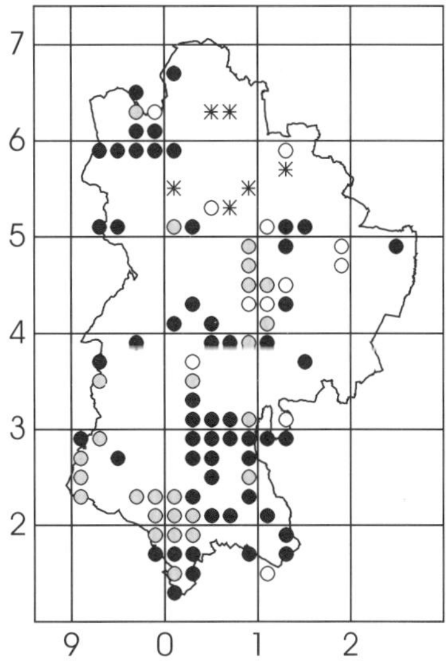

Specimens in collections: The Wilderness, near Colesden, 1927 and 1934 (Natural History Museum); Bedford 1937 and Wilden 1929 & 1934(Tebbs).

In 1975, W.J.Champkin released stock on Sharnbrook Summit whence it has spread, being seen in Bromham in 1993. There was also a release by R.C.Revels of the Marbled White on the Old Warden Tunnel Nature Reserve in 1977 (N.Dawson *in litt.* 1995). In this instance 4 males and 12 females were released on 24 July 1977 and 17 more females on 2 August 1977. They were all captured on the Chilterns near Tring. From 1979 to 1984 the colony was very abundant spreading northward to Cotton End and Cople and as far as Willington by 1982 and along the old railway line between Willington and Blunham in the 1980s. The population declined in the late 1980s and early 1990s but had increased again by 1994.

The Marbled White has also been reported at the western end of the Greensand Ridge, from Stockgrove Country Park, King's Wood (Heath and Reach) and Aspley Wood. In 1976 one was seen in Maulden Wood. It has been recorded since 1977 in 93 tetrads, 55 of which are new records in the 1990s. More than 100 have been counted on several transect walks and 231 on a walk on Dunstable Downs in 1992.

Flight: June to September (weeks 25 to 36, peak 27 to 29)⋆.

Larval Foodplants: Red fescue, sheep's-fescue, smooth meadow-grass⋆ and possibly other grasses.

Grayling *Hipparchia semele semele* (Linnaeus) (1621)

Pre VCH: Abbot (MS1) recorded the Grayling in September 1797 without giving a locality and on 29 August 1799 on Barton Hills.

VCH: Not listed.

Post VCH: H.Nicholls is quoted as reporting in 1915 that the Grayling had been found "once on a roadside at Clapham" (Anon, 1915). West (1949) found it at Ravensburgh Castle in 1944 and 1948. A.W.Guppy (MS) noted seeing one "at the same place" in 1920. The only other records are from Dunstable Downs in 1972 by B.Johnson and at Woburn Sands in 1991 by N.Bowles. Given the absence of recent records within a radius of some 80 km it seems likely that these were releases.

For key to butterfly maps see page 3.

Gatekeeper or Hedge Brown *Pyronia tithonus* (Linnaeus) ssp. *britanniae* (Verity) (1625) (Plate 71)

Pre VCH: Abbot (MS1) noted the Gatekeeper on 20 July 1799, no locality given. Listed by Lucas (1855) as "everywhere abundant" in the neighbourhood of Luton.

VCH: "Generally common".

Post VCH: Present on Knocking Hoe in 1917-21 (Bowden, 1965). West (1949) recorded it as "very common throughout the county". This remains the present position. The Gatekeeper has been recorded since 1977 in 360 tetrads and is most commonly found along woodland rides, hedgerows and roadside verges and in downland scrub rather than on open grassland. Counts often exceed 80 on transect walks and 123 were seen on a walk on Dunstable Downs in 1993.

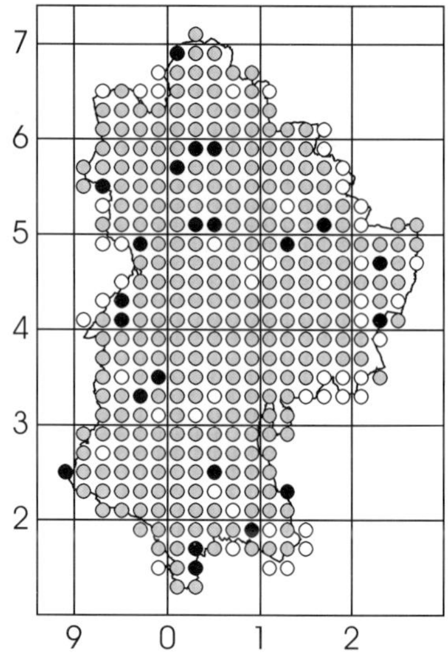

Specimens in collections: Ampthill 1946 (Buckinghamshire Museum); Dunstable Downs 1949 (G.F.B.Prior); Totternhoe Knolls 1956 and 1964 (Graveley-Edwards); Pegsdon 1937, Putnoe 1927-37 and Wilden 1937(Tebbs); Kensworth 1930, Luton 1916 and Sharpenhoe 1930 (Luton Museum).

Flight: Late June to August with a few lasting into September (weeks 26 to 36, peak 29 to 32)*.

Larval Foodplants: Bents, fescues and other narrow-leaved grasses.

Meadow Brown *Maniola jurtina* (Linnaeus) ssp. *insularis* Thomson (1626)
(Drawing on title page)

Pre VCH: Abbot (MS1) found the Meadow Brown "very common 1797" and also noted it on 15 July 1799, no locality given. J.C.Dale (MS3) recorded it at Clapham Park Wood on 13 July 1819. "Extremely common" in the neighbourhood of Luton (Lucas, 1855).

VCH: as *Epinephile janira* Linn. "Generally common".

Post VCH: S.R.Bowden (1965) found it on Knocking Hoe in 1917-21 and "exceptionally numerous" there in 1946. "Very common, especially in meadow land that has remained unploughed for a considerable time" noted West (1949). Reported in 1954 as "plentiful" in King's Wood, Heath and Reach (Kershaw, 1954).

Specimens in collections: Ampthill 1946 (Buckinghamshire Museum); Dunstable Downs 1937-46 (G.F.B.Prior); Totternhoe Knolls 1952 (Graveley-Edwards); Bedford 1937, Putnoe 1927-34 (Tebbs); Skimpot 1929 (Luton Museum).

Currently widespread and common, the Meadow Brown can be seen in almost any grassy area, including road verges, green lanes and woodland rides. Recorded since 1977 in 356 tetrads. Transect counts often exceed 100 and over 200 have been seen on

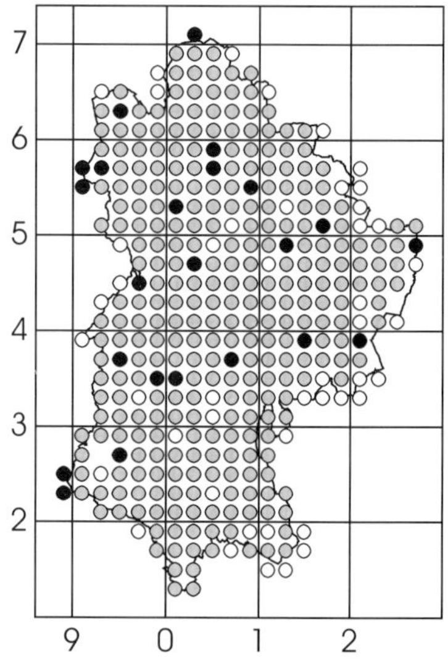

For details of standard weeks see page 6.

several occasions with 346 counted on a walk on Blow's Downs in 1994.
Flight: June to September (weeks 24 to 39, peak 28 to 32)*.
Larval Foodplants: Various fine grass species including meadow-grasses and bents.

Ringlet *Aphantopus hyperantus* (Linnaeus) (1629) (Drawing on page 30)
Pre VCH: Charles Abbot (MS1) recorded the Ringlet as "common at Clapham between woods in the Slipe. June 1798" and also found it on 15 July 1799. J.C.Dale found it on 13 July 1819 in Clapham Park Wood (MS3). "Abundant" in the neighbourhood of Luton wrote Lucas (1855).
VCH: "Plentiful in woods".
Post VCH: West (1949) described it as "common, but rather more restricted to woodland than open country, though found on the lower chalk at Barton". The increase in scrub especially on the chalk downs since the 1950s has provided this butterfly with an opportunity to expand its range and it is now very abundant in such sites, preferring the shaded grassy areas. It can also be seen along many roadside verges, especially if bordered by damp ditches, and in green lanes and other grassy fragments of uncultivated land.

Specimens in collections: Putnoe 1929-31 (Tebbs); King's Wood, Heath and Reach 1957 (Humphrey-Kershaw).

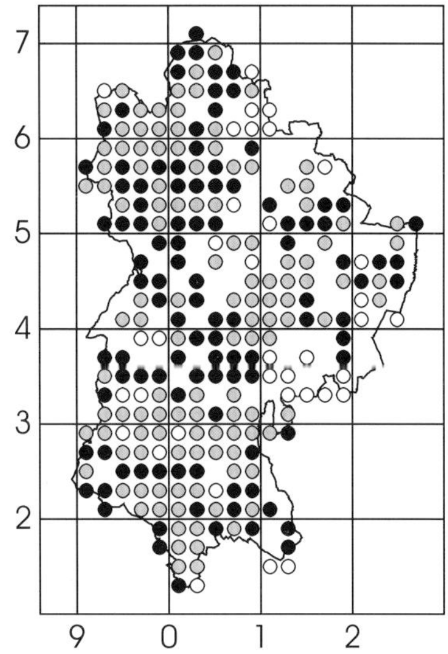

It has been recorded since 1977 in 259 tetrads of which 102 are new records in the 1990s. The latter probably represent a real expansion in range. Like the Speckled Wood, the total numbers recorded on transects increased up to 1992 and have remained high since then. Over 200 have been counted on some walks and 340 on a walk on Blow's Downs in 1994.
Flight: June to August (weeks 24 to 34, peak 27 to 29)*.
Larval Foodplants: Tufted hair-grass, creeping bent and other grasses.

Small Heath *Coenonympha pamphilus pamphilus* (Linnaeus) (1627) (Drawing on page 253)
Pre VCH: Abbot's notebook (MS1) mentions the Small Heath as "far from rare. Clapham Wood 1797" and also on 10 June 1799 without saying where. J.C.Dale (MS3) recorded finding it on 14 July 1818, from the context clearly in the Bedford area. Lucas listed it in 1855 as "common" in the neighbourhood of Luton and Hasted noted it at Bedford in 1890.
VCH: "Common in every grass field".
Post VCH: S.R.Bowden (1965) found the Small Heath on Knocking Hoe in 1917-21 but West did not mention it in his 1949 review.

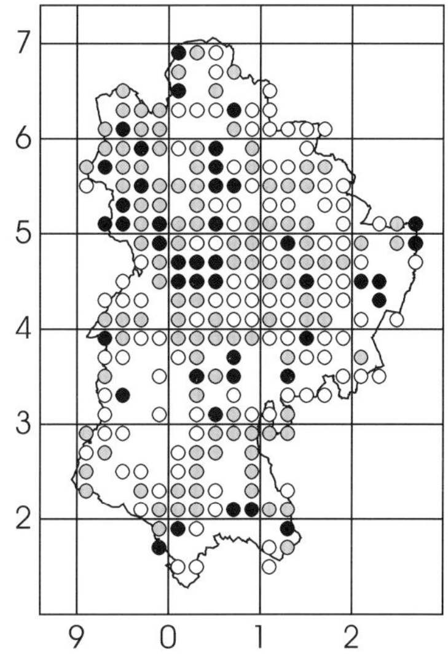

For key to butterfly maps see page 3.

Specimens in collections: Dunstable Downs 1932-64 (G.F.B.Prior); Dunstable Downs 1941, Totternhoe Knolls 1961 (Graveley-Edwards); Pegsdon 1933, Putnoe 1922-33 and Wilden 1934 (Tebbs).

Currently the Small Heath is widespread (recorded since 1977 in 256 tetrads) but rarely very common. The comment made in the VCH would certainly not have applied in recent years. Thirty-six were counted on a single transect walk on Barton Hills in 1995 but counts of 10-15 are more usual. It is occasionally found on road verges but more often on open grassland and in green lanes. In recent years, Barton Hills has been one of the best sites on the chalk for this species though numbers were exceptionally high on Whipsnade Downs in 1989. Numbers were low at both sites in 1993. Away from the chalk, the largest numbers have been seen on restored grassland as at Bromham Lake Local Nature Reserve and Centenary Wood.

Flight: April to September (weeks 17 to 39, peaks 21 to 28 and 34 to 36)*.

Larval Foodplants: Fescues, Meadow-grasses and bents.

Subfamily: **Danainae**

Many species of the Danainae accumulate toxic chemicals, usually from their larval foodplants, in their bodies. This makes them poisonous or distasteful to predators. Only one species, the Monarch, occasionally reaches Britain. Wingspan 95-100 mm.

Monarch or Milkweed *Danaus plexippus* (Linnaeus) (1630)

Post VCH: The only known report of this species was on 16 July 1995 in a garden in Willington by G.H.Pickerell. This was probably an escape from captivity as it is unlikely to have been a natural immigrant at that time of year.

For details of standard weeks see page 6.

Eggars and their allies

(Lasiocampidae and Saturniidae)

V.W.Arnold

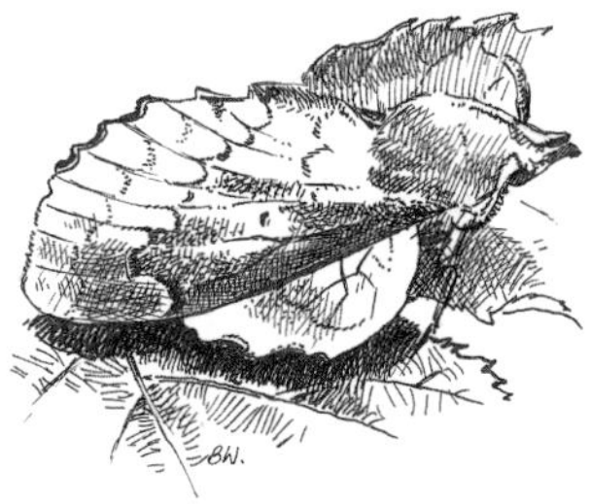

The Lappet

Family: **Lasiocampidae**

Mostly rather fat-bodied 'furry' moths with yellowish-brown wings. Wingspans range from 32 to 99 mm. The proboscis is reduced or absent and the moths do not feed. Some species are entirely nocturnal while the day-flying males of the Oak Eggar are attracted by scent to newly-emerged females from considerable distances. The caterpillars are hairy and in some species, such as the Lackey, are brightly coloured and gregarious. Eight of the 12 British species occur in Bedfordshire.

December Moth *Poecilocampa populi* (Linnaeus) (1631)

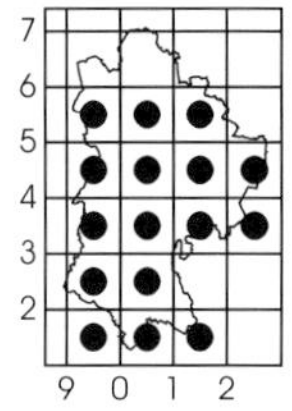

Pre VCH: Recorded by J.C.Dale (MS3) on 1 June 1820 as "Larvas of *B. Populeus* trunk of oak &c". From the adjacent entries Dale was collecting in Clapham Park Wood at that time.
VCH: "Bedford, Luton, Potton; sometimes to be seen flying around gas lamps in December."
Post VCH: Well distributed and common throughout the County.
Flight: October to end of December (weeks 41 to 52, peak 43 to 50)*.
Larval Foodplants: Polyphagous on deciduous trees including blackthorn*, oaks, birches, hawthorns and poplars.

Pale Eggar *Trichiura crataegi* (Linnaeus) (1632)

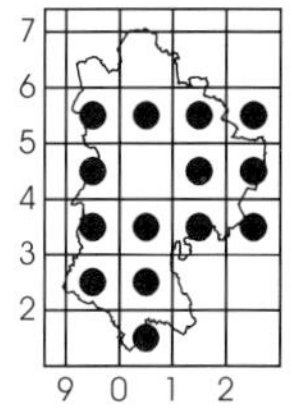

Pre VCH: Recorded in the Curtis diaries from "Bedfordsh" [*sic*] but with no date.
VCH: "Bedford, Luton, Potton; but scarce."
Post VCH: Well distributed but never recorded in large numbers.
Flight: August and September (weeks 32 to 39, peak 35 to 38)*.
Larval Foodplants: Blackthorn, hawthorns, birches, oaks.

Small Eggar *Eriogaster lanestris* (Linnaeus) (1633) (Plate 74)
Pre VCH: J.C.Dale (MS2) recorded receiving this species from Abbot's collection from near Bedford but not dated.
VCH: The entry brackets the Small Eggar with the Lackey: "The large silken habitations of the larvae of these two species are not uncommon on hawthorn hedges and fruit trees." It is not clear whether this meant that each species was "not uncommon" or whether the larval webs were often not distinguished.
Post VCH: R.M.Craske recalled the Small Eggar as "local, Putnoe Lane, Bedford" between 1918 and 1927. Foster (1934) described it as "quite common in the north western quarters

For key to moth maps see page 3.

of our district" by which he probably meant the Flitwick area. K.Parsons found a web of caterpillars in June 1984 on blackthorn on a roadside verge between Upper Dean and Shelton and V.W.Arnold found a web in the same area in 1987. G.Ping recorded webs at Carlton in 1985, 1986 and 1987 on blackthorn. H.A.Smith found a colony north of Odell Great Wood in 1985 and 1993 and larvae at Dungee Wood in 1993 and Harrold in 1994. In 1995, larvae were found at Wymington Meadow Nature Reserve during a Bedfordshire Natural History Society meeting and on Sharnbrook Summit Nature Reserve by M.Hammond and S.Wantling. In 1996 larvae were found at Thurleigh Cutting, Bletsoe, Felmersham Nature Reserve, Little Staughton, Wollaston Roman Road, near Odell Great Wood and Colworth House, Sharnbrook by D.V.Manning, D.Tyler, R.C.Revels, H.A.Smith, M.J.Hammond and S.Wantling. Despite this apparant increase in range in 1996, the Small Eggar is still scarce in the County. It has declined throughout its range in the British Isles, no doubt affected by habitat loss, modern methods of hedge management and the use of pesticides.

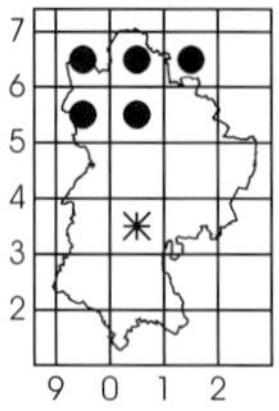

Flight: February and March. (All the Bedfordshire records have been for caterpillars.)
Larval Foodplants: Blackthorn*, hawthorns* and elm*. Living in a large web.

The Lackey *Malacosoma neustria* (Linnaeus) (1634)
Pre VCH: Abbot (MS1) noted rearing *Neustria* in 1799. He also sent to Sowerby, with a letter dated 16 May 1799, "a spray of Hawthorn with the empty egg-shells of *Bombyx Neustria* curiously arranged". In neither case did he give the locality. Emily Shore (Anon, 1891) wrote a very accurate description of the larva from Woodbury, near Everton, on 23 June 1832. Graham (1878) described the Lackey as "well known for its ravages on fruit trees and hedges".
VCH: See the entry for the previous species.
Post VCH: This is a common and widely distributed species. It is the large silken webs, in which the larvae live together until nearly fully grown, that are usually reported.

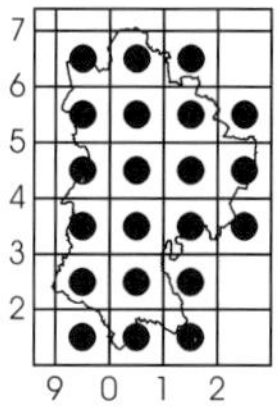

Flight: End of June to August (weeks 25 to 35, peak 26 to 33)*.
Larval Foodplants: A wide variety of trees including hawthorns*, blackthorn*, sallow and various fruit trees such as apple* and cherry*.

Grass Eggar *Lasiocampa trifolii trifolii* ([Denis and Schiffermüller]) (1636)
VCH: "Dr. W.G.Nash reports that he has reared this species at Bedford."
Notes: This species is confined to coastal areas and has only been included here because it was mentioned in the VCH.

Oak Eggar *Lasiocampa quercus quercus* (Linnaeus) (1637)
Pre VCH: Found frequently near Bedford by C.Abbot (Haworth, 1803) and reared by him in 1799 (Abbot, MS1).
VCH: "Generally distributed."
Post VCH: R.M.Craske recalled finding this species in Green Lane, Clapham between 1918 and 1927. There is a specimen in B.B.West's collection labelled "Putnoe 6th August

For details of standard weeks see page 6.

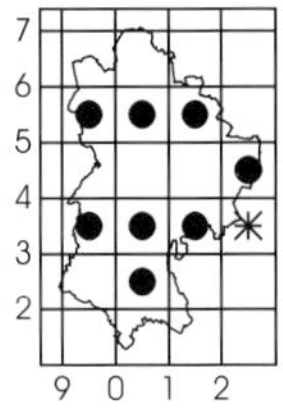

1928. W.G.Nash". More recent records are from Stotfold in the 1950s where D.Tyler recalled the larvae as quite numerous on brambles, Biggleswade in the 1960s by R.C.Revels, Clapham in 1979 by G. Ping, Luton in 1979 by K.F.Webb, Meppershall in 1977 by V.H.Chambers, Salford in 1983, 1995 and 1996 by J. Moore, in the RIS trap at Cockayne Hatley in 1976, 1981 and 1995 and Shefford in 1991 by D.Parsons. During 1995 C.R.B. and P.M.Baker recorded it from Wilden and near Warren Wood and a female came to H.A.Smith's light at Carlton.
Flight: July and August (weeks 27 to 32)★.
Larval Foodplants: A variety of trees and shrubs, including brambles★, sallow, oaks and hazel.

Fox Moth *Macrothylacia rubi* (Linnaeus) (1638)
Post VCH: R.M.Craske recalled this species as common at Sharpenhoe between 1918 and 1927. "Common on Barton Hills and also on Pegsdon Hills" (Foster, 1934). Also recorded from Cooper's Hill in the 1950s, Pegsdon Hills (1985 and 1986), Sharpenhoe (1958), Totternhoe Knolls (1946, 1957), Warden and Galley Hills (1957 and 1978) and the RIS trap at Houghton Regis (1991).
Flight: May, June and July (weeks 24 and 30)★. Most records are of larvae.
Larval Foodplants: Many plants including brambles, heather and bilberry.

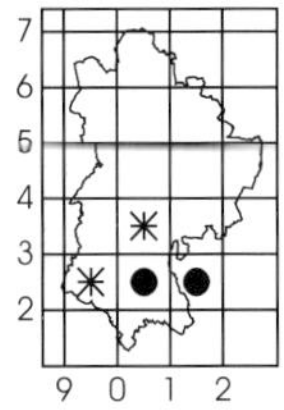

The Drinker *Euthrix potatoria* (Linnaeus) (1640)
Pre VCH: Abbot (MS1) recorded rearing this species in 1799.
VCH: "Generally distributed."
Post VCH: Common throughout the County, particularly in damp areas.
Flight: June to September (weeks 23 to 35, peak 27 to 32)★.
Larval Foodplants: Many species of grasses★ and reeds.

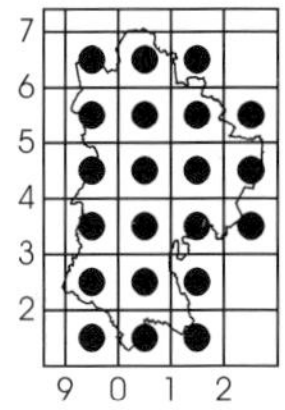

The Lappet *Gastropacha quercifolia* (Linnaeus) (1642)
(Drawing on page 259)
Pre VCH: J.C.Dale (MS2) recorded receiving this species from Abbot's collection from near Bedford dated "July 24 1799" and Abbot (MS1) noted it emerging on that date.
VCH: "Bedford, Woburn, Potton."
Post VCH: Widespread but never found in large numbers.
Flight: July and August (weeks 27 to 32)★.
Larval Foodplants: Hawthorns★, blackthorn, buckthorn and apple★.

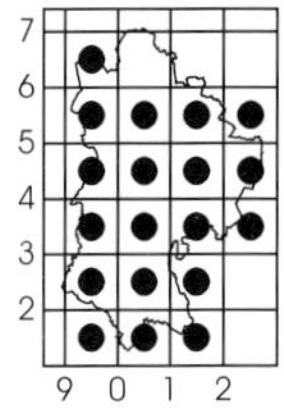

For key to moth maps see page 3.

Family: Saturniidae

Emperor Moth

The Emperor Moth is the only British representative of this family of 'silk moths', which includes some of the largest moths in the world. The adults do not feed and the male antennae are large and feather-like. The larva has short spines arising from small coloured 'warts'. The pupa, which overwinters, is enclosed in a remarkable tough cocoon the exit of which is guarded by a ring of stiff outward-pointing bristles.

Emperor Moth *Pavonia pavonia* (Linnaeus) (1643) (Plates 8 and 9)
Pre VCH: Charles Abbot recorded in his notebook (MS1) "9 *Pavonia* caterpillars found at Grubb's Wood near Stagsden July 8th 1799". On 30 May 1820 J.C.Dale (MS3) noted "small larva *B . Pavonus* blackthorn". He was collecting near Bedford that day. Elsewhere (MS2) he recorded receiving this species from Abbot's collection from near Bedford but not dated.
VCH: "Bedford, Woburn, Potton."
Post VCH: Found throughout the County, but never recorded in large numbers. Larvae of this species were collected from Bison Hill, from a small hawthorn bush on the 8 June 1978. These pupated in August 1978. On the 8 May 1979 a bilateral gynandromorph emerged from pupation. This is only the third known British specimen (Arnold,1979b) and only the second with full data. It is now in the Natural History Museum, South Kensington. A.J.Martin (1980b, 1981a) investigated assembling behaviour. In 1979 he took a cage of virgin females to Flitwick Moor and marked 12 males that were attracted to them. He then moved the females 2 km to Ampthill and noted the arrival of four of the marked males. In the following year he found that males were attracted to a cage of females despite their being surrounded by a selection of strong-smelling substances.

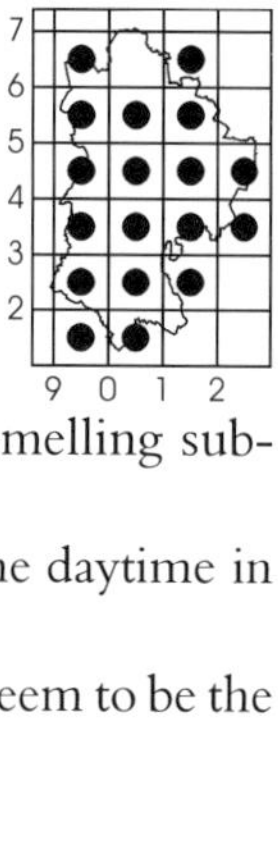

Flight: April and May (weeks 15 to 22)★. The male can be seen flying in the daytime in search of females which are nocturnal.
Larval Foodplants: Heather★, hawthorns★, brambles★ and meadowsweet★ seem to be the favoured plants in Bedfordshire.

For details of standard weeks see page 6.

Hook-tips, Lutestrings and Geometers - Part 1

(Drepanidae to Sterrhinae)

V.W.Arnold

Pebble Hook-tip

Family: **Drepanidae The Hook-tips**

These moths get their name from the elongated and hooked tip to the forewings. The adult moth has no proboscis and does not feed. With yellowish-brown wings, the moths are well-camouflaged when at rest. Wingspan 26-42 mm. The Chinese Character differs from the other species in being smaller (22-27 mm), coloured white with black markings and lacking the hooked tip to the forewings. Its larva is however of the typical drepanid form, humped and lacking the hind claspers. There are seven species in Britain of which five have been found in Bedfordshire.

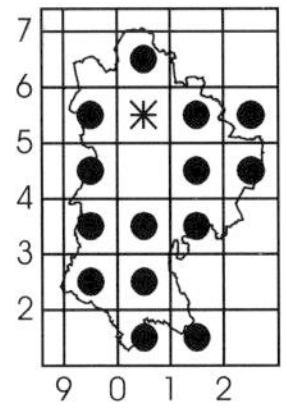

Scalloped Hook-tip ***Falcaria lacertinaria*** **(Linnaeus) (1645)**
Post VCH: A local species, found in woods with birch, throughout the County. Good sites are Flitwick Moor and Maulden Woods. S.H.Kershaw recorded it at Aspley Heath in 1936, 1945 and 1952.
Flight: Between May and September in two broods (weeks 18 to 34 with the only clear peak at 31 to 32)★.
Larval Foodplants: Birches★.

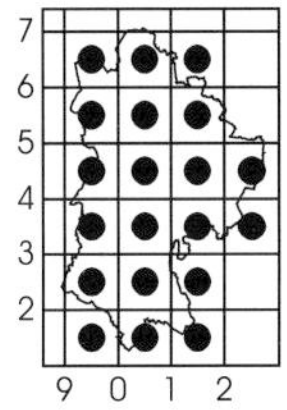

Oak Hook-tip ***Drepana binaria*** **(Hufnagel) (1646)** (Plate 35)
Pre VCH: Recorded by J.C.Dale (MS2, MS3) (as *Falcaria Hamula*) on 31 May 1820 from Clapham Park Wood.
Post VCH: Widespread and common throughout the County.
Flight: Between May and September in two broods (weeks 20 to 38, peaks 22 to 23 and 30 to 34)★.
Larval Foodplants: Oaks★.

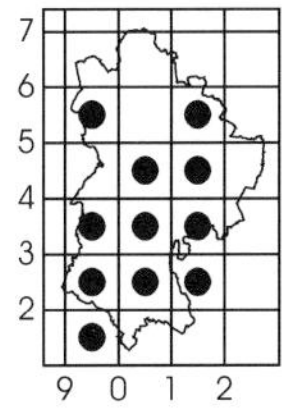

Barred Hook-tip ***Drepana cultraria*** **(Fabricius) (1647)**
Post VCH: A local and uncommon species in Bedfordshire found in areas where its foodplant occurs. S.H.Kershaw noted it at Aspley Heath in 1954.
Flight: May and June (weeks 20 to 24)★ and August (weeks 31 to 35)★.
Larval Foodplant: Beech.

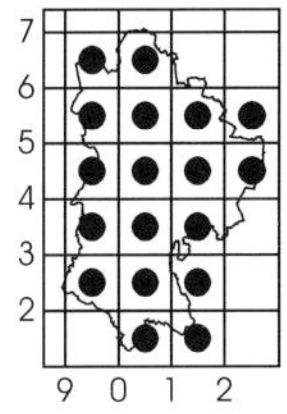

Pebble Hook-tip ***Drepana falcataria falcataria*** **(Linnaeus) (1648)**
Post VCH: Local but well distributed. Maulden Wood and Flitwick Moor are good sites for this species.
Flight: Between May and September in two broods (weeks 20 to 35 with the only clear peak at 31 to 32)★.
Larval Foodplants: Birches.

For key to moth maps see page 3.

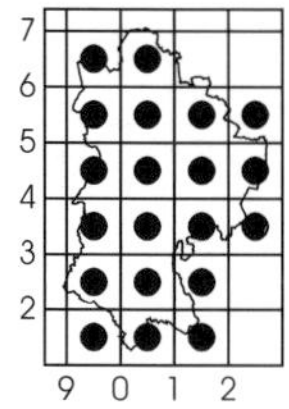

Chinese Character *Cilix glaucata* (Scopoli) (1651)
VCH: "Generally distributed about hawthorn."
Post VCH: Common throughout the County.
Flight: Between April and September in two broods (weeks 17 to 37, peaks 20 to 23 and 28 to 36)*.
Larval Foodplants: Hawthorns* and blackthorn.

Family: **Thyatiridae**

The species in this family look superficially like noctuids (see later) but are grouped close to the geometers on morphological grounds. Although most of the moths are a rather dull grey and white in appearance, the Buff Arches and the Peach Blossom are among the most beautiful of British moths. Wingspan 25-44 mm. All the nine British species have been found in Bedfordshire.

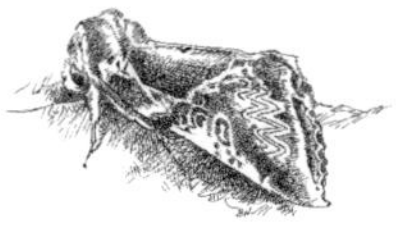

Buff Arches

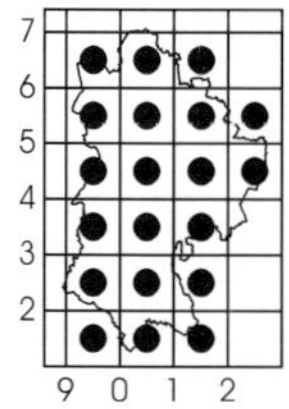

Peach Blossom *Thyatira batis* (Linnaeus) (1652) (Plate 34)
Post VCH: Common in wooded areas throughout the County.
Flight: May to August (weeks 20 to 35, peak 24 to 29)*.
Larval Foodplants: Brambles.

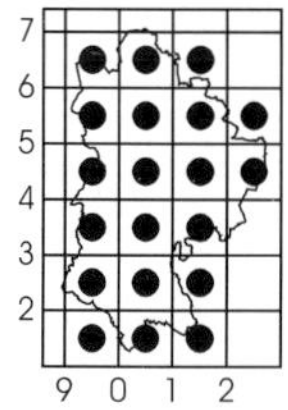

Buff Arches *Habrosyne pyritoides* (Hufnagel) (1653)
VCH: (as *Gonophora derasa* Linn.) "Bedford, in woods."
Post VCH: A common and widespread species.
Flight: June to August (weeks 24 to 33, peak 26 to 31)*.
Larval Foodplants: Brambles.

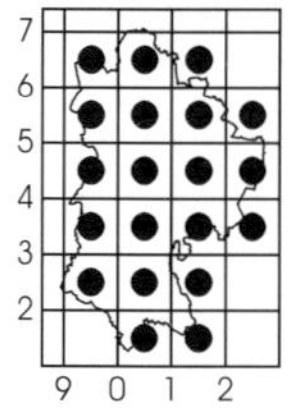

Figure of Eighty *Tethea ocularis* (Linnaeus) ssp. *octogesimea* (Hübner) (1654)
VCH: "Bedford, taken at sugar and the pupa dug up from roots of poplar."
Post VCH: Common and widespread.
Flight: May to July (weeks 23 to 29)*.
Larval Foodplants: Poplars* and aspen.

Poplar Lutestring *Tethea or or* ([Denis & Schiffermüller]) (1655)
Pre VCH: There is a specimen in the Dale collection side-labelled "Bedford" but no mention of this could be found in J.C.Dale's notebooks.
Post VCH: Normally found in old woodland where its food plant occurs. Recorded from Aspley Heath (1936, 1946 and 1954), King's Wood, Heath and Reach (1981 and 1987), Marston Thrift (1983, 1985 and 1986), Maulden Wood (1979 and 1990), Odell Great Wood (1990), Potton Wood (1976) and its northern end (1992), Sandy (1959), West Wood (1988 and 1989) and the RIS trap at Cockayne Hatley (1983).
Flight: May to August (weeks 20 to 33)*.
Larval Foodplants: Aspen and poplars.

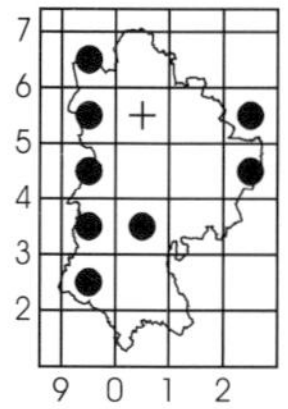

For details of standard weeks see page 6.

Satin Lutestring ***Tetheella fluctuosa*** **(Hübner) (1656)**
Post VCH: Recorded in S.H.Kershaw's notebook as found at Aspley Heath on 7-8 May 1934. The date is rather early and no specimen has been seen.
Flight: June to August.
Larval Foodplants: Birches.

Common Lutestring ***Ochropacha duplaris*** **(Linnaeus) (1657)**

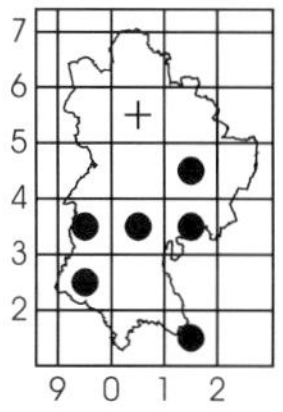

VCH: "Bedford, in woods."
Post VCH: An uncommon species found only in old woodlands, such as Aspley Heath, Flitwick Moor, Maulden Wood, Old Warden and The Lodge at Sandy,
Flight: June to August (weeks 23 to 32, peak 31)★.
Larval Foodplants: Birches, alder and oaks.

Oak Lutestring ***Cymatophorima diluta*** **([Denis & Schiffermüller]) ssp.** ***hartwiegi*** **(Reisser) (1658)**
VCH: "Luton."

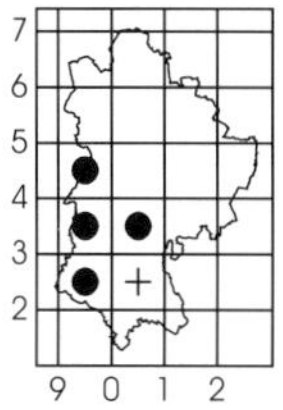

Post VCH: A local species that can be abundant where it occurs. Found at: Aspley Heath (most years 1932-47), Cranfield (1982), King's Wood, Heath and Reach (1981, 1985 and 1987), Maulden Wood (1976, 1977, 1980, 1981, 1983 and 1986) and Shire Oak (1983). On the 7 September 1981 a large number were attracted to light in King's Wood, Heath and Reach.
Flight: August and September (weeks 35 to 39)★.
Larval Foodplants: Oaks.

Yellow Horned ***Achlya flavicornis*** **(Linnaeus) ssp.** ***galbanus*** **(Tutt) (1659)**
Pre VCH: J.C.Dale (MS2) recorded receiving this species, as *Luteicornis*, from Abbot's collection from Bedford but not dated.

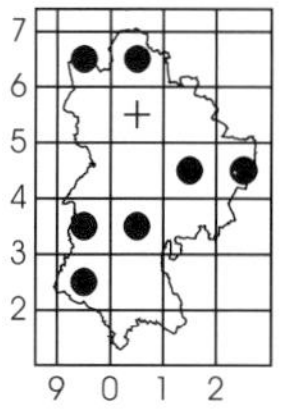

Post VCH: R.M.Craske recalled that between 1918 and 1927 this species was common at Rowney Warren. Foster (1934) stated: "has been taken by Temple, of Bedford, at Rowney Warren". It occurs in areas where its foodplant, birch, occurs. Examples are Aspley Heath, Flitwick Moor, The Lodge at Sandy, Warren Wood and West Wood.
Flight: February to April (weeks 8 to 15, peak 11)★.
Larval Foodplants: Birches★.

Frosted Green ***Polyploca ridens*** **(Fabricius) (1660)**

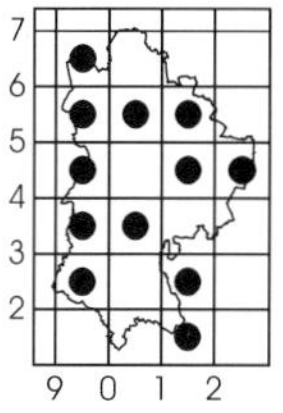

Post VCH: A local species that can be found in old woodlands: Aspley Heath, Flitwick Moor, Luton Hoo, Marston Thrift, Maulden Wood, Old Warden, Stockgrove Country Park, and West Wood.
Flight: April and May (weeks 15 to 20, peak 18)★.
Larval Foodplants: Oaks.

For key to moth maps see page 3.

Family: **Geometridae**

The moth usually has a proboscis. Most species rest with their wings held flat and are well camouflaged. They have a hearing organ (tympanum) on each side of the first segment of the abdomen which may help them evade predation by bats.The larvae lack abdominal prolegs and their 'looping' gait is a feature of the family.

Subfamily: **Archiearinae The Orange Underwings**

The species in this subfamily spend around nine months in the pupal stage, emerging to fly in early spring. There are two British species, both of which have been found in Bedfordshire. Wingspan 33-39 mm.

Orange Underwing ***Archiearis parthenias*** **(Linnaeus) (1661)**
VCH: "Bedford."
Post VCH: Recorded from Flitwick Moor (1947, 1979 and 1982), Maulden Wood (1974), Shire Oak (1979 and 1980) and The Lodge, Sandy (1990).
Flight: March and April (weeks 13 to 16)*, flying in bright sunshine around birch trees.
Larval Foodplants: Birches.

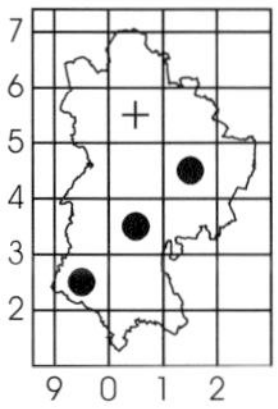

Light Orange Underwing ***Archiearis notha*** **(Hübner) (1662)**
Post VCH: Marston Thrift (1976), Maulden Wood (1982, 1983 and 1991) and Potton Wood (in most years since 1976).
Flight: March and April (weeks 13 to 14)*, flying in bright sunshine around aspen trees.
Larval Foodplant: Aspen.

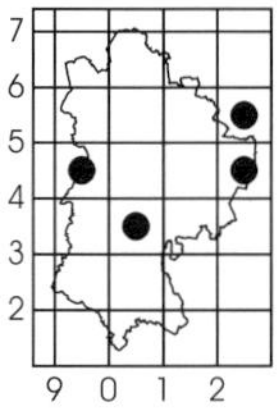

Subfamily: **Oenochrominae**

The March Moth is the only British species. It overwinters as a pupa. Wingspan of the male is 34-38 mm. The female is wingless.

March Moth ***Alsophila aescularia*** **([Denis & Schiffermüller]) (1663)**
VCH: "Bedford, Luton."
Post VCH: Well distributed and common.
Flight: January to May (weeks 2 to 20, peak 8 to 16)*.
Larval Foodplants: Polyphagous on deciduous trees.

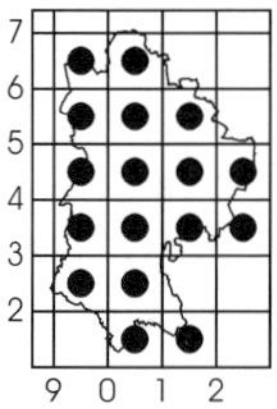

Subfamily: **Geometrinae The Emeralds etc.**

The various species of Emerald are pale green in colour though this often fades with age. Wingspan 23-64 mm. Most species overwinter as larvae. Ten British species, six in Bedfordshire.

For details of standard weeks see page 6.

Grass Emerald *Pseudoterpna pruinata* (Hufnagel) ssp. *atropunctaria* (Walker) (1665)
VCH: "Generally distributed."

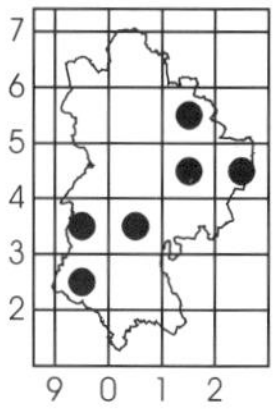

Post VCH: Confined to rough heathland and acid woodlands. Recorded from the RIS traps at Cockayne Hatley (1983), Old Warden (1975) and The Lodge, Sandy (1969-1972 and to MV light in 1989). Also from Aspley Heath (1934-52, 1986), Maulden Wood (1974, 1976 and 1977), Rowney Warren (1983), Stockgrove Country Park (1979 and 1984), Waterloo Thorns (1986) and Woburn Sands (1945).

Flight: June and July (weeks 26 to 29, peak 28)*.
Larval Foodplants: Gorse, broom and dyer's greenweed.

Large Emerald *Geometra papilionaria* (Linnaeus) (1666)

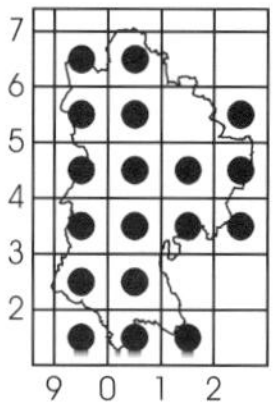

Pre VCH: Recorded in the Natural History Notebooks of T.Orlebar Marsh (MS1) "1799 Clapham between Twin Woods".
VCH: "Bedford district."
Post VCH: Recorded throughout the County, usually in wooded areas.
Flight: June to August (weeks 26 to 31, peak 29)*.
Larval Foodplants: Birches* and occasionally alder, hazel and beech.

Blotched Emerald *Comibaena bajularia* ([Denis & Schiffermüller]) (1667) (Plate 36)

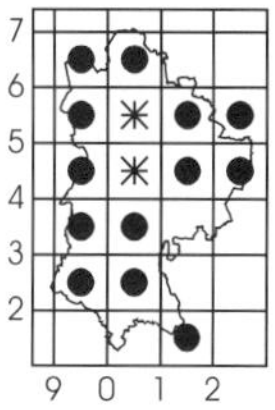

VCH: "Recorded at Potton by Mr. W.Bond-Smith."
Post VCH: Widely distributed in old oak woodlands. Although a local species, it can be common where it occurs. A good site is Maulden Wood.
Flight: June and July (weeks 24 to 28, peak 26 and 27)*.
Larval Foodplants: Oaks*.

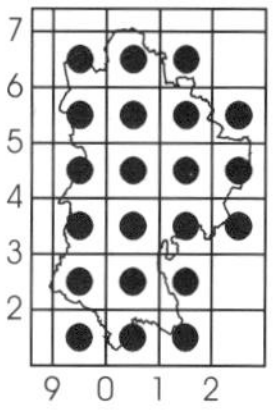

Common Emerald *Hemithea aestivaria* (Hübner) (1669)
VCH: (as *Hemithea thymiaria* Linn.) "Bedford, Luton."
Post VCH: Common throughout the County.
Flight: June to August (weeks 25 to 31, peak 27 to 29)*.
Larval Foodplants: Polyphagous on deciduous trees and bushes.

Small Grass Emerald *Chlorissa viridata* (Linnaeus) (1670)
VCH: "Recorded at Bedford by Mr. J.Sharpin." It is possible that this species was incorrectly identified. It is more likely to have been the Little Emerald, *J. lactearia* (L.).
Post VCH: In his notebooks S.H.Kershaw recorded finding *viridata* at Aspley Heath on 19 July 1937 and 13 July 1946 but no voucher specimens have been seen. Skinner (1984) does not include Bedfordshire in his list of known sites for this species.

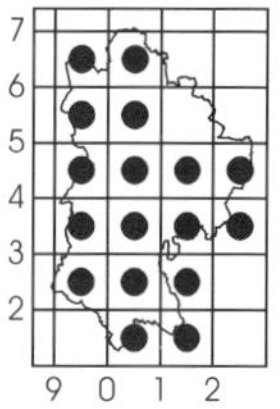

Small Emerald *Hemistola chrysoprasaria* (Esper) (1673)
VCH: (as *Iodis vernaria* Linn.) "Bedford district."
Post VCH: A local species that never appears to be common.
Flight: June to August (weeks 26 to 31, peak 30)*.
Larval Foodplant: Traveller's-joy.

Little Emerald *Jodis lactearia* (Linnaeus) (1674)
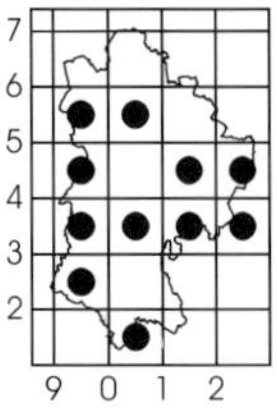

VCH: "Bedford district."
Post VCH: A local species found throughout the County in woodland areas.
Flight: June to September (weeks 23 to 35)*.
Larval Foodplants: Polyphagous on trees and shrubs.

Subfamily: **Sterrhinae**
Mochas, Waves etc.

Riband Wave

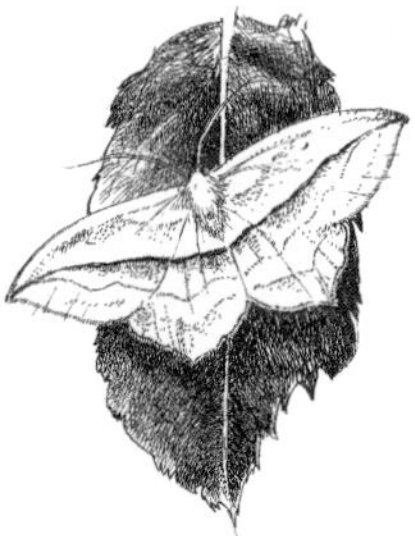
Blood Vein

The moths of most species have a delicate pattern of lines or dots which extends across both fore- and hind-wings. There is often a central dot on each wing.

Wingspan 18-35 mm. There are 38 British species of which 22 have definitely been found in Bedfordshire, together with a further three where the records are in doubt.

Dingy Mocha *Cyclophora pendularia* (Clerck) (1675)
Post VCH: Recorded from the RIS trap at Sandy (1969). This species was recorded in error and is not known from Bedfordshire.

The Mocha *Cyclophora annulata* (Schulze) (1676)
Pre VCH: J.C.Dale (MS3) recorded finding this species (as *Geometra Omicronaria*) in Clapham Park Wood between 31 May and 2 June 1820. Elsewhere (MS2) he noted receiving this species from Abbot's collection from near Bedford but not dated.
VCH: "Bedford district, among maple."

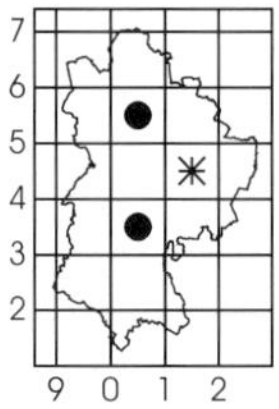

Post VCH: A very uncommon species. There are specimens in the Temple collection from Twin Wood dated June 1906, 1907 and 1909. R.M.Craske recalled the Mocha as "local at Rowney Warren" between 1918 and 1927. Only two recent records: Putnoe Wood (1968) and Flitwick Moor (1976).
Flight: Between May and August (weeks 31 and 34)* in two broods.
Larval Foodplant: Field maple.

Birch Mocha *Cyclophora albipunctata* (Hufnagel) (1677)
VCH: (as *Ephyra pendularia* Linn.) "Bedford, among birch."

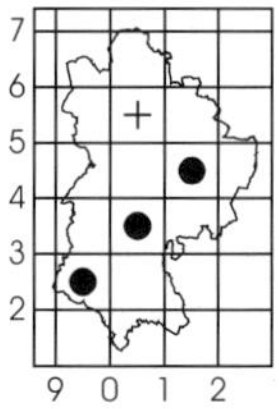

Post VCH: In 1958 it was common at Folly Wood, Flitwick (West, 1959) but has since become scarce. Recorded in the RIS trap at The Lodge, Sandy, every year between 1969 and 1975. Also from King's Wood, Heath and Reach (1987) and Warren Wood (1984).
Flight: May and June and again in late July and August in two broods (weeks 18 to 21, peak 20, and weeks 30 to 35, peak 32)*.
Larval Foodplants: Birches.

For details of standard weeks see page 6.

False Mocha *Cyclophora porata* (Linnaeus) (1679)
VCH: "Bedford, among oak."

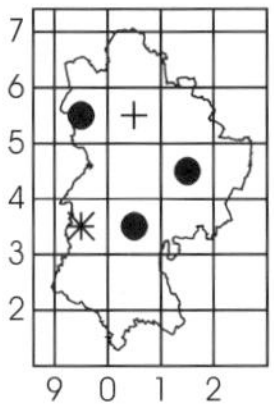

Post VCH: A specimen in the Kershaw collection is from Aspley Heath (1939). More recently found in Maulden Wood (1976, 1977, 1979, 1980), Sharnbrook (1974, 1976) and in the RIS trap at The Lodge, Sandy (1970). A scarce species in Bedfordshire.
Flight: Double-brooded, flying in May and June (weeks 23 to 25)★ and August (weeks 32 to 34)★ and September.

Larval Foodplants: Oaks.

Maiden's Blush *Cyclophora punctaria* (Linnaeus) (1680) (Plate 37)
VCH: "Bedford, among oak."

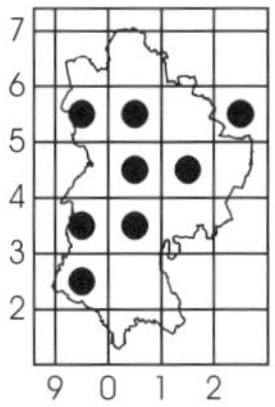

Post VCH: An uncommon species, recorded mainly from sites along the Greensand Ridge, such as Aspley Heath, Clophill, King's Wood (Heath and Reach) and The Lodge, Sandy. It was also recorded in 1961 from Bedford.
Flight: Double-brooded flying in May and June and again in August and September (weeks 18 to 27, peak 21, and weeks 30 to 37, peak 32 to 35)★.
Larval Foodplants: Oaks.

Clay Triple-lines *Cyclophora linearia* (Hübner) (1681)

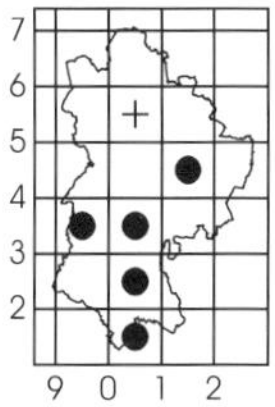

VCH: "Bedford district, among beech."
Post VCH: Scarce in Bedfordshire. Recorded by S.H.Kershaw from Aspley Heath (1937-55). Also reported from Luton (1980, 1982 and 1992), Maulden Wood (1976 and 1981) and in the RIS trap at Old Warden (1976).
Flight: May to July (weeks 21 and 25)★ and sometimes between August (week 34)★ and October.
Larval Foodplant: Beech.

Blood-vein *Timandra griseata* (Petersen) (1682) (Drawing on page 268)
Pre VCH: J.C.Dale (MS3) recorded finding this species (as *Geometra Amataria*) on 14 July 1819, probably by the River Ouse near Bedford.

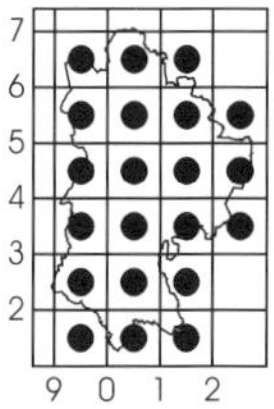

VCH: (as *Bradyepetes amataria* Linn.) "Bedford, Luton."
Post VCH: Common throughout the County.
Flight: Between May and September (weeks 20 to 40, peak 24 to 35)★.
Larval Foodplants: Docks, sorrels and knotgrass.

Lace Border *Scopula ornata* (Scopoli) (1687)

Pre VCH: J.C.Dale (MS2, MS3) recorded finding this species (as *Geometra Paludata* or *Ornata*) probably at Mouse's Pasture, Bromham on 14 July 1819.

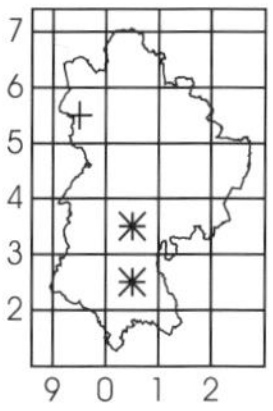

Post VCH: There are specimens in the Temple collection from Barton dated June 1906, 1909 and August 1911. "Common on Barton Hills" (Foster (1934) citing Nash). Although this species has been looked for in recent years, so far it has not been rediscovered.
Flight: Between May and September.
Larval Foodplants: Wild thyme and marjoram.

For key to moth maps see page 3.

Mullein Wave *Scopula marginepunctata* (Goeze) (1689)
VCH: Listed without comment.
Post VCH: Not recorded.
Flight: Between June and September in two broods.
Larval Foodplants: Mugwort, yarrow, plantains and other low-growing plants.

Small Blood-vein *Scopula imitaria* (Hübner) (1690)
Pre VCH: J.C.Dale (MS3) noted "*imitaria* female near Bedford" on 15 July 1819. Elsewhere (MS2) he recorded receiving this species from Abbot's collection from Bedford but not dated.
VCH: "Bedford, Luton."
Post VCH: Widespread and common.
Flight: June to September (weeks 24 to 37, peak 26 to 31)*.
Larval Foodplants: Privets and probably a variety of low-growing plants.

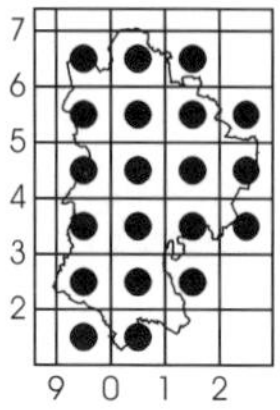

Lesser Cream Wave *Scopula immutata* (Linnaeus) (1692)
VCH: "Luton."
Post VCH: Found in damp meadows and marshes. It appears to be a local and scarce species in Bedfordshire. Entries in S.H.Kershaw's notebooks note it at Aspley Heath in 1936 and 1955. Recorded more recently from sites such as Felmersham Nature Reserve, Flitwick Moor and Waterloo Thorns.
Flight: June, July (week 27 to 30)* and August.
Larval Foodplants: Common valerian and meadowsweet.

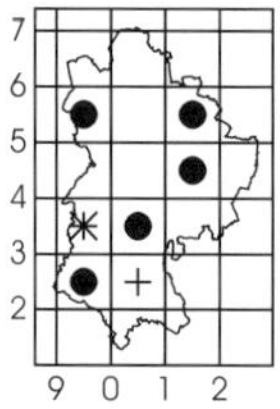

Cream Wave *Scopula floslactata floslactata* (Haworth) (1693)
VCH: (as *Acidalia remutata* Hb.) "Bedford, Potton, probably in all woods."
Post VCH: Never appears to be common but is recorded in most years from woodlands.
Flight: May to July (weeks 18 to 28, peak 22)*.
Larval Foodplants: Dandelions and knotgrass and probably a variety of low-growing plants.

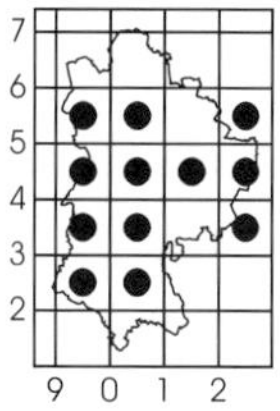

Smoky Wave *Scopula ternata* Schrank (1694)
Post VCH: Recorded only from Kershaw's notebook (as *fumata*) as coming to light at Aspley Heath on 21-22 July 1950. No specimen has been seen.
Flight: June and July.
Larval Foodplants: Bilberry and heather.

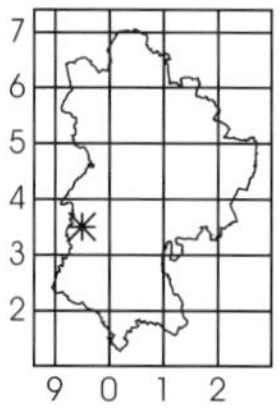

Least Carpet *Idaea vulpinaria* (Herrich-Schäffer) ssp. *atrosignaria* Lempke (1699)
Post VCH: Recorded only from the RIS trap at Cockayne Hatley in 1976, 1980 and 1996.
Flight: June to August (weeks 26, 30 and 32)*.
Larval Foodplants: Ivy, traveller's-joy and probably many other plants.

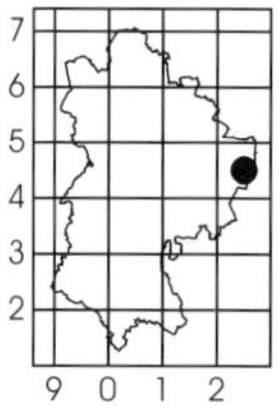

For details of standard weeks see page 6.

Dotted Border Wave *Idaea sylvestraria* (Hübner) (1701)
Post VCH: Recorded in error by Arnold (1995b) from a misplaced specimen in Kershaw's collection dated 12 July 1946. Kershaw also recorded this species in his notebook as *circellata* at Aspley Heath on 27 July 1948. As no voucher specimen has been seen for the latter record it must remain in doubt.

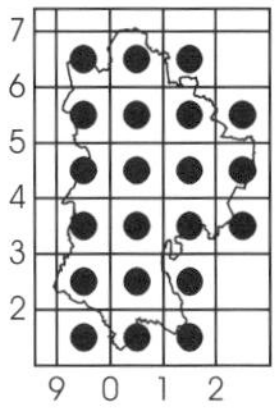

Small Fan-footed Wave *Idaea biselata* (Hufnagel) (1702)
VCH: "Common in woods."
Post VCH: Common throughout the County.
Flight: June to September (weeks 24 to 35, peak 27 to 33)*.
Larval Foodplants: Dandelions, knotgrass, plantains and brambles.

Silky Wave *Idaea dilutaria* (Hübner) (1704)
VCH: (as *Acidalia dilutaria* Hb.) "Bedford." This was probably an error. The Dwarf Cream Wave, *Idaea fuscovenosa* (Goeze), was also referred to as *Acidalia dilutaria* (Hübner).
Post VCH: Recorded in S.H.Kershaw's notebooks between 1932 and 1947 but no voucher specimens have been seen. The record from the RIS trap at Old Warden in 1979 was subsequently deleted as a misidentification (Arnold, 1982 and 1985).

Rusty Wave *Idaea inquinata* (Scopoli) (1703)
Post VCH: A moth was reared in October 1996 from a larva found in Luton on dried flowers, probably imported (det. A.M.Riley).

Dwarf Cream Wave *Idaea fuscovenosa* (Goeze) (1705)

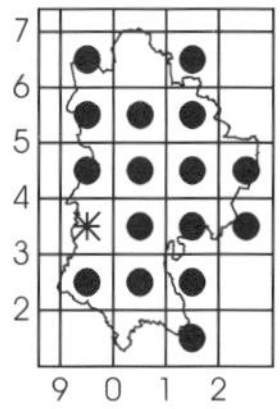

VCH: Not recorded but this seems likely to have been the species listed as *Acidalia dilutaria* (Hübner).
Post VCH: Well distributed but never common.
Flight: June to August (weeks 24 to 33, peak 26 to 31)*.
Larval Foodplants: Dandelions and also brambles in captivity. Probably feeds on a variety of low-growing plants.

Small Dusty Wave *Idaea seriata* (Schrank) (1707)

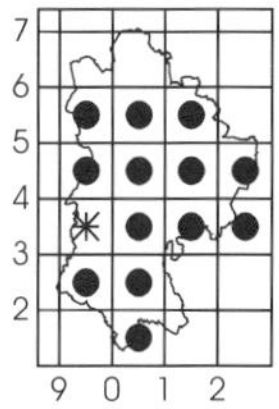

Pre VCH: J.C.Dale (MS2) recorded receiving this species as *Virgulata* from Abbot's collection from "Bedford ?" but not dated.
VCH: (as *Acidalia incanaria* Hb.) "Generally common in gardens."
Post VCH: Common throughout the County.
Flight: Between May and October (weeks 21 to 41, peak 26 to 31)*.
Larval Foodplants: Various low-growing plants and ivy.

For key to moth maps see page 3.

Single-dotted Wave *Idaea dimidiata* (Hufnagel) (1708)

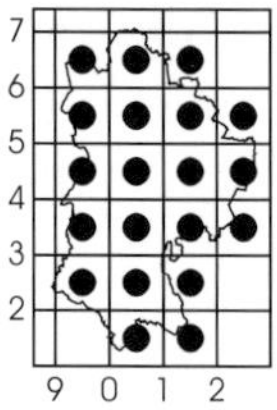

VCH: "Generally common."
Post VCH: Widely distributed and common.
Flight: Between late May and September (weeks 22 to 37, peak 26 to 32)*.
Larval Foodplants: Burnet-saxifrage and cow parsley.

Satin Wave *Idaea subsericeata* (Haworth) (1709)

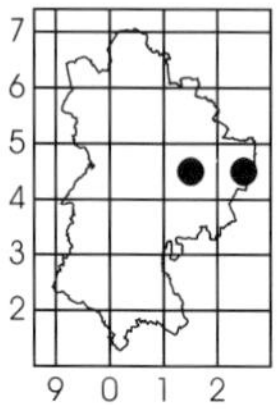

Post VCH: Known only from RIS traps at Cockayne Hatley (1979) and The Lodge, Sandy (1973, 1974).
Flight: June and July (weeks 24 to 30)*.
Larval Foodplants: Dandelions, knotgrass, plantains and probably a variety of low-growing plants.

Treble Brown Spot *Idaea trigeminata* (Haworth) (1711)

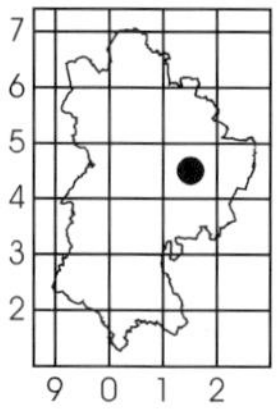

Post VCH: Known only from the RIS trap at The Lodge, Sandy on 11 and 14 July 1971 and 2 August 1973. A specimen in the Kershaw collection (Arnold, 1995b) was subsequently found to be misplaced.
Flight: Partly double-brooded June, July (week 28)*, August (week 31)*.
Larval Foodplants: A variety of low-growing plants.

Small Scallop *Idaea emarginata* (Linnaeus) (1712)

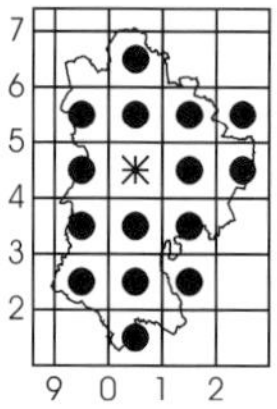

VCH: "Bedford, Luton."
Post VCH: Widely distributed but never found in large numbers.
Flight: June to September (weeks 26 to 37, peak 29 to 31)*.
Larval Foodplants: Bedstraws and a variety of low-growing plants.

Riband Wave *Idaea aversata* (Linnaeus) (1713)

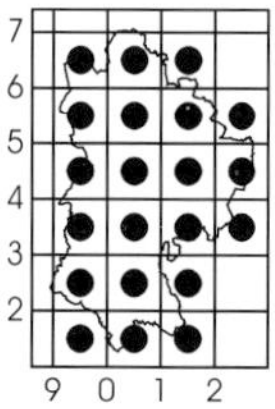

(Drawing on page 268)
VCH: "Generally distributed."
Post VCH: Common throughout the County.
Flight: May to September (weeks 22 to 39, peak 26 to 33)*.
Larval Foodplants: Various low-growing plants.

For details of standard weeks see page 6.

Plain Wave *Idaea straminata* (Borkhausen) (1715)

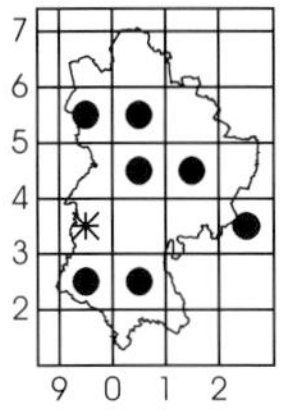

Post VCH: A scarce moth with very few records. There are specimens in the Temple collection from "near Shefford" dated 20 July 1908 and 16 August 1909. Records are in S.H.Kershaw's notebooks for Aspley Heath between 1936 and 1958. More recent records are from: King's Wood, Heath and Reach (1981), Luton (1992), Pavenham (1986), Stockgrove Country Park (1984), Stotfold (1989-1991, 1993), Sharnbrook (1995) and The Lodge, Sandy (RIS trap 1969-1973, MV trap 1989 and 1991),
Flight: July and August (weeks 27 to 34, peak 29 and 30)*.
Larval Foodplants: Probably a variety of low-growing plants.

The Vestal *Rhodometra sacraria* (Linnaeus) (1716)

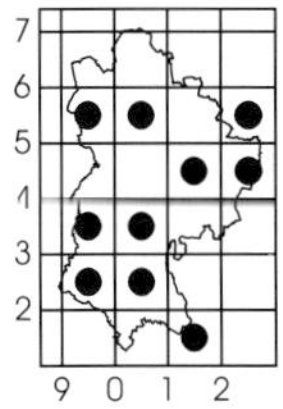

Post VCH: This immigrant species was found by A.H.Chapman at Everton on 1 September 1983. Later in the same month it was reported by others from Aspley Heath, Biggleswade, Bromham, Carlton, Cockayne Hatley, Eaton Bray, Luton and Luton Hoo. Other records from subsequent years are: Carlton (1985); Cockayne Hatley (1987); The Lodge, Sandy (1990); Ampthill Park (1994).
Flight: August and September (weeks 33 to 39)* and October.
Larval Foodplants: Docks and knotgrass.

Geometers - Part 2

(Larentiinae)

V.W.Arnold

Treble-bar

Family: **Geometridae**

Subfamily: **Larentiinae** **Carpets, Pugs etc.**

The 'carpets' and their allies (wingspan 18-48 mm) usually have strongly patterned forewings and pale uniform hindwings. The 'pugs' are smaller moths (wingspan 12-24 mm) with uniformly patterned wings. They are often difficult to identify to species. About 160 species have been found in Britain, 116 in Bedfordshire plus a further five for which the records are in some doubt.

Oblique Carpet *Orthonama vittata* (Borkhausen) (1719)

VCH: "Luton, in damp meadows."

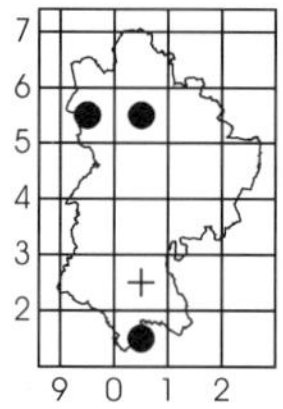

Post VCH: A scarce species in Bedfordshire, with very few records. A specimen in the Temple collection is labelled "Bedford 11/6/1910". More recently from: Bedford (1965), Bromham (1973), Putnoe Wood (1965), Stevington (1965) and the RIS trap at Whipsnade (1972).

Flight: Double-brooded in May and June (weeks 19 to 23)★ and August and September (week 36)★.

Larval Foodplants: Bedstraws.

The Gem *Orthonama obstipata* (Fabricius) (1720)

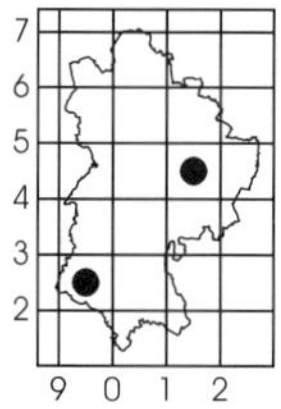

Post VCH: An immigrant species known only from the RIS traps at Eaton Bray (1981) and The Lodge, Sandy (1969).

Flight: Could occur at any time between spring and autumn. Recorded in Bedfordshire between July and October (weeks 30 to 42)★.

Larval Foodplants: Probably a variety of low-growing plants. Fed on knotgrass in captivity (A.M.Riley, pers. comm.).

Flame Carpet *Xanthorhoe designata* (Hufnagel) (1722)

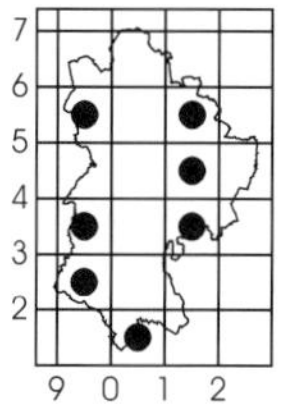

Post VCH: A local and scarce species in Bedfordshire. There is a specimen in the Kershaw collection from Aspley Heath dated 23 May 1933. Subsequently it has been recorded from a variety of sites, including the following RIS traps: Eaton Bray (1983), Old Warden (1974, 1975, 1976, 1979) and The Lodge, Sandy (1970).

Flight: May to September (weeks 22 to 37, peak 31 to 33)★.

Larval Foodplants: Species of Cruciferae in damp woodlands.

For details of standard weeks see page 6.

Red Twin-spot Carpet ***Xanthorhoe spadicearia*** **([Denis & Schiffermüller]) (1724)**

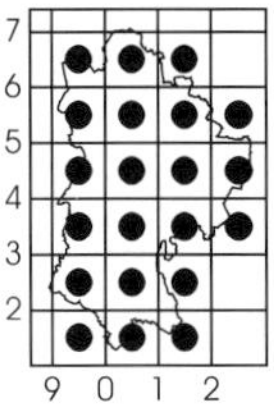

VCH: (as *Coremia ferrugata* Linn.) "Everywhere common."
Post VCH: Found commonly throughout the County.
Flight: April to September (weeks 16 to 38, peaks 20 to 23 and 30 to 34)*.
Larval Foodplants: Bedstraws and a variety of other low-growing plants.

Dark-barred Twin-spot Carpet ***Xanthorhoe ferrugata*** **(Clerck) (1725)**

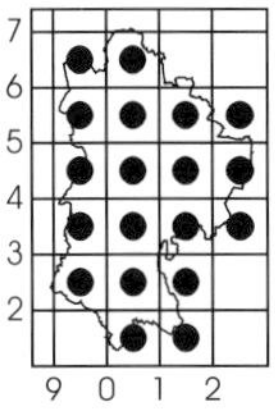

VCH: (as *Coremia unidentaria* Haw.) "Generally distributed."
Post VCH: Common throughout the County.
Flight: April to September (weeks 18 to 39, peaks 21 to 23 and 29 to 34)*.
Larval Foodplants: Polyphagous on low-growing plants.

Large Twin-spot Carpet ***Xanthorhoe quadrifasiata*** **(Clerck) (1726)**

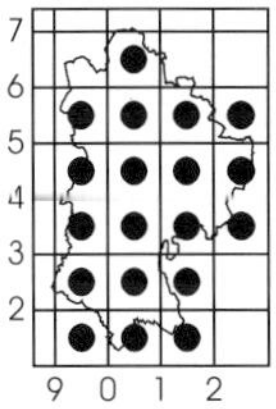

VCH: "Bedford, Luton."
Post VCH: Recorded throughout the County, normally in wooded areas. Not usually found in large numbers.
Flight: June to August (weeks 24 to 33, peaks 28 to 30)*.
Larval Foodplants: Polyphagous on low-growing plants.

Silver-ground Carpet ***Xanthorhoe montanata montanata*** **([Denis & Schiffermüller]) (1727)**

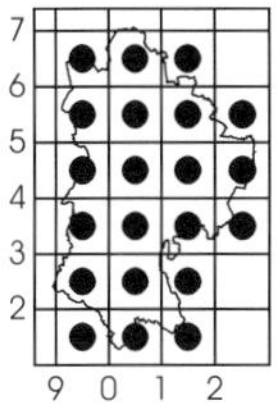

VCH: "Abundant in all woods."
Post VCH: Common throughout the County.
Flight: May to August (weeks 20 to 32, peak 21 to 26)*.
Larval Foodplants: Polyphagous on low-growing plants.

Garden Carpet ***Xanthorhoe fluctuata fluctuata*** **(Linnaeus) (1728)**

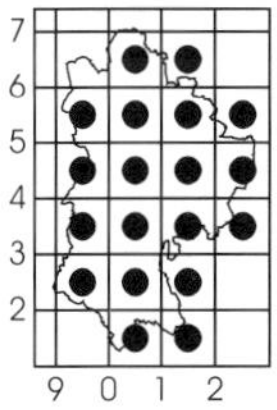

VCH: "Abundant in all gardens."
Post VCH: Common throughout the County.
Flight: Between May and October (weeks 17 to 44, common 20 to 39 with a peak 33 to 37)*.
Larval Foodplants: Various crucifers.

Chalk Carpet ***Scotopteryx bipunctaria*** **([Denis & Schiffermüller])ssp.** ***cretata*** **(Prout) (1731)**

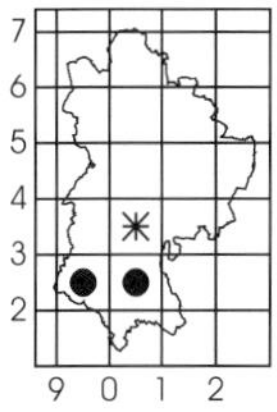

VCH: "Luton, on chalk hills."
Post VCH: Sometimes common on chalk downland in the Luton and Dunstable areas. There are 12 specimens in the Temple collection all labelled "Barton 24/8/1909". S.H.Kershaw found it at Sharpenhoe on 5 July 1934. Also recorded from King's Wood, Heath and Reach on 27 July 1981 and from the RIS trap at Eaton Bray (1981, 1986 and 1987).
Flight: July and August. (weeks 29 to 33)*.
Larval Foodplants: Trefoils and clovers.

For key to moth maps see page 3.

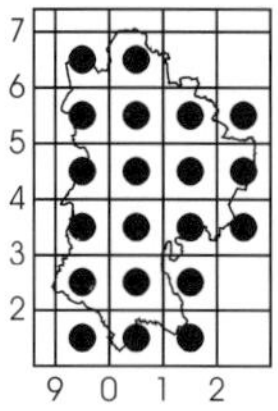

Shaded Broad-bar ***Scotopteryx chenopodiata*** **(Linnaeus) (1732)**
VCH: (as *Eubolia mensuraria* Schiff.) "Generally common."
Post VCH: Common throughout the County.
Flight: May to October (weeks 22 to 40, peak 28 to 33)*.
Larval Foodplants: Vetches and clovers.

July Belle ***Scotopteryx luridata*** **(Hufnagel) ssp.** ***plumbaria*** **(Fabricius) (1734)**
Pre VCH: Steuart (1891) described this species as "common" in Bedfordshire.
VCH: (as *Eubolia palumbaria* Schiff.) "Bedford, Luton."

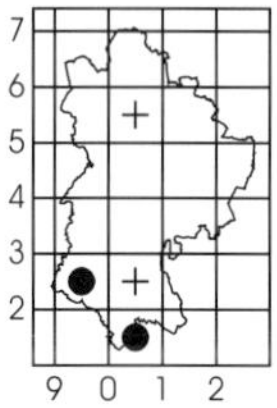

Post VCH: The July Belle has only been recorded at two sites since the publication of the VCH: from the RIS traps at Eaton Bray (1981) and Whipsnade (1973). Records of *luridata* in S.H.Kershaw's notebooks appear to refer to Brindled White-spot (No. 1950).
Flight: June to August(weeks 26 to 34)*.
Larval Foodplant: Gorse.

Ruddy Carpet ***Catarhoe rubidata*** **([Denis & Schiffermüller]) (1735)**

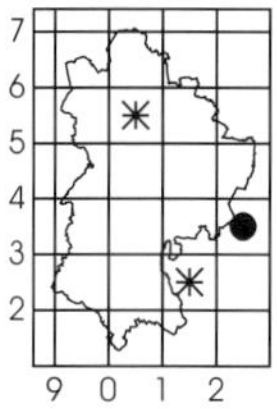

Post VCH: There are specimens in the Temple collection from Putnoe dated 16 June 1908, 29 June 1909 and 8 July 1909. The Rylands collection contains a specimen labelled "Putnoe June 1911". Foster (1917) recorded this species on "Pegsdon Hills; by beating but not commonly" and (1934) also mention it as "at Pegsdon". One specimen came to light on 15 July 1995 in a garden in Stotfold (E. and B.Bowskill).
Flight: June and July (week 28)*.
Larval Foodplants: Hedge-bedstraw and lady's bedstraw.

Royal Mantle ***Catarhoe cuculata*** **(Hufnagel) (1736)**

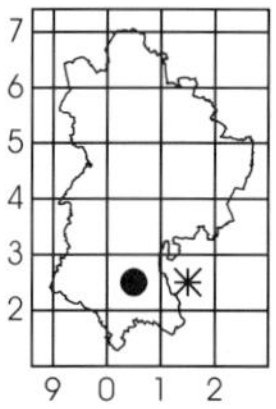

Post VCH: Recorded "at Pegsdon" by Foster (1934). One specimen was caught at a garden moth trap in Luton, by K.F.Webb (13 July 1982). Subsequently one specimen came to a light on Sharpenhoe Clappers operated by V.W.Arnold and L.Field on 29 June 1987.
Flight: June and July (weeks 26 and 28)*.
Larval Foodplants: Hedge-bedstraw and lady's bedstraw.

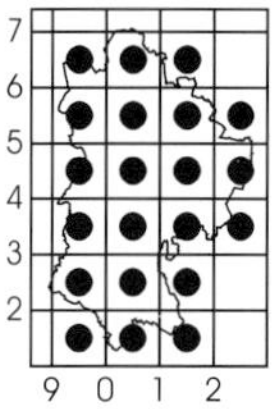

Common Carpet ***Epirrhoe alternata alternata*** **(Müller) (1738)**
VCH: (as *Melanippe subtristata* Haw.) "Common everywhere."
Post VCH: Common throughout the County.
Flight: May to September (weeks 19 to 37, peaks 21 to 25 and 30 to 35)*.
Larval Foodplants: Bedstraws.

Wood Carpet *Epirrhoe rivata* (Hübner) (1739)
Pre VCH: J.C.Dale (MS2) recorded receiving this species as *Sylvaticata* from Abbot's collection from near Bedford but not dated.
Post VCH: Scarce in Bedfordshire. There are specimens in the Temple collection from Putnoe dated 29 June 1909 and 8 July 1909 and in the Rylands collection from "Putnoe June 1911". Also from Aspley Heath (1952), Hardwick Spinney, King's Wood (Heath and Reach) (1954), Stagsden (1972), Sheerhatch Wood (1958) and from the RIS traps at: Cockayne Hatley (1976), Old Warden (1975) and The Lodge, Sandy (1970).
Flight: June to early August (weeks 25 to 33)*.

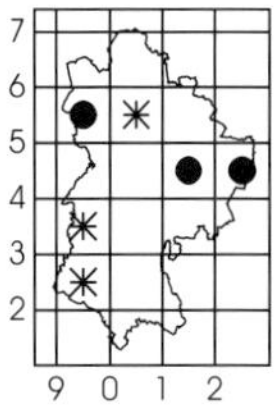

Larval Foodplants: Hedge-bedstraw and lady's bedstraw.

Galium Carpet *Epirrhoe galiata* ([Denis & Schiffermüller]) (1740)
Post VCH: Recorded in S.H.Kershaw's notebooks from Aspley Heath on 31 August 1954 as *galeata* and from Totternhoe on 23 May 1956. No voucher specimens have been seen.
Flight: Late May to mid July and a partial second generation in August.
Larval Foodplants: Bedstraws.

Yellow Shell *Camptogramma bilineata bilineata* (Linnaeus) (1742)
VCH: "Abundant in every hedge."
Post VCH: Common throughout the County. (Plate 14)
Flight: May to September (weeks 22 to 36, peak 27 to 33)*.
Larval Foodplants: Polyphagous on low-growing plants.

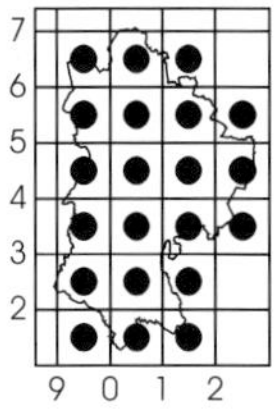

The Mallow *Larentia clavaria* (Haworth) (1745)
Pre VCH: J.C.Dale (MS2) recorded receiving this species as *Cervinata* from Abbot's collection from Bedford but not dated.
VCH: (as *Eubolia cervinata* Schiff.) "Luton, Potton; among mallow."
Post VCH: Widely distributed but local. Comes readily to light.
Flight: September and October (weeks 38 to 43, peak 39 to 41)*.
Larval Foodplants: Common mallow and hollyhock.

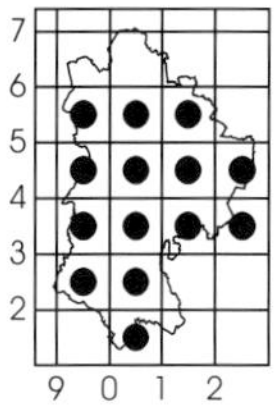

Shoulder-stripe *Anticlea badiata* ([Denis & Schiffermüller]) (1746)
VCH: "Bedford, Potton."
Post VCH: Common throughout the County.
Flight: Late February to early June (weeks 8 to 23, peak 15 to 18)*.
Larval Foodplants: Roses.

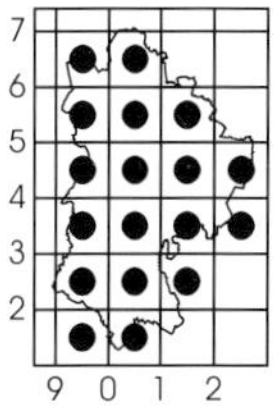

The Streamer *Anticlea derivata derivata* ([Denis & Schiffermüller]) (1747)
VCH: "Bedford, Potton, Luton."
Post VCH: A local, but widespread species. Comes to light in small numbers.
Flight: March to May (weeks 13 to 21, peak 17 and 18, and a single record in week 31)*.
Larval Foodplant: Dog-rose.

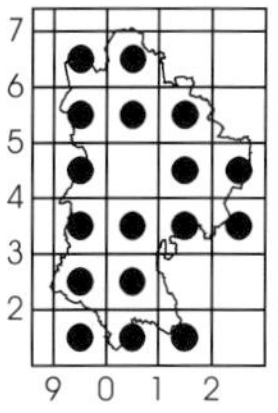

For key to moth maps see page 3.

Beautiful Carpet ***Mesoleuca albicillata*** **(Linnaeus) (1748)**

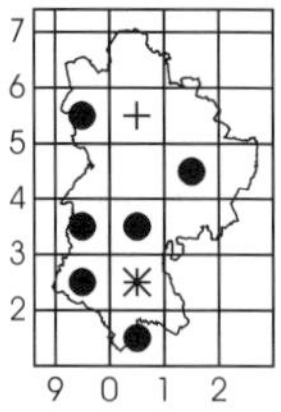

VCH: "Bedford, Woburn."
Post VCH: An uncommon species, usually found in woodlands, including: Flitwick 20 June 1907 and Putnoe 8 June 1910 (specimens in the Temple collection), Aspley Guise (1996), Hardwick Spinney, Stagsden (1953); Maulden Wood (1975); Odell Great Wood (1990), Sharpenhoe (1933). Also recorded from the RIS trap at The Lodge, Sandy (1969, 1970, 1973, 1975).
Flight: June and July (weeks 25 to 30)★.

Larval Foodplants: Brambles and raspberry.

Dark Spinach ***Pelurga comitata*** **(Linnaeus) (1749)**

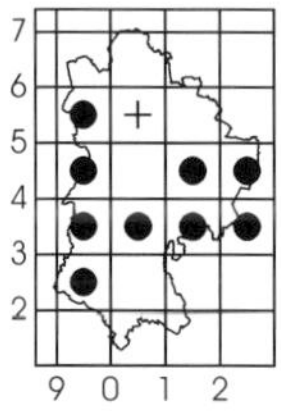

Pre VCH: J.C.Dale (MS2) recorded receiving this species from Abbot's collection from near Bedford but not dated.
Post VCH: A local and uncommon species in Bedfordshire. Found in the RIS traps at Cockayne Hatley (1976, 1977, 1978, 1980, 1984, 1985), Eaton Bray (1980, 1986) and The Lodge, Sandy (1969).
Flight: July and August (weeks 27 to 34, peak 32 and 33)★.

Larval Foodplants: Goosefoots and oraches.

Water Carpet ***Lampropteryx suffumata*** **([Denis & Schiffermüller]) (1750)**

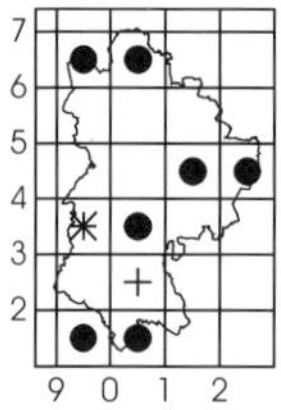

VCH: "Luton."
Post VCH: An uncommon local species. It has been found on downlands in the south of the County, such as Bison Hill, as well as in woodlands in the north, including Coppice Wood.
Flight: April and May (weeks 14 to 21)★.

Larval Foodplants: Bedstraws.

Purple Bar ***Cosmorhoe ocellata*** **(Linnaeus) (1752)**

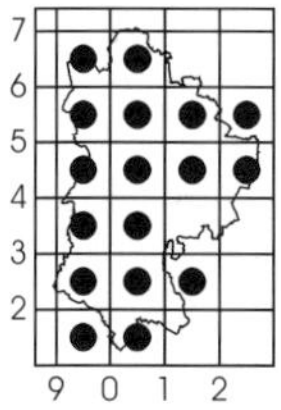

VCH: "Generally distributed."
Post VCH: A local but widespread species.
Flight: May and June and again in August and September (weeks 18 to 37, peaks 22 to 23 and 32 to 34)★.
Larval Foodplants: Bedstraws.

The Phoenix ***Eulithis prunata*** **(Linnaeus) (1754)**

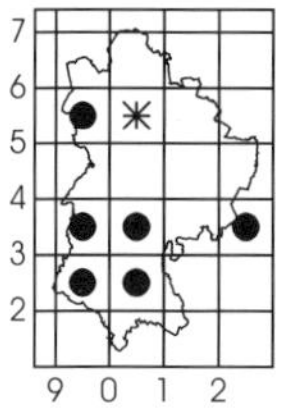

VCH: "Luton, in gardens."
Post VCH: A local species. Although it comes readily to light, it is never common. Records for this species still come from gardens where its foodplants grow.
Flight: June to August (weeks 26 to 32)★.
Larval Foodplants: Black currant, red currant and gooseberry.

For details of standard weeks see page 6.

The Chevron *Eulithis testata* (Linnaeus) (1755)
VCH: "Luton."
Post VCH: Uncommon. Recorded at light in most years, but only in very low numbers. Usually found in open areas of woodland such as Flitwick Moor and Coppice Wood.
Flight: July to September (weeks 27 to 37, peak 31 and 32)*.
Larval Foodplants: Sallows, willows, aspen and birches.

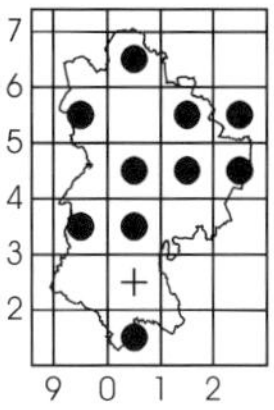

Northern Spinach *Eulithis populata* (Linnaeus) (1756)
Post VCH: S.H.Kershaw found it at Aspley Heath (August 1937 and 1954). Only two more recent records: in the RIS trap at The Lodge, Sandy (1971) and at Sharnbrook (1976). Dony (1976) does not show bilberry to be present in either of these last locations but it is present at Aspley Heath.
Flight: July and August(weeks 30 and 31)*.
Larval Foodplant: Bilberry.

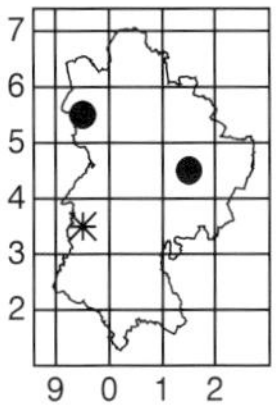

The Spinach *Eulithis mellinata* (Fabricius) (1757)
VCH: (as *Cidaria dotata* Linn.) "Bedford, Potton, Luton; in gardens."
Post VCH: A local species, never seen in large numbers.
Flight: June to August (weeks 26 to 33)*.
Larval Foodplants: Red currant and black currant.

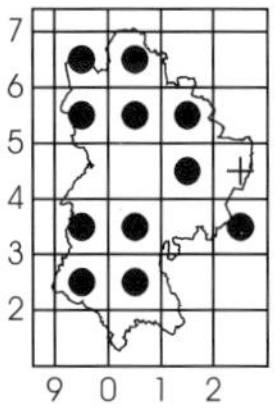

Barred Straw *Eulithis pyraliata* ([Denis & Schiffermüller]) (1758)
VCH: "Luton."
Post VCH: Common throughout the County.
Flight: Late May to early September (weeks 22 to 35, peak 25 to 30)*.
Larval Foodplants: Bedstraws.

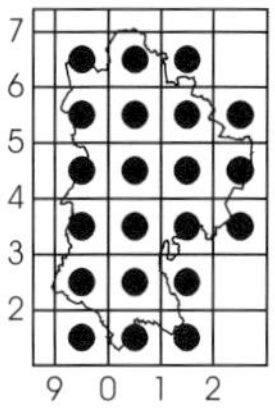

Small Phoenix *Ecliptopera silaceata* ([Denis & Schiffermüller]) (1759)
Post VCH: Common throughout the County.
Flight: May to September (weeks 18 to 37, peak 30 to 34)*.
Larval Foodplants: Willowherbs.

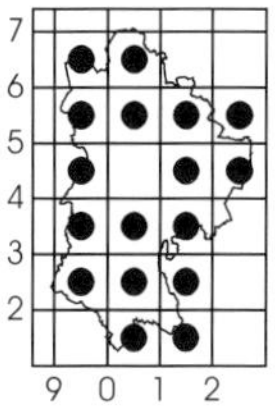

Red-green Carpet *Chloroclysta siterata* (Hufnagel) (1760)
Post VCH: Recorded only once, Bedford at MV light (1956) (West, 1959).
Flight: September, October and, after hibernation, in April and May.
Larval Foodplants: Oaks, rowan, possibly on other deciduous trees.

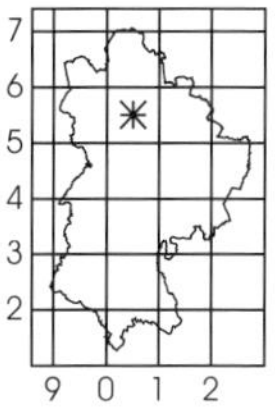

For key to moth maps see page 3.

Autumn Green Carpet *Chloroclysta miata* (Linnaeus) (1761)
VCH: "Bedford, Potton, Luton."
Post VCH: Two specimens in the Temple collection are labelled "Bedford 28/10/1908". According to his notebooks, S.H.Kershaw found it at Aspley Heath betwen 1933 and 1948. RIS trap at The Lodge, Sandy (1975).
Flight: September, October (week 40)★ and, after hibernation, in April and May.
Larval Foodplants: Sallows, rowan, birches, oaks and probably on other deciduous trees.

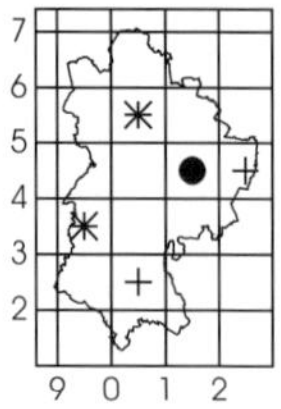

Dark Marbled Carpet *Chloroclysta citrata citrata* (Linnaeus) (1762)
VCH: Not recorded. This species is easily confused with *C. truncata* (Hufnagel) which could explain its absence from the VCH.
Post VCH: Local but widespread, found mainly in wooded areas.
Flight: June to September (weeks 24 to 39)★.
Larval Foodplants: Sallows, birches, bilberry and wild strawberry.

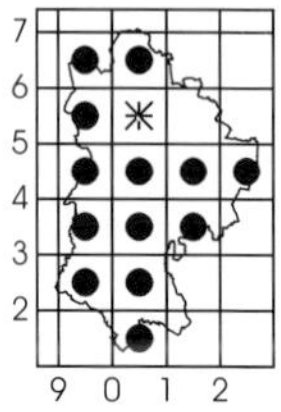

Common Marbled Carpet *Chloroclysta truncata* (Hufnagel) (1764)
VCH: "Generally abundant."
Post VCH: Common throughout the County.
Flight: May to October (weeks 20 to 43, peaks 23 to 26, 35 to 38)★ in what appear to be several overlapping broods.
Larval Foodplants: Polyphagous, mainly on deciduous trees and shrubs.

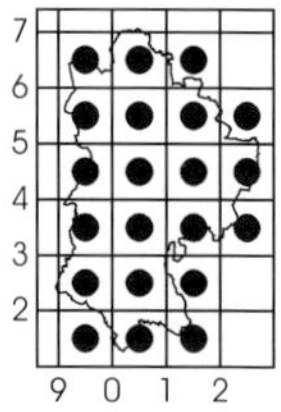

Barred Yellow *Cidaria fulvata* (Forster) (1765)
VCH: "Bedford, Luton."
Post VCH: Common throughout the County.
Flight: June to August (weeks 25 to 31, peak 27 and 28)★.
Larval Foodplant: Dog-rose.

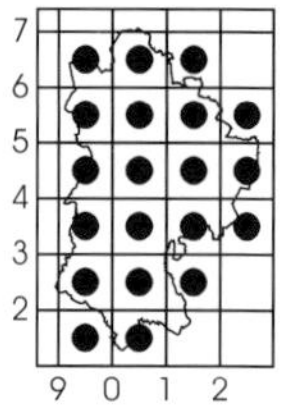

Blue-bordered Carpet *Plemyria rubiginata rubiginata* ([Denis & Schiffermüller]) (1766)
VCH: "Luton."
Post VCH: A local species which is found mainly in wooded areas, such as Marston Thrift. It comes readily to light, but only in small numbers.
Flight: June and July (weeks 26 to 28)★.
Larval Foodplants: Various trees including alder, blackthorn and apple.

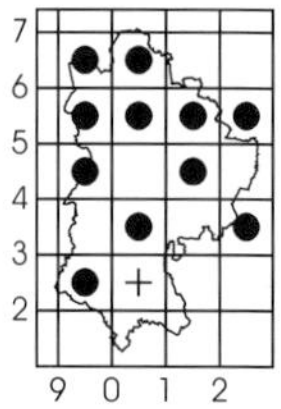

Pine Carpet *Thera firmata* (Hübner) (1767)
Post VCH: A scarce local species. Recorded at Aspley Heath by S.H. Kershaw between 1932 and 1960 but no specimens have been seen. More recently found in Maulden Wood, by V.W.Arnold (1977) and subsequently at Aspley Guise by J.B.Barnwell (1985, 1986, 1988, 1993).
Flight: July (week 28)★ to November.
Larval Foodplant: Scots pine.

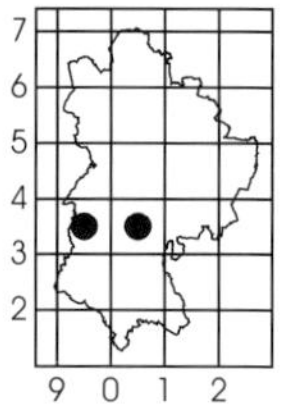

For details of standard weeks see page 6.

Grey Pine Carpet *Thera obeliscata* (Hübner) (1768)

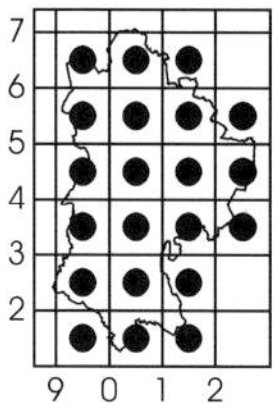

VCH: (as *T. variata* Schiff.) "Bedford, Luton among fir." *T. variata* was subsequently separated into two species so it is not clear whether the VCH entry refers to the Grey Pine Carpet or to the Spruce Carpet.
Post VCH: Found, wherever its food plant occurs, throughout the County.
Flight: May to July (weeks 20 to 27, peak 24)⋆ and again in September to November (weeks 35 to 47, peak 37 to 41)⋆ in two broods.
Larval Foodplants: Scots pine, Norway spruce and Douglas fir.

Spruce Carpet *Thera britannica* (Turner) (= *variata* auctt.) (1769)

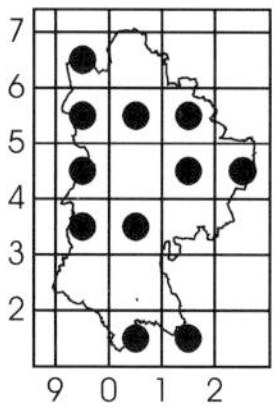

VCH: See Grey Pine Carpet.
Post VCH: This species is recorded sporadically from areas where its foodplants occur, such as Aspley Heath (1935, Kershaw MS), Maulden Wood and Aspley Guise. Recorded as "commonly at Rowney Warren" (Foster, 1934).
Flight: May to June (weeks 22 to 24)⋆ and September to October (weeks 35 to 43)⋆.
Larval Foodplants: Spruces and Douglas fir.

Juniper Carpet *Thera juniperata juniperata* (Linnaeus) (1771)

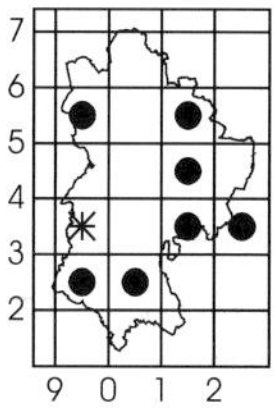

Post VCH: A scarce species in Bedfordshire. Recorded from Aspley Heath on 14 October 1933 (Kershaw MS), Sharnbrook by D.V. Manning in October 1979 (Arnold, 1980c). Subsequently at Clifton (1985-1988, 1990, 1991), Luton (1992, 1993), Stotfold (1985, 1988 -1991, 1993-1995) and the RIS traps at Eaton Bray (1986, 1989) and Houghton Regis (1991).
Flight: October (weeks 40 to 42)⋆.
Larval Foodplants: Juniper and possibly cypresses. All records for this species have been from gardens where it probably feeds on cultivated junipers and cypresses.

Broken-barred Carpet *Electrophaes corylata* (Thunberg) (1773)

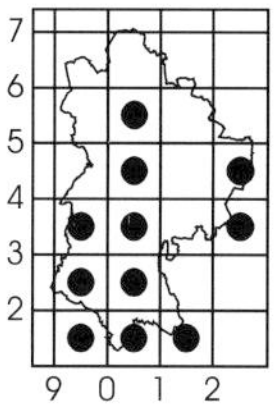

Pre VCH: J.C.Dale (MS3) recorded finding this species (as *Pha. ruptata*) on 1 June 1820 in Clapham Park Wood.
VCH: "Luton, in woods."
Post VCH: A local species which is usually found in woodland.
Flight: May to July (weeks 21 to 27, peak 24)⋆.
Larval Foodplants: A variety of deciduous trees, including birches, oaks and hawthorns.

Mottled Grey *Colostygia multistrigaria* (Haworth) (1775)

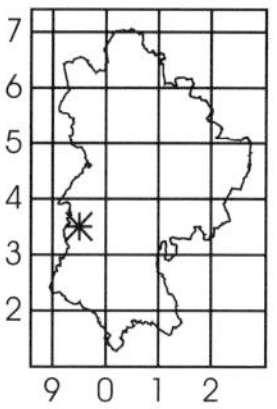

Post VCH: There are specimens in the Kershaw collection from Aspley Heath dated 21 March 1938 and 11 April 1939, also records in his notebooks for 1934, 1937 and 1947.
Flight: March and April (weeks 12 and 15)⋆.
Larval Foodplants: Bedstraws.

For key to moth maps see page 3.

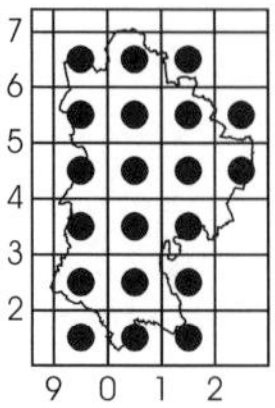

Green Carpet *Colostygia pectinataria* (Knoch) (1776)
VCH: "Luton."
Post VCH: Widespread and common throughout the County.
Flight: May to October (weeks 21 to 40, peak 26 to 30)*.
Larval Foodplants: Bedstraws.

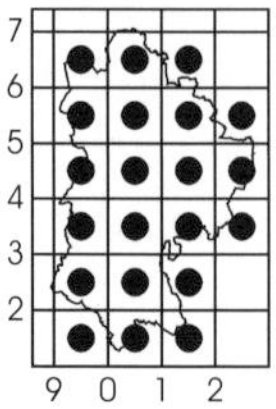

July Highflyer *Hydriomena furcata* (Thunberg) (1777)
VCH: (as *Hypsipetes elutata* Schiff.) "Generally abundant."
Post VCH: Common throughout the County.
Flight: June to September (weeks 25 to 36, peak 27 to 33)*.
Larval Foodplants: Sallows, bilberry, heather and hazel*.

May Highflyer *Hydriomena impluviata* ([Denis & Schiffermüller]) (1778)
Pre VCH: "Recorded once only by Samuel Tuke from Pegsdon in 1870" (Foster, 1934).

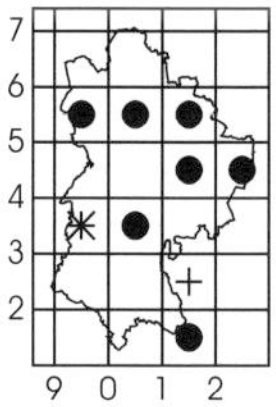

VCH: "Bedford, among alder."
Post VCH: A scarce and local species. A specimen in the Temple collection is labelled "Bedford 11/6/1910". Noted by S.H.Kershaw at Aspley Heath on 23 July 1955, "very late even for this late season". More recently recorded at: Flitwick Moor (1978, 1982, 1984), Luton Hoo (1984, 1985), Tempsford (1992) and in the RIS traps at Cockayne Hatley (1992) and Old Warden (1974-1976).
Flight: Late May to July (weeks 22 to 26)*.
Larval Foodplant: Alder.

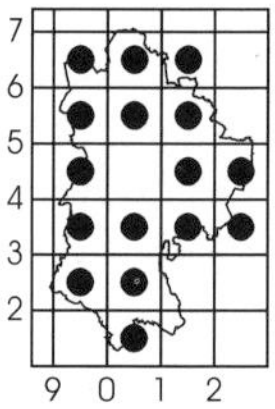

Small Waved Umber *Horisme vitalbata* ([Denis & Schiffermüller]) (1781)
VCH: "Bedford, Potton, Luton; among *Clematis vitalba.*"
Post VCH: Found throughout the County, but not common.
Flight: May to September (weeks 20 to 36)*.
Larval Foodplant: Traveller's-joy.

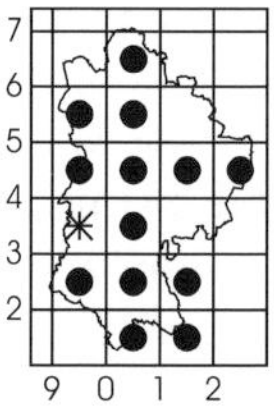

Fern *Horisme tersata* ([Denis & Schiffermüller]) (1782)
VCH: "Luton, among *Clematis vitalba.*"
Post VCH: A local species, found in areas where Traveller's Joy grows.
Flight: June to August (weeks 25 to 32, one record in week 37)*.
Larval Foodplant: Traveller's-joy.

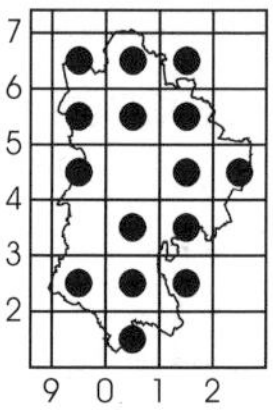

Pretty Chalk Carpet *Melanthia procellata* ([Denis & Schiffermüller]) (1784)
Post VCH: Widely distributed but only recorded in low numbers.
Flight: June to August (weeks 25 to 30, peak 27 to 30)*.
Larval Foodplant: Traveller's-joy.

Argent and Sable ***Rheumaptera hastata hastata*** **(Linnaeus) (1787)**
Post VCH: S.H.Kershaw noted seeing it in King's Wood, Heath and Reach on 26 May 1956. Another unconfirmed record is from Bromham Lake on 26 May 1995 (P.Almond).
Flight: May (week 21)* and June flying in the daytime.
Larval Foodplants: Birches.

Scarce Tissue ***Rheumaptera cervinalis*** **(Scopoli) (1788)**
VCH: (as *Scotosia certata* Hb.) "Luton, Potton; among *Berberis* and *Mahonia*."

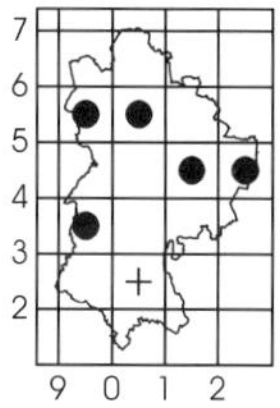

Post VCH: A very scarce species for which there are few records. A specimen in the Kershaw collection from Aspley Heath in 1932 was misplaced. He also noted seeing it there on 9 May 1957 but no specimen has been seen. Recorded from the RIS traps at Cockayne Hatley (1987) and The Lodge, Sandy (1971, 1973, 1974). Also from Bromham (1980), Aspley Heath (1983, 1987, 1991, 1993) and Sharnbrook (1996).
Flight: Late April to early June (weeks 18 to 22)*.
Larval Foodplants: Barberry and cultivated species of *Berberis*.

Scalloped Shell ***Rheumaptera undulata*** **(Linnaeus) (1789)**

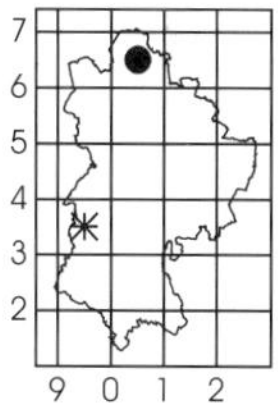

Post VCH: There are two specimens in the Kershaw collection from Aspley Heath dated 28 July 1945 and 13 July 1946. The only recent records are from Melchbourne by D.V.Manning on 22 June 1986 and 15 July 1995.
Flight: June and July (weeks 25 to 30)*.
Larval Foodplants: Sallows, aspen and bilberry.

The Tissue ***Triphosa dubitata*** **(Linnaeus) (1790)**
VCH: "Bedford, Luton, Potton; comes to 'light' ".

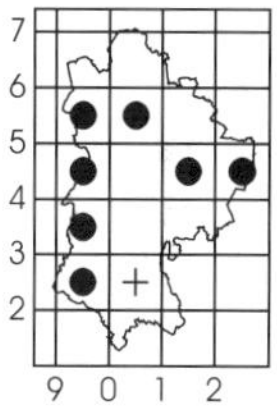

Post VCH: A scarce species in Bedfordshire. There are specimens in the Temple collection from Bedford dated 2 and 3 August 1906 and 20 August 1907 and from Twin Wood on 21 August 1909. R.M.Craske recalled the Tissue as "very local" in the Bedford area (1918-1927). The Kershaw collection contains specimens from Aspley Heath in 1936, 1937 and 1955 and he also noted seeing it there in 1932 and 1933. More recently found in the RIS traps at Cockayne Hatley (1979, 1982), Eaton Bray (1982), Old Warden (1975) and The Lodge, Sandy (1970). Also from Aspley Guise (1985, 1986), Marston Thrift (1985), Putnoe Wood (1965), Sheerhatch Wood (1958) and Stevington (1965).
Flight: July (week 28)*, August (weeks 31 to 33)* and September and, after hibernation, in April and May (weeks 16 to 20)*.
Larval Foodplants: Buckthorn and alder buckthorn.

Brown Scallop ***Philereme vetulata*** **([Denis & Schiffermüller]) (1791)**

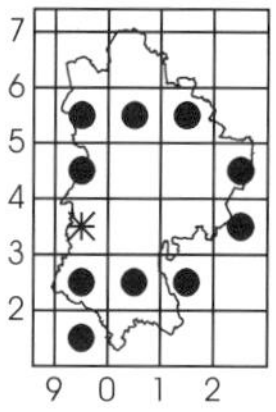

Pre VCH: J.C.Dale (MS3) recorded finding this species on 14 July 1819 at Mouse's Pasture, Bromham.
VCH: "Bedford, among *Clematis vitalba.*"
Post VCH: A local species usually found in areas where buckthorn grows.
Flight: June and July (weeks 25 to 30, peak 29)*.
Larval Foodplant: Buckthorn.

For key to moth maps see page 3.

Dark Umber ***Phileremе transversata*** **(Hufnagel) ssp.** ***britannica*** **Lempke (1792)**

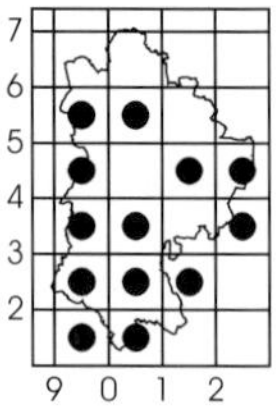

VCH: (as *Scotosia rhamnata* Schiff.) "Bedford, Luton; among *Clematis vitalba.*"
Post VCH: A local species usually found in areas where buckthorn grows.
Flight: Late June to August (weeks 26 to 35, peak 28 to 31)*.
Larval Foodplant: Buckthorn.

Sharp-angled Carpet ***Euphyia unangulata*** **(Haworth) (1794)**

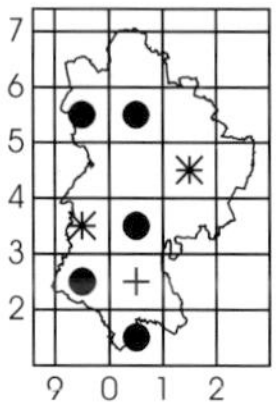

VCH: "Luton."
Post VCH: A scarce woodland species for which there are very few records. There are specimens in the Temple collection from "near Shefford" dated July 1908 and July and August 1909. S.H.Kershaw noted seeing it at Aspley Heath in 1960. In the area around Heath and Reach this species has been recorded from King's Wood (1987), Shire Oak (1979,1980) and Stockgrove Country Park (1986). Other locations are Hardwick Spinney (1972) and Maulden Wood (1981).
Flight: June to August (weeks 25 to 33)*.
Larval Foodplants: Chickweeds and stitchworts.

Note on the genus ***Epirrita*****:**
All members of this genus are so alike that it is unwise to identify them without examination of the genitalia.

November Moth ***Epirrita dilutata*** **([Denis & Schiffermüller]) (1795)**

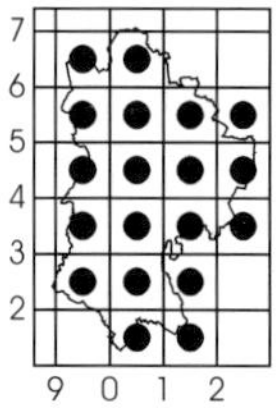

VCH: "Generally distributed."
Post VCH: Common throughout the County.
Flight: September to December (weeks 38 to 48, peak 40 to 45)*.
Larval Foodplants: Polyphagous on deciduous trees.

Pale November Moth ***Epirrita christyi*** **(Allen) (1796)**

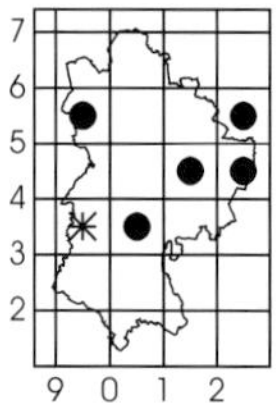

Post VCH: There are few records of this woodland species in Bedfordshire. The Kershaw collection contains a specimen from Aspley Heath on 30 October 1937. Found in the RIS traps at Cockayne Hatley (1976, 1978, 1988, 1989, 1993) and Old Warden (1976-1979). Also from Flitwick Moor (1977), Maulden Wood (1977, 1979) and the northern section of Potton Wood (1992). Specimens in G.Ping's collection from Carlton (between 1984-1986).
Flight: October and November (weeks 42 to 44, peak 43)*.
Larval Foodplants: Polyphagous on deciduous trees.

For details of standard weeks see page 6.

Autumnal Moth *Epirrita autumnata* (Borkhausen) (1797)

Post VCH: S.H.Kershaw noted finding it at Aspley Heath in 1937 and 1947. Most recent records of the Autumnal Moth, a woodland species, have come from the RIS traps at Eaton Bray (1986), Old Warden (1975, 1976, 1978) and The Lodge, Sandy (1974-1975) and Whipsnade Wild Animal Park (1973). Also from Flitwick Moor (1977) and Maulden Wood (1977, 1979).
Flight: October and November (weeks 41 to 45)*.
Larval Foodplants: Birches, alder and possibly larches.

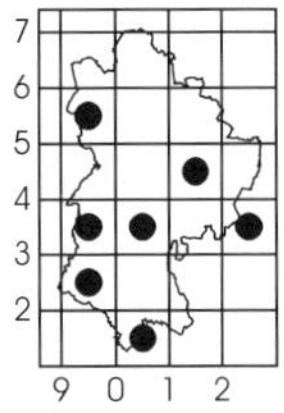

Small Autumnal Moth *Epirrita filigrammaria* (Herrich-Schäffer) (1798)

Post VCH: Two records only: a specimen in the Temple collection from Hanger Wood on 29 October 1908 and in the RIS trap at Whipsnade Wild Animal Park (1973).
Flight: August to October (week 41)*.
Larval Foodplants: Heather and bilberry.

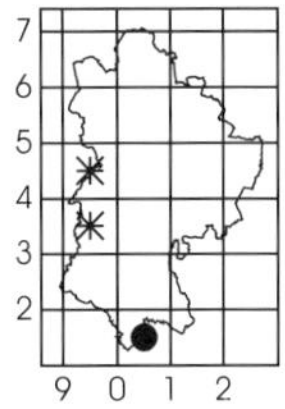

Winter Moth *Operophtera brumata* (Linnaeus) (1799)

VCH: "Everywhere abundant."
Post VCH: Common throughout the County.
Flight: October to February (weeks 40 to 5, peak 48 to 51)*.
Larval Foodplants: Apple*, field maple*, hawthorns*, hazel*, lilac* and other trees and shrubs.

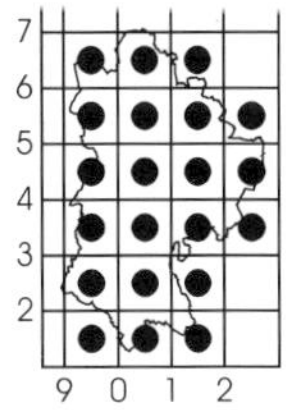

Northern Winter Moth *Operophtera fagata* (Scharfenberg) (1800)

Post VCH: Very few records, mainly from the RIS traps at Cockayne Hatley (1977), Old Warden (1976, 1978) and The Lodge, Sandy (1969, 1971, 1973 and at MV light in 1990).
Flight: November to December (weeks 46 to 50, peak 47)*.
Larval Foodplants: Birches, apple, plum and cherry.
Notes: As this species and the previous one are superficially very similar, the Northern Winter Moth may be more common than the records suggest.

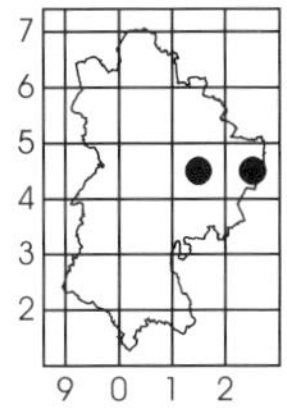

The Rivulet *Perizoma affinitata* (Stephens) (1802)

VCH: "Luton, among *Lychnis*."
Post VCH: Scarce: found at Bromham (1973), Luton (1976) and in the RIS traps at Eaton Bray (1988) and Old Warden (1974, 1978).
Flight: May to August (weeks 18 to 33)*.
Larval Foodplants: Red campion.

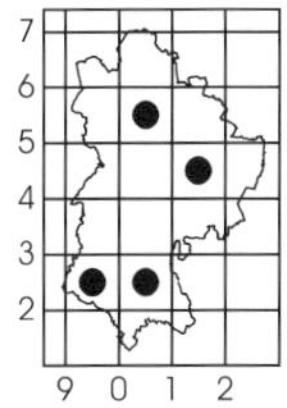

Small Rivulet *Perizoma alchemillata* (Linnaeus) (1803)

VCH: "Luton, among *Galeopsis*."
Post VCH: Common throughout the County.
Flight: June to September (weeks 24 to 36, peak 27 to 32)*.
Larval Foodplants: Hemp-nettles.

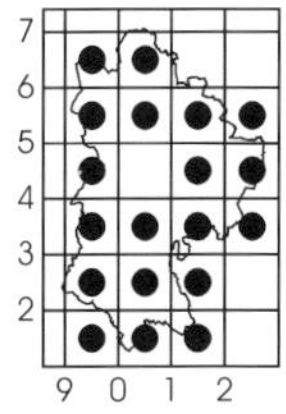

For key to moth maps see page 3.

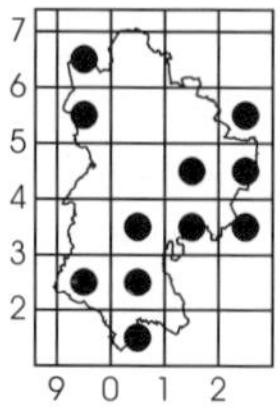

Barred Rivulet *Perizoma bifaciata* (Haworth) (1804)
Post VCH: An uncommon and local species. It comes to light and can be found at sites such as Maulden Wood, King's Wood (Heath and Reach) and West Wood.
Flight: July and August (weeks 28 to 34)*.
Larval Foodplant: Red bartsia.

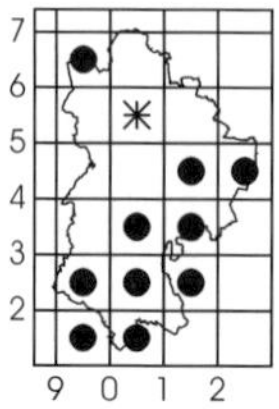

Grass Rivulet *Perizoma albulata* ([Denis & Schiffermüller]) (1807)
VCH: "Luton, in meadows among yellow-rattle."
Post VCH: This species can be found in grassy areas, such as Totternhoe Knolls and Warden Hills. It comes to light and has been found in the RIS trap at Eaton Bray (1980, 1982, 1983, 1985-1989). A specimen is in the Rylands collection from Twin Wood. It has no date but other specimens in the collection date from 1907 to 1911. "Pegsdon" (Foster, 1934).
Flight: May to July (weeks 22 to 30)*.
Larval Foodplant: Yellow-rattle.

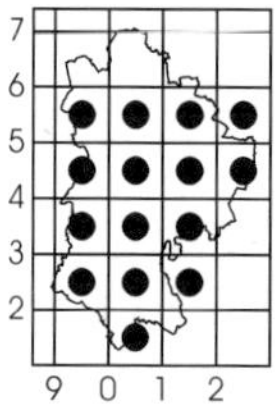

Sandy Carpet *Perizoma flavofasciata* (Thunberg) (1808)
VCH: "Bedford, among *Lychnis*."
Post VCH: Widespread and fairly common.
Flight: May to August (weeks 21 to 33, peak 26 and 27)*.
Larval Foodplants: Red campion, white campion and bladder campion.

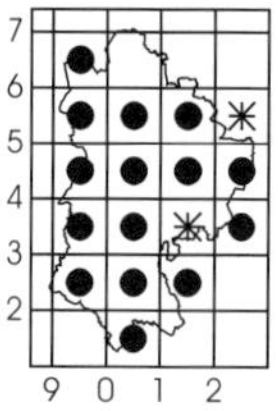

Twin-spot Carpet *Perizoma didymata didymata* (Linnaeus) (1809)
VCH: "Bedford, Luton; probably everywhere."
Post VCH: Common throughout the County.
Flight: June to August (weeks 24 to 33, peak 26 to 29)*.
Larval Foodplants: Polyphagous on low-growing plants.

The Pug moths (genera *Eupithecia, Chloroclystis* and *Gymnoscelis*)

Apart from a few species, the Pug moths are very difficult to identify with certainty. A number of species may have been misidentified over the years and many will have been overlooked or deliberately ignored. The author is indebted to A.M.Riley of the Rothamsted Insect Survey for his assistance with this group over the last few years.

Tawny Speckled Pug

For details of standard weeks see page 6.

Slender Pug *Eupithecia tenuiata* (Hübner) (1811)

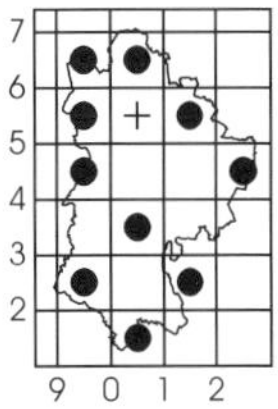

VCH: "Bedford, among sallow."
Post VCH: A local species, almost certain to be more common than records suggest. Searching for larvae among sallow catkins is probably the best way to discover its true distribution. It has been recorded in this way from Maulden Wood and Clophill Sand Quarry (1984).
Flight: July to September (weeks 28 to 35)*.
Larval Foodplant: Sallow*.

Maple Pug *Eupithecia inturbata* (Hübner) (1812)

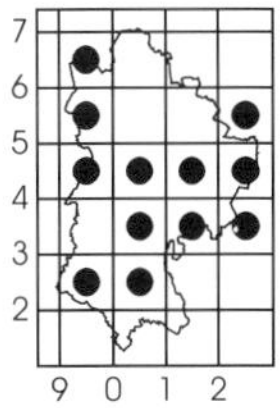

Post VCH: A local species which is usually found in areas where field maple occurs. It has been recorded from the RIS traps at Eaton Bray (1981-1983, 1986-1989, 1994, 1995)) and Cockayne Hatley (1987-1991). Also found at Lower Alders, Campton (1981), Maulden Wood (1981), and northern section of Potton Wood (1992).
Flight: July to September (weeks 29 to 35, peak 33)*.
Larval Foodplant: Field maple*.

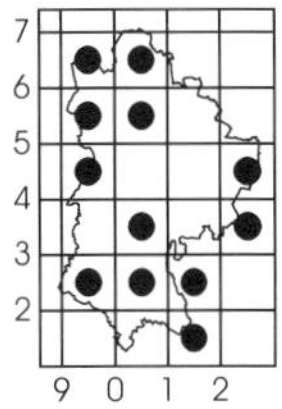

Haworth's Pug *Eupithecia haworthiata* Doubleday (1813)
Post VCH: Recorded by W.J.Champkin at Bromham Park in 1974. Distributed throughout the County, but it is probably overlooked.
Flight: June to August (weeks 24 to 31)*.
Larval Foodplant: Traveller's-joy.

Cloaked Pug *Eupithecia abietaria* (Goeze) (1815)

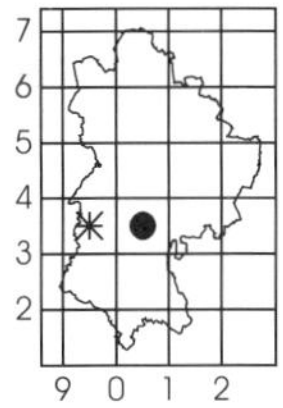

Post VCH: Recorded only twice: by S.H.Kershaw (MS) at Aspley Heath 19 July 1935 (no specimen has been seen) and by V.W.Arnold, in Maulden Wood on 4 July 1977 (Arnold, 1979c). Despite various attempts to find this species again, no more moths have been found. The site, in Maulden Wood, was clear-felled in about 1980. It will therefore be difficult to confirm this record.
Flight: July (week 27)*.
Larval Foodplant: Norway spruce.

Toadflax Pug *Eupithecia linariata* ([Denis & Schiffermüller]) (1816)

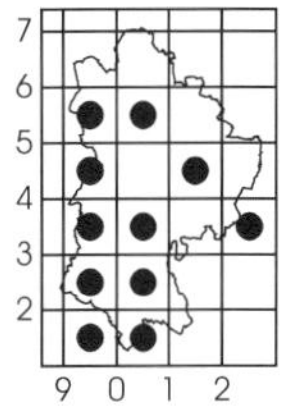

Post VCH: Found commonly throughout the County. Recorded in S.H. Kershaw's notebooks from Aspley Heath in 1937, 1938 and 1947.
Flight: May to August (weeks 21 to 33, peak 24)*.
Larval Foodplants: Common toadflax and cultivated *Antirrhinum*.

For key to moth maps see page 3.

Foxglove Pug *Eupithecia pulchellata pulchellata* Stephens (1817)

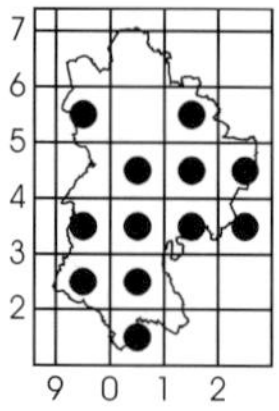

Post VCH: Recorded in S.H.Kershaw's notebooks from Aspley Heath between 1932 and 1953. Currently fairly common throughout the County. Foxglove is found wild mainly on the Greensand Ridge. Records away from this area are from gardens where the foodplant has been introduced.
Flight: May to August (weeks 18 to 31, peak 23)★.
Larval Foodplant: Foxglove★.

Marbled Pug *Eupithecia irriguata* (Hübner) (1818)

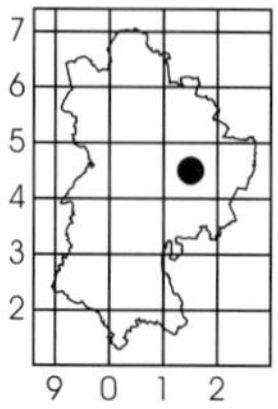

Post VCH: Only two records: Bunkers Hill, Sandy in 1960 (West, 1961) and Sandy Warren in 1961 (West, 1962).
Flight: April, May (week 21)★ and June★.
Larval Foodplants: Oaks.

Mottled Pug *Eupithecia exiguata exiguata* (Hübner) (1819)

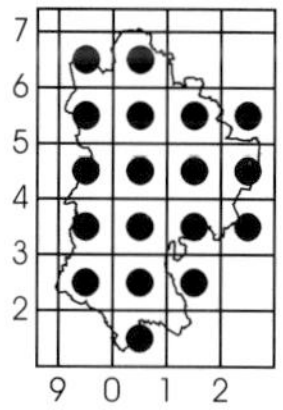

Post VCH: Common throughout the County. There are specimens in the Temple collection from Twin Wood (May 1909) and Putnoc (8 June 1909). Recorded in S.H.Kershaw's notebooks from Aspley Heath in1937 and 1947.
Flight: May and June (weeks 20 to 26, peak 21 to 24)★.
Larval Foodplants: Hawthorns★, blackthorn and sycamore.

Pinion-spotted Pug *Eupithecia insigniata* (Hübner) (1820)

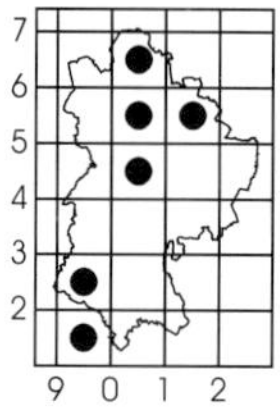

Post VCH: A scarce species in Bedfordshire. Recorded from the RIS trap at Eaton Bray (1981, 1982, 1985, 1989). Other sites include: Bison Hill (1985), Bromham (1982), Coppice Wood (1987), Tempsford (1990) and Wootton (1984).
Flight: May (weeks 18 to 22)★.
Larval Foodplants: Hawthorns★ and apple.

Marsh Pug *Eupithecia pygmaeata* (Hübner) (1822)

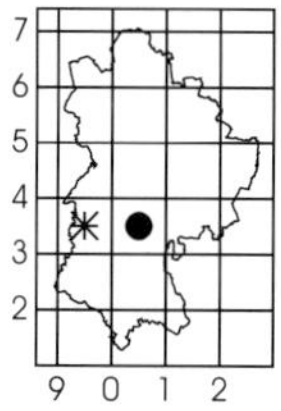

Post VCH: Recorded in S.H.Kershaw's notebook from Aspley Heath on 22 August 1952. The date is very late and no specimen has been seen so this record is doubtful. Found more recently at Sandy Banks Nature Reserve (June 1984, 1985) by A.M. Riley, K.F. Webb and V.W.Arnold (Webb, 1985b). Also recorded at Flitwick Moor, by V.W.Arnold (June 1984).
Flight: May and June (weeks 23 to 25)★.
Larval Foodplants: Field mouse-ear★, possibly other mouse-ears, chick-weeds and stitchworts.

Netted Pug *Eupithecia venosata venosata* (Fabricius) (1823)

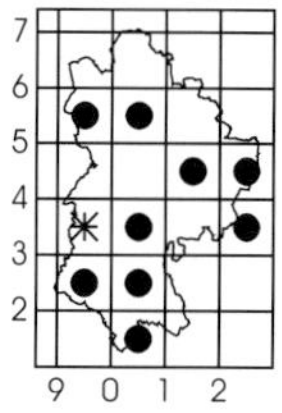

VCH: "Bedford, Potton; among *Silene inflata.*"
Post VCH: An uncommon but widespread species, found mainly on calcareous soils. There is a specimen in the Temple collection from Bedford dated 7 June 1910.
Flight: Late May and June (weeks 22 to 28)★.
Larval Foodplant: Bladder campion★.

For details of standard weeks see page 6.

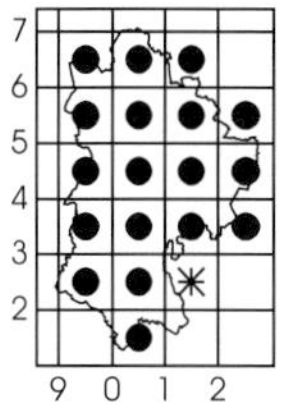

Lime-speck Pug *Eupithecia centaureata* ([Denis & Schiffermüller]) (1825)
VCH: "Common in gardens."
Post VCH: Common throughout the County.
Flight: May to September (weeks 20 to 38, peak 31 to 35)*.
Larval Foodplants: Common ragwort*, mugwort* and other herbaceous plants.

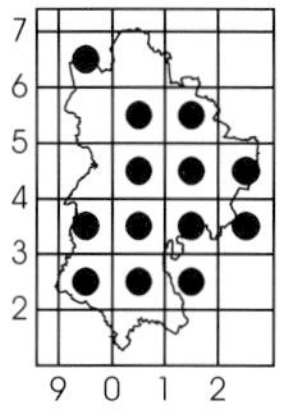

Freyer's Pug *Eupithecia intricata* (Zetterstedt) ssp. *arceuthata* (Freyer) (1827)
Post VCH: Widespread and fairly common in gardens. Recorded in S.H. Kershaw's notebook from Aspley Heath on 4 April 1946 as "Edinburgh Pug". No specimen has been seen and this record is very early in the year.
Flight: May to July (weeks 21 to 28, peak 22 to 27)*.
Larval Foodplants: Cypresses*.

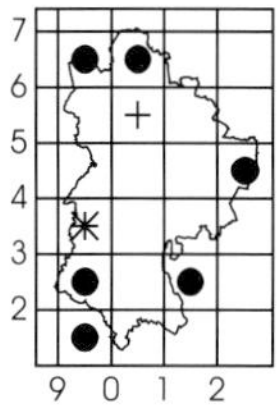

Satyr Pug *Eupithecia satyrata satyrata* (Hübner) (1828)
VCH: "Bedford."
Post VCH: Recorded in S.H.Kershaw's notebook from Aspley Heath between 1934 and 1951 and in the RIS traps at Cockayne Hatley (1981, 1992, 1995) and at Eaton Bray (1995). Also from Bison Hill (1988), Coppice Wood (1990), King's Wood, Heath and Reach (1985), Pegsdon Hills (1986) and West Wood (1987).
Flight: May to July (weeks 22 to 29)*.
Larval Foodplants: Mugwort* and other herbaceous plants, on the flowers.

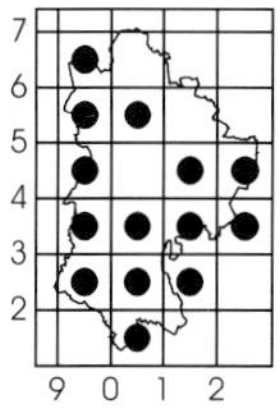

Wormwood Pug *Eupithecia absinthiata* (Clerck) (1830)
Post VCH: Widespread and fairly common. Recorded in S.H.Kershaw's notebook from Aspley Heath in 1935, 1936, 1952 and 1959.
Flight: Late May to August (weeks 22 to 32, peak 29)*.
Larval Foodplants: Polyphagous on plants such as mugwort*, common ragwort* and yarrow*.

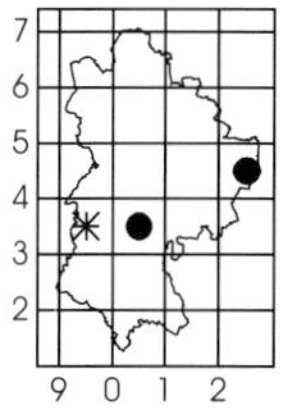

Ling Pug *Eupithecia goossensiata* Mabille (1831)
Post VCH: Recorded in S.H.Kershaw's notebook from Aspley Heath on 16 July 1933 but no specimen has been seen. Only two recent records: RIS trap at Cockayne Hatley (1981) and from Clophill Sand Quarry by K.F. Webb (1984).
Flight: June, July and late August (weeks 34 and 35)*.
Larval Foodplant: Heather.
Notes: Although listed separately here, *E. goossensiata* is regarded as a form of *E. absinthiata*.

For key to moth maps see page 3.

Currant Pug *Eupithecia assimilata* Doubleday (1832)

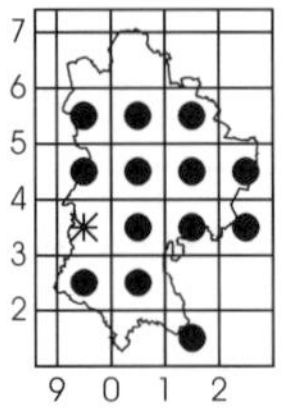

Post VCH: Widespread and fairly common. Recorded in S.H.Kershaw's notebook from Aspley Heath in 1945.
Flight: May and June (weeks 21 to 25)★ and again in August and September (weeks 31 to 37)★ in two broods.
Larval Foodplants: Hop, black currant and red currant.

Common Pug *Eupithecia vulgata* (Haworth) (1834)

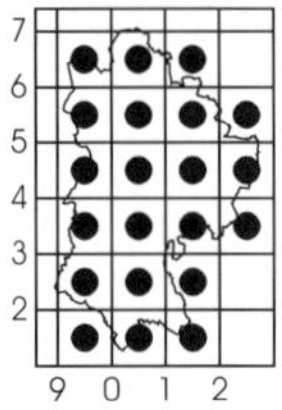

VCH: "Common everywhere."
Post VCH: Common throughout the County.
Flight: April to early August (weeks 17 to 31, peak 22 to 26)★.
Larval Foodplants: Polyphagous on shrubs.

White-spotted Pug *Eupithecia tripunctaria* Herrich-Schäffer (1835)

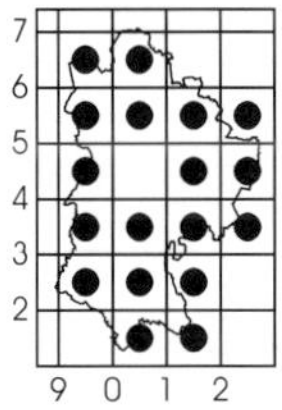

Post VCH: Widespread and locally common. Recorded in S.H.Kershaw's notebooks from Aspley Heath in 1947, 1952 and 1956.
Flight: May to September (weeks 18 to 36, peaks 22 and 31)★.
Larval Foodplants: Elder★, wild angelica and wild parsnip.

Campanula Pug *Eupithecia denotata denotata* (Hübner) (1836)
Post VCH: Recorded in S.H.Kershaw's notebook from Aspley Heath on 28 May 1947 but no specimen has been seen. Also reported from Sharnbrook by D.V.Manning in 1975 and 1976 but as no specimens were kept these records are in doubt.
Flight: June and July.
Larval Foodplants: Nettle-leaved bellflower and giant bellflower.

Grey Pug *Eupithecia subfuscata* (Haworth) (1837)

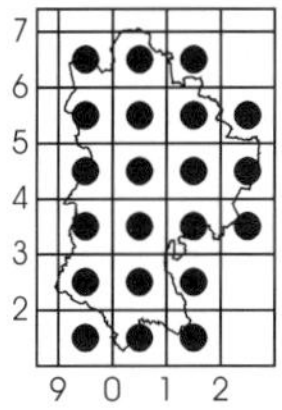

VCH: (as *E. castigata* Haw.) "Generally common."
Post VCH: Widespread and generally common.
Flight: May to August (weeks 20 to 33, peak 23 to 27)★.
Larval Foodplants: Common ragwort★, mugwort★ and other herbaceous plants.

Tawny-speckled Pug *Eupithecia icterata* (Villers) ssp. *subfulvata* (Haworth) (1838) (Drawing on page 286)

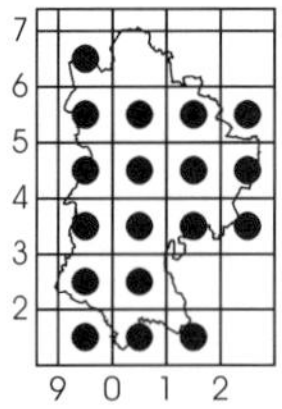

VCH: (as *E. subfulvata* Haw.) "Bedford, Luton."
Post VCH: Fairly common throughout the County.
Flight: July to September (weeks 28 to 37, peak 31 to 34)★.
Larval Foodplant: Yarrow★.

Bordered Pug *Eupithecia succenturiata* (Linnaeus) (1839)

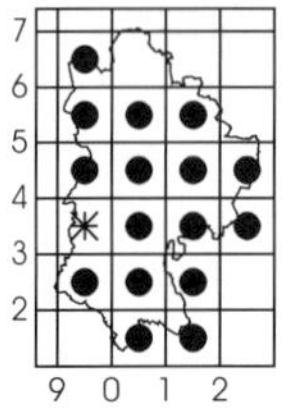

VCH: "Potton."
Post VCH: Fairly common throughout the County.
Flight: Late June to August (weeks 26 to 34, peak 29 to 32)★.
Larval Foodplants: Mugwort★ and yarrow★.

For details of standard weeks see page 6.

Shaded Pug *Eupithecia subumbrata* ([Denis & Schiffermüller]) (1840)

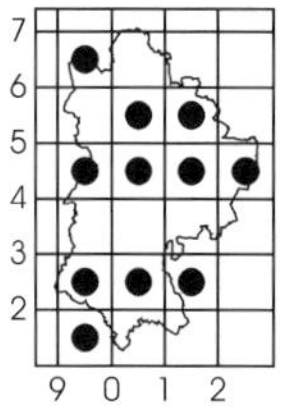

Post VCH: Local but widespread. Recorded by Foster (1934) under the name Scabious Pug, *E. scabiosata* from "Pegsdon Hills by myself, Nash and Brocklehurst". Also found by S.H.Kershaw at Totternhoe on 9 June 1947.
Flight: June and July (weeks 22 to 30, peak 28)*.
Larval Foodplants: Common ragwort*, fox-and-cubs* and other herbaceous plants.

Plain Pug *Eupithecia simpliciata* (Haworth) (1842)

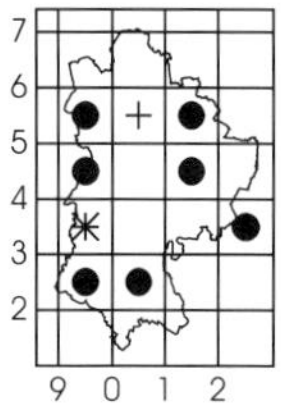

VCH: (as *E. subnotata* Hb.) "Bedford."
Post VCH: A scarce species in Bedfordshire: Luton (1981), Marston Thrift (1981), Old Warden Tunnel (1972), Stotfold (1994) and Tempsford (1990, 1991). Also in the RIS trap at Eaton Bray (1980).
Flight: July and August (weeks 28 to 33)*.
Larval Foodplants: Goosefoots and oraches.

Thyme Pug *Eupithecia distinctaria* Herrich-Schäffer ssp. *constrictata* Guenée (1843)

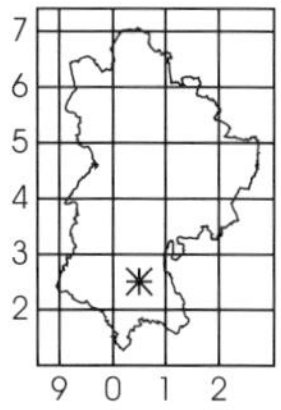

Post VCH: Two specimens in the Fryer collection at Rothamsted Experimental Station, Harpenden labelled "Sharpenhoe 25th June 1948".
Flight: June and July.
Larval Foodplant: Wild thyme.

Ochreous Pug *Eupithecia indigata* (Hübner) (1844)

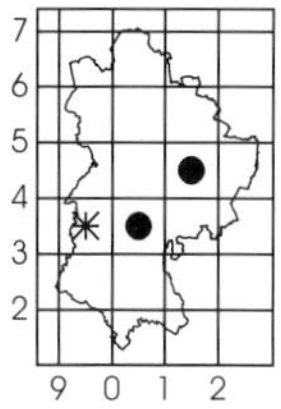

Post VCH: A scarce species that can be found in conifer plantations. Entered in S.H.Kershaw's notebooks as found at Aspley Heath on 8 June 1946 and 26 May 1953. More recent records are from the RIS trap at Old Warden on 31 May 1979 and from Maulden Wood on 1 June 1983. Some other records have been deleted owing to lack of reliable data or specimens.
Flight: April to early June (week 22)*.

Larval Foodplant: Scots pine.

Pimpinel Pug *Eupithecia pimpinellata* (Hübner) (1845)

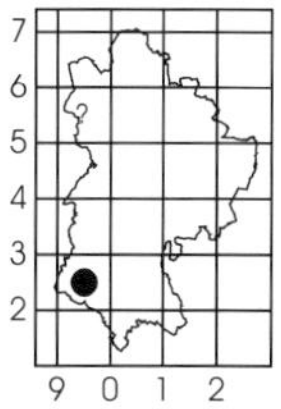

Post VCH: Scarce: RIS trap at Eaton Bray (1981, 1983, 1989). Also doubtfully recorded from Sharnbrook in 1975 and 1976.
Flight: July and August (weeks 30 to 32)*.
Larval Foodplant: Burnet-saxifrage.

Narrow-winged Pug *Eupithecia nanata* (Hübner) ssp. *angusta* Prout (1846)

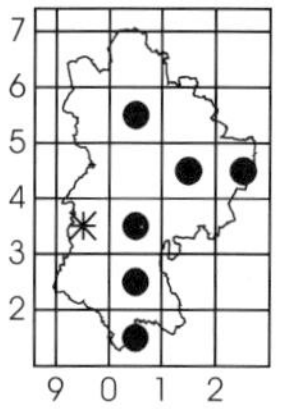

VCH: "Luton."
Post VCH: An uncommon species found mainly along the Greensand Ridge but the larval foodplant is commonly cultivated in gardens.
Flight: April to September (weeks 15 to 36, slight peaks: 21 to 22 and 31)*.
Larval Foodplant: Heather.

For key to moth maps see page 3.

Ash Pug *Eupithecia fraxinata* Crewe (1849)

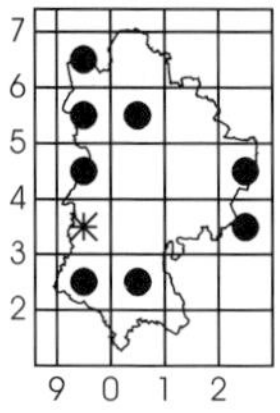

Post VCH: A scarce, local species, mainly found in woodlands where ash occurs. Recorded in S.H.Kershaw's notebooks from Aspley Heath between 1946 and 1959 but no specimens have been seen. Recorded at Hardwick Spinney (1973), Sharnbrook (1976), Stotfold (1982, 1987) and, among other sites, in the RIS trap at Eaton Bray (1983, 1989, 1994).
Flight: Late June and July and again in late August and early September (weeks 26 to 31 and 35)★.
Larval Foodplant: Ash.
Notes: In some earlier records for the County this species was referred to as *E. innotata* (Hufnagel), Angle-barred Pug.

Golden-rod Pug *Eupithecia virgaureata* Doubleday (1851)

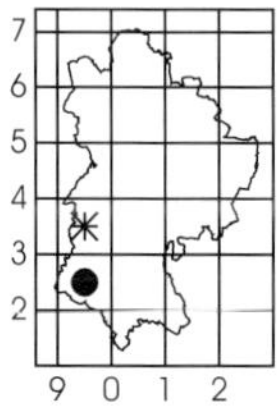

Post VCH: Recorded in S.H.Kershaw's notebooks from Aspley Heath on 23 July 1935, 19 July 1937 and 10 August 1946 but no specimens have been seen. One recent record only, from the RIS trap at Eaton Bray on 17 August 1983.
Flight: May and June, and again in August (week 33)★.
Larval Foodplants: Goldenrod and common ragwort.

Brindled Pug *Eupithecia abbreviata* Stephens (1852)

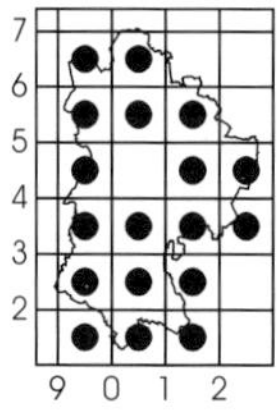

Post VCH: Common throughout the County. Recorded in S.H.Kershaw's notebooks from Aspley Heath in 1936 and 1938 (no specimens have been seen). The melanic f. *nigra* Cockayne is widespread.
Flight: April to July (weeks 13 to 30, peak 15)★.
Larval Foodplants: Oaks.

Oak-tree Pug *Eupithecia dodoneata* Guenée (1853)

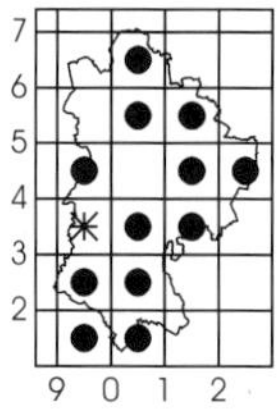

Post VCH: Widespread and local, but can be common where it occurs. Recorded in S.H.Kershaw's notebook from Aspley Heath on14 April 1946 but no specimens have been seen.
Flight: May and June (weeks 18 to 24, peak 20)★.
Larval Foodplants: Hawthorns★ and oaks.

Juniper Pug *Eupithecia pusillata pusillata* ([Denis & Schiffermüller]) (1854)

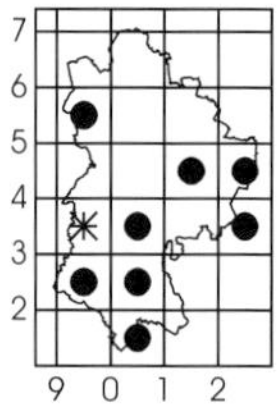

VCH: (as *E. sobrinata* Hb.) "Luton, among juniper."
Post VCH: A scarce species in Bedfordshire. It has been recorded from a number of gardens and in S.H.Kershaw's notebooks from Aspley Heath in 1935, 1946 and 1954 (no specimens seen). Also from the RIS traps at Cockayne Hatley (1991, 1995), Eaton Bray (1980, 1989) and Old Warden (1979). K.F.Webb found larvae on junipers in Caddington churchyard.
Flight: May to August (weeks 20 to 32)★.
Larval Foodplants: Juniper★ and possibly other cultivated conifers.

For details of standard weeks see page 6.

Larch Pug *Eupithecia lariciata* (Freyer) (1856)

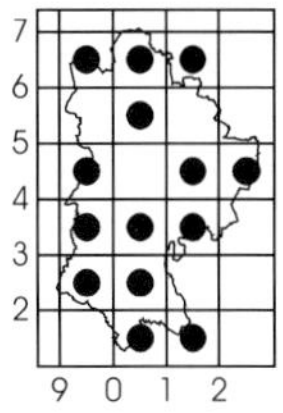

Post VCH: A local, but widespread species usually occurring among larch trees. "Common at Rowney Warren" Foster (1934). Recorded in S.H. Kershaw's notebooks from Aspley Heath between 1932 and 1959 (no specimens seen).
Flight: July to early August (weeks 27 to 31)*.
Larval Foodplants: Larches.

Dwarf Pug *Eupithecia tantillaria* Boisduval (1857)

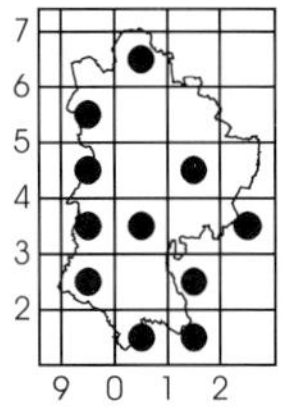

Post VCH: A widespread but local species, usually found in conifer plantations.
Flight: May to July (weeks 21 to 27)*.
Larval Foodplants: Norway spruce and Douglas fir.

V-Pug *Chloroclystis v-ata* (Haworth) (1858)

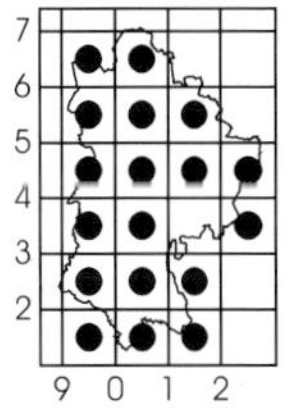

VCH: (as *E. coronata* Hb.) "Bedford, Luton."
Post VCH: Widespread and common.
Flight: June to August (weeks 20 to 34, peak 30)*.
Larval Foodplants: Elder* and herbaceous plants.

Sloe Pug *Chloroclystis chloerata* (Mabille) (1859)

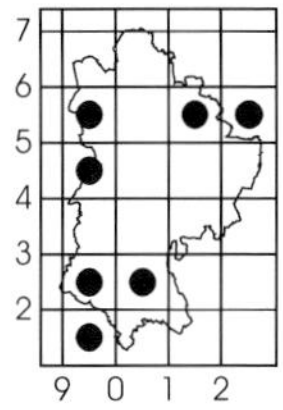

Post VCH: Recorded in 1984 by K.F. Webb, from Warden Hill, as larvae (Webb, 1985b). Since then it has been found at a variety of sites but usually in low numbers.
Flight: June and July (weeks 24 to 28)*.
Larval Foodplant: Blackthorn*.

Green Pug *Chloroclystis rectangulata* (Linnaeus) (1860)

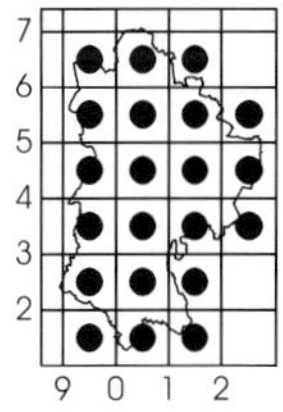

VCH: "Generally common in orchards."
Post VCH: Common throughout the County.
Flight: June to early August (weeks 23 to 31, peak 26 to 29)*.
Larval Foodplants: Apple*, pear, cherry and blackthorn*.

Bilberry Pug *Chloroclystis debiliata* (Hübner) (1861)
Post VCH: Recorded in S.H.Kershaw's notebooks from Aspley Heath on 31 July 1936 and 11 June 1947 but no specimens have been seen.
Flight: June and July.
Larval Foodplants: Bilberry

Double-striped Pug *Gymnoscelis rufifasciata* (Haworth) (1862)

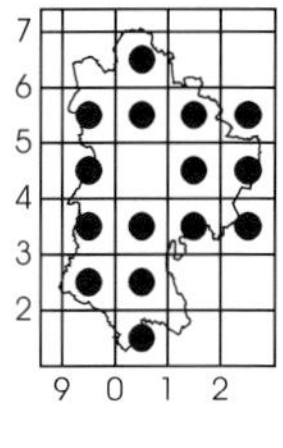

Post VCH: Widespread and common. Recorded in S.H.Kershaw's notebooks from Aspley Heath between 1935 and 1959 (no specimens).
Flight: April to September (weeks 15 to 35, peaks 16 to 20 and 27 to 31)*.
Larval Foodplants: Common ragwort* and other herbaceous plants.

For key to moth maps see page 3.

The Streak *Chesias legatella* ([Denis & Schiffermüller]) (1864) (Plate 55)
VCH: (as *C. spartiata* Schiff.) "Potton, among broom."

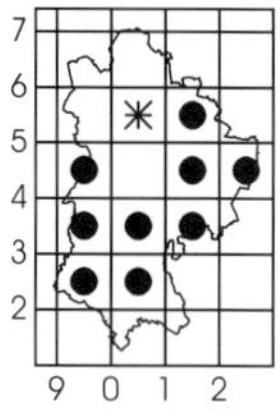

Post VCH: A local species which is never common. There are two specimens in the Temple collection from Bedford dated 7 October 1908 and 18 October 1909. Recorded in S.H.Kershaw's notebooks from Aspley Heath between 1933 and 1958 (no specimens). Current sites include Aspley Guise, Maulden Wood and The Lodge, Sandy.
Flight: September to November (weeks 39 to 45, peak 41 to 43)*.
Larval Foodplant: Broom.

Broom-tip *Chesias rufata rufata* (Fabricius) (1865)

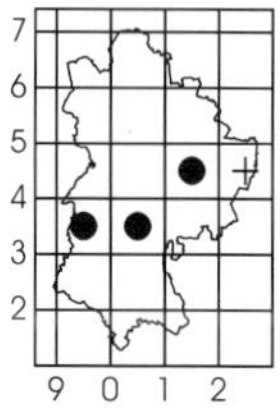

VCH: "Among broom, Potton."
Post VCH: A scarce insect, only recorded in a few locations such as Aspley Heath between 1932 and 1959 (Kershaw MS, no specimens), Aspley Guise, Maulden Wood, Old Warden and The Lodge, Sandy.
Flight: March to August (weeks 11 to 34, peak 28 to 31)*.
Larval Foodplant: Broom.

Treble-bar *Aplocera plagiata plagiata* (Linnaeus) (1867)

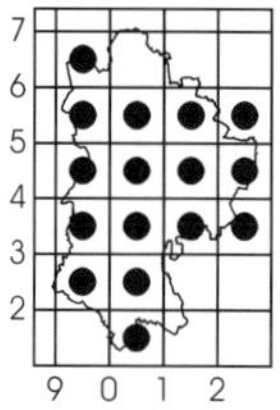

VCH: "Generally distributed." (Drawing on page 274)
Post VCH: Found locally throughout the County.
Flight: Double-brooded, flying in late May to July (weeks 22 to 27)* and again in August to October (weeks 33 to 42, peak 35)*.
Larval Foodplants: St John's-worts.

Lesser Treble-bar *Aplocera efformata* (Guenée) (1868)

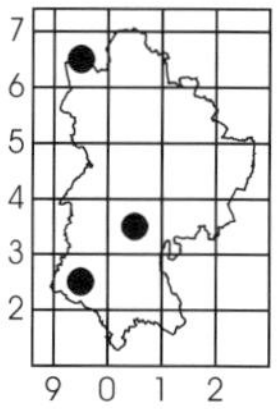

Post VCH: Recorded by R.F.Bretherton from King's Wood, Heath and Reach on 13-15 July 1945. Also from Cooper's Hill and Sharnbrook Summit by W.J.Champkin (1984) and from the RIS trap at Eaton Bray (1985, 1994).
Flight: May to September (weeks 28 and 38)* in two broods.
Larval Foodplants: St John's-worts.

Chimney Sweeper *Odezia atrata* (Linnaeus) (1870)
(Drawing on page 25)

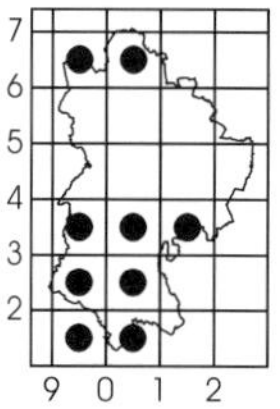

Post VCH: Found by S.H.Kershaw (MS) at Totternhoe in 1945, 1946 and 1955. A local species that can be abundant where it occurs. Good locations include Dunstable Downs, Totternhoe Knolls and Flitwick Moor.
Flight: June and July (weeks 23 to 30)* flying by day.
Larval Foodplant: Pignut, feeding on the flowers.

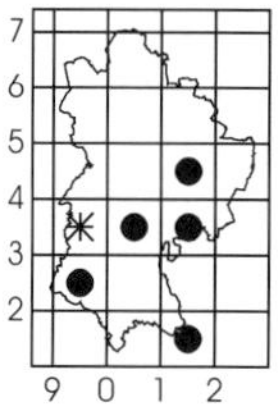

Dingy Shell *Euchoeca nebulata* (Scopoli) (1874)
Post VCH: There are specimens from Flitwick in the Temple collection dated 18 June 1908 and 13 July 1909 and also the Rylands collection dated15 June 1908 and 20 July 1909. Reported from "Flitwick Marsh" (Foster,

1934). Also recorded in S.H.Kershaw's notebooks from Aspley Heath on 13 July 1946 and more recently at Flitwick Moor (1976, 1978, 1985), Lower Alders (1981, 1982), Luton Hoo (1983), Sewell Cutting (1980) and the RIS trap at Old Warden (1979).
Flight: June to September (weeks 29 to 36)*.
Larval Foodplant: Alder.

Small White Wave *Asthena albulata* (Hufnagel) (1875)
Pre VCH: J.C.Dale (MS2) recorded receiving this species (as *Candidulata*) from Abbot's collection from Bedford but not dated.
VCH: (as *A. candidata* Schiff.) "Bedford, Luton."
Post VCH: A scarce and local species which is usually found in woodlands, such as Maulden Wood where it was recorded in 1976, 1978 and 1986.
Flight: May to July and occasionally in August.
Larval Foodplants: Various trees including hazel, birches and hornbeam.

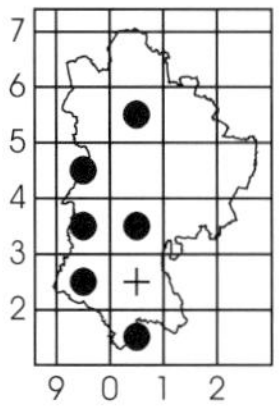

Small Yellow Wave *Hydrelia flammeolaria* (Hufnagel) (1876)
Pre VCH: J.C.Dale (MS2) recorded receiving this species (as *Luteata*) from Abbot's collection from Bedford but not dated.
VCH: (as *Asthena luteata* Schiff.) "Bedford, Potton, Luton."
Post VCH: Widespread but local, found mainly in woodlands.
Flight: June and July (weeks 25 to 30, peak 28)*.
Larval Foodplant: Field maple.

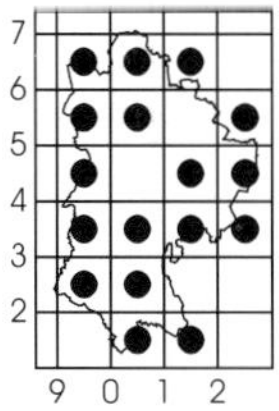

Drab Looper *Minoa murinata* (Scopoli) (1878)
Pre VCH: J.C.Dale (MS3) recorded finding this species (as *Phalaena Euphorbiata*) on 1 June 1820 in Clapham Park Wood "in plenty".
Post VCH: Recorded in S.H.Kershaw's notebook from Aspley Heath on 15 July 1949 as *euphorbiata*. The entry is flagged as important but no specimen has been seen. No other record is known.
Flight: May and June.
Larval Foodplant: Wood spurge.

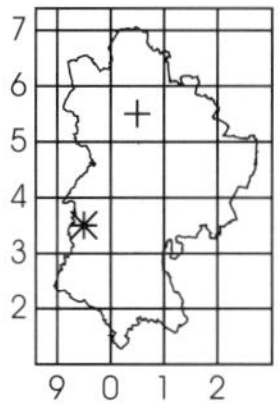

The Seraphim *Lobophora halterata* (Hufnagel) (1879)
Post VCH: Widespread but very local, usually found in woodlands. It has been recorded from Aspley Heath (Kershaw MS) in 1935, 1936 and 1947 and more recently in sites such as Coppice Wood (1985-1987, 1990) and Maulden Wood (1976-1978, 1980, 1983).
Flight: May to July (weeks 19 to 27)*.
Larval Foodplants: Aspen and poplars.

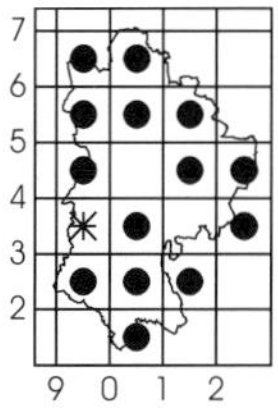

Early Tooth-striped *Trichopteryx carpinata* (Borkhausen) (1881)
Post VCH: Very few records: Sandy Warren, Sandy (1961); King's Wood, Heath and Reach (1984, 1985, 1987); Stockgrove Country Park (1984).
Flight: April and May (weeks 15 to 19)*.
Larval Foodplants: Honeysuckle, sallows, birches and alder.

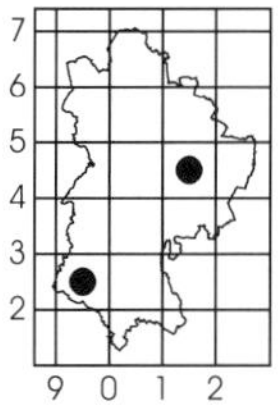

For key to moth maps see page 3.

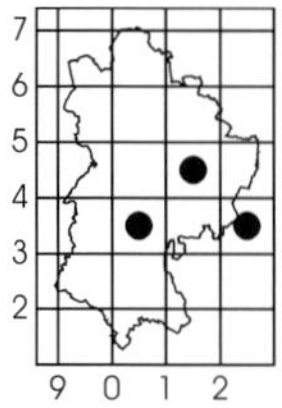

Small Seraphim *Pterapherapteryx sexalata* (Retzius) (1882)
Post VCH: A scarce and local species for which there are only four records: Flitwick Moor (1977, 1978), Sandy (1975) and Stotfold (1977).
Flight: Flying between May and August (weeks 28 & 29)* in two broods.
Larval Foodplants: Sallows.

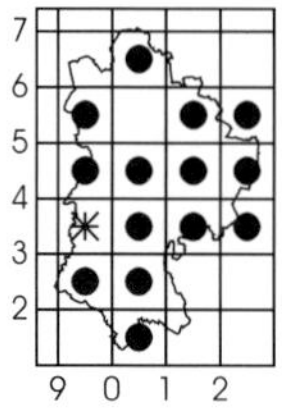

Yellow-barred Brindle *Acasis viretata* (Hübner) (1883)
Post VCH: Recorded in S.H.Kershaw's notebook from Aspley Heath in 1947. Currently widespread but local. Mainly found in woodlands, hedgerows and mature gardens.
Flight: Flying in May (weeks 19 to 22)* and July to September (weeks 30 to 35, peak 31 to 33)* in two broods.
Larval Foodplants: Holly, ivy, wild privet, dogwood and guelder-rose.

For details of standard weeks see page 6.

Geometers - Part 3

(Ennominae)

V.W.Arnold

Purple Thorn

Clouded Border

Family: **Geometridae**

Subfamily: **Ennominae** **Thorns, Beauties etc.**

The moths in this subfamily are variable in size (wingspan 22-68 mm) and pattern but the hindwings are patterned in most species. The larvae of some species mimic twigs in form and posture to a remarkable extent. Of the 81 British species, 51 have been found in Bedfordshire, plus a further three species for which the records are in doubt.

The Magpie *Abraxas grossulariata* (Linnaeus) (1884) (Plate 90)

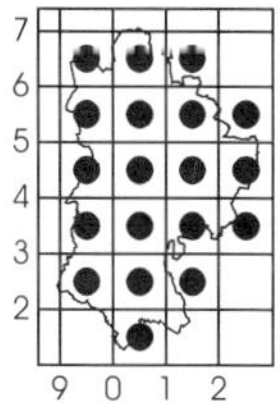

Pre VCH: Recorded by T. Orlebar Marsh (MS1) from Clapham and Biddenham in 1798.
VCH: "Abundant in gardens everywhere."
Post VCH: Common throughout the County.
Flight: July to September (weeks 27 to 38, peak 30 to 34)★.
Larval Foodplants: Currants★, gooseberry★, polyphagous on herbaceous plants and shrubs.

Clouded Magpie *Abraxas sylvata* (Scopoli) (1885)

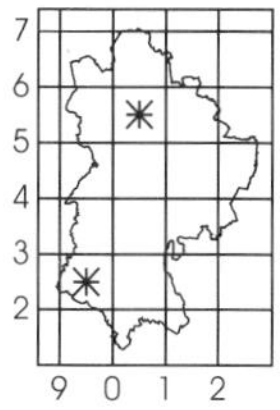

VCH: "Bedford district, in woods."
Post VCH: J.M. Schofield collected records of this species from King's Wood, Heath and Reach before 1970. Also came to light at Bedford School on 22 July 1959.
Flight: May to July (week 29)★.
Larval Foodplants: Wych elm and English elm.

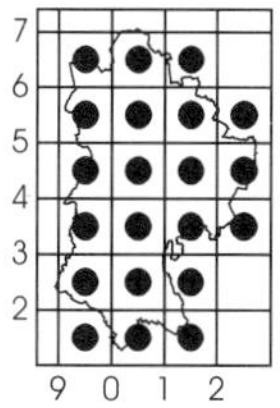

Clouded Border *Lomaspilis marginata* (Linnaeus) (1887)
VCH: "Bedford, Luton; among sallow."
Post VCH: Common throughout the County.
Flight: May to August (weeks 18 to 34, peak 25 to 31)★.
Larval Foodplants: Sallows, aspen, poplars and hazel.

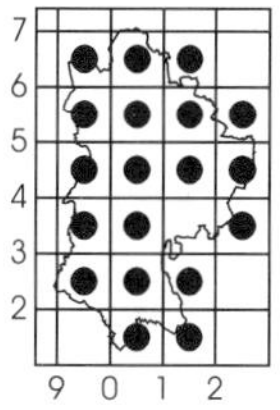

Scorched Carpet *Ligdia adustata* ([Denis & Schiffermüller]) (1888)
VCH: "Bedford, Luton; among spindle."
Post VCH: An uncommon local species, found throughout the County.
Flight: Late April to early September (weeks 18 to 35)★.
Larval Foodplant: Spindle.

For key to moth maps see page 3.

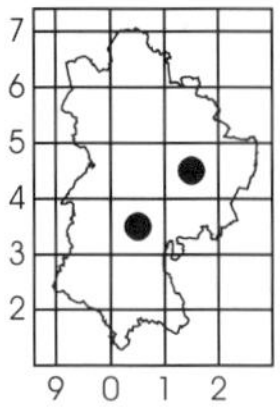

Peacock Moth *Semiothisa notata* (Linnaeus) (1889)
Post VCH: Only three records: Flitwick Moor (1977), The Lodge, Sandy (1989) and in the RIS trap at Old Warden (1976).
Flight: May to July (weeks 24 to 27)* and August in two broods.
Larval Foodplants: Birches.

Sharp-angled Peacock *Semiothisa alternaria* (Hübner) (1890)
Post VCH: Recorded only once. A drawing was made of a specimen seen on a willow by the Embankment, Bedford in 1959 (West, 1960). Without a voucher specimen, confusion with *S. notata* must remain a possibility.

Tawny-barred Angle *Semiothisa liturata* (Clerck) (1893) (Plate 57)

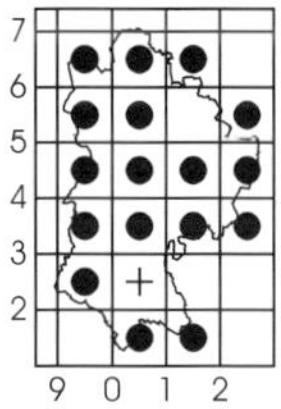

VCH: "Luton, Bedford; among Scotch fir."
Post VCH: Common in and around conifer plantations throughout the County. The melanic form *nigrofulvata* Collins was recorded at Shire Oak in 1979 and in the RIS trap at Cockayne Hatley in 1993.
Flight: June to August (weeks 23 to 33, peak 31 and 32)*.
Larval Foodplants: Scots pine and Norway spruce.

Latticed Heath *Semiothisa clathrata clathrata* (Linnaeus) (1894) (Drawing page 54)

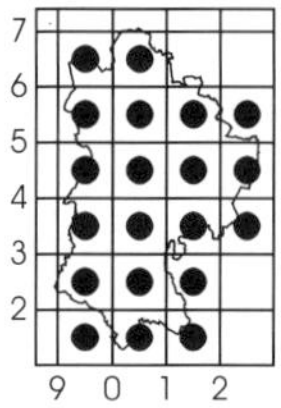

Pre VCH: J.C.Dale (MS3) recorded finding this species in Clapham Park Wood on 1 June 1820. Elsewhere (MS2) he noted receiving this species from Abbot's collection from Bedford but not dated.
VCH: "Bedford, Potton, Luton; common among clover."
Post VCH: Common throughout the County.
Flight: Between May and September (weeks 19 to 36, peaks 23 and 31 to 32)* in two overlapping broods. This species is both diurnal and nocturnal in its flight pattern.
Larval Foodplants: Trefoils, clovers and lucerne.

V-moth *Semiothisa wauaria* (Linnaeus) (1897)

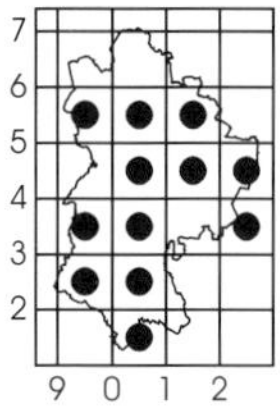

Pre VCH: J.C.Dale (MS2) recorded receiving this species (as *Vauaria*) from Abbot's collection from near Bedford but not dated.
VCH: "Everywhere in gardens among currant bushes."
Post VCH: Widespread but local. Often found near its foodplants in gardens and allotments.
Flight: June to August(weeks 25 to 33)*.
Larval Foodplants: Gooseberry, black currant and red currant.

Frosted Yellow *Isturgia limbaria* (Fabricius) (1899)
Pre VCH: J.C.Dale (MS2) recorded receiving this species from Abbot's collection from near Bedford but not dated.
Post VCH: Not recorded. Last reported in England in 1914 (Skinner, 1984).

For details of standard weeks see page 6.

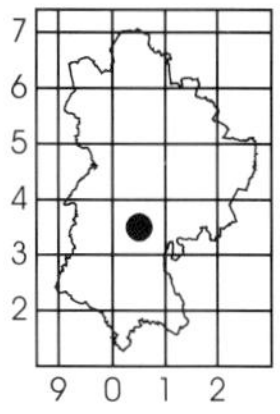

Little Thorn *Cepphis advenaria* (Hübner) (1901)
Post VCH: At light at Flitwick Moor on30 April 1981.
Flight: April (week 18)★ to June.
Larval Foodplant: Bilberry. Skinner (1984) states that "where this foodplant is absent, it must have an alternative foodplant and among those suggested are bramble, wild rose and dogwood."

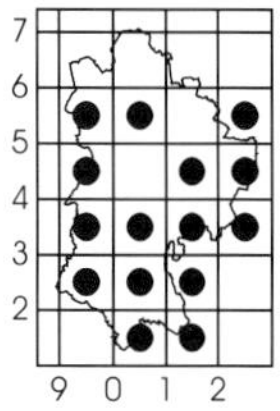

Brown Silver-lines *Petrophora chlorosata* (Scopoli) (1902)
Pre VCH: J.C.Dale (MS2) recorded receiving this species (as *Petrata*) from Abbot's collection from near Bedford but not dated.
VCH: (as *Panagra petraria* Hb.) "Near Bedford, among brake-fern."
Post VCH: Widespread and often common in areas where bracken occurs.
Flight: April to July (weeks 15 to 30, peak 20 to 25)★.
Larval Foodplant: Bracken.

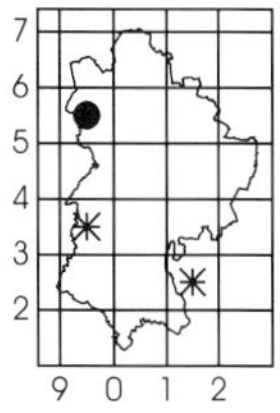

Barred Umber *Plagodis pulveraria* (Linnaeus) (1903)
Post VCH: Recorded in S.H.Kershaw's notebooks from Aspley Heath on 7 July1933 and 19 June 1935 and from Pegsdon on 1 August 1934. All these records are rather late, the last exceptionally so unless it was an unusual second generation. No specimens have been seen. Also from Manor Farm, Stevington, by W.J.Champkin on 2 April 1965.
Flight: April (week 14)★ to June.
Larval Foodplants: Sallows and birches.

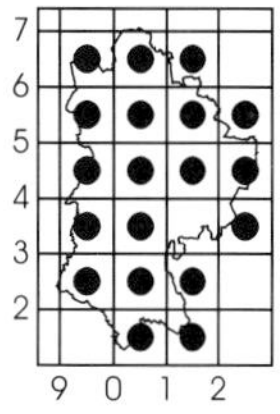

Scorched Wing *Plagodis dolabraria* (Linnaeus) (1904)
Pre VCH: J.C.Dale (MS3) noted finding this species on 1 June 1820 in Clapham Park Wood.
Post VCH: Widespread, usually found in woodlands.
Flight: May to July (weeks 22 to 29)★.
Larval Foodplants: Oaks, birches and sallows.

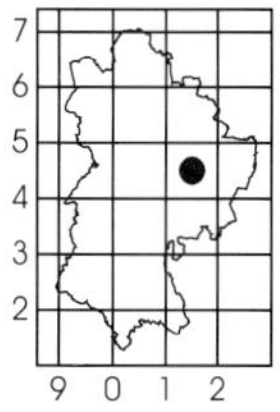

Horse Chestnut *Pachycnemia hippocastanaria* (Hübner) (1905)
Post VCH: Found in the RIS trap at The Lodge, Sandy on 24 July 1971, 15 August 1972 and 8 September 1974.
Flight: April and May and again between late July and early September (weeks 30 to 36)★.
Larval Foodplant: Heather.

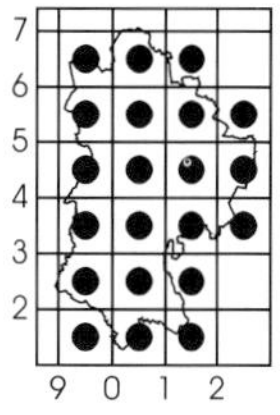

Brimstone Moth *Opisthograptis luteolata* (Linnaeus) (1906)
VCH: (as *Rumia cratagata* Linn.) "Generally common."
Post VCH: Common throughout the County.
Flight: April to October (weeks 16 to 41, peaks 21 to 24, 28 to 30 and 34 to 36)★, in three broods.
Larval Foodplants: Polyphagous on deciduous trees.

For key to moth maps see page 3.

Bordered Beauty *Epione repandaria* (Hufnagel) (1907)
VCH: (as *E. apiciaria* Schiff.) "Bedford, Luton; in lanes among sallow."
Post VCH: A local, but widespread species. It is usually found in damp areas where sallow occurs but it is never common.
Flight: Late June to September (weeks 26 to 39)*.
Larval Foodplants: Sallows.

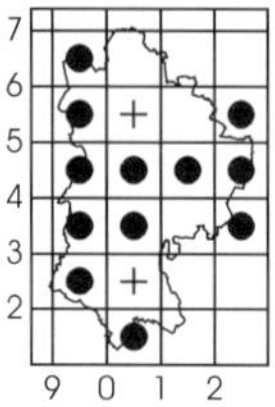

Speckled Yellow *Pseudopanthera macularia* (Linnaeus) (1909)
VCH: "Woods near Luton."
Post VCH: R.M.Craske recalled this species as "very local in Hanger Wood, Stagsden" between 1918 and 1927. Foster (1934) reported it as found "near Luton". In his diaries R. Palmer noted that the Speckled Yellow was to be found in the Luton area in the late 1940s and early 1950s. This species has now almost certainly become extinct in Bedfordshire, a victim of urbanisation and habitat destruction.
Flight: Flies by day in May and June.
Larval Foodplants: Wood sage, woundworts, yellow archangel and dead-nettles.

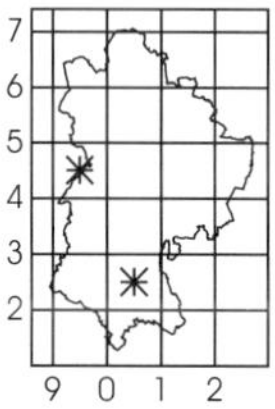

Lilac Beauty *Apeira syringaria* (Linnaeus) (1910)
VCH: "Bedford."
Post VCH: A widespread, but local species, that can be found in woodlands and mature gardens.
Flight: June and July (weeks 25 to 30, peak 28)*.
Larval Foodplants: Honeysuckle, ash and wild privet.

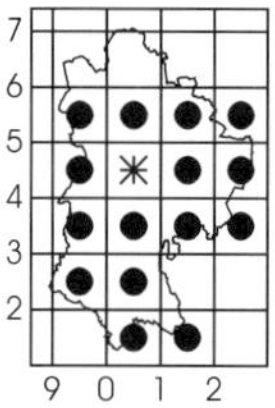

Large Thorn *Ennomos autumnaria* (Werneberg) (1911)
Post VCH: A scarce and local species. Found at Bedford (1958), Biggleswade (1990), Tempsford (1994) and at the RIS trap sites at Cockayne Hatley (1976, 1978, 1979, 1982-1995), Old Warden (1974, 1977) and The Lodge, Sandy (1969, 1970). The Large Thorn is a resident species but it is also suspected to be an immigrant.
Flight: August to October (weeks 34 to 41, peak 38 to 40)*.
Larval Foodplants: Polyphagous on deciduous trees.

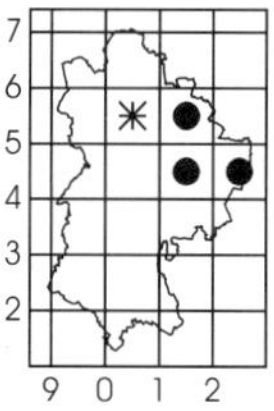

August Thorn *Ennomos quercinaria* (Hufnagel) (1912)
VCH: "Bedford."
Post VCH: A woodland species that is widespread but local.
Flight: August and September (weeks 30 to 39, peak 30 to 31)*.
Larval Foodplants: Polyphagous on deciduous trees.

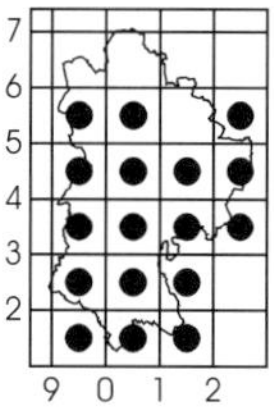

Canary-shouldered Thorn *Ennomos alniaria* (Linnaeus) (1913)
VCH: "Bedford, Luton; among alder."
Post VCH: Widespread and common.
Flight: July to October (weeks 29 to 42, peak 31 to 38)*.
Larval Foodplants: Polyphagous on deciduous trees.

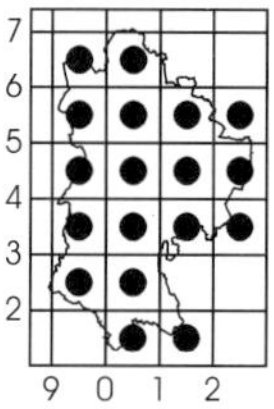

For details of standard weeks see page 6.

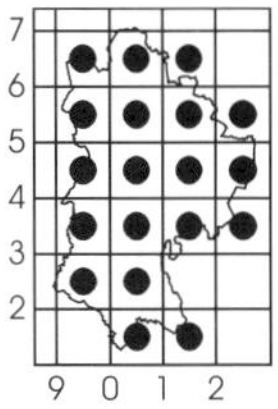

Dusky Thorn *Ennomos fuscantaria* (Haworth) (1914)
VCH: "Potton, among ash."
Post VCH: A common and widespread species that inhabits woodlands and mature gardens.
Flight: July to October (weeks 28 to 40, peak 33 to 38)*.
Larval Foodplant: Ash.

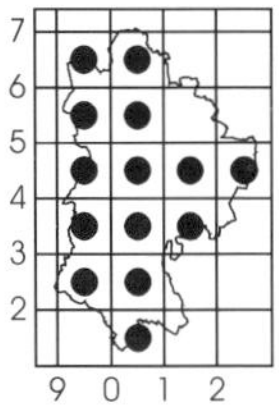

September Thorn *Ennomos erosaria* ([Denis & Schiffermüller]) (1915)
Post VCH: Local and uncommon but widespread throughout the County. Recorded by S.H.Kershaw from Aspley Heath between 1935 and 1954.
Flight: July to October (weeks 28 to 40, peak 31 to 33)*.
Larval Foodplants: Oaks, limes and birches.

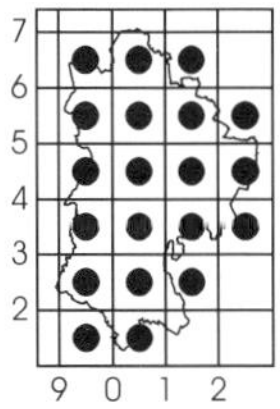

Early Thorn *Selenia dentaria* (Fabricius) (1917)
VCH: (as *S. illunaria* Hb.) "Generally common in lanes."
Post VCH: Common throughout the County.
Flight: Late March to June (weeks 13 to 24, peak 15 to 21)* and again in July to September (weeks 27 to 35, peak 29 to 33)*.
Larval Foodplants: Polyphagous on deciduous trees.

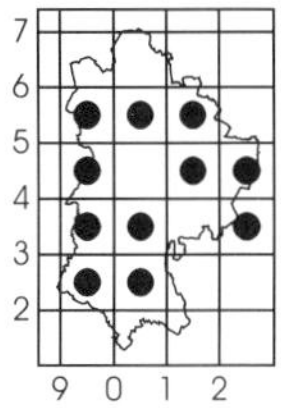

Lunar Thorn *Selenia lunularia* (Hübner) (1918)
Post VCH: Local and uncommon in woodlands throughout the County. Recorded by S.H.Kershaw from Aspley Heath in 1936, 1947 and 1952.
Flight: May to July (weeks 21 to 30)*.
Larval Foodplants: Polyphagous on deciduous trees.

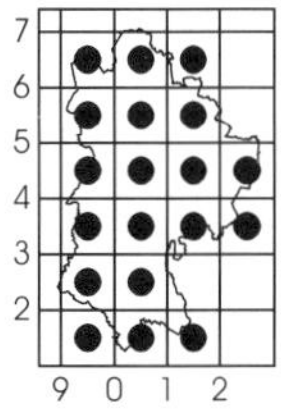

Purple Thorn *Selenia tetralunaria* (Hufnagel) (1919)
(Drawing on page 297)
VCH: "Recorded at Bedford by the Rev. O. W.Harries."
Post VCH: Common throughout the County.
Flight: Double-brooded, flying in April and May (weeks 15 to 21)* and again in late June to August (weeks 25 to 34, peak 30 to 32)*.
Larval Foodplants: Polyphagous on deciduous trees.

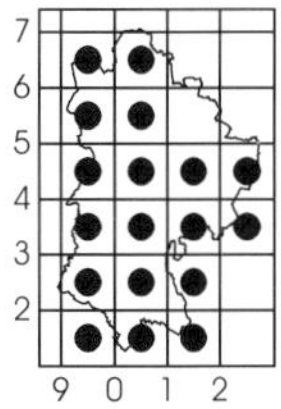

Scalloped Hazel *Odontopera bidentata* (Clerck) (1920)
VCH: "Generally distributed."
Post VCH: Common throughout the County.
Flight: April to June (weeks 15 to 25, peak 20 to 23)*.
Larval Foodplants: Polyphagous on deciduous and coniferous trees.

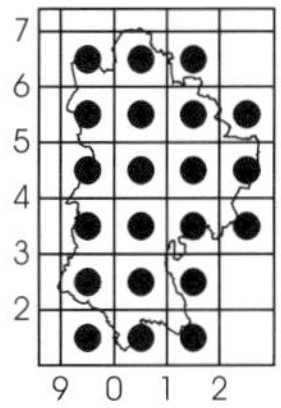

Scalloped Oak *Crocallis elinguaria* (Linnaeus) (1921)
VCH: "Generally distributed, on hedge banks."
Post VCH: Common throughout the County.
Flight: June to September (weeks 22 to 36, peak 28 to 33)*.
Larval Foodplants: Polyphagous on deciduous trees and shrubs.

For key to moth maps see page 3.

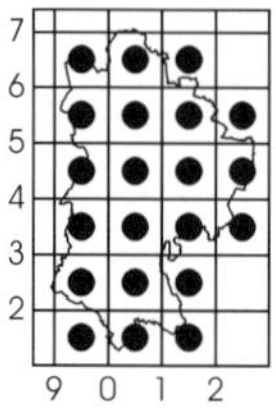

Swallow-tailed Moth *Ourapteryx sambucaria* (Linnaeus) (1922)
VCH: "Generally common."
Post VCH: Common throughout the County.
Flight: Late June to early August (weeks 26 to 31, peak 28 to 30)*.
Larval Foodplants: On ivy and a variety of trees and shrubs.

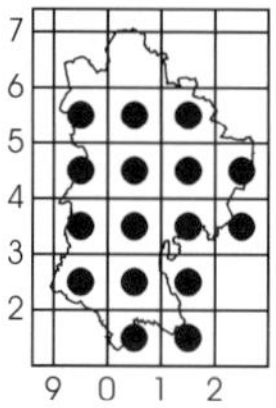

Feathered Thorn *Colotois pennaria* (Linnaeus) (1923)
Pre VCH: J.C.Dale (MS2) recorded receiving this species from Abbot's collection from near Bedford but not dated.
VCH: "Bedford, Luton; common in woods."
Post VCH: Common in woodlands throughout the County.
Flight: September to early December (weeks 38 to 48, peak 41 to 45)*.
Larval Foodplants: Hawthorns*, poplars*, polyphagous on deciduous trees and shrubs.

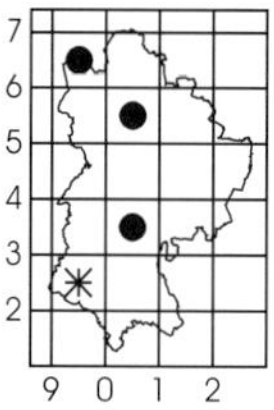

Orange Moth *Angerona prunaria* (Linnaeus) (1924)
Pre VCH: J.C.Dale (MS2, MS3) recorded finding this species on 19 June 1818 and 13 July 1819 in Clapham Park Wood.
VCH: "Woods near Bedford."
Post VCH: A scarce and local species. Recorded from King's and Baker's Woods at Heath and Reach by J.M.Schofield (no date but pre 1970). Also from Bromham (1983), Hinwick Dungee (1960) and Maulden Wood (1976).
Flight: June and July (weeks 26 and 28)*.
Larval Foodplants: Polyphagous on deciduous trees and shrubs.

Small Brindled Beauty *Apocheima hispidaria* ([Denis & Schiffermüller]) (1925)
Post VCH: A scarce and local woodland species. There is a specimen in the Temple collection from Bedford dated 9 March 1910. Recorded in S.H.Kershaw's notebook from Aspley Heath on 11 March 1959. Recorded more recently from Maulden Wood (1976, 1977, 1981), West Wood (1987-1990, 1995) and the RIS traps at Cockayne Hatley (1992, 1993) and The Lodge, Sandy (1971, 1972).

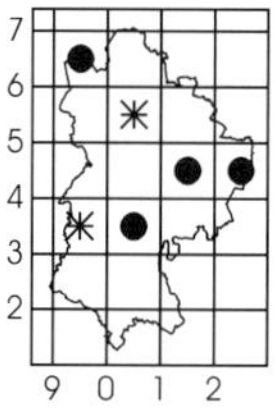

Flight: February to April (weeks 8 to 11 and 16)*.
Larval Foodplants: Oaks, and occasionally on hazel, elms and sweet chestnut.

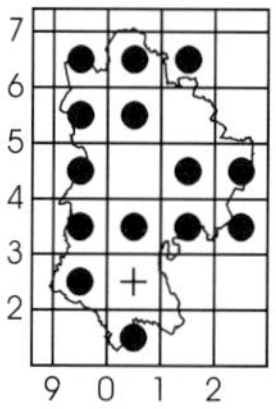

Pale Brindled Beauty *Apocheima pilosaria* ([Denis & Schiffermüller]) (1926)
VCH: "Luton, Potton."
Post VCH: Found commonly in a variety of habitats, throughout the County. The melanic form *monachraria* Staudinger was recorded from Maulden Wood in 1975.
Flight: January to April (weeks 2 to 16, peaks 5 and 8)*.
Larval Foodplants: Hazel*, wayfaring-tree* and other deciduous trees and shrubs.

For details of standard weeks see page 6.

Brindled Beauty *Lycia hirtaria* (Clerck) (1927)

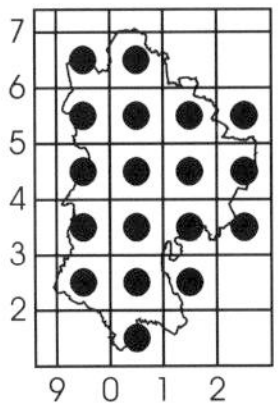

Pre VCH: J.C.Dale (MS2) recorded receiving this species from Abbot's collection from Bedford but not dated.
VCH: "Bedford, Luton."
Post VCH: Common throughout the County. Often comes to light.
Flight: March to early June (weeks 12 to 22, peak 15 to 20)*.
Larval Foodplants: Hazel*, sallow* and other deciduous trees and shrubs.

Oak Beauty *Biston strataria* (Hufnagel) (1930)

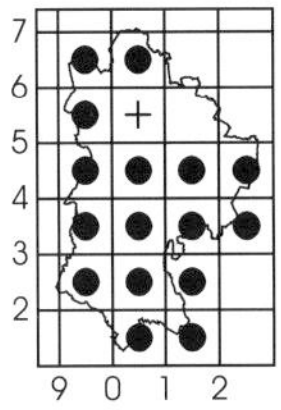

VCH: (as *B. prodromarius* Schiff.) "Bedford, Luton."
Post VCH: Well distributed in woodlands throughout the County.
Flight: March and April (weeks 10 to 17, peak 12 to 14)*.
Larval Foodplants: Polyphagous on deciduous trees.

Peppered Moth *Biston betularia* (Linnaeus) (1931)

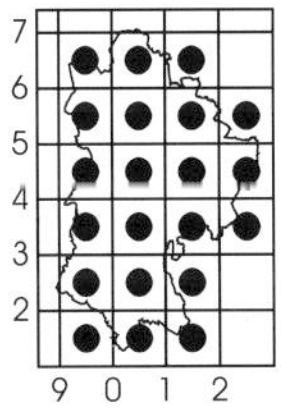

VCH: "Generally distributed."
Post VCH: Common throughout the County.
Flight: Late May to early September (weeks 22 to 36, peak 27 to 29)*.
Larval Foodplants: Hawthorns*, plum*, polyphagous on deciduous trees and herbaceous plants, such as asters*.
Notes: The proportion of melanic forms in populations of the Peppered Moth have been the subject of many studies on the evolution of 'industrial melanism'. Populations in Bedfordshire include the melanic form *carbonaria* Jordan and the form *insularia* Thierry-Mieg which is intermediate in appearance between the melanic and typical forms. The latter two forms have been the most common. Specimens in the Temple collection show that both *carbonaria* and *insularia* were present in Bedford in 1906 but we do not know how common they were. Observations elsewhere in Britain (Clarke *et al.*, 1990) suggest that the typical form has become more common as air pollution has decreased. Catches of this species in RIS light-traps in Bedfordshire show an increase in the proportion of the typical form from 25% between 1975 and 1985 to 66% between 1985 and 1995. Unfortunately the numbers are too low to allow this change to be verified statistically.

Spring Usher *Agriopis leucophaearia* ([Denis & Schiffermüller]) (1932) (Drawing on page 41)

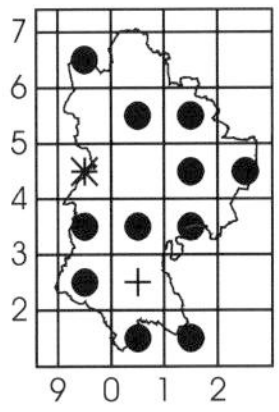

VCH: "Luton."
Post VCH: A local species which is found in woodlands, such as Maulden Wood and West Wood.
Flight: January to March (weeks 2 to 12)*.
Larval Foodplants: Oaks.

Scarce Umber *Agriopis aurantiaria* (Hübner) (1933)

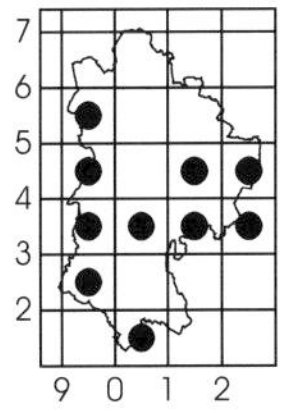

Post VCH: A local and uncommon species which is usually found in wooded areas. There are specimens from Hanger Wood in the Temple collection dated 9 and 11 November 1909 and also in the Rylands collection from the latter date.
Flight: October to early December (weeks 40 to 49, peak 47)*.
Larval Foodplants: Polyphagous on deciduous trees.

For key to moth maps see page 3.

Dotted Border *Agriopis marginaria* (Fabricius) (1934)
VCH: "Everywhere abundant."
Post VCH: Common throughout the County.
Flight: January to May (weeks 3 to 20, peak 9 to 16)★.
Larval Foodplants: Polyphagous on deciduous trees and shrubs.

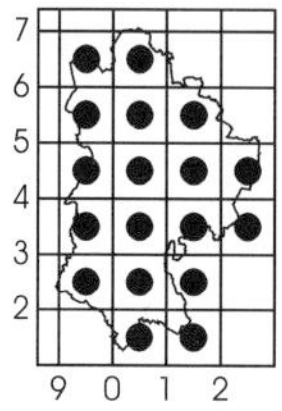

Mottled Umber *Erannis defoliaria* (Clerck) (1935)
Pre VCH: J.C.Dale (MS2) recorded receiving this species from Abbot's collection from Bedford but not dated.
VCH: "Generally distributed in woods." (Drawing on page 36)
Post VCH: Common throughout the County.
Flight: October to February (weeks 40 to 8, peak 46 to 3)★.
Larval Foodplants: Birches★, field maple★, hawthorns★, hornbeam★, sallow★, sycamore★ and other deciduous trees and shrubs.

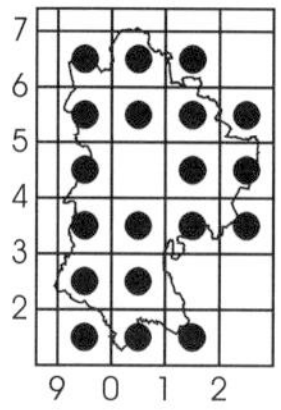

Waved Umber *Menophra abruptaria* (Thunberg) (1936)
VCH: "Bedford, Luton."
Post VCH: Widespread but never common. Found in woodlands and mature gardens throughout the County.
Flight: April to June (weeks 17 to 27, peak 19 to 21)★.
Larval Foodplants: Garden privet and lilac.

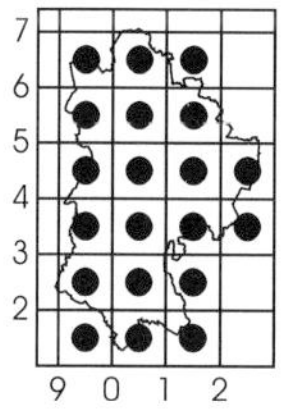

Willow Beauty *Peribatodes rhomboidaria* ([Denis & Schiffermüller]) (1937)
Pre VCH: J.C.Dale (MS3) found this species on 15 July 1819 near Bedford.
VCH: "Generally distributed."
Post VCH: Found in a variety of habitats throughout the County.
Flight: June to September (weeks 24 to 36, peak 27 to 34)★.
Larval Foodplants: Polyphagous on deciduous trees.

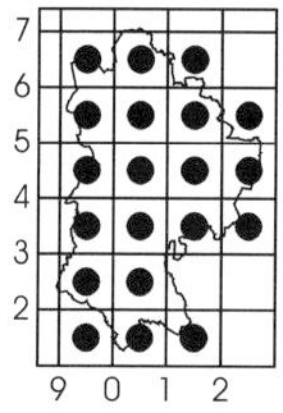

Satin Beauty *Deileptenia ribeata* (Clerck) (1940)
Post VCH: A scarce species, that has been overlooked in the past. A specimen in the Kershaw collection thought to have been this species (Arnold, 1995b) was subsequently found to have been misidentified. Found at Aspley Heath (1989), Dunstable (1971), Potton Wood (northern section) (1976) and in the RIS trap at Eaton Bray (1981).
Flight: June, July (week 27)★ and August.
Larval Foodplants: Polyphagous on various conifers, also oaks and birches.

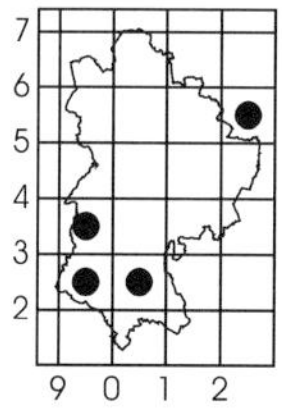

Mottled Beauty *Alcis repandata repandata* (Linnaeus) (1941)
VCH: "Bedford, Luton, probably everywhere."
Post VCH: A common, sometimes abundant, species throughout the County.
Flight: June to August (weeks 23 to 34, peak 26 to 28)★.
Larval Foodplants: Heather★ and other plants.

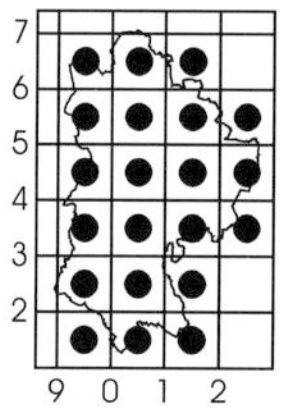

For details of standard weeks see page 6.

Great Oak Beauty ***Hypomecis roboraria*** **([Denis & Schiffermüller]) (1943)**

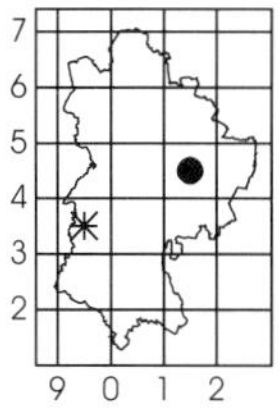

Post VCH: Scarce: a specimen in the Kershaw collection from Aspley Heath is dated 25 May 1953 and there are records in Kershaw's notebooks from there in 1934, 1949, 1950 and 1951. West (1959) recorded it under Heslop's (1947) list number "854" but no site was given. It has also been found in the RIS traps at Old Warden (1975) and The Lodge, Sandy (1969).
Flight: May and June (weeks 19, 23, 24)*.
Larval Foodplants: Oaks.

Pale Oak Beauty ***Serraca punctinalis*** **(Scopoli) (1944)**

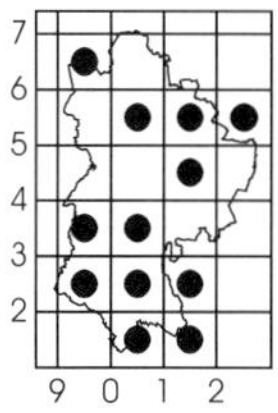

Pre VCH: J.C.Dale (MS3) recorded finding this species (as *Geometra Consortaria*) on 19 July 1818 at Clapham Park Wood.
Post VCH: Uncommon but widespread in woodlands. Recorded in S.H.Kershaw's notebook from Aspley Heath between 1946 and 1953.
Flight: May to July (weeks 21 to 29, peak 23 to 25)*.
Larval Foodplants: Oaks, birches and sallows.

Brussel's Lace ***Cleorodes lichenaria*** **(Hufnagel) (1945)**
Pre VCH: J.C.Dale (MS3) recorded finding this species on 15 July 1819 near Bedford.
VCH: "Luton."

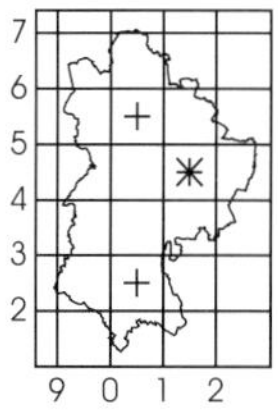

Post VCH: Recorded in S.H.Kershaw's notebook from Aspley Heath in 1936 and 1937 but no specimens have been seen for these years. A specimen in his collection dated 1947 was misplaced. West (1963) reported: "Willington, late July, on a fence, but I know of no area in the vicinity where one could expect to find the habitat of a lichen feeder, unless one assumes a colony in Sheerhatch Wood".
Flight: June to August.
Larval Foodplants: Lichens growing on oaks, blackthorn and old fences.

The Engrailed ***Ectropis bistortata*** **(Goeze) (1947)**

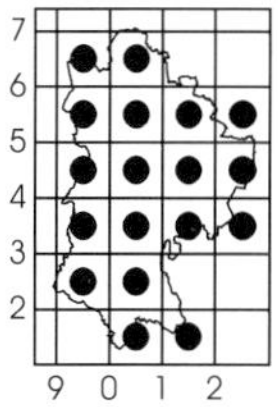

VCH: (as *Tephrosia biundularia* Esp.) "Bedford, on tree trunks."
Post VCH: Common and widespread in woods and mature gardens.
Flight: February to October (weeks 8 to 40, peaks 15 to 16 and 26 to 33)* in two broods.
Larval Foodplants: Polyphagous on deciduous trees and shrubs.

Small Engrailed ***Ectropis crepuscularia*** **([Denis & Schiffermüller]) (1948)**
Pre VCH: J.C.Dale (MS3) recorded finding this species on 30 May 1820 near Bedford.
VCH: "Bedford, on tree trunks."

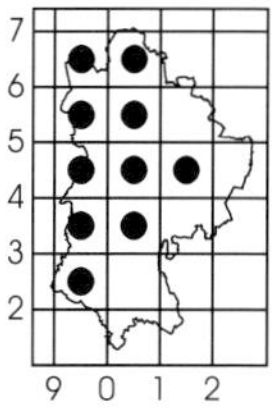

Post VCH: Local and uncommon but widespread in woodlands throughout the County. Re-examination of the records suggested possible confusion with the previous species and some records have therefore been discarded.
Flight: April to June (weeks 15 to 21 and 24)*.
Larval Foodplants: Polyphagous on deciduous trees and shrubs.

For key to moth maps see page 3.

Square Spot *Paradarisa consonaria* (Hübner) (1949)
Post VCH: South (1908) stated "it occurs in some of the woods in Bedfordshire." Recorded in S.H.Kershaw's notebook from Aspley Heath in 1946, 1947, 1950, 1952 and 1955. All these records were in July and the only specimen seen (Arnold, 1995b) proved on subsequent examination to be misidentified. Kershaw's record from King's Wood, Heath and Reach on 7 August 1954 and W.J.Champkin's from Hardwick Spinney on 8 August 1953 are even later, making the evidence for the occurrence of this species in Bedfordshire somewhat doubtful.
Flight: April to June.
Larval Foodplants: Polyphagous on deciduous and coniferous trees.

Brindled White-spot *Paradarisa extersaria* (Hübner) (1950)

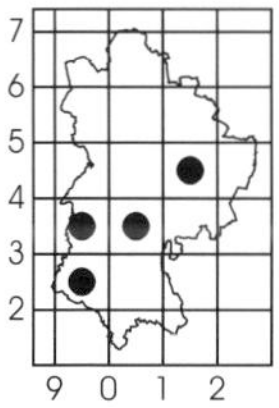

Post VCH: A very local woodland species. Specimens in Kershaw's collection from Aspley Heath are dated 4 June 1937, 13 June 1939 and 11 June 1947. More recently recorded from Aspley Heath (1981, 1984), King's Wood, Heath and Reach (1984, 1985), Maulden Wood (1985, 1991) and the RIS trap at Old Warden (1974).
Flight: June (weeks 22 to 26)*.
Larval Foodplants: Oaks and birches.

Grey Birch *Aethalura punctulata* ([Denis & Schiffermüller]) (1951)

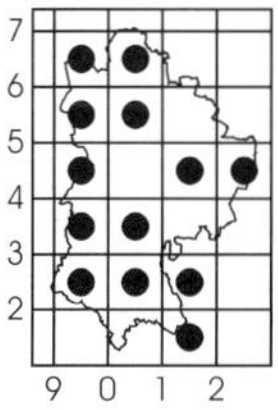

Pre VCH: J.C.Dale (MS2) recorded receiving this species (as *Punctularia*) from Abbot's collection from Bedford but not dated.
VCH: "Luton."
Post VCH: A local species, found in woodland throughout the County.
Flight: May and June (weeks 22 to 27)*.
Larval Foodplants: Birches and alder.

Common Heath *Ematurga atomaria atomaria* (Linnaeus) (1952)
(Drawing on page 53)

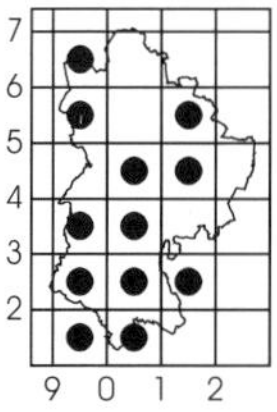

VCH: "Luton, common on heaths."
Post VCH: A local species, found on chalk downlands, woodland and heathland.
Flight: Flies by day from May to early July (weeks 19 to 27)* and again in late July (week 30)* and August.
Larval Foodplants: Trefoils, clovers, heaths and heather.

Bordered White *Bupalus piniaria* (Linnaeus) (1954)
(Drawing on page 45)

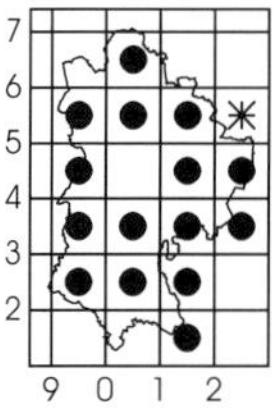

VCH: "Plentiful in all fir woods."
Post VCH: Widespread and sometimes abundant in coniferous woodland throughout the County.
Flight: Late May to August (weeks 22 to 32, peak 27 to 29)*.
Larval Foodplants: Scots pine, Corsican pine and probably other conifers.

Common White Wave *Cabera pusaria* (Linnaeus) (1955)
VCH: "Generally common in woods; the var. *rotundaria* has been found near Bedford by Mr. J. Sharpin." (See Notes)

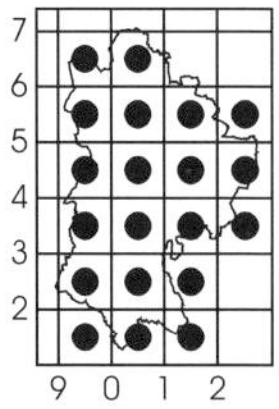

Post VCH: Common throughout the County in a variety of habitats, including woodlands and gardens.
Flight: May to September (weeks 18 to 36, peaks 24 and 28 to 30)*.
Larval Foodplants: Polyphagous on deciduous trees and shrubs.
Notes: The Round-winged White Wave (*C. rotundaria*) is described in Newman (1869) as a distinct species. Riley (1991b) explained that it is now known to be a form of *C. pusaria* which can be produced by underfeeding the larvae.

Common Wave *Cabera exanthemata* (Scopoli) (1956)

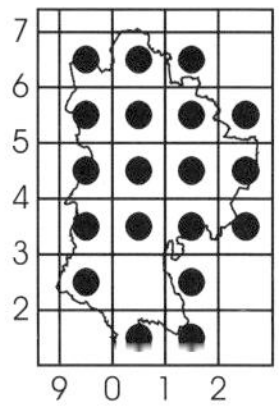

VCH: "Generally distributed."
Post VCH: Widespread in woodlands and damp areas. Less common than *C. pusaria*.
Flight: May to September (weeks 20 to 36, peak 26 to 31)*.
Larval Foodplants: Sallows and aspen.

White-pinion Spotted *Lomographa bimaculata* (Fabricius) (1957)

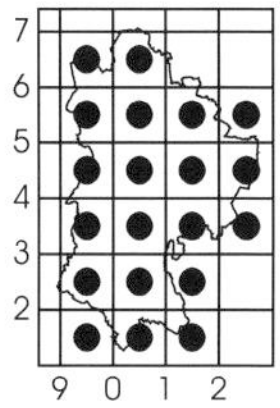

Pre VCH: J.C.Dale (MS2) recorded receiving this species from Abbot's collection from Bedford but not dated.
VCH: (as *Bapta taminata* Schiff.) "Potton, Bedford, at the edges of woods."
Post VCH: Widespread and common in a variety of woodland habitats.
Flight: May to July (weeks 20 to 28, peak 22 to 24)*.
Larval Foodplants: Blackthorn and hawthorns.

Clouded Silver *Lomographa temerata* ([Denis & Schiffermüller]) (1958)

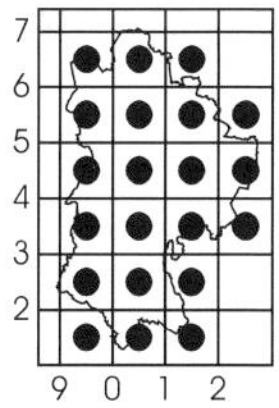

Pre VCH: J.C.Dale (MS3) recorded finding this species (as "*Phalaena Nubeculata* or *Punctata* of Mr Stephens") on 1 and 2 June 1820 at Clapham Park Wood.
VCH: "Bedford, at the margins of woods."
Post VCH: Common in woodlands and mature gardens throughout the County.
Flight: May to early August (weeks 18 to 31, peak 23 to 28)*.
Larval Foodplants: Hawthorns, blackthorn, plum, wild cherry, apple and aspen.

Early Moth *Theria primaria* (Haworth) (1960)

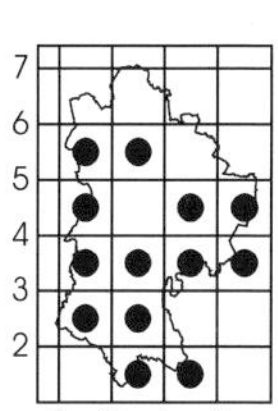

VCH: (as *Hibernia rupicapraria* Schiff.) "Bedford, Luton."
Post VCH: A local species, found throughout the County along woodland edges, rides and hedgerows.
Flight: January to March (weeks 1 to 12, peaks 5 and 10)*.
Larval Foodplants: Hawthorns and blackthorn.

For key to moth maps see page 3.

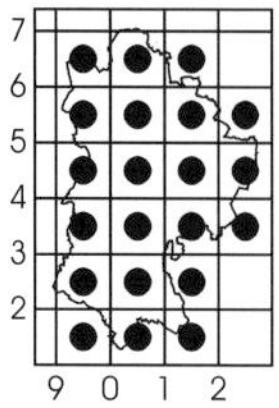

Light Emerald ***Campaea margaritata*** **(Linnaeus) (1961)**
VCH: "Generally common in woods."
Post VCH: Common throughout the County.
Flight: Late May to early September (weeks 22 to 35, peak 25 to 30)*.
Larval Foodplants: Polyphagous on deciduous trees.

Barred Red ***Hylaea fasciaria*** **(Linnaeus) (1962)**

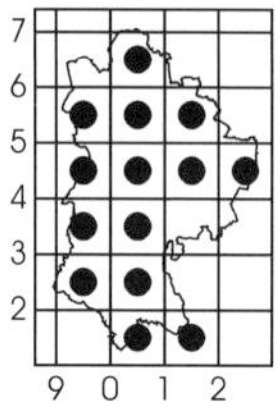

Pre VCH: J.C.Dale (MS2) recorded receiving this species (as *Prosapiaria*) from Abbot's collection from near Bedford but not dated.
VCH: "Luton, among Scotch fir."
Post VCH: A local species found in coniferous woodlands throughout the County.
Flight: June to September (weeks 23 to 38, peak 26 to 32)*.
Larval Foodplants: Various conifers including Scots pine, Norway spruce, and Douglas fir.

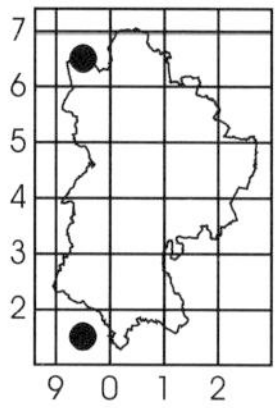

The Annulet ***Gnophos obscurata*** **([Denis & Schiffermüller]) (1964)**
Post VCH: Found at Sharnbrook Summit by W.J.Champkin on 12 July 1964 and on Bison Hill on 16 August 1995 by C.R.B.Baker.
Flight: July (week 28)* and August (week 33)*.
Larval Foodplants: Heather, bird's-foot-trefoils, common rock-rose, salad burnet and probably other herbaceous plants.

The Black-veined Moth ***Siona lineata*** **(Scopoli) (1966)**
Pre VCH: J.C.Dale (MS2) recorded receiving this species (as *Dealbata*) from Abbot's collection from near Bedford "?" but not dated. The fact that Dale queried the locality suggests that he had some doubt about the origin of the specimen(s). This species is now "confined to a few localities in south-east Kent" (Skinner, 1984).

For details of standard weeks see page 6.

Hawk-moths, Prominents and Tigers

(Sphingidae to Arctiidae)

V.W.Arnold

Family: **Sphingidae** **Hawk-moths**

This family includes the largest of the British moths. All have large bodies and may spend several minutes vibrating their wings before they become warm enough to fly. They are mostly strong fliers and some occur only as immigrants from mainland Europe. In some species the moth feeds on the wing, hovering in front of flowers drinking nectar through an unusually long proboscis. By contrast other species have no proboscis. The larva usually has a prominent 'horn' at the hind end.

Subfamily: **Sphinginae**

Eyed Hawk-moth

A varied group. Some moths are streamlined in appearance and rest with their narrow forewings held back close to their bodies. Others have broader and more irregularly-shaped wings and rest with the wings held horizontally. In these species the proboscis is less well-developed . Wingspan 70-135 mm. The larvae are marked with oblique stripes along their sides. All of the five resident and two immigrant species in Britain have been found in Bedfordshire.

Convolvulus Hawk-moth *Agrius convolvuli* (Linnaeus) (1972)
Pre VCH: A letter survives from Charles Abbot which gives a flavour of the age:

> "Dr. Abbot, with Compliments, feels very much obliged to Mr. Lee Antonie for his attention in sending to him the Moth he received this morning: it has received much damage from the mode of killing and carriage is however the *Sphinx Convolvuli*, or Unicorn Hawk Moth, which he never met with in Bedfordshire before, had it been taken in perfection, would have been a valuable acquisition to his Cabinet, which before was only possessed of one foreign specimen. Bedford. October. 1. 1809."

Other pre-VCH records are very sparse. Records from Biggleswade, Broom and Colworth were reported by Graham (1878). South (1907) mentioned Bedfordshire and Bedford (1901). Nash (1902) reported four moths at Elstow in 1901 and five larvae found in the area later that year.

VCH: "Bedford, Potton; an occasional visitor."

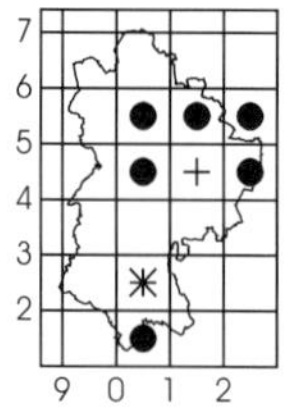

Post VCH: A rare immigrant. Reported from Bedford (1922, 1982, 1995), Biggleswade (1965), Bromham (1992), Caddington (1970), Colmworth (1995), Dunstable (1946), Everton (1983), Luton (1911) and Pavenham (1983).

Flight: Between July and November (weeks 28 and 35 to 37)*.

Larval Foodplants: Bindweeds. Nash (1902) reported "Scarlet runners or french beans".

Death's-head Hawk-moth *Acherontia atropos* (Linnaeus) (1973)

Pre VCH: Larvae were abundant in the County in 1858. They were found at Sharnbrook on potatoes and at Felmersham on *Lycium barbarum* Graham (1878). Near Luton (Jennings, 1865). Stagsden (Greenwell-Lax, 1878). Larvae were to be found in 1896 (Bond-Smith, 1896).

VCH: "Occasionally found; larva in potato fields."

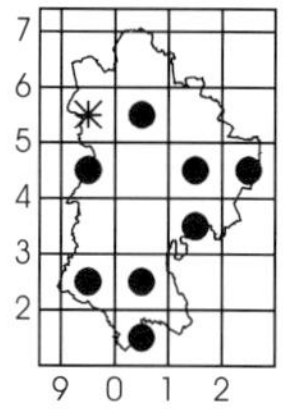

Post VCH: A rare immigrant, usually associated with potato fields, as larvae, or pupae. Reported from: Beeston in 1923 (Palmer, MS1), Bedford in 1947 (Palmer, MS2) and 1967 (Knight, 1967), Biggleswade in 1974 and 1982, Billington in 1982, Clifton in 1990, Cranfield in 1991, Kensworth in 1970, Luton in 1941 and 1964, Pavenham in 1958 and 1959 and Sandy in 1996.

Flight: May to September (weeks 36 and 38)*.

Larval Foodplants: Potato* and in captivity, on garden privet.

Privet Hawk-moth *Sphinx ligustri* Linnaeus (1976)

Pre VCH: Abbot (MS1) noted rearing this species in 1799.

VCH: "Generally distributed, larva on privet hedges."

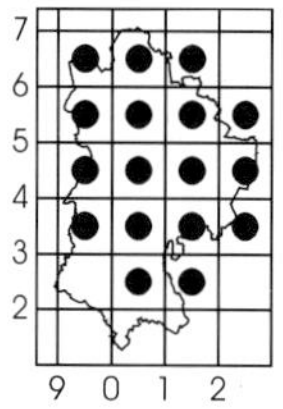

Post VCH: A local species, found in woods and gardens throughout the County. It comes readily to light, but a number of records are from finds of larvae. Both R.C.Revels from Biggleswade and K.F.Webb from Luton recalled that in the late 1950s and early 1960s the larva of this species was very plentiful and easy to collect. Revels (pers. comm., 1995) recorded in his diary finding 70 on 2 September 1962 and 30 on 27 August 1963, all feeding on privet hedges or on small ash trees. Such numbers have not been reported in recent years.

Flight: Late May (week 21)*, June and July (weeks 26 to 30)*.

Larval Foodplants: Privets*, lilac*, ash*, holly*, annual garden scabious* and cultivated species of *Viburnum** (Revels, 1971).

For details of standard weeks see page 6.

Pine Hawk-moth *Hyloicus pinastri* (Linnaeus) (1978)
(Plate 52 and drawing on page 42)
Post VCH: A species that is usually found in the coniferous plantations on the Greensand Ridge. S.H.Kershaw's notebook contains records of *pinastri* at Aspley Heath from 1935 on but the records are ambiguous as the same specific name appears to have been used for more than one other species. Pine Hawk-moth has been found at Bunkers Hill, Sandy, Maulden Wood, Rowney Warren, Stockgrove Country Park and The Lodge, Sandy. Sometimes it is abundant at Aspley Heath and Aspley Guise where J.B.Barnwell has watched the moths feeding at honeysuckle. (See also Webb, 1984a.) It is occasionally recorded from other areas of the County, as in 1995 when it came to light at Little Staughton and West Wood.

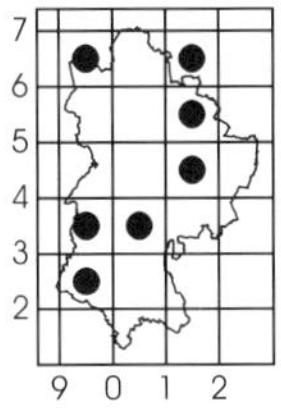

Flight: June and July (weeks 24 to 30)★.
Larval Foodplants: Scots pine★ and Norway spruce.

Lime Hawk-moth *Mimas tiliae* (Linnaeus) (1979)
Pre VCH: J.C.Dale (MS2) recorded receiving this species from Abbot's collection from Bedford but not dated. Abbot (MS1) noted rearing it in 1799.
VCH: "Widely distributed, about limes and elms."
Post VCH: Found fairly commonly throughout the County, in areas where its foodplants occur.
Flight: April to July (weeks 17 to 27)★.
Larval Foodplants: Limes★, English elm★, alder and birches. Also on the purple cultivar of Norway maple★ in Cockayne Hatley in August 1995.

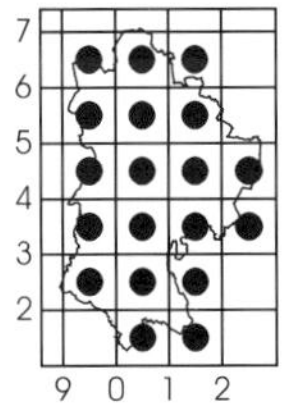

Eyed Hawk-moth *Smerinthus ocellata* (Linnaeus) (1980)
(Drawing on page 309)
Pre VCH: J.C.Dale (MS3) recorded finding this species on 14 July 1819 "by ye river Ouze" and on 31 May and 1 June 1820 in Clapham Park Wood. Elsewhere (MS2) he noted receiving this species from Abbot's collection from Bedford but not dated.
VCH: "Bedford, Potton, common at Woburn."
Post VCH: Widely distributed but not common. Found in gardens and woodlands.
Flight: May to July (weeks 21 to 29)★.
Larval Foodplants: Apple★, willows★, sallows★ and aspen.

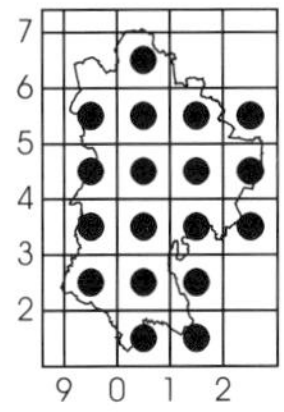

Poplar Hawk-moth *Laothoe populi* (Linnaeus) (1981)
Pre VCH: J.C.Dale (MS2) recorded receiving this species from Abbot's collection from Bedford but not dated. Abbot (MS1) noted rearing it in 1799.
VCH: "Generally distributed, on poplars."
Post VCH: Common throughout the County.
Flight: May to August (weeks 19 to 36, peak 21 to 22)★.
Larval Foodplants: Poplars★, willows, aspen and sallows.

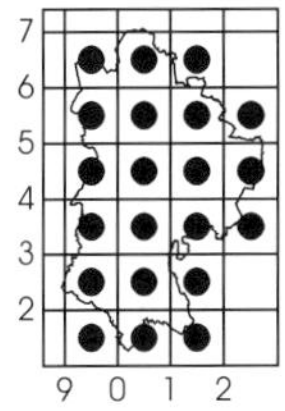

For key to moth maps see page 3.

Subfamily: **Macroglossinae**

All the species in this subfamily have narrow, sharply-pointed, forewings and rest with the wings held horizontally. Wingspan 41-115 mm. Three species fly by day. The larvae do not have lateral stripes and some have remarkable colour patterns. All the four resident and four of the six immigrant species in Britain have been found in Bedfordshire.

Broad-bordered Bee Hawk-moth

Narrow-bordered Bee Hawk-moth *Hemaris tityus* (Linnaeus) (1982)

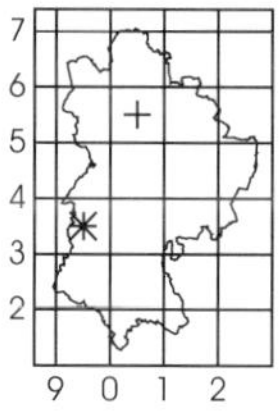

VCH: as *Macroglossa bombyliformis* Esp. "Dr. Nash also records this species in woods near Bedford."
Post VCH: S.H.Kershaw noted a female "searching for scabious" in King's Wood, Heath and Reach on 2 June 1955. He also noted a "Bee Hawk" in the wood on 28 May 1953 but did not identify it to species.
Flight: Flies by day in May and June.
Larval Foodplant: Devils'-bit scabious.

Broad-bordered Bee Hawk-moth *Hemaris fuciformis* (Linnaeus) (1983)

Pre VCH: J.C.Dale (MS2) recorded receiving this species from Abbot's collection from near Bedford but not dated.

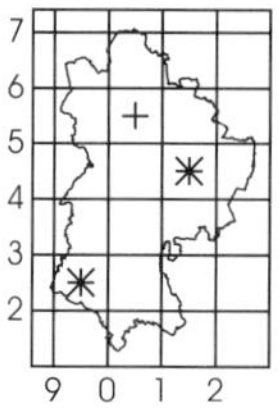

VCH: "Dr. Nash records this species in woods near Bedford."
Post VCH: Foster (1934) states "Rowney Warren in 1905 by C.Down". Recorded at King's Wood, Heath and Reach in July 1945 by R.F.Bretherton (pers. comm.). Also listed from King's Wood and Baker's Wood, Heath and Reach by J.M.Schofield (pre 1970).
Flight: Flies by day in May, June and July*.
Larval Foodplant: Honeysuckle.

Humming-bird Hawk-moth *Macroglossum stellatarum* (Linnaeus) (1984)

(Plate 94)
Pre VCH: In a note to the Linnean Society dated 1 November 1798, Charles Abbot mentioned that he took it twice "this last summer" and bred it once. As his moth emerged in October, he disputed Donovan's conclusion that this species overwintered as a pupa. Emily Shore gave a good description of this species in her diary for 21 July 1835, seen at Everton (Anon, 1891).

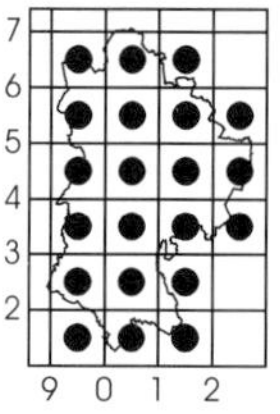

VCH: "Generally distributed; to be seen occasionally in gardens, hovering at tubular flowers."
Post VCH: Found throughout the County. As an immigrant this species can occur anywhere. The moth is most often seen in gardens hovering in front of flowers of buddleia, red valerian, honeysuckle and petunia.
Flight: Flies by day. Most records are from June to October, but it was recorded in Bedford in November 1959 and 1976. A recently dead specimen was found in Bedford on 12 February 1960.
Larval Foodplants: Hedge-bedstraw, lady's bedstraw* and wild madder.

For details of standard weeks see page 6.

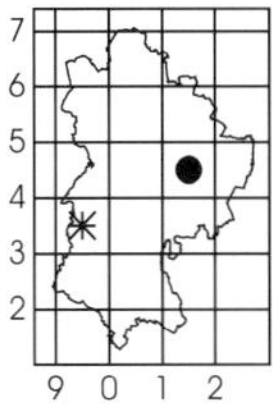

Bedstraw Hawk-moth *Hyles gallii* (Rottemburg) (1987)
Post VCH: A very rare immigrant. S.H.Kershaw found this species at Aspley Heath in June 1943 and R.C.Revels had single specimens in his light-trap in Biggleswade in 1987 and 1989.
Flight: May to August (week 30)★.
Larval Foodplants: Bedstraws, willowherbs and fuchsia.

Striped Hawk-moth *Hyles livornica* (Esper)(= *lineata* (Fabricius) ssp. *livornica* (Esper)) (1990)
Post VCH: R.F.Bretherton in Heath and Emmet (1979) recorded this immigrant species for VC30 Bedfordshire. Later he stated (pers. comm.) "that this was an error."

Elephant Hawk-moth *Deilephila elpenor* (Linnaeus) (1991)
Pre VCH: Abbot (MS1) reared this species in 1799. Steuart (1891b) found larvae of this species on purple loosestrife on the banks of the River Ouse. Recorded in the minute book of the Bedford Amateur Natural History Society for 15 July 1896 as found in Bedford.
VCH: "Bedford, Woburn."

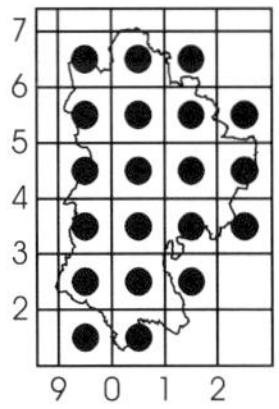

Post VCH: Common throughout the County. The larvae are often found feeding on cultivated fuchsias resulting in newspaper articles, where they are reported as resembling anything from a snake to a gecko!
Flight: May to July (weeks 22 to 31)★.
Larval Foodplants: Rosebay willowherb★ and other willowherbs, bedstraws★, fuchsia★, grape-vine★, orange balsam★, purple-loosestrife★ and bogbean★.

Small Elephant Hawk-moth *Deilephila porcellus* (Linnaeus) (1992) (Plate 53)
Pre VCH: Steuart (1891b) reported finding larvae of this species on purple loosestrife on the banks of the River Ouse. Recorded in the minute book of the Bedford Amateur Natural History Society for 15 July 1896 as found in Bedford and "a remarkable capture of 32 by a gentleman at Elstow".

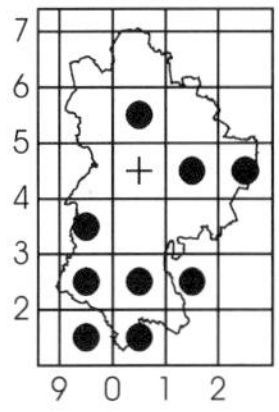

VCH: "Bedford, Potton; among ladies' bedstraw."
Post VCH: Usually an uncommon and local species but can be abundant on occasions. Widely distributed, most often found on chalk downlands or heathlands. Stockgrove Country Park has proved a good site for this species.
Flight: May to July (weeks 22 to 28)★.
Larval Foodplants: Lady's bedstraw★ and other bedstraws, and purple-loosestrife★.

Silver-striped Hawk-moth *Hippotion celerio* (Linnaeus) (1993)
VCH: "Dr. Nash reports 'A specimen is said to have been taken in Bedford, twenty years ago' ".
Post VCH: This immigrant species has been found once, at Milton Ernest on 6 December 1948 by J.B.Purser (Dannreuther, 1949; Palmer, 1949). Newman (1952) illustrated the actual specimen from B.B.West's collection.
Flight: Between May and December.
Larval Foodplants: Bedstraws, fuchsia, willowherbs, grape-vine and virginia creeper.

For key to moth maps see page 3.

Family: **Notodontidae** **The Prominents**

The family gets its name from the protruding tufts of scales on the forewings of some of the species. The moth has a proboscis but usually does not feed. Wingspan 24-80 mm. The larvae often rest with the head and tail segments raised. Those of some species, such as the Puss Moth and Lobster Moth, have unusually complicated shapes. There are 22 resident species in Britain of which 20 have been found in Bedfordshire.

Buff-tip

Buff-tip *Phalera bucephala* (Linnaeus) (1994)

Pre VCH: Abbot (MS1) noted 23 September 1799 "Twenty larvae of *Phalaena bucephala* found by Mrs Abbot on a young lime tree in St. Paul's Churchyard - The wind was at North and the stone coping was covered with their excrement which was the cause of her making the discovery." "One appeared from Pupa May 31 1800. Two more June 2nd". Graham (1878) reported "most destructive to elm-trees. I saw many young elms completely defoliated by the larvae at Sharnbrook one year".

VCH: "Generally common."

Post VCH: Common in a variety of woodland habitats.

Flight: May to August (weeks 19 to 33, peak 25 to 30)★

Larval Foodplants: Oaks★, willows★, limes★, elms★, birches★ and other deciduous trees and shrubs.

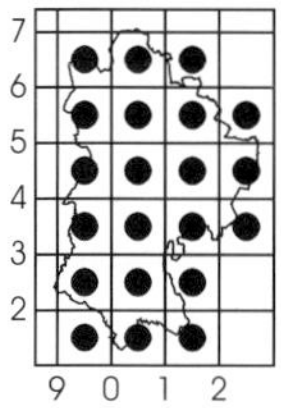

Puss Moth *Cerura vinula* (Linnaeus) (1995) (Plates 31 and 32)

Pre VCH: Abbot (MS1) recorded rearing this species in 1799 but did not note where he found it.

VCH: "Generally distributed among willow."

Post VCH: Local and uncommon but generally distributed.

Flight: May to July (weeks 19 to 29)★. Many records are of larvae.

Larval Foodplants: Aspen★, willows★, poplars★, sallows★.

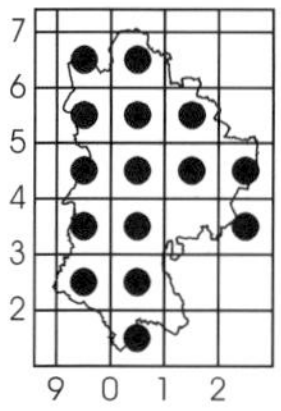

Sallow Kitten *Furcula furcula* (Clerck) (1997)

Pre VCH: J.C.Dale (MS2) recorded receiving this species from Abbot's collection from near Bedford but not dated.

VCH: "Bedford, Luton; about sallow."

Post VCH: Local and uncommon but generally distributed.

Flight: May and June (weeks 18 to 25)★ and again in August (weeks 30 to 34)★, in two broods.

Larval Foodplants: Sallows, aspen and poplars.

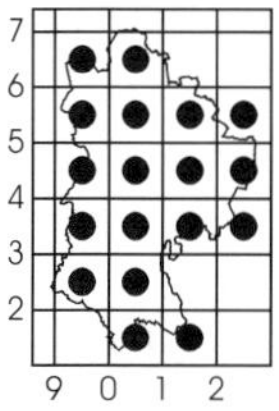

Poplar Kitten *Furcula bifida* (Brahm) (1998)

VCH: "Recorded at Bedford by Dr. W.G.Nash."

Post VCH: A scarce and local species found in woods where its larval foodplants occur. Examples are Coppice Wood, Flitwick Moor, Marston Thrift and Maulden Wood.

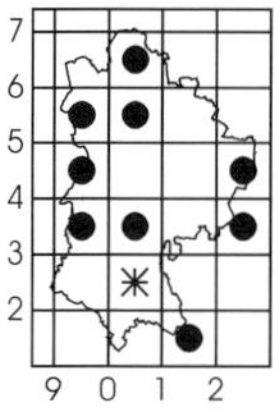

For details of standard weeks see page 6.

Flight: May to August (weeks 21 to 33)*.
Larval Foodplants: Aspen, poplars and sallows.

Lobster Moth *Stauropus fagi* (Linnaeus) (1999)
Post VCH: S.H.Kershaw noted this species in his light-trap at Aspley Heath in 1934-37, 1947-48, 1950 and 1953 but it is currently a scarce and local species found in mature woodlands, such as Aspley Heath, Maulden Wood and King's Wood, Heath and Reach. Occasionally it is found in gardens.
Flight: May to July (weeks 22 to 29)*.
Larval Foodplants: Beech*, oaks*, birches and hazel.

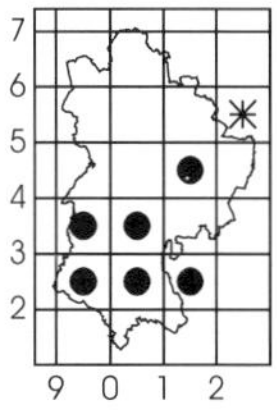

Iron Prominent *Notodonta dromedarius* (Linnaeus) (2000)
VCH: "Luton."
Post VCH: Common throughout the County.
Flight: May to August (weeks 18 to 35)*, in two overlapping broods.
Larval Foodplants: Birches, alder, hazel and oaks.

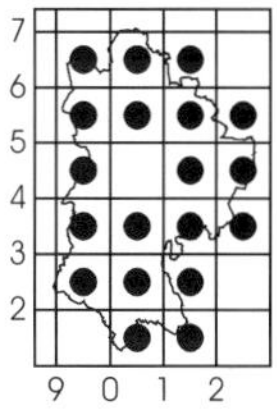

Three-humped Prominent *Tritophia tritophus* ([Denis & Schiffermüller]) (2002)
Post VCH: A specimen of this rare immigrant was captured in Bedford on 13 May 1907 by W.S.Brocklehurst (Brocklehurst, 1908a, 1908b). South (1939) mentions this record. R.M.Craske recalled that Nash and Brocklehurst kept this specimen in their respective collections for six months at a time until Nash died in 1935.

Pebble Prominent *Eligmodonta ziczac* (Linnaeus) (2003)
VCH: "Bedford."
Post VCH: Common throughout the County.
Flight: May to August, in two broods (weeks 18 to 35)*.
Larval Foodplants: Sallows, aspen, willows* and poplars.

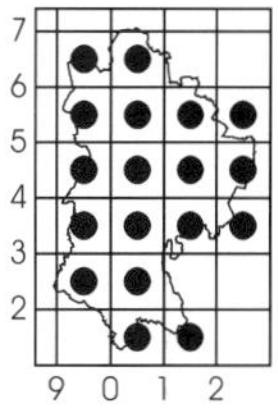

Great Prominent *Peridea anceps* (Goeze) (2005)

Post VCH: A local species which can be abundant where it occurs. A specimen in the Kershaw collection is labelled "Aspley Heath 1936" and his notebook contains records for 1935, 1946, 1951 and 1953. Locations where this species has been recorded more recently include: The Lodge at Sandy, Aspley Heath, Aspley Guise, Stockgrove Country Park and King's Wood, Heath and Reach.

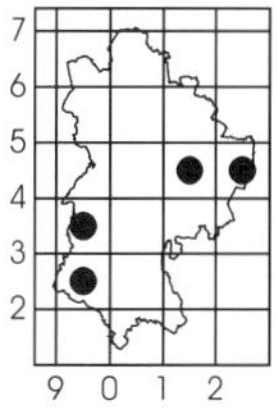

Flight: April, May (weeks 18 to 22)* and June.
Larval Foodplants: Oaks.

Lesser Swallow Prominent *Pheosia gnoma* (Fabricius) (2006)

Post VCH: Locally common throughout the County. Recorded in S.H. Kershaw's notebooks from Aspley Heath between 1934 and 1952.
Flight: April to June and again in August and September, in two broods (weeks 17 to 38, peaks 18 to 20 and 32 to 36)*.
Larval Foodplants: Birches.

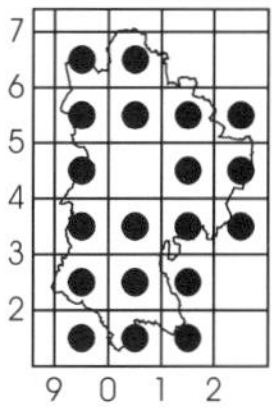

For key to moth maps see page 3.

Swallow Prominent *Pheosia tremula* (Clerck) (2007)
VCH: "Bedford, Luton; among poplar."
Post VCH: Widely distributed and common throughout the County.
Flight: April to June (weeks 17 to 25)* and again in August (weeks 30 to 34)*, in two broods.
Larval Foodplants: Poplars, aspen, sallows and willows.

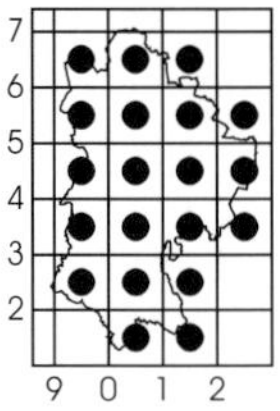

Coxcomb Prominent *Ptilodon capucina* (Linnaeus) (2008)
VCH: (as *Lophopteryx camelina* Linn.) "Bedford, Luton."
Post VCH: Common throughout the County.
Flight: May to September, in two broods which probably overlap (weeks 18 to 36, peaks 23 to 25 and 28 to 33)*.
Larval Foodplants: . Polyphagous on deciduous trees, including beech*, oaks* and birches*.

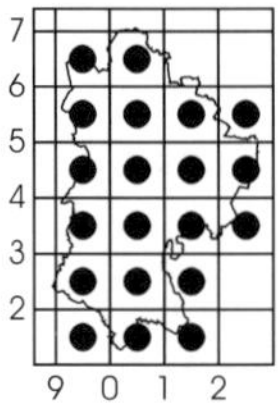

Maple Prominent *Ptilodontella cucullina* ([Denis & Schiffermüller]) (2009)
Post VCH: An uncommon species found throughout the County, usually in woodlands.
Flight: June to August (weeks 25 to 32)*.
Larval Foodplants: Field maple and sycamore*.

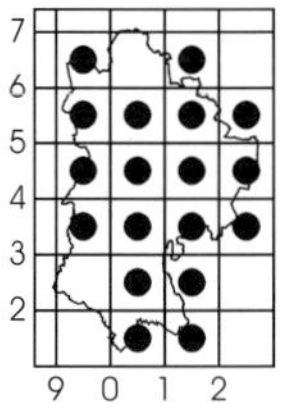

Scarce Prominent *Odontosia carmelita* (Esper) (2010)
Post VCH: A scarce and local species. Specimens in the Kershaw collection from Aspley Heath are dated 6 May 1936, May 1937 and 1939 and his notebooks also contain records for 1932, 1935 and 1950. It was not recorded again until April 1981 when several moths were attracted to light at Aspley Heath and Flitwick Moor. Since then it has been found in several mature birch woodlands in the County.
Flight: April and May (weeks 16 to 19)*.
Larval Foodplants: Birches.

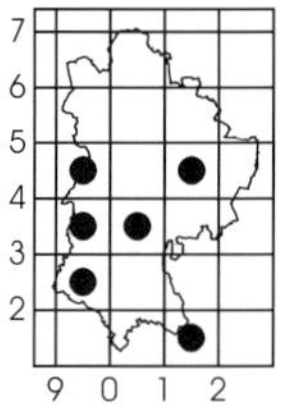

Pale Prominent *Pterostoma palpina* (Clerck) (2011)
Pre VCH: J.C.Dale (MS2) recorded receiving this species from Abbot's collection from near Bedford but not dated.
VCH: "Bedford, Potton; among poplar."
Post VCH: Common throughout the County.
Flight: Late April to the end of August, in two broods which may overlap (weeks 17 to 35 with the largest numbers in 30 to 33).
Larval Foodplants: Sallows*, aspen and willows.

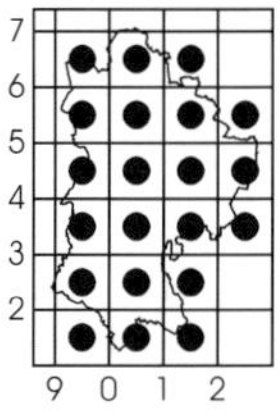

For details of standard weeks see page 6.

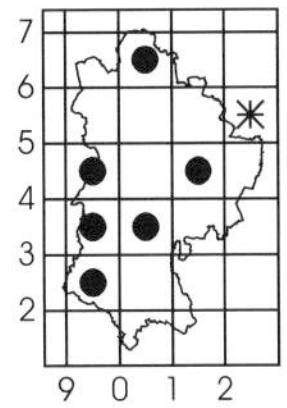

Marbled Brown *Drymonia dodonaea* ([Denis & Schiffermüller]) (2014)
Post VCH: A local and uncommon species which is found in old oak woods such as Maulden Wood and King's Wood, Heath and Reach. Recorded in S.H.Kershaw's notebooks from Aspley Heath in 1935-38, 1946 and 1948-49.
Flight: May to July (weeks 20 to 28, peak 22 to 26)*.
Larval Foodplants: Oaks.

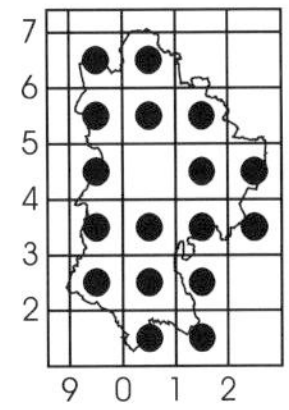

Lunar Marbled Brown *Drymonia ruficornis* (Hufnagel) (2015)
Post VCH: An uncommon species found in oak woodlands throughout the County. Recorded in S.H.Kershaw's notebooks from Aspley Heath in 1934 and 1946-48.
Flight: April to June (weeks 16 to 25)*.
Larval Foodplants: Oaks.

Small Chocolate-tip *Clostera pigra* (Hufnagel) (2017)
Pre VCH: J.C.Dale (MS2) listed this species (as *Reclusus*) in his collection catalogue "Clapham Park Wood Bedford J.C.Dale beat from hazle [*sic*] May 30 1820." However, in his diary (MS3) for that day he recorded finding *Bombyx Curtulus* and it is the Chocolate Tip, side-labelled "n Bedford", that remains in the Dale collection. So it seems possible that the entry in his collection catalogue may be an error. However, Haworth (1803) reported Abbot's finding this species "*in Bedfordia*". Not recorded since.

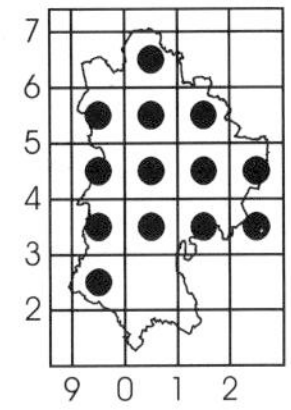

Chocolate-tip *Clostera curtula* (Linnaeus) (2019)
Pre VCH: J.C.Dale (MS3) recorded finding this species on 30 May 1820. The first entry for the day refers to "nr Bedford" so it is likely that all the specimens listed were found there, probably in Clapham Park Wood (see previous species). The Dale collection contains four specimens side-labelled "n Bedford".
Post VCH: An uncommon and local species which is found in damp woodlands throughout the County. Recorded in S.H.Kershaw's notebooks from Aspley Heath in 1947.
Flight: May to August, in two broods (weeks 18 to 33)*.
Larval Foodplants: Aspen, poplars, sallows and willows.

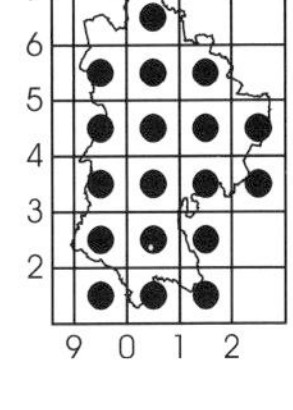

Figure of Eight *Diloba caeruleocephala* (Linnaeus) (2020)
VCH: "Generally common."
Post VCH: Common and widespread in woodlands and areas of scrub.
Flight: September to November (weeks 39 to 46, peak 41 to 43)*.
Larval Foodplants: Hawthorns*, blackthorn, apple and probably other trees.

For key to moth maps see page 3.

Family: **Lymantriidae The Tussocks**

Most of the moths in this family are nocturnal and have a ground colour of white or grey. The Vapourer differs in that the males are brown and fly in the daytime while the females are wingless. Wingspan 34-70 mm. Most of the larvae have hairs that are urticating to some extent, some extremely so. Of the ten British species, seven have been found in Bedfordshire.

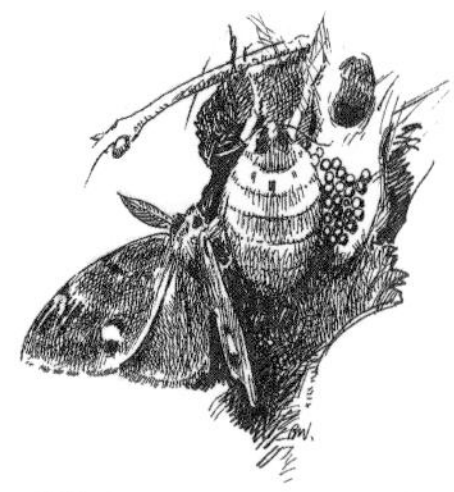

Vapourer - male and wingless female

The Vapourer *Orgyia antiqua* (Linnaeus) (2026)
VCH: "Common everywhere, and conspicuous in the autumn by its lively dancing flight, about roads and shrubberies, in the sunshine."
Post VCH: Widespread, but local. The males are most often seen and the VCH (above) describes their flight well. Appears to be less common than formerly.
Flight: July to October (weeks 31 to 43)★.
Larval Foodplants: Birches★, blackthorn★, elms★, hawthorns★, oaks★, roses★, rowan★ and other deciduous trees and shrubs. Has also been found on *Cotoneaster horizontalis*★, honeysuckle★, pelargonium★ and mistletoe★.

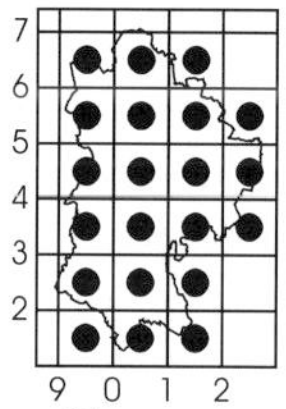

Dark Tussock *Dicallomera fascelina* (Linnaeus) (2027)
Pre VCH: Abbot (MS1) noted the dates in June 1799 when larvae of *Phal. Fascelina* that he was rearing "spun up" and recorded the time spent in the pupal stage. Unfortunately he did not note where he found the larvae.
VCH: "Taken near Bedford, by Dr. W.G.Nash."
Post VCH: Not recorded.
Flight: July and August.
Larval Foodplants: Heather, sallows, broom, hawthorns and brambles.

Pale Tussock *Calliteara pudibunda* (Linnaeus) (2028)
VCH: "Bedford, Potton."
Post VCH: Common and sometimes abundant throughout the County.
Flight: May and June (weeks 18 to 26, peak 21 to 24)★.
Larval Foodplants: Polyphagous on deciduous trees and shrubs.

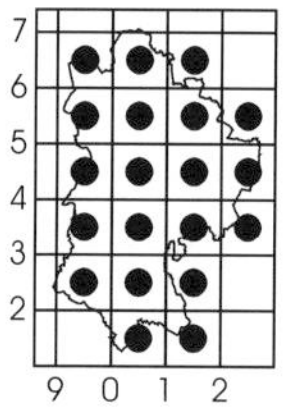

Brown-tail *Euproctis chrysorrhoea* (Linnaeus) (2029)
Pre VCH: Reports of *chrysorrhoea* in Marsh (MS1) and Steuart (1891b) may refer either to this species or the next as the name has been applied to both.
VCH: "Reported at Bedford by the Rev. W.O.Harries, and at Woburn by Mr. H.Studman."

For details of standard weeks see page 6.

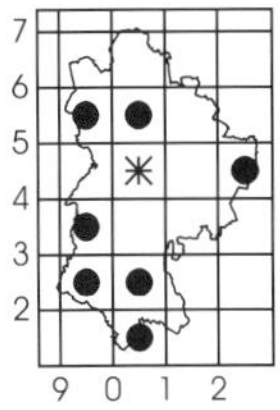

Post VCH: Reported mainly as singletons in light-traps at a variety of sites. There is little evidence that the Browntail breeds in the County; records probable reflect chance immigration.
Flight: July and August (weeks 28 and 30)*.
Larval Foodplants: Polyphagous on deciduous trees and shrubs.
Notes: The hairs on the larvae are strongly urticating and can cause intense irritation. They should be handled with great care.

Yellow-tail *Euproctis similis* (Fuessly) (2030)
Pre VCH: Noted at Everton on 21 July 1835 by Emily Shore as Brown-tail, *Porthesia auriflua*, "tail is yellow-brown"(Anon, 1891).
VCH: "Generally common on hawthorn hedges."

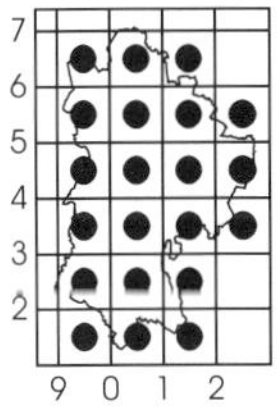

Post VCH: Common, sometimes abundant.
Flight: June to September (weeks 25 to 38, peak 27 to 34)*.
Larval Foodplants: Apple*, blackthorn*, brambles*, elder*, hawthorns* and other deciduous trees and shrubs.
Notes: The hairs on the larvae are strongly urticating and can cause intense irritation. They should be handled with great care.

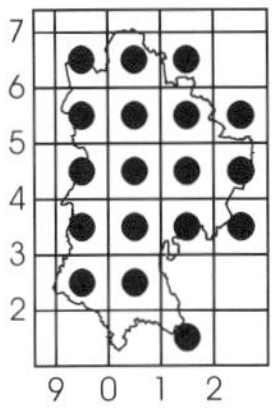

White Satin *Leucoma salicis* (Linnaeus) (2031)
VCH: "Bedford, Potton; about willow or poplar."
Post VCH: Local and uncommon, but widely distributed throughout the County.
Flight: July and August (weeks 27 to 32)*.
Larval Foodplants: Poplars, sallows and willows.

Black Arches *Lymantria monacha* (Linnaeus) (2033) (Plate 40)

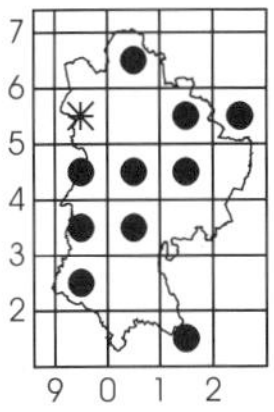

Post VCH: A woodland species that can be abundant where it occurs. R.M.Craske recalled this species as "very local at Salem Thrift between 1918 and 1927". "Old Warden by Dr. Nash" (Foster, 1934). Recorded in S.H. Kershaw's notebooks from Aspley Heath only in 1935, 1936, 1947 and 1955. His collection contains a specimen labelled "Aspley Heath 1936". Currently found for example at Aspley Guise, Coppice Wood, Flitwick Moor, Luton Hoo, Old Warden and The Lodge, Sandy.
Flight: July and August (weeks 30 to 33)*.
Larval Foodplants: Oaks*.

For key to moth maps see page 3.

Family: **Arctiidae**

Subfamily: **Lithosiinae** **The Footman moths**

Common Footman

The moths are narrow-winged, mostly greyish or straw coloured. Their probosces are well developed and they feed actively. Wing-span 19-55 mm. The larvae are slightly hairy and feed on lichens. Ten of the 17 British species have been found in Bedfordshire.

Round-winged Muslin *Thumatha senex* (Hübner) (2035)

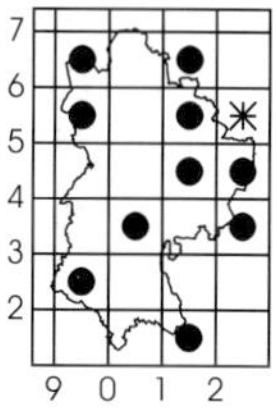

Post VCH: Local and uncommon. Found in fens and marshes, such as Flitwick Moor (1977, 1978, 1980) and in woodland areas, such as The Lodge, Sandy (1973, 1989, 1990) and West Wood (1990). This species has also been found in the RIS traps at Eaton Bray (1994) and Cockayne Hatley (1983-1985, 1987, 1990, 1991, 1993, 1994).
Flight: July (weeks 27 to 30)*.

Larval Foodplants: Various mosses and lichens.

Rosy Footman *Miltochrista miniata* (Forster) (2037) (Plate 54)

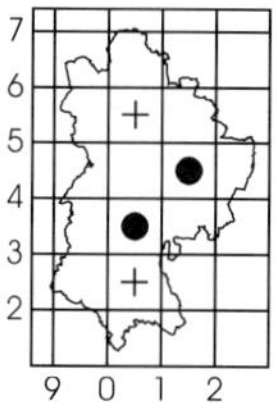

VCH: "Bedford, Luton."
Post VCH: A local species that can be abundant where it is found: Clophill Sand Quarry (1984), Maulden Wood (1983, 1989), Warren Wood (1983) and at Sandy at Stratford Lane (1959) and The Lodge (RIS trap in 1969-75, MV light in 1989-1991 and 1994).
Flight: June to August (weeks 26 to 33, peak 26 to 31)*.

Larval Foodplants: Lichens growing on trees.

Muslin Footman *Nudaria mundana* (Linnaeus) (2038)

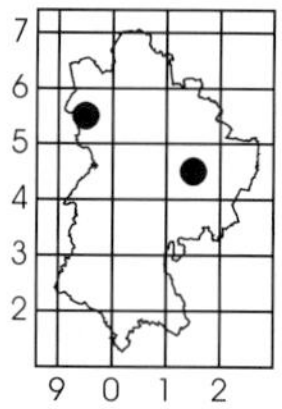

Post VCH: Scarce and very local: Felmersham Nature Reserve (1979), Sharnbrook (1979, 1986) and The Lodge, Sandy (RIS trap in 1972, MV light in 1989). Also in G.Ping's collection from Carlton 1984-86.
Flight: June (week 25)*, July (weeks 28 to 30)* and August.
Larval Foodplants: Lichens growing on walls and fences.

Red-necked Footman *Atolmis rubricollis* (Linnaeus) (2039)
Pre VCH: J.C.Dale (MS3) recorded finding *L. Rubricollis* in Clapham Park Wood on 1 June 1820. Not recorded since.

Four-dotted Footman *Cybosia mesomella* (Linnaeus) (2040)

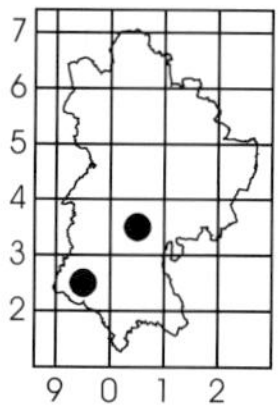

Post VCH: "Reported from Flitwick Marsh by Nash and Brocklehurst" (Foster, 1934). A specimen was caught at Flitwick Moor on 22 June 1977 and another at Stockgrove Country Park on 21 June 1996 by V.W.Arnold.
Flight: June (week 25)* to August.
Larval Foodplants: Lichens and algae.

For details of standard weeks see page 6.

Dingy Footman *Eilema griseola* (Hübner) (2044)

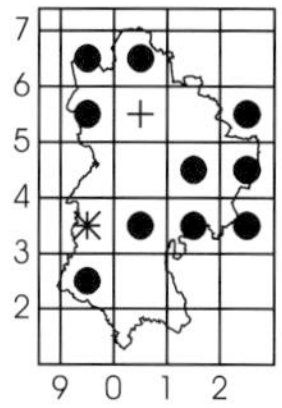

VCH: "Bedford."
Post VCH: Local and uncommon but widespread in damp woodlands, such as Flitwick Moor.
Flight: July and August(weeks 26 to 35, peak 29 to 33)*.
Larval Foodplants: Lichens.

Scarce Footman *Eilema complana* (Linnaeus) (2047)

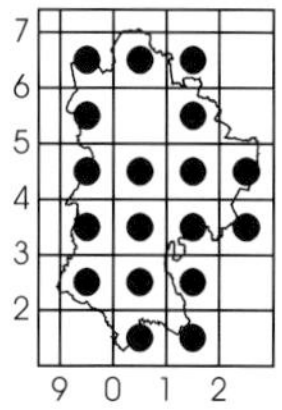

Pre VCH: J.C.Dale (MS3) recorded finding this species on 15 July 1819, probably near Bedford.
VCH: "Taken near Potton by Mr. W.Bond-Smith."
Post VCH: Local and uncommon but widespread in damp woodlands throughout the County. In the Kershaw collection there is a specimen of the Scarce Footman from Aspley Heath dated 7 September 1943. It has grey scales on the hindwings resembling the Northern Footman, *Eilema sericea*. His notebook also records it there in 1936, 1946, 1947 and 1948.
Flight: June to September (weeks 25 to 36, peak 27 to 33)*.
Larval Foodplants: Lichens.

Buff Footman *Eilema deplana* (Esper) (2049)

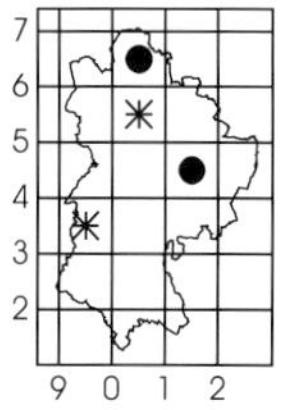

Post VCH: A scarce and local species. R.M.Craske recalled that the Buff Footman was "local in Bedford and Clapham" between 1918 and 1927. The Kershaw collection contains specimens from Aspley Heath dated 30 July 1934 and 18 July 1952. More recently found at Coppice Wood (1986, 1989) and in the RIS traps at Old Warden (1974) and The Lodge, Sandy (1969, 1970; also at MV light in 1990).
Flight: June, July and August (weeks 26 and 29 to 32)*.
Larval Foodplants: Lichens and algae, growing on trees.

Common Footman *Eilema lurideola* (Zincken) (2050)

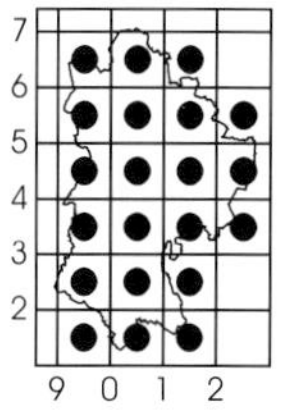

(Drawing on page 320)
VCH: "Taken at lamps near Bedford and Luton."
Post VCH: Common and widespread.
Flight: May to September (weeks 22 to 39, peak 26 to 33)*.
Larval Foodplants: Lichens and algae growing on fences, trees and walls.

Four-spotted Footman *Lithosia quadra* (Linnaeus) (2051)
Post VCH: Recorded in S.H.Kershaw's notebook from Aspley Heath on 31 July 1946. This individual was probably an immigrant.
Flight: June to August.
Larval Foodplants: Lichens.

For key to moth maps see page 3.

Subfamily: **Arctiinae** **The Tiger Moths**

Cinnabar - moth and larva

The colouring and size of the moths in this subfamily are very variable. Some species, such as the Garden Tiger and Cinnabar, have brightly coloured hindwings while others, such as the Ermines, are plainly coloured. Wingspans range from 28 to 78 mm. The moth usually has only a small proboscis and does not feed. The larvae are often very hairy and may be urticating. Of the 14 British species, 11 have been found in Bedfordshire.

Crimson Speckled *Utetheisa pulchella* (Linnaeus) (2054)
Pre VCH: "Taken by Dr Nash at Biggleswade in 1875" (Foster, 1934). Other finds were reported by King (1875) and F.W.F. (1895).
VCH: "One specimen taken near County School by Dr. Nash, July 1894."
Post VCH: This immigrant species has been recorded only once (Nash, 1924). It is also described in Stevens' catalogue for the sale of Nash's collection on 11 February 1936, "*pulchella* - a very fine and perfect female, Bedford 29/5/24, Dr Nash".

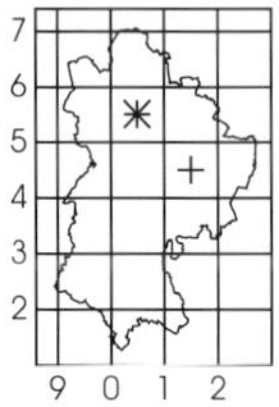

Wood Tiger *Parasemia plantaginis plantaginis* (Linnaeus) (2056)
Pre VCH: J.C.Dale (MS3) recorded finding this species in Clapham Park Wood between 30 May and 1 June 1820 and noted "no females took 4 males". There are three specimens, side-labelled "n. Bedford" in the Dale collection.
Post VCH: Scarce and local. Recorded from chalk downlands between Bison Hill and Dunstable, flying in bright sunshine (1959, 1965, 1975, 1978, 1982). Also listed by Schofield from King's Wood and Baker's Wood, Heath and Reach but the finder and the date are not known.
Flight: May, June (weeks 23 and 24)*, July. Active during the day but also flies at night.
Larval Foodplants: Polyphagous on herbaceous plants.

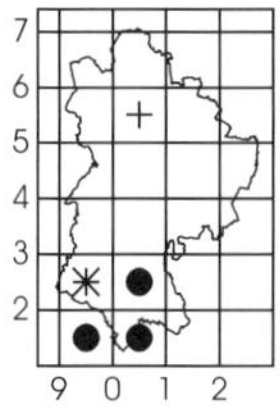

Garden Tiger *Arctia caja* (Linnaeus) (2057) (Plate 92)
Pre VCH: Abbot (MS1) noted rearing this species in 1799.
VCH: "Everywhere common."
Post VCH: Widespread but seems less common in recent years.
Flight: June to August (weeks 25 to 34, peak 27 to 32)*.
Larval Foodplants: Burdocks*, docks*, nettles*, dandelions* and other herbaceous plants.

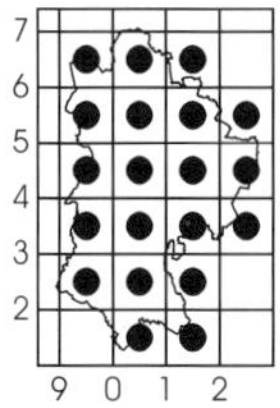

Cream-spot Tiger *Arctia villica* (Linnaeus) ssp. *britannica* Oberthür (2058)
VCH: "Reported by Mr. W.Bond-Smith at Potton." (Foster's (1916) report "Cream-spot Tiger at Potton" may refer to the same record.)
Post VCH: Two records only: Bunkers Hill, Sandy on 27 May 1960 and larvae feeding on tamarisk in Bedford, (no date) (West, 1961).
Flight: May (week 21)* and June.

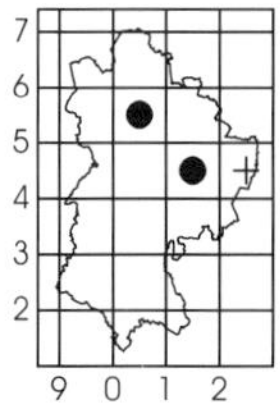

For details of standard weeks see page 6.

Larval Foodplants: Polyphagous on herbaceous plants. Also tamarisk★.

Clouded Buff ***Diacrisia sannio*** **(Linnaeus) (2059)**

Pre VCH: Recorded by T.Orlebar Marsh (MS1), as *Phalaena Russula* "1798, Clapham".
Post VCH: R.M.Craske recalled finding this species at "Sharpenhoe between 1920 and 1925". Also recorded in S.H.Kershaw's notebook from Aspley Heath on 31 July 1949 and 20 August 1955.
Flight: June and July. Active during the day but also flies at night.
Larval Foodplants: Polyphagous on herbaceous plants, including heaths and heather.

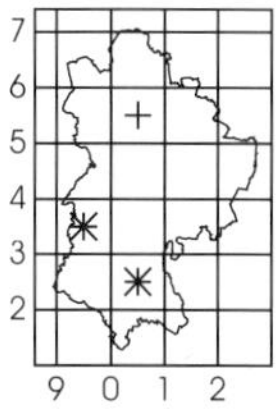

White Ermine ***Spilosoma lubricipeda*** **(Linnaeus) (2060)**

VCH: (as *S. menthastri* Schiff.) "Common everywhere."
Post VCH: Widespread and common.
Flight: May to July (weeks 18 to 30, peak 20 to 28)★.
Larval Foodplants: Chickweed★ and other herbaceous plants.

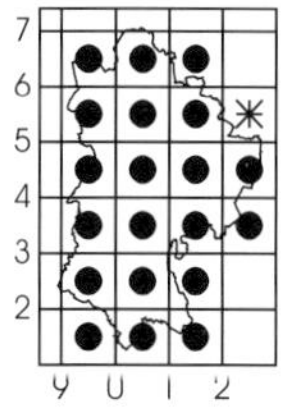

Buff Ermine ***Spilosoma lutea*** **(Hufnagel) (2061)**

Pre VCH: J.C.Dale (MS3) recorded finding this species (as *Lubricipedatus*) in Clapham Park Wood on 1 June 1820. Elsewhere (MS2) he noted receiving this species from Abbot's collection from Bedford but not dated.
VCH: (as *S. lubricipeda* Linn.) "Common everywhere."
Post VCH: Widespread and common.
Flight: May to September (weeks 18 to 37, peak 23 to 32)★.
Larval Foodplants: Polyphagous on herbaceous plants.

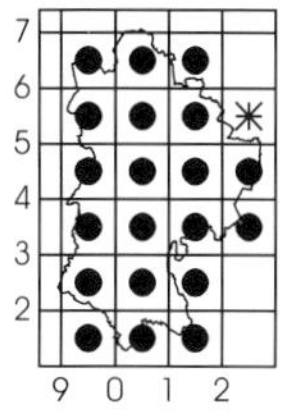

Water Ermine ***Spilosoma urticae*** **(Esper) (2062)**

Post VCH: Not recorded. Specimens in J.B.Barnwell's collection are from just over the county boundary in Buckinghamshire, not Bedfordshire as previously reported (Arnold, 1981b).

Muslin Moth ***Diaphora mendica*** **(Clerck) (2063)**

VCH: "Bedford, Potton."
Post VCH: Widespread, local and uncommon. Found in woods, downland and gardens.
Flight: April to June (weeks 17 to 25, peak 18 to 23)★. Active during the day but also flies at night.
Larval Foodplants: Polyphagous on herbaceous plants.

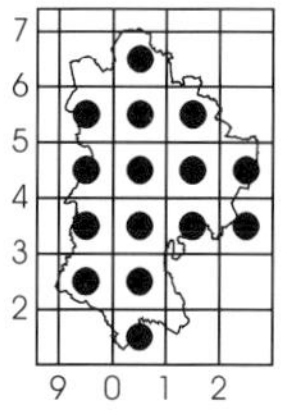

Ruby Tiger ***Phragmatobia fuliginosa fuliginosa*** **(Linnaeus) (2064)**

VCH: "Bedford, Potton."
Post VCH: Common and widespread. It comes readily to light.
Flight: May to September (weeks 18 to 35 with the largest numbers in 29 to 34)★. One specimen came to light at Sharnbrook on 13 February 1981.
Larval Foodplants: Plantains★ and other herbaceous plants.

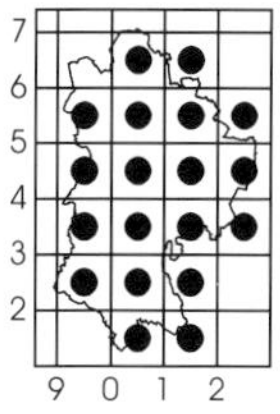

For key to moth maps see page 3.

Scarlet Tiger *Callimorpha dominula* (Linnaeus) (2068)
Post VCH: There are no definite records of this species in Bedfordshire. A bred series in the Kershaw collection includes two specimens of the form *bimaculata* labelled "Aspley Heath", September 1953 which should probably have been labelled "bred". Kershaw also noted without comment a larva in King's Wood, Heath and Reach on 3 June 1954.

The Cinnabar *Tyria jacobaeae* (Linnaeus) (2069) (Drawing p. 322)
VCH: "Generally common among ragwort and groundsel."
Post VCH: Common throughout the County on rough ground. The larvae are seen more often than the moths.
Flight: May to July (weeks 19 to 30)★. Day-flying and also comes to light.
Larval Foodplants: Common ragwort★, groundsel★ and other *Senecio* species.

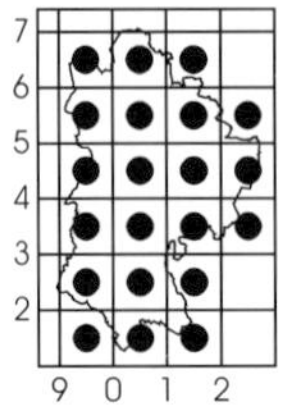

Family: **Nolidae**

A group of small moths, wingspan 15-24 mm, which in the new classification (Emmet, 1996) are placed as a subfamily of the Noctuidae. There are five species in Britain.

Short - cloaked Moth (x 1.6)

Small Black Arches *Meganola strigula* ([Denis & Schiffermüller]) (2075)
Post VCH: One record only by R.F.Bretherton from King's Wood, Heath and Reach in July 1945 (J.Heath pers. comm.). S.H.Kershaw's notebook contains records of *strigula* at Aspley Heath from 1934 onwards but the True Lover's Knot was also known as *strigula*.
Flight: June and July★.
Larval Foodplants: Oaks.

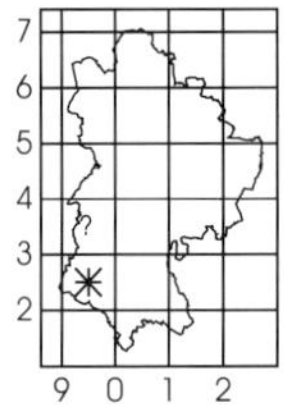

Short-cloaked Moth *Nola cucullatella* (Linnaeus) (2077)
VCH: "Bedford, Luton; among fruit trees."
Post VCH: Widespread and fairly common in woodlands, old orchards and mature gardens.
Flight: June to August (weeks 24 to 33, peak 26 to 32)★.
Larval Foodplants: Blackthorn, hawthorns★, apple and plum.

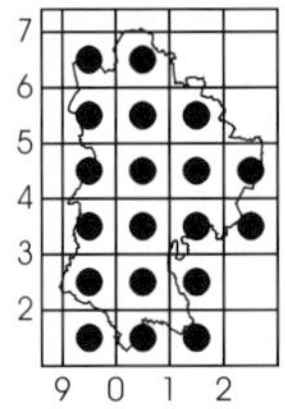

Least Black Arches *Nola confusalis* (Herrich-Schäffer) (2078)
Post VCH: A scarce and local species. Recorded by S.H.Kershaw at Aspley Heath in 1934 and 1935 with specimens dated 1946, 1947 and 1949. More recently found at Ampthill (1984), Biggleswade (1995), King's Wood, Heath and Reach (1987, 1988), Little Staughton (1995), Stockgrove Country Park (1983, 1985) and West Wood (1989). Also in the RIS traps at The Lodge, Sandy (1969) and Cockayne Hatley (1986, 1988, 1989, 1992, 1994).
Flight: April to June (weeks 17 to 26)★.
Larval Foodplants: Lichens on trees.

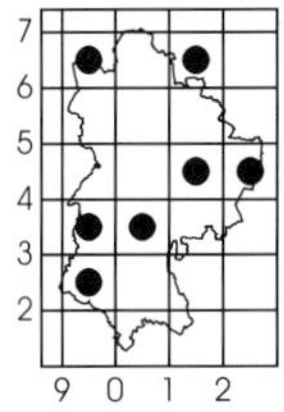

Noctuids - Part 1

(Noctuinae and Hadeninae)

V.W.Arnold

Family: **Noctuidae**

This is a large family with some 340 species in Britain. The moths are usually medium-sized (wingspan around 28-60 mm) with narrow forewings which they hold close to the body when at rest. The colour patterns on the forewings are often complex and variable within a species so many species are not easy to identify even to the practised eye. In a few species the moths cannot be distinguished unless the genitalia are removed and examined though the larvae may be quite distinct. The moths have a hearing organ (tympanum) on each side of the thorax and have been filmed taking evasive action when a bat approaches. The larvae typically have four pairs of prolegs and a pair of anal claspers but the prolegs are sometimes reduced in number, as in the Plusiinae.

Subfamily: **Noctuinae** **The Darts and Yellow Underwings.**

Many moths in this subfamily are rather dull brown or greyish but the Yellow Underwings, as their name implies, have bright yellow hindwings bordered with black. The moths of some species, such as the Large Yellow Underwing, are particularly active and fast-moving. Wingspan 28-60 mm. The larvae have few, if any, obvious hairs and tend to feed at night hiding in the soil during the day. Some are the notorious 'cutworms' which remain in the soil and eat roots and stem bases, sometimes causing a great deal of damage to crops and garden plants. There are about 53 British species of which 39 have been found in Bedfordshire as well as four for which the records are doubtful.

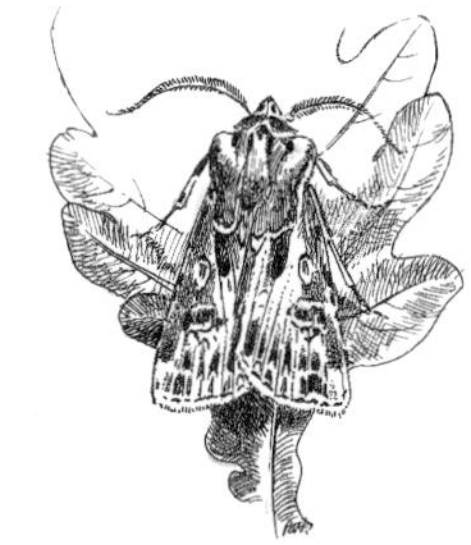

Archer's Dart

Square-spot Dart *Euxoa obelisca* ([Denis & Schiffermüller]) (2080)
Post VCH: Recorded in S.H.Kershaw's notebooks from Aspley Heath on 8 August 1933. A specimen in his collection dated 1939 is misplaced and the 1933 record seems very doubtful as this is primarily a coastal species in Britain.

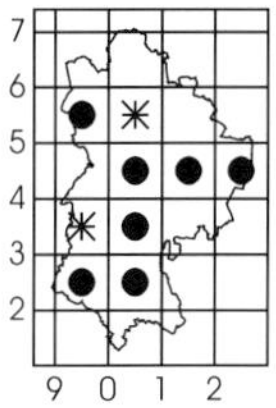

White-line Dart *Euxoa tritici* (Linnaeus) (2081)
Post VCH: A local and uncommon species, normally found in heathland areas, such as The Lodge, Sandy. There are specimens in the Kershaw collection from Aspley Heath in 1935 and 1936.
Flight: July and August (weeks 29 to 35)*.
Larval Foodplants: Polyphagous on herbaceous plants.

For key to moth maps see page 3.

Garden Dart *Euxoa nigricans* (Linnaeus) (2082)

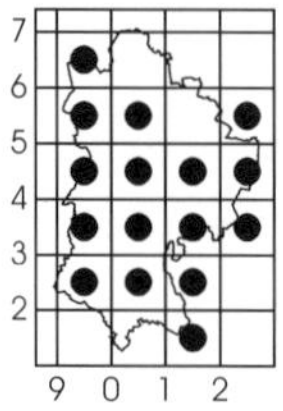

VCH: "Luton."
Post VCH: Widespread but not common. Found in a variety of habitats including gardens, heathlands and waste ground.
Flight: June to September (weeks 23 to 36, peak 31 to 33)*.
Larval Foodplants: Polyphagous on herbaceous plants.

Light Feathered Rustic *Agrotis cinerea* ([Denis & Schiffermüller]) (2084)

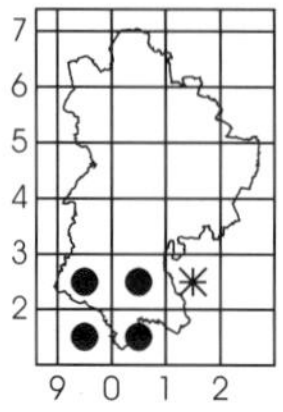

Post VCH: In the main a species of the chalk downland. Foster (1934) stated "Pegsdon and Barton Hills by myself". Other records from Bison Hill (1985, 1995), Dunstable Downs (1971, 1972, 1978), Luton (1980), Totternhoe Knolls (1978) and from the RIS traps at Eaton Bray (1985, 1987, 1988) and Whipsnade (1973).
Flight: May and June (weeks 21 to 25)*.
Larval Foodplant: Wild thyme.

Archer's Dart *Agrotis vestigialis* ((Hufnagel)) (2085)

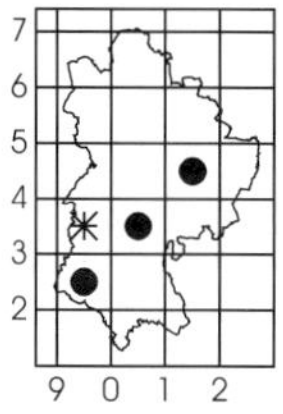

(Drawing on page 325)
Post VCH: A local and scarce species. Recorded in S.H.Kershaw's notebooks from Aspley Heath in 1934-36. Only six recent records, all confined to the Greensand Ridge: Cooper's Hill (1965), Sandy (1958, 1965), Shire Oak (1980) and Stockgrove Country Park (1975, 1980).
Flight: July to September (weeks 29 to 35)*.
Larval Foodplants: Polyphagous on grasses and herbaceous plants.

Turnip Moth *Agrotis segetum* ([Denis & Schiffermüller]) (2087)

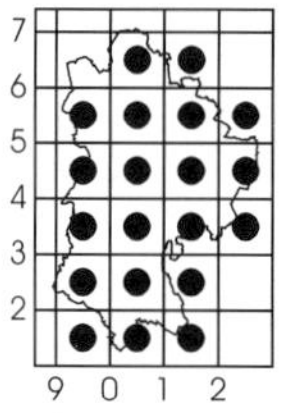

VCH: "Everywhere abundant; very injurious in turnip fields."
Post VCH: Common throughout the County.
Flight: May to November (weeks 22 to 45 with the largest numbers 23 to 34)*. The late records represent an occasional second generation.
Larval Foodplants: Roots of herbaceous plants and cultivated crops. Sometimes a pest on root crops.

Heart and Club *Agrotis clavis* (Hufnagel) (2088)

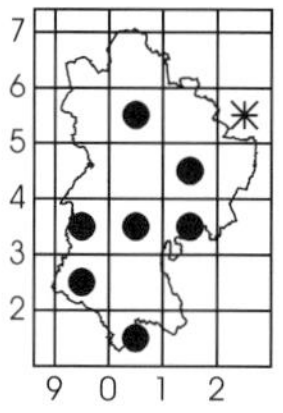

Post VCH: A local and uncommon species with few records. Specimens are in the Kershaw collection from Aspley Heath dated 1946 and 14 July 1953 and it is in his notebook from there in 1932. Other records are mainly from the RIS traps at Eaton Bray (1983, 1987), Old Warden (1975), The Lodge, Sandy (1971, 1975) and Whipsnade (1973).
Flight: June to August (weeks 25 to 35, peak 33)*.
Larval Foodplants: Polyphagous on herbaceous plants.
Notes: In the past this species may have been confused with *A. exclamationis* (L.).

For details of standard weeks see page 6.

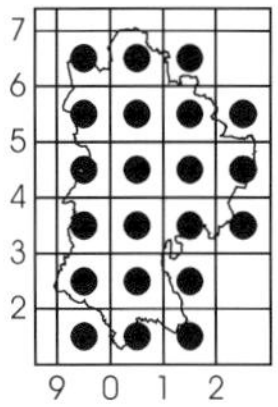

Heart and Dart *Agrotis exclamationis* (Linnaeus) (2089)
VCH: "Most abundant, and mischievous to growing turnips."
Post VCH: Widespread and common. Can be abundant at light.
Flight: May to September (weeks 19 to 39, peak 24 to 31)★.
Larval Foodplants: Polyphagous on herbaceous plants.

Crescent Dart *Agrotis trux* (Hübner) ssp. *lunigera* Stephens (2090)
Post VCH: *lunigera* is recorded in S.H.Kershaw's notebooks from Aspley Heath in 1935, 1946 and 1953. These records seem very doubtful as the Crescent Dart is a coastal species in Britain.

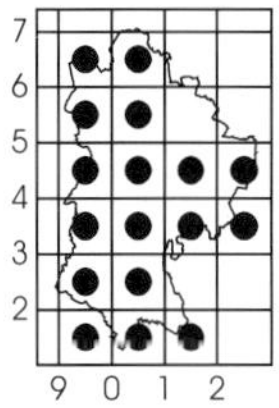

Dark Sword-grass *Agrotis ipsilon* (Hufnagel) (2091)
VCH: (as *A. suffusa* Hb.) "Bedford, Luton."
Post VCH: An immigrant that can be found anywhere in the County but is not common.
Flight: March to November (weeks 20 and 33 to 45)★. Most often found in September and October (weeks 37 to 41)★.
Larval Foodplants: Polyphagous on herbaceous plants.

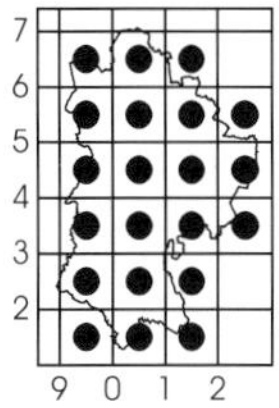

Shuttle-shaped Dart *Agrotis puta puta* (Hübner) (2092)
VCH: "Bedford; not very common."
Post VCH: Common throughout the County.
Flight: Continuously brooded between May and October (weeks 19 to 44, peaks 21 and 31 to 34)★.
Larval Foodplants: Polyphagous on herbaceous plants.

Tawny Shoulder *Feltia subterranea* (Fabricius) (2096)
Post VCH: "Tawny Shoulder" is entered in S.H.Kershaw's notebook as in his moth trap at Aspley Heath on 24-25 June 1934 without comment. This is a North American species for which there are only three unconfirmed 19th century records in Britain (Emmet, 1991). Kershaw would surely have highlighted the record as special if he had really meant this species.

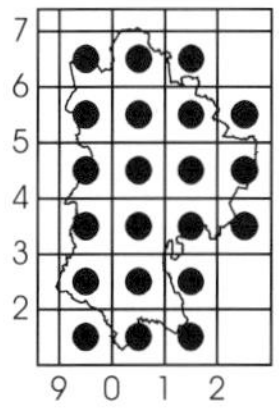

The Flame *Axylia putris* (Linnaeus) (2098)
VCH: "Generally distributed."
Post VCH: Common throughout the County.
Flight: May to September (weeks 19 to 36, peak 25 to 30)★.
Larval Foodplants: Polyphagous on herbaceous plants.

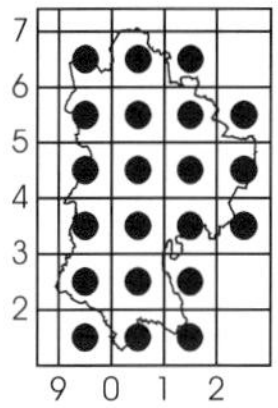

Flame Shoulder *Ochropleura plecta* (Linnaeus) (2102)
VCH: "Bedford, Luton."
Post VCH: Common throughout the County.
Flight: May to September (weeks 19 to 39, peaks 23 to 26 and 32 to 35)★, in two broods which probably overlap.
Larval Foodplants: *Mentha* sp.★ Polyphagous on herbaceous plants.

For key to moth maps see page 3.

Plain Clay *Eugnorisma depuncta* (Linnaeus) (2103)
Post VCH: Recorded by Champkin (1968, 1969,1972) in error. Otherwise not recorded in Bedfordshire.

Dotted Rustic *Rhyacia simulans* (Hufnagel) (2105)

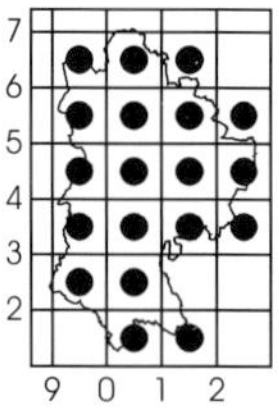

Post VCH: First recorded in the County in 1974 from Hardwick Spinney by W.J.Champkin. This species was recorded throughout the County between 1984 and 1988. Many records came from the Bedfordshire Bat Group by finding wings at bat roosts, especially in 1988. It appears to have become much less common since then but is still recorded singly.
Flight: Between June and late September (weeks 26 to 39)*. For part of this time the moths aestivate in outhouses, etc.
Larval Foodplants: Unknown in the wild.

Large Yellow Underwing *Noctua pronuba* (Linnaeus) (2107)

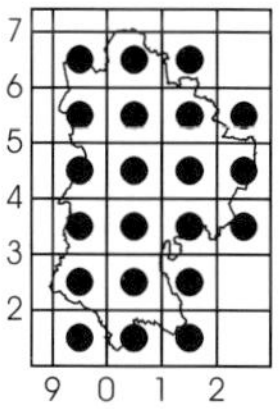

VCH: "Everywhere abundant."
Post VCH: Very common throughout the County.
Flight: June to November (weeks 23 to 45, peak 31 to 37)* It is not clear if there are several broods or whether some individuals aestivate.
Larval Foodplants: Polyphagous on grasses and herbaceous plants.

Lunar Yellow Underwing *Noctua orbona* (Hufnagel) (2108)

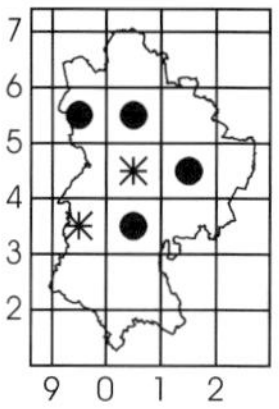

Post VCH: A local and uncommon species, that has declined in Britain in recent years. Recorded in S.H.Kershaw's notebooks from Aspley Heath between 1936 and 1959, more frequently than the Lesser Yellow Underwing which today is the more common of the two. However, the name *orbona* has been applied to both species and they are easily confused so it is difficult to be sure if these records have been interpreted correctly. The same comment would apply to many earlier records of this species.
Flight: June to September(weeks 24 and 32 to 36)*.
Larval Foodplants: Polyphagous on grasses and herbaceous plants.

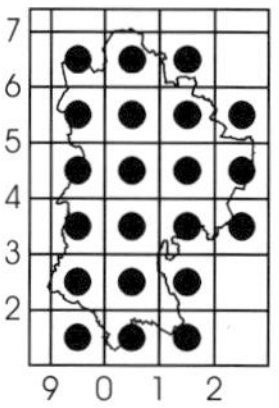

Lesser Yellow Underwing *Noctua comes* Hübner (2109)
VCH: (as *N. orbona* Fab.) "Everywhere abundant."
Post VCH: Very common throughout the County.
Flight: July to October (weeks 27 to 42, peak 33 to 37)*.
Larval Foodplants: Polyphagous on deciduous trees and shrubs.

Broad-bordered Yellow Underwing *Noctua fimbriata* (Schreber) (2110) (Plate 75)

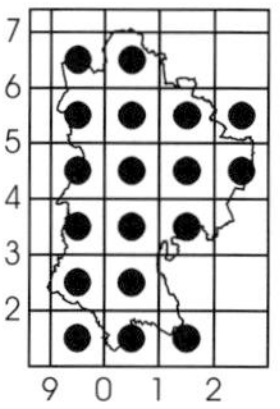

VCH: "Bedford, in woods."
Post VCH: Local, but widespread. Found most commonly in wooded areas.
Flight: July to October (weeks 28 to 42)*.
Larval Foodplants: Cultivated primrose* and other herbaceous plants.

For details of standard weeks see page 6.

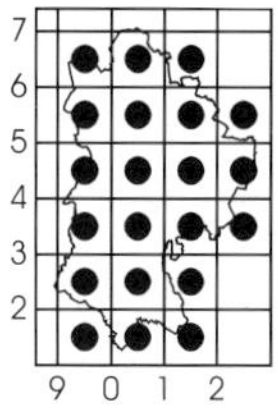

Lesser Broad-bordered Yellow Underwing ***Noctua janthe*** **Borkhausen (=*janthina* auctt.) (2111)**
VCH: "Bedford, Potton; in gardens and woods."
Post VCH: Common throughout the County.
Flight: July to September (weeks 27 to 37, peak 30 to 34)*.
Larval Foodplants: Polyphagous on herbaceous plants.

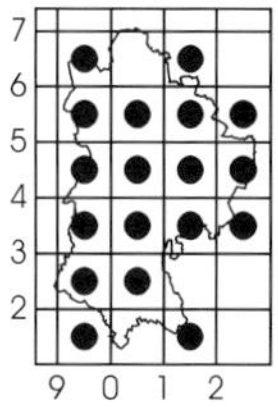

Least Yellow Underwing ***Noctua interjecta*** **Hübner ssp.** ***caliginosa*** **(Schawerda) (2112)**
VCH: "Bedford, Luton; in woods and hedges."
Post VCH: Widespread but uncommon and local.
Flight: July and August (weeks 28 to 36)*.
Larval Foodplants: Polyphagous on herbaceous plants.

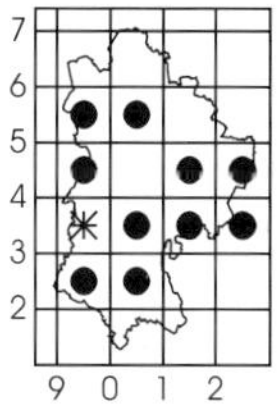

Stout Dart ***Spaelotis ravida*** **([Denis & Schiffermüller]) (2113)**
VCH: "Bedford; very local."
Post VCH: Widespread but local and uncommon.
Flight: July to September (weeks 28 to 39)*.
Larval Foodplants: Unknown. In captivity will eat docks and dandelions.

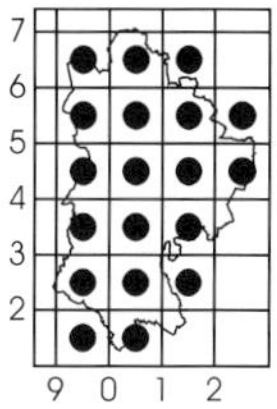

Double Dart ***Graphiphora augur*** **(Fabricius) (2114)**
VCH: "Bedford, Luton."
Post VCH: A local species usually found in woodlands throughout the County.
Flight: June to September (weeks 26 to 36)*.
Larval Foodplants: Docks and deciduous trees.

Autumnal Rustic ***Paradiarsia glareosa glareosa*** **(Esper) (2117)**

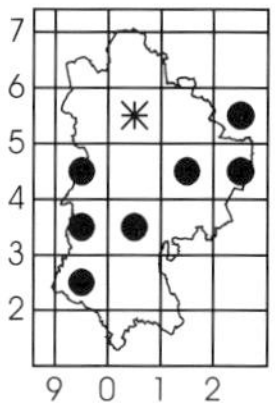

Post VCH: A local and uncommon species, found mainly in heathy areas along the Greensand Ridge. A specimen in Bedford Museum is labelled "Putnoe, R.P.K.Rylands" but without a date. "At Rowney, by Brocklehurst" (Foster, 1934). By "Rowney" Foster probably meant Rowney Warren. Recorded in S.H.Kershaw's notebooks from Aspley Heath between 1932 and 1954 and a specimen in his collection is labelled "Aspley Heath 1936".

Flight: September to October (weeks 36 to 40, peak 37)*.
Larval Foodplants: Polyphagous on grasses and herbaceous plants.

True Lover's Knot ***Lycophotia porphyrea*** **([Denis & Schiffermüller]) (2118)**
VCH: "Luton."

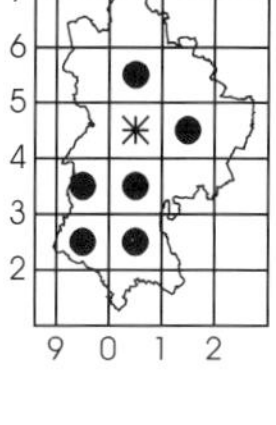

Post VCH: A local and uncommon species, usually confined to the Greensand Ridge. Occasional records have been received from gardens where cultivated heathers are grown.
Flight: Late May to September (weeks 22 to 37, peak 27 to 30)*.
Larval Foodplant: Heather*.

For key to moth maps see page 3.

Pearly Underwing *Peridroma saucia* (Hübner) (2119)

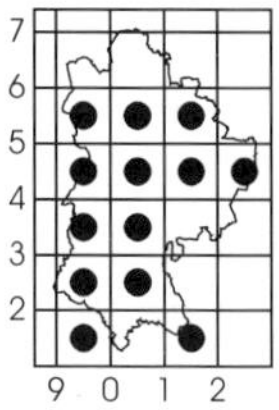

VCH: "Bedford."
Post VCH: An immigrant species that can be found throughout the County, but is never common.
Flight: July (week 29)★ and August to November (weeks 33 and 45)★.
Larval Foodplants: Polyphagous on herbaceous plants.

Ingrailed Clay *Diarsia mendica mendica* (Fabricius) (2120)

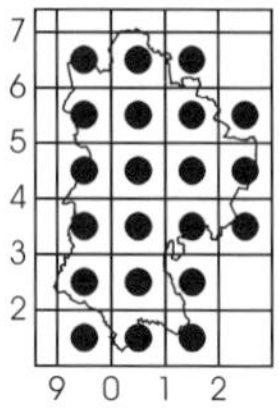

VCH: (as *Noctua festiva* Hb.) "Bedford, Luton; in woods."
Post VCH: Common and widespread, especially in wooded areas.
Flight: May to August (weeks 21 to 31, peak 23 to 28)★.
Larval Foodplants: Polyphagous on herbaceous plants.

Barred Chestnut *Diarsia dahlii* (Hübner) (2121)

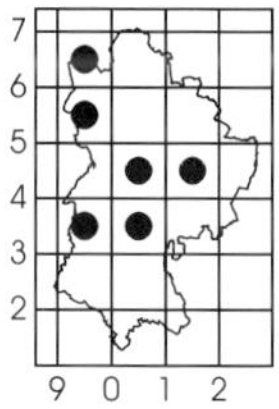

Post VCH: A specimen in the Kershaw collection labelled "Aspley Heath" is dated 27 August 1946 and there are records in his notebooks for 22 July and1 August 1936. Recorded by W.J.Champkin from Cooper's Hill (1965), Cople Pits (1964), Hardwick Spinney (1974), Sandy (1965) and Sharnbrook Summit (1965) but it has not been seen since.
Flight: August and September (weeks 31 to 36)★.
Larval Foodplants: Birches and bilberry.

Purple Clay *Diarsia brunnea* ([Denis & Schiffermüller]) (2122)

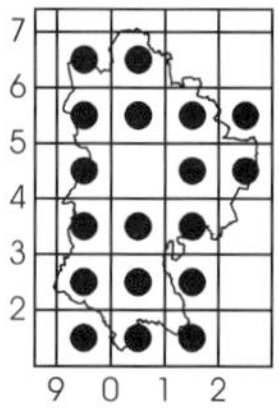

Post VCH: A local species found in woodlands throughout the County. Foster (1934) stated "at Flitwick, by Brocklehurst". Recorded in S.H.Kershaw's notebooks from Aspley Heath between 1934 and 1955.
Flight: June to August (weeks 24 to 31, peak 26 to 28)★.
Larval Foodplants: Polyphagous on deciduous trees and shrubs.

Small Square-spot *Diarsia rubi* (Vieweg) (2123)

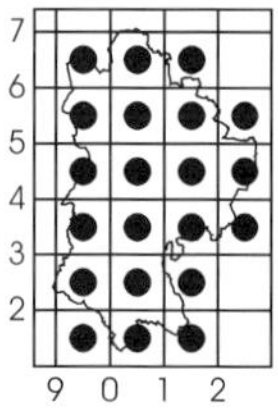

VCH: "Bedford, Luton, in woods."
Post VCH: Common and widespread.
Flight: May to October (weeks 18 to 42, peaks 21 to 26 and 30 to 38)★, in two overlapping broods.
Larval Foodplants: Polyphagous on herbaceous plants.

Setaceous Hebrew Character *Xestia c-nigrum* (Linnaeus) (2126)

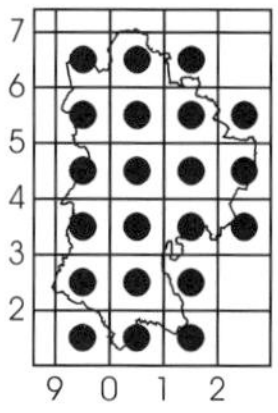

VCH: "Bedford, Luton, Potton."
Post VCH: Common and widespread.
Flight: May to October (weeks 20 to 45, peaks 24 to 28 and 33 to 41)★, in two overlapping broods.
Larval Foodplants: Polyphagous on herbaceous plants.

For details of standard weeks see page 6.

Triple-spotted Clay ***Xestia ditrapezium*** **([Denis & Schiffermüller]) (2127)**
Post VCH: A local and uncommon species, found in a few wooded locations in the County. Recorded in S.H.Kershaw's notebooks from Aspley Heath in 1947 and 1953. Most recent records originate from the following RIS traps: Cockayne Hatley (1981, 1987), Old Warden (1974-1975), The Lodge, Sandy (1969-1974) and Whipsnade Wild Animal Park (1973). Also from Aspley Heath (1984), Clophill Sand Quarry (1984) and Stockgrove Country Park (1980, 1986).
Flight: June to August (weeks 25 to 33, peak 27 to 31)*.
Larval Foodplants: Polyphagous on deciduous trees and shrubs.

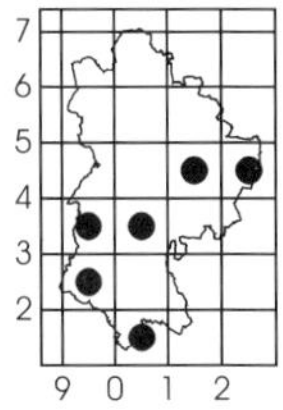

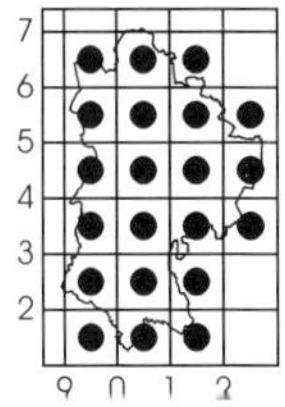

Double Square-spot ***Xestia triangulum*** **(Hufnagel) (2128)**
VCH: "Bedford, Luton; in woods."
Post VCH: Widespread and common in woodland.
Flight: May to August (weeks 22 to 33, peak 27 to 31)*.
Larval Foodplants: Polyphagous on deciduous trees and shrubs.

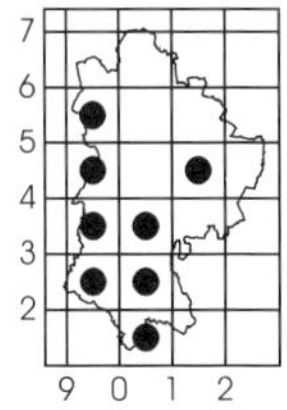

Dotted Clay ***Xestia baja*** **([Denis & Schiffermüller]) (2130)**
Post VCH: A local and uncommon species, found in woodland and heathland areas, such as Maulden Wood and The Lodge, Sandy.
Flight: June and July (weeks 27 to 34)*.
Larval Foodplants: Polyphagous on deciduous trees and shrubs.

Square-spotted Clay ***Xestia rhomboidea*** **(Esper) (2131)**
Post VCH: Shown as occurring in Bedfordshire by Heath and Emmet (1979) but J.Heath (pers. comm.) considered that this was not an acceptable record. Recorded as *stigmatica* in S.H.Kershaw's notebook from Aspley Heath on 30 June 1946, a very early date but the entry is flagged as "new". No specimen has been seen.

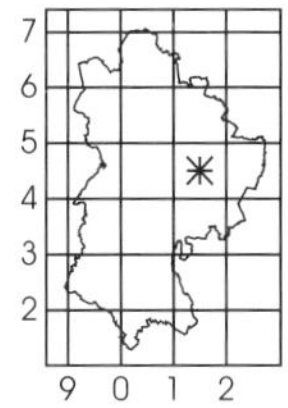

Neglected Rustic ***Xestia castanea*** **(Esper) (2132)**
Post VCH: Recorded only once, at Sandy in August 1958 (West, 1959).
Flight: August and September.
Larval Foodplants: Heaths and heather.

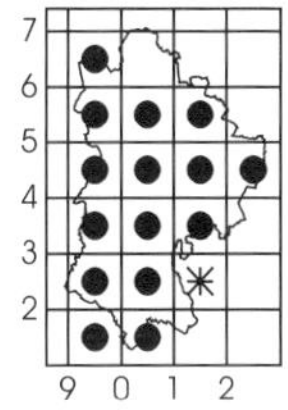

Six-striped Rustic ***Xestia sexstrigata*** **(Haworth) (2133)**
Post VCH: Widespread but local and uncommon. Recorded in S.H.Kershaw's notebook from Aspley Heath between 1933 and 1955 and at Pegsdon in 1938.
Flight: June to September (weeks 26 to 36, peak 33 to 34)*.
Larval Foodplants: Polyphagous on herbaceous plants.

For key to moth maps see page 3.

Square-spot Rustic ***Xestia xanthographa*** **([Denis & Schiffermüller]) (2134)**

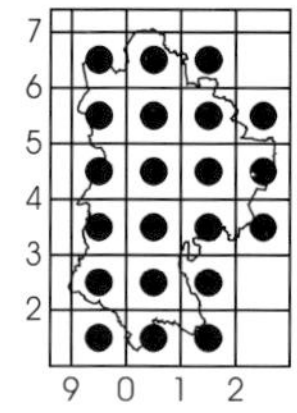

VCH: "Everywhere abundant."
Post VCH: Common and widespread.
Flight: July to November (weeks 27 to 45, peak 33 to 39)*.
Larval Foodplants: Polyphagous on grasses, deciduous trees and herbaceous plants.

Heath Rustic ***Xestia agathina agathina*** **(Duponchel) (2135)**

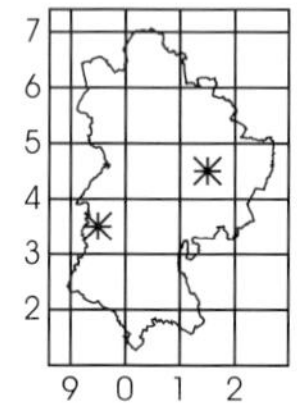

Post VCH: Recorded "at Rowney Warren only, by Nash, Brocklehurst and C.Downs" (Foster, 1934). Specimens in the Kershaw collection are labelled "Aspley Heath" and dated 25 August 1938 and 21 August 1949 and there are also entries in his notebooks for 1933, 1935, 1936 and 1946.
Flight: Late August and September.
Larval Foodplant: Heather.

The Gothic ***Naenia typica*** **(Linnaeus) (2136)**

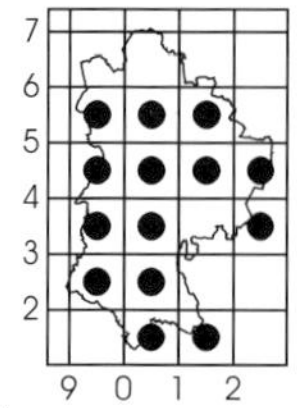

VCH: "Common everywhere."
Post VCH: Found throughout the County, but local and uncommon.
Flight: June to September (weeks 24 to 35)*.
Larval Foodplants: Polyphagous on herbaceous plants.

Great Brocade ***Eurois occulta*** **(Linnaeus) (2137)**

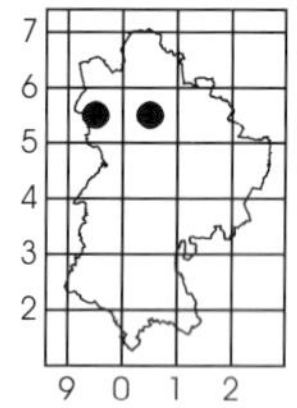

Post VCH: A rare immigrant. Found at Bedford (1976), Carlton (1983) and Stevington (1964).
Flight: July to September (week 33)*.
Larval Foodplants: Birches and sallows.

Green Arches ***Anaplectoides prasina*** **([Denis & Schiffermüller]) (2138)**

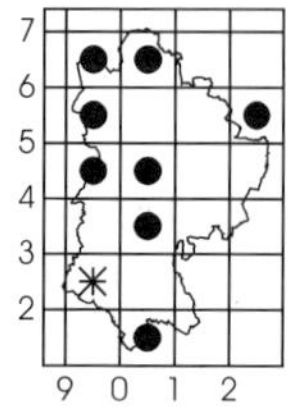

Post VCH: A local moth that is not uncommon in some of the old oak woods in the north of the County, such as West Wood and Coppice Wood.
Flight: June and July (weeks 25 to 28)*.
Larval Foodplants: Polyphagous, including honeysuckle and sallow.

Red Chestnut ***Cerastis rubricosa*** **([Denis & Schiffermüller]) (2139)**

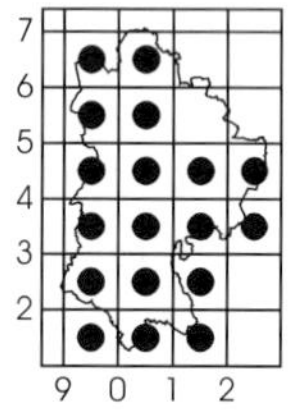

VCH: "Bedford."
Post VCH: Widespread and common, found mainly in woodlands. Kershaw (1958) recorded specimens of the Scottish form, Ab. *mucida* Esper, at his window in Aspley Heath on 17 and 22 April 1958.
Flight: February to May (weeks 8 to 20, peak 14 to 17)*.
Larval Foodplants: Polyphagous on herbaceous plants.

For details of standard weeks see page 6.

Subfamily: **Hadeninae**

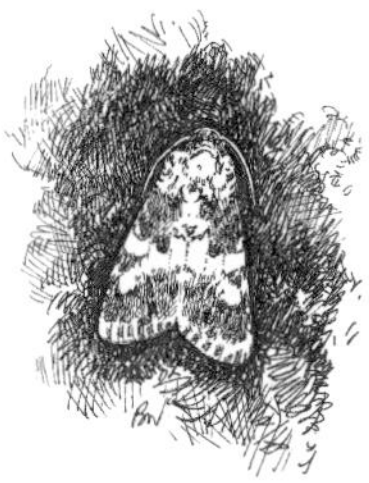

Varied Coronet

Dot Moth

This is a large and variable subfamily. Many of the moths are dull brownish-grey or straw coloured but others have more complex patterns on the forewings. Wingspan 24-58 mm. They have hairy eyes which distinguishes them from all other noctuids found in Bedfordshire, except the Nut-tree Tussock (Pantheinae). The larvae of almost all species feed above ground. There are about 63 British species of which 40 have been found in Bedfordshire together with one doubtful record.

Beautiful Yellow Underwing ***Anarta myrtilli*** **(Linnaeus) (2142)**

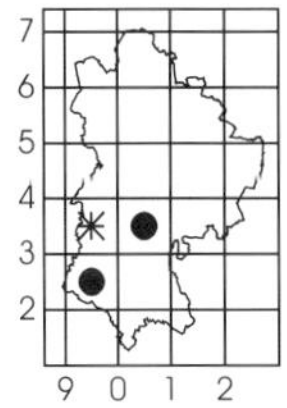

Post VCH: A scarce species in Bedfordshire. R.M.Craske recalled it as "local on greensand" between 1918 and 1927. Recorded in S.H.Kershaw's notebook from Aspley Heath in 1936. At light at Cooper's Hill (August 1965, W.J.Champkin) and one in sunshine at Shire Oak (2 June 1979, V.W.Arnold).
Flight: Double-brooded between April and August. Flies by day but also may come to light.
Larval Foodplants: Heather and heaths.

The Nutmeg ***Discestra trifolii*** **(Hufnagel) (2145)**

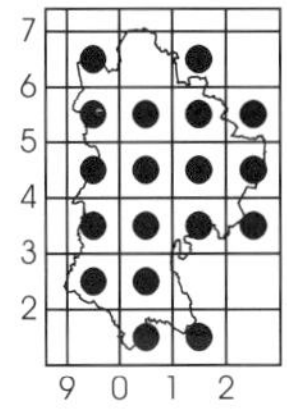

VCH: "Generally distributed."
Post VCH: Common throughout the County.
Flight: May to September (weeks 20 to 37, peaks 24 to 26 and 30 to 34)*.
Larval Foodplants: Goosefoots and oraches.

The Shears ***Hada plebeja*** **(Linnaeus) (=** ***nana*** **(Hufnagel)) (2147)**

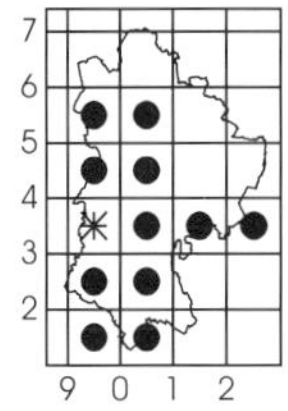

VCH: (as *Hadena dentina* Esp.) "Bedford."
Post VCH: Widely distributed but local and uncommon.
Flight: May to July (weeks 22 to 30, peak 25)*.
Larval Foodplants: Dandelions, chickweeds, hawkweeds and hawk's-beards.

Pale Shining Brown ***Polia bombycina*** **(Hufnagel) (2148)**

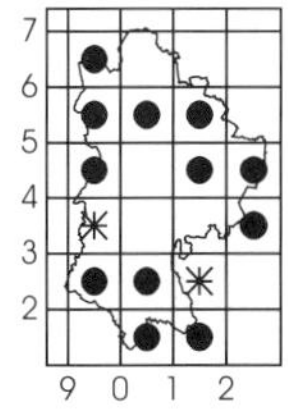

VCH: (as *Aplecta advena* Fab.) "Bedford."
Post VCH: Widespread but local and uncommon. Not recorded in the County since 1987. This species has become scarce nationally.
Flight: June and July (weeks 25 to 31, peak 28)*.
Larval Foodplants: Unknown in the wild, but probably polyphagous on herbaceous plants.

For key to moth maps see page 3.

Silvery Arches ***Polia trimaculosa*** **(Esper) (2149)**
Post VCH: Shown as occurring in Bedfordshire by Heath and Emmet (1979) but J. Heath (pers. comm.) considered that this was not an acceptable record.

Grey Arches ***Polia nebulosa*** **(Hufnagel) (2150)**
VCH: "Bedford."
Post VCH: Widely distributed in woodlands, but local and never common.
Flight: June and July (weeks 24 to 29, peak 26 to 27)*.
Larval Foodplants: Polyphagous on deciduous trees and shrubs.

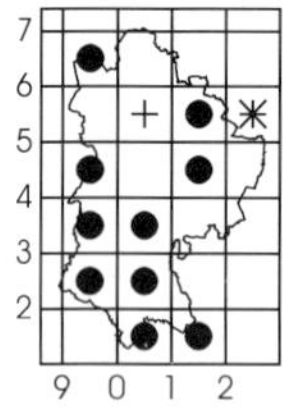

Bordered Gothic ***Heliophobus reticulata*** **(Goeze) ssp.** ***marginosa*** **(Haworth) (2153)**
Post VCH: A scarce species in Bedfordshire with only three records. A specimen in the Kershaw collection is labelled "Aspley Heath" and dated 25 June 1935. R.Passley's collection contains a specimen labelled "Bedfordshire 1964". The locality was Stevington (pers. comm.). Recorded at MV light at Chapel Field, Great Barford, by A.Muir-Howie on 18 July 1981.
Flight: June and July (weeks 26 and 29)*.
Larval Foodplants: Polyphagous on flowers.

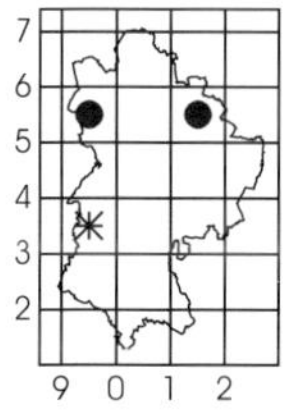

Cabbage Moth ***Mamestra brassicae*** **(Linnaeus) (2154)**
VCH: "Universally abundant, and mischievous in gardens."
Post VCH: Common and widespread.
Flight: Between June and October (weeks 21 to 41, peak 30 to 32)*.
Larval Foodplants: Polyphagous on herbaceous plants especially *Brassica* spp*.

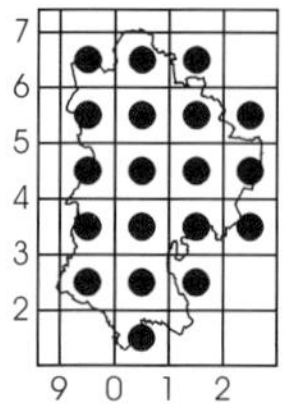

Dot Moth ***Melanchra persicariae*** **(Linnaeus) (2155)**
(Drawing on page 333)
VCH: "Bedford, Luton, Potton."
Post VCH: Common and widespread.
Flight: June to September (weeks 25 to 35, peak 28 to 30)*.
Larval Foodplants: Polyphagous on herbaceous plants.

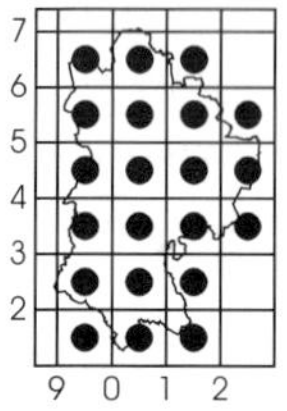

Beautiful Brocade ***Lacanobia contigua*** **([Denis & Schiffermüller]) (2156)**
Post VCH: Recorded in error by Arnold (1983). Not otherwise known in Bedfordshire.

Light Brocade ***Lacanobia w-latinum*** **(Hufnagel) (2157)**
Post VCH: A local and uncommon species, usually found on calcareous soils at sites such as Totternhoe Knolls. A specimen in Bedford Museum is labelled "Flitwick, R.P.K.Rylands" but without a date. Recorded in S.H. Kershaw's notebook from Aspley Heath between 1934 and 1953, in some years as early as 28 May.
Flight: June and July (weeks 24 to 29)*.
Larval Foodplants: Polyphagous on herbaceous plants.

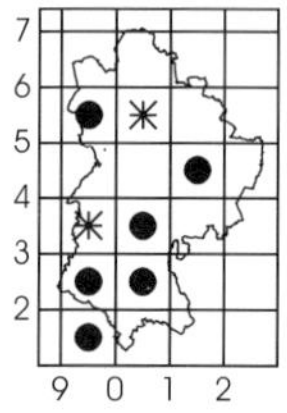

For details of standard weeks see page 6.

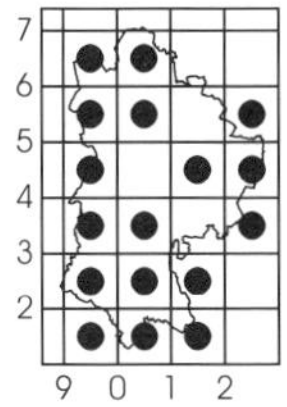

Pale-shouldered Brocade ***Lacanobia thalassina*** **(Hufnagel) (2158)**
VCH: "Bedford."
Post VCH: Widespread in wooded areas, but local and uncommon.
Flight: May to August (weeks 20 to 31, peak 24)*.
Larval Foodplants: Polyphagous on deciduous trees and herbaceous plants.

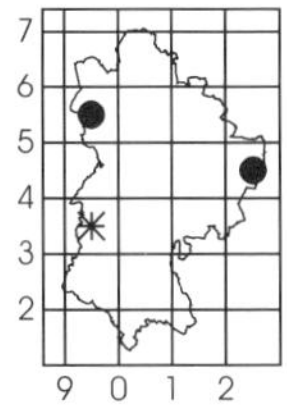

Dog's Tooth ***Lacanobia suasa*** **([Denis & Schiffermüller]) (2159)**
Post VCH: Only five records: Aspley Heath by S.H.Kershaw on 9 June 1933 and 30 June 1936, at Stevington by W.J.Champkin on 14 August 1964 and in the RIS trap at Cockayne Hatley on 20 July 1976 and 7 August 1995.
Flight: May to September (weeks 29 and 32)*, in two broods.
Larval Foodplants: Polyphagous on herbaceous plants.

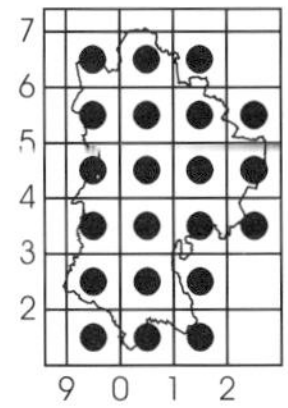

Bright-line Brown-eye ***Lacanobia oleracea*** **(Linnaeus) (2160)**
VCH: "Common in gardens everywhere."
Post VCH: Common and widespread.
Flight: May to September (weeks 18 to 38, peak 26 to 32)*.
Larval Foodplants: Polyphagous on herbaceous plants including tomato*.

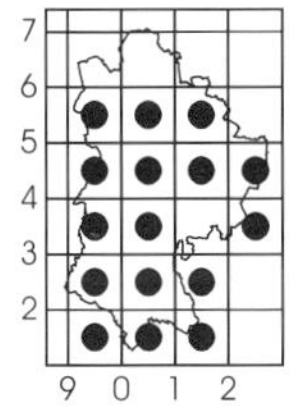

Broom Moth ***Ceramica pisi*** **(Linnaeus) (2163)**
Pre VCH: J.C.Dale (MS2) recorded receiving this species from Abbot's collection from Bedford but not dated.
VCH: "Bedford, Potton."
Post VCH: Widespread and fairly common.
Flight: May to July (weeks 21 to 30, peak 25)*.
Larval Foodplants: Polyphagous on deciduous trees, shrubs and herbaceous plants.

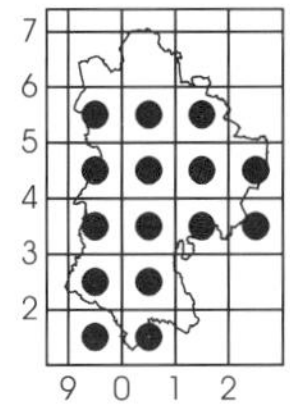

Broad-barred White ***Hecatera bicolorata*** **(Hufnagel) (2164)**
VCH: (as *H. serena* Fab.) "Bedford, Luton; a very pretty object on a tree trunk."
Post VCH: Widespread and fairly common in a variety of habitats.
Flight: June to August (weeks 24 to 34)*.
Larval Foodplants: Hawkweeds, hawk's-beards and possibly other herbaceous plants.

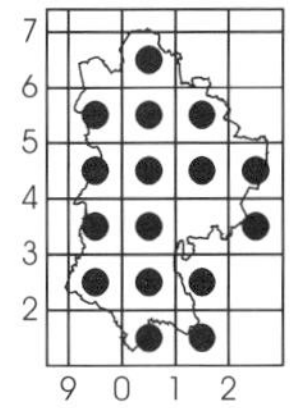

The Campion ***Hadena rivularis*** **(Fabricius) (2166)**
VCH: (as *Dianthecia cucubali* Fuessl.) "Luton."
Post VCH: Widespread, but local and uncommon.
Flight: May to August (weeks 20 to 34)*.
Larval Foodplants: White campion*.

For key to moth maps see page 3.

Tawny Shears *Hadena perplexa perplexa* ([Denis & Schiffermüller]) (2167)

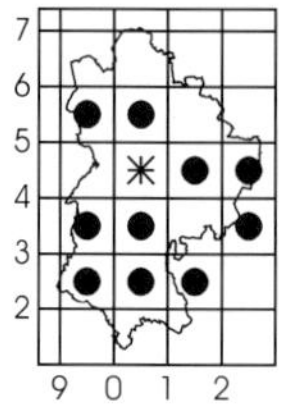

VCH: (as *Dianthecia carpophaga* Bkh.) "Luton."
Post VCH: Widespread, but local and uncommon.
Flight: May to July (weeks 21 to 27)*.
Larval Foodplants: Campions*.

Varied Coronet *Hadena compta* ([Denis & Schiffermüller]) (2170)

(Drawing on page 333)

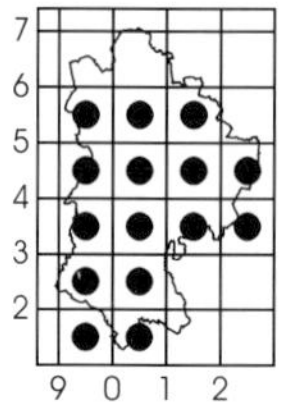

Post VCH: Widespread but local. Usually recorded from gardens where its foodplant is grown. This species has spread since it was discovered in England in 1948. The first Bedfordshire specimen appears to have been found at The Lodge, Sandy, by W.J.Champkin in 1962.
Flight: June to August (weeks 24 to 32)*.
Larval Foodplants: Sweet-William and bladder campion.

Marbled Coronet *Hadena confusa* (Hufnagel) (2171)

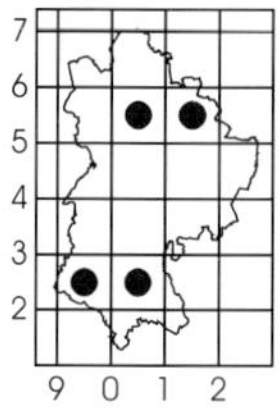

VCH: (as *Dianthecia conspersa* Esp.) "Luton."
Post VCH: A scarce and very local species that is known from only a few sites, mainly on calcareous soils, including Luton and Sewell Cutting.
Flight: May, June, July (weeks 23 to 28)*.
Larval Foodplants: Campions.

White Spot *Hadena albimacula* (Borkhausen) (2172)
Post VCH: Recorded in Kitchener (1964) and Champkin (1976) in error. Otherwise unknown in Bedfordshire.

The Lychnis *Hadena bicruris* (Hufnagel) (2173)

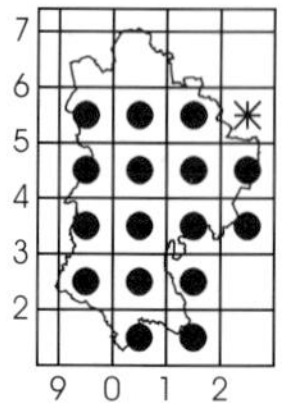

VCH: (as *Dianthecia capsinicola* Hb.) "Potton."
Post VCH: Widespread but local and uncommon.
Flight: May to August (weeks 21 to 34)*.
Larval Foodplants: Sweet-William and other campions.

Antler Moth *Cerapteryx graminis* (Linnaeus) (2176)

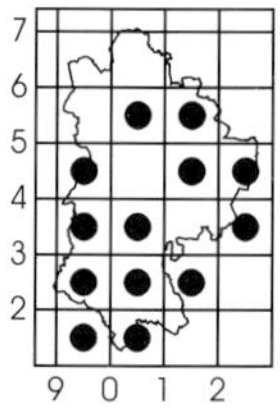

VCH: "Bedford." (Drawing on page 31)
Post VCH: Widespread on grassland, but local and uncommon.
Flight: July to September (weeks 28 to 37, peak 32 to 34)*.
Larval Foodplants: Grasses.

Hedge Rustic *Tholera cespitis* ([Denis & Schiffermüller]) (2177)

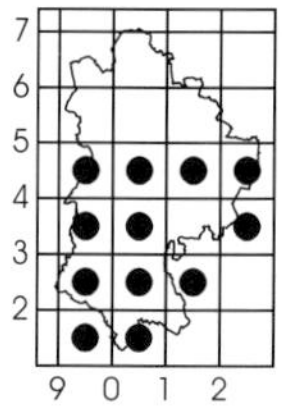

VCH: "Potton."
Post VCH: A grassland species that can sometimes be abundant where it occurs. Widespread but local.
Flight: August and September (weeks 32 to 39, peak 34 and 35)*.
Larval Foodplants: Grasses.

For details of standard weeks see page 6.

Feathered Gothic *Tholera decimalis* (Poda) (2178)

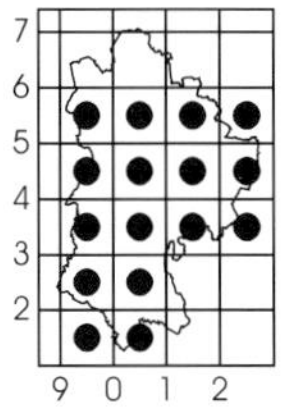

VCH: (as *Heliophobus popularis* Fab.) "Luton, Bedford, Potton."
Post VCH: Widespread and locally common in grassy areas.
Flight: July to October (weeks 30 to 42, peak 34 to 36)*.
Larval Foodplants: Polyphagous on grasses.

Pine Beauty *Panolis flammea* ([Denis & Schiffermüller]) (2179)

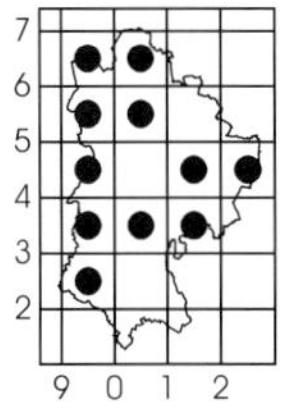

(Plate 56)
Post VCH: Locally abundant in coniferous woodlands, mainly along the central Greensand Ridge. Recorded in S.H.Kershaw's notebooks from Aspley Heath between 1933 and 1959 and a specimen in his collection is labelled Aspley Heath 1938.
Flight: March to June (weeks 13 to 24, peak 18 and 19)*.
Larval Foodplants: Pines.

Small Quaker *Orthosia cruda* ([Denis & Schiffermüller]) (2182)

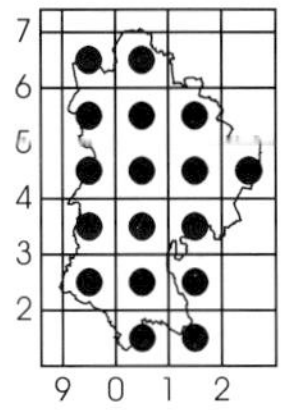

VCH: "Abundant about sallows."
Post VCH: Widespread in woodlands. Can be abundant in some years.
Flight: February to May (weeks 8 to 19, peak 11 to 15)*.
Larval Foodplants: Polyphagous on deciduous trees and shrubs.

Blossom Underwing *Orthosia miniosa* ([Denis & Schiffermüller]) (2183)
Post VCH: Recorded in Arnold (1995b) from a misidentified specimen. The record is therefore withdrawn.

Northern Drab *Orthosia opima* (Hübner) (2184)

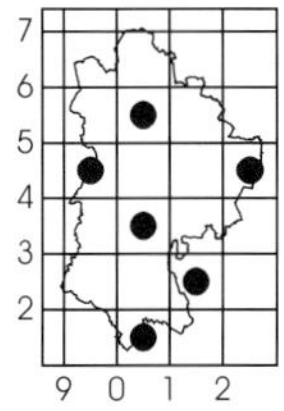

Post VCH: A very scarce and local species. Recorded from the following locations: Bedford School (1963), Cranfield (1981), Maulden Wood (1977), Sandy (1974), Whitehill Wood (1984) and the RIS traps at Cockayne Hatley (1976) and Whipsnade Wild Animal Park (1972).
Flight: April and May (weeks 18 and 19)*.
Larval Foodplants: Polyphagous on deciduous trees and shrubs.

Lead-coloured Drab *Orthosia populeti* (Fabricius) (2185)

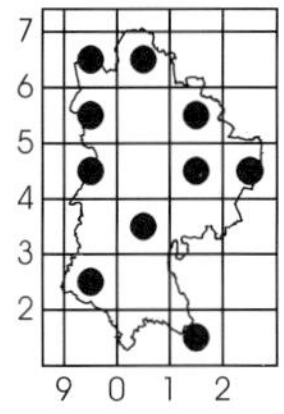

Post VCH: Local and uncommon: found in woodlands, such as Maulden Wood and Coppice Wood, where its foodplant occurs.
Flight: April and May (weeks 11 to 19)*.
Larval Foodplant: Aspen.

Powdered Quaker *Orthosia gracilis* ([Denis & Schiffermüller]) (2186)

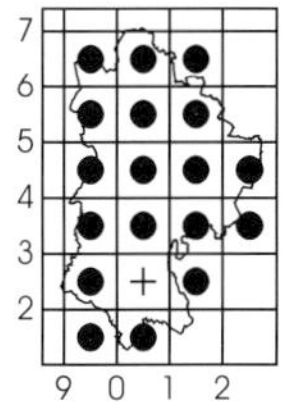

VCH: "Bedford, Luton."
Post VCH: Widespread but local and uncommon.
Flight: March to late May (weeks 12 to 22, peak 18 and 19)*.
Larval Foodplants: Polyphagous on shrubs and herbaceous plants.

For key to moth maps see page 3.

Common Quaker *Orthosia cerasi* (Fabricius) (2187)
VCH: (as *Taeniocampa stabilis* View.) "Abundant about sallows."
Post VCH: Common throughout the County.
Flight: February to June (weeks 8 to 23, peak 13 to 19)★.
Larval Foodplants: Polyphagous on deciduous trees.

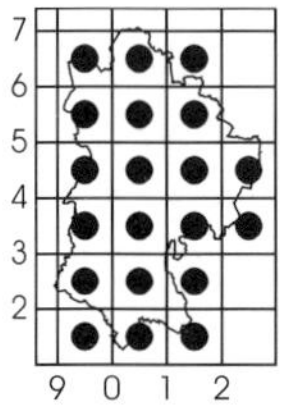

Clouded Drab *Orthosia incerta* (Hufnagel) (2188)
VCH: "Common about sallows."
Post VCH: Common and widespread.
Flight: March to June (weeks 10 to 23, peak 13 to 18)★.
Larval Foodplants: Polyphagous on deciduous trees and shrubs.

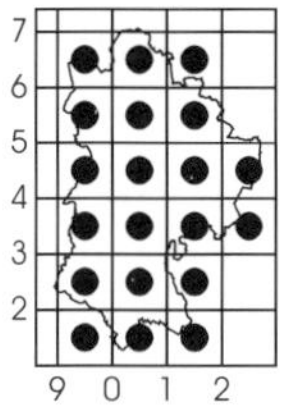

Twin-spotted Quaker *Orthosia munda* ([Denis & Schiffermüller]) (2189)
Post VCH: Widespread in woodlands but local and uncommon. Recorded in S.H.Kershaw's notebooks from Aspley Heath between 1934 and 1959.
Flight: March and April (weeks 10 to 18, peak 13 to 16)★.
Larval Foodplants: Hawthorns★, hazel★, sallow★ and other deciduous trees.

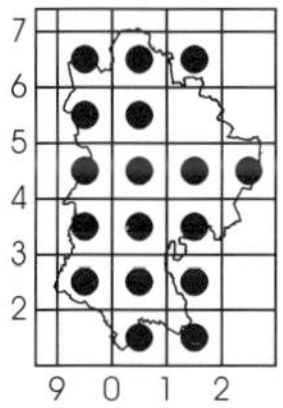

Hebrew Character *Orthosia gothica* (Linnaeus) (2190)
(Drawing on page 54)
VCH: "Generally common at sallow bloom."
Post VCH: Common and widespread.
Flight: January to June (weeks 1 to 23, peak 10 to 19)★.
Larval Foodplants: Polyphagous on deciduous trees and shrubs.

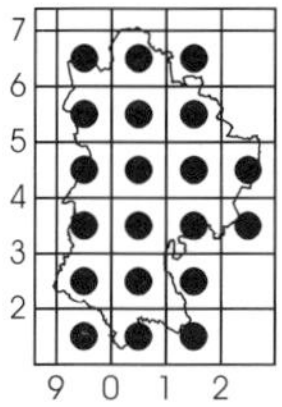

Brown-line Bright-eye *Mythimna conigera* ([Denis & Schiffermüller]) (2192)
VCH: "Bedford, Luton."
Post VCH: Common and widespread.
Flight: July and August (weeks 27 to 33, peak 29 to 32)★.
Larval Foodplants: Grasses.

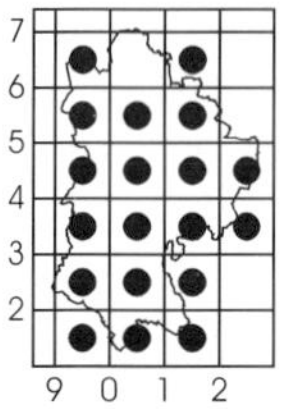

The Clay *Mythimna ferrago* (Fabricius) (2193)
VCH: (as *Leucania lithargyria* Esp.) "Bedford; probably everywhere."
Post VCH: Common and widespread.
Flight: June to August (weeks 22 to 35, peak 27 to 33)★.
Larval Foodplants: Grasses.

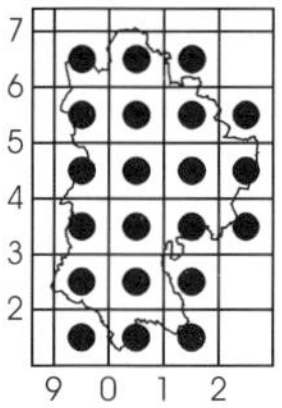

White-point *Mythimna albipuncta* ([Denis & Schiffermüller]) (2194)
Post VCH: One record only for this rare immigrant, in the RIS trap at Cockayne Hatley on 3 August 1995 (Woiwod & Manning, 1996).
Flight: August (week 31)★ to October.
Larval Foodplants: Grasses.

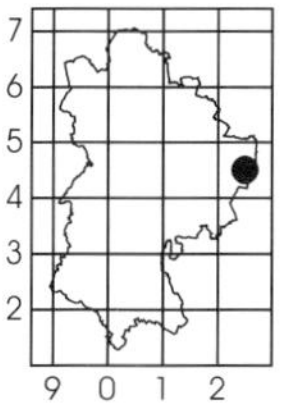

For details of standard weeks see page 6.

Striped Wainscot *Mythimna pudorina* ([Denis & Schiffermüller]) (2196)

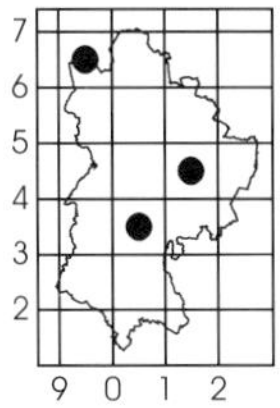

Post VCH: Recorded only three times, all in 1965: Cooper's Hill on 21 August, Sharnbrook Summit on 25 August and The Lodge, Sandy by W.J.Champkin on 20 August.
Flight: June, July, August (week 34)*.
Larval Foodplants: Common reed and various grasses.

Southern Wainscot *Mythimna straminea* (Treitschke) (2197)

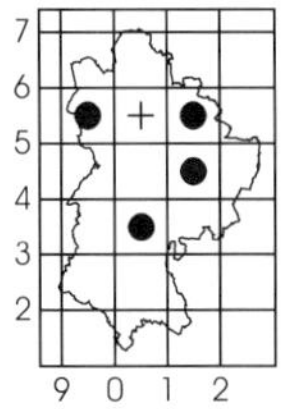

VCH: "Reported at Bedford by Mr. A.Sharpin."
Post VCH: A scarce and local species. Only four records: Carlton (1982), Flitwick Moor (1985), Tempsford (1990) and in the RIS trap at The Lodge, Sandy (1971).
Flight: July (week 29)* and August.
Larval Foodplants: Common reed and canary-grasses.

Smoky Wainscot *Mythimna impura impura* (Hübner) (2198)

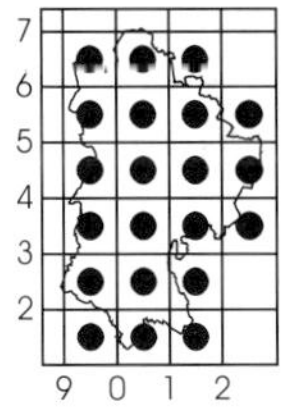

VCH: "Everywhere abundant."
Post VCH: Widespread and common.
Flight: June to October (weeks 22 to 41, peak 26 to 33)*.
Larval Foodplants: Grasses.

Common Wainscot *Mythimna pallens* (Linnaeus) (2199)

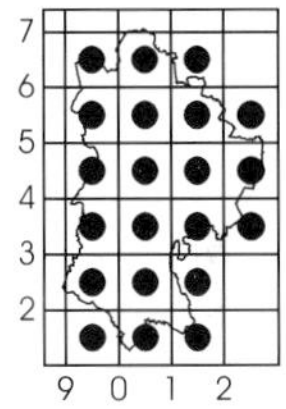

VCH: "Everywhere abundant."
Post VCH: Widespread and common.
Flight: May to October (weeks 22 to 42 with large numbers between 26 and 38 and peaks in 30 and 36)*. These records probably represent two overlapping broods.
Larval Foodplants: Grasses.

Shoulder-striped Wainscot *Mythimna comma* (Linnaeus) (2205)

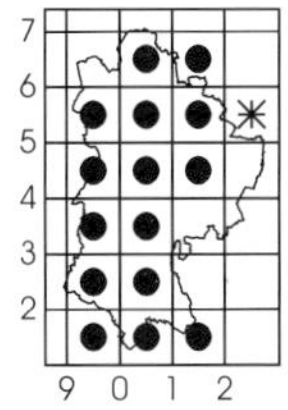

VCH: "Bedford."
Post VCH: Widespread but local and uncommon.
Flight: June and July (weeks 23 to 29, peak 24)*.
Larval Foodplants: Grasses.

Devonshire Wainscot *Mythimna putrescens* (Hübner) (2206)
Post VCH: There is a specimen in the Kershaw collection labelled "Aspley Heath 6.7.1933". This was no doubt mislabelled as there is no entry in Kershaw's notebook for that date. There is no other record from Bedfordshire.

For key to moth maps see page 3.

Noctuids - Part 2

(Cuculliinae and Acronictinae)

V.W.Arnold

Family: **Noctuidae**

The Mullein and larva

Subfamily: **Cuculliinae**

A group of species in which many of the moths are dull brownish in colour, superficially similar to many other noctuids. Some species, of which the beautiful Merveille du Jour is the most striking, have more complex forewing patterns. A few species, the Sharks, have unusually narrow forewings. Wingspan 28-68 mm. There are about 52 British species of which 41 have been found in Bedfordshire.

The Wormwood *Cucullia absinthii* (Linnaeus) (2211)

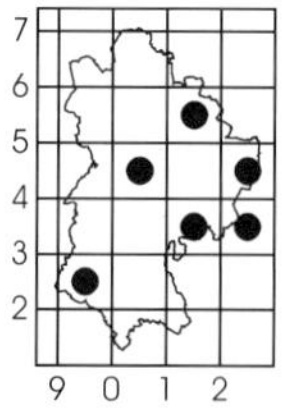

Post VCH: A scarce and local species with only a few records. A specimen in the P.N.Crow collection is labelled "Eaton Bray 24.vii.63". Larvae were found by W.J.Champkin in 1964 on mugwort at Barkers Lane, Bedford, and at Cople Pits. At light at Topfield Farm, Biggleswade, by R.C.Revels (July 1969), Blunham by A.Muir-Howie (1982), Clifton by A.R.Outen (1985, 1986) and Stotfold by E. and B.Bowskill (1991,1993, 1994) who also found larvae on wormwood there in 1993.

Flight: July and August (weeks 28 to 32)*.
Larval Foodplants: Wormwood* and mugwort*.

Chamomile Shark *Cucullia chamomillae* ([Denis & Schiffermüller]) (2214)

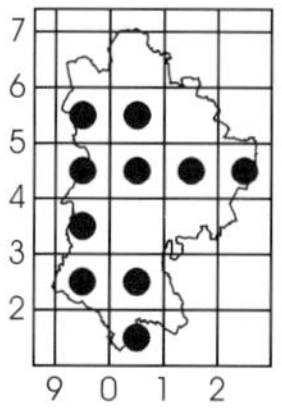

Post VCH: Found throughout the County, but local and uncommon. Recorded in S.H.Kershaw's notebooks from Aspley Heath in 1936.
Flight: April, May (weeks 19 and 21)*, June. Most records have been of larvae.
Larval Foodplants: Mayweeds* and chamomiles*.

The Shark *Cucullia umbratica* (Linnaeus) (2216)

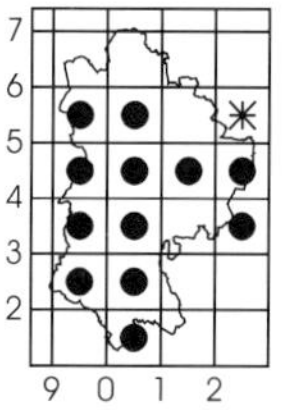

VCH: "Bedford, Luton; at flowers in gardens in the evening."
Post VCH: Widespread but local and uncommon.
Flight: June and July (weeks 25 to 29)*.
Larval Foodplants: Sow-thistles.

For details of standard weeks see page 6.

Water Betony *Cucullia scrophulariae* ([Denis & Schiffermüller]) (2220)
Pre VCH: "Larvae found about a week ago on *Scrophularia aquatica* (water betony) in a ditch by the side of the Corporation Farm" (Graham, 1878). This was probably a misidentified *C. verbasci* (The Mullein). For a full description of this species, see Heath and Emmet (1983).

The Mullein *Cucullia verbasci* (Linnaeus) (2221) (Drawing on page 340)

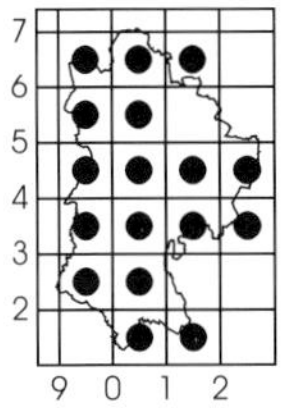

Pre VCH: J.C.Dale (MS2) recorded receiving this species from Abbot's collection from near Bedford but not dated. Abbot (MS1) noted rearing it in 1799.
VCH: "Bedford, Potton; larvae on *Verbascum* and *Scrophularia*."
Post VCH: Widespread but local and uncommon.
Flight: April and May (weeks 17 to 22)★. Many records have been of larvae.
Larval Foodplants: Mulleins★, figworts★ and *Buddleia globosa*★.

Minor Shoulder-knot *Brachylomia viminalis* (Fabricius) (2225)

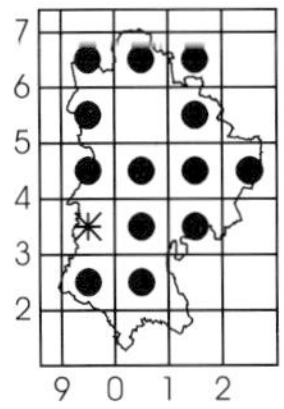

Post VCH: Widespread but local, in woodlands, fens and marshes. "Flitwick" (Foster, 1934). Recorded in S.H.Kershaw's notebooks from Aspley Heath on 9 August 1935. Some of the sites where this species has been found include Coppice Wood (1985, 1987, 1990, 1995) and Maulden Wood (1977, 1982) and also in the RIS traps at Cockayne Hatley (1976-1987, 1989-1992, 1994-1996) and Old Warden (1974, 1979).
Flight: June to August (weeks 24 to 33, peak 28 to 31)★.
Larval Foodplants: Sallows and willows.

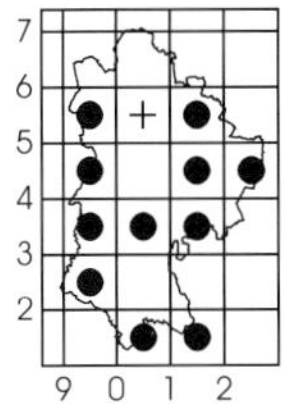

The Sprawler *Brachionycha sphinx* (Hufnagel) (2227)
VCH: (as *Petasia cassinea* Schiff.) "Bedford."
Post VCH: Widespread in woodlands. A local species that is attracted to light.
Flight: October to December (weeks 40 to 48, peak 43 to 46)★.
Larval Foodplants: Blackthorn★, ash★ and other deciduous trees.

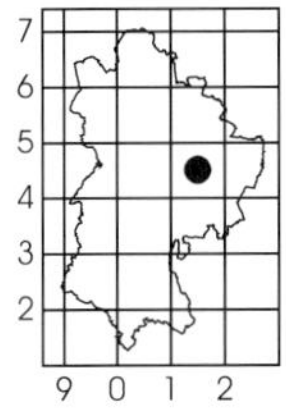

Brindled Ochre *Dasypolia templi* (Thunberg) (2229)
Post VCH: One at light at The Lodge, Sandy on 7 November 1990 by M.Kemp.
Flight: September to April.
Larval Foodplants: Hogweed and wild angelica, in the stems and roots.

Deep-brown Dart *Aporophyla lutulenta lutulenta* ([Denis & Schiffermüller]) (2231)

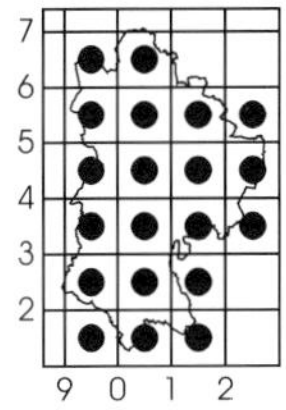

Post VCH: Common throughout the County. Recorded in S.H.Kershaw's notebooks from Aspley Heath in 1933 and 1938.There is also a specimen in the Kershaw collection from Aspley Heath in 1934.
Flight: September and October (weeks 36 to 43, peak 37 to 40)★.
Larval Foodplants: Polyphagous on grasses, hawthorns, blackthorn and broom.

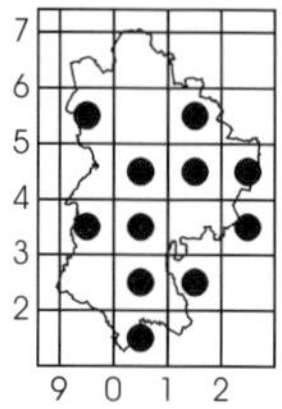

Black Rustic *Aporophyla nigra* (Haworth) (2232)
Post VCH: Widespread but local and uncommon.
Flight: September and October (weeks 38 to 44)*.
Larval Foodplants: Polyphagous on grasses and herbaceous plants.

Golden-rod Brindle *Lithomoia solidaginis* (Hübner) (2233)

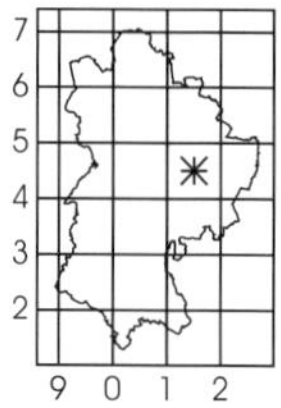

Post VCH: An immigrant species. Foster (1934) comments "Known as the Golden-rod Brindle, *Polia solidaginis*; Rowney Warren by Wightman". West (1959) includes this species in his list of Bedfordshire Lepidoptera but no locality is given.
Flight: August and September.
Larval Foodplants: Polyphagous on moorland and heathland plants.

Tawny Pinion *Lithophane semibrunnea* (Haworth) (2235)

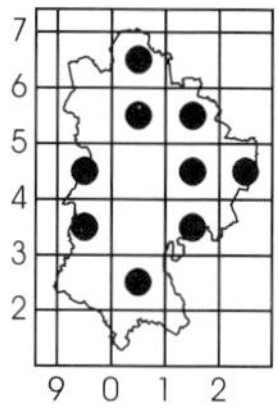

VCH: "Bedford, Potton; at ivy blossom."
Post VCH: Local, uncommon species in the County. Some of the sites where this species has been found include Aspley Heath (1934, 1983), Biggleswade (1980), Luton (1980, 1993) and Putnoe Wood (1965). Also in the RIS traps at Cockayne Hatley (1982, 1985, 1986) and Old Warden (1974).
Flight: September to November (weeks 38 to 44)* and, after hibernation, from March to May (weeks 15 to 17)*.
Larval Foodplant: Ash.

Pale Pinion *Lithophane hepatica* (Clerck) (= *socia* Hufnagel)) (2236)
Post VCH: Shown as occurring in Bedfordshire by Heath and Emmet (1983) but J. Heath (pers. comm.) considered this record erroneous.

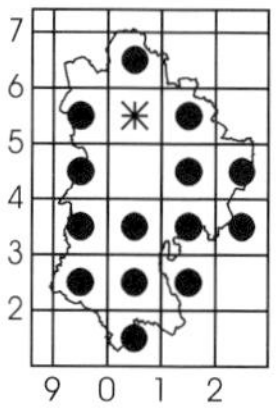

Grey Shoulder-knot *Lithophane ornitopus* (Hufnagel) ssp. *lactipennis* (Dadd) (2237)
Post VCH: Widespread in woodlands but local and uncommon.
Flight: September to April (weeks 38 to 44 and 1 to 13)*.
Larval Foodplants: Oaks.

Blair's Shoulder-knot *Lithophane leautieri* (Boisduval) ssp. *hesperica* Boursin (2240) (Drawing on page 57)

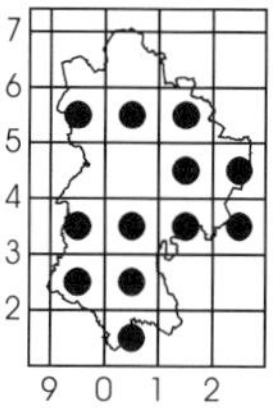

Post VCH: Found at Clifton by A.R.Outen in October 1985. It has since been recorded, mainly from gardens, throughout the County but in small numbers.
Flight: September to November (weeks 39 to 45, peak 40 and 41)*.
Larval Foodplants: Monterey cypress and other cypress cultivars*.

For details of standard weeks see page 6.

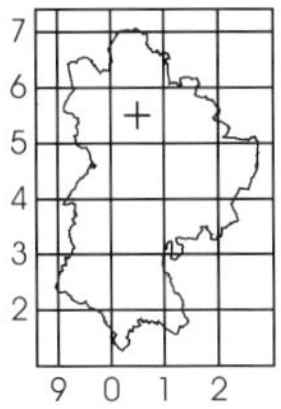

Red Sword-grass *Xylena vetusta* (Hübner) (2241)
VCH: "Bedford."
Post VCH: Not recorded.
Flight: September, October and, after hibernation, March and April.
Larval Foodplants: Polyphagous on grasses, deciduous trees and shrubs.

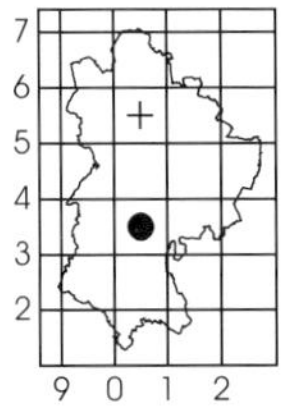

Sword-grass *Xylena exsoleta* (Linnaeus) (2242)
VCH: "Bedford."
Post VCH: One at light in Maulden Wood on 31 October 1977. A suspected immigrant.
Flight: September, October (week 44)* and, after hibernation, March and April.
Larval Foodplants: Polyphagous on grasses, deciduous trees and shrubs.

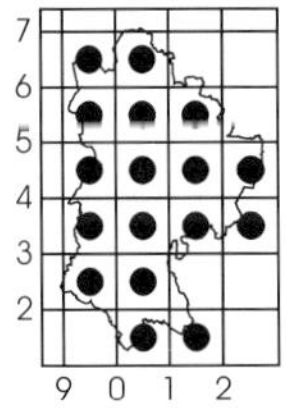

Early Grey *Xylocampa areola* (Esper) (2243)
VCH: "Bedford."
Post VCH: Widespread and common in woodlands and gardens.
Flight: March to June (weeks 10 to 23)*.
Larval Foodplant: Honeysuckle*.

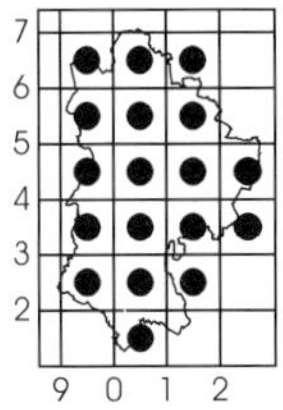

Green-brindled Crescent *Allophyes oxyacanthae* (Linnaeus) (2245)
VCH: "Bedford, Potton; its dark variety, *capucina*, occasionally."
Post VCH: Widespread and common in woods and gardens. The melanic form *capucina* is still common.
Flight: September to November (weeks 38 to 45, peak 40 to 43)*.
Larval Foodplants: Blackthorn* and hawthorns*.

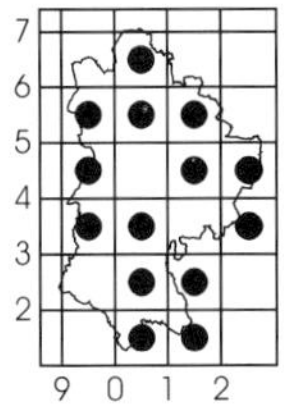

Merveille du Jour *Dichonia aprilina* (Linnaeus) (2247) (Plate 33)
VCH: "Bedford, Luton, Potton; about oaks."
Post VCH: Widespread in oak woodlands but a local and uncommon species.
Flight: September and October (weeks 39 to 42)*.
Larval Foodplants: Oaks*.

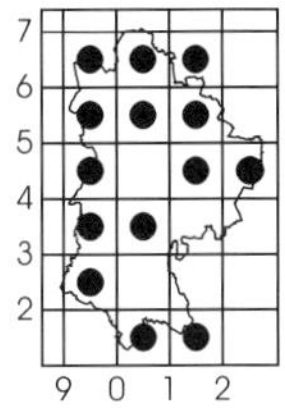

Brindled Green *Dryobotodes eremita* (Fabricius) (2248)
Pre VCH: J.C.Dale (MS2) recorded receiving this species (as *Seladonia*) from Abbot's collection from Bedford but not dated.
VCH: (as *Dryobota protea* Bkh.) "Bedford."
Post VCH: A local and uncommon species found in oak woodlands throughout the County.
Flight: September and October (weeks 35 to 42, peak 39)*.
Larval Foodplants: Oaks and hawthorns.

For key to moth maps see page 3.

Dark Brocade ***Mniotype adusta*** **(Esper) (2250)**

VCH: "Luton, in woods."
Post VCH: A local and uncommon species which has been found at the following sites: Bedford (1959, 1960), Cople Pits (1982), Flitwick Moor (1987), Marston Thrift (1986), Pavenham (1983, 1986), Sharnbrook (1977), Stotfold (1977) and Totternhoe Knolls (1978).
Flight: June to August (weeks 23, 27 and 32)*.
Larval Foodplants: Polyphagous on grasses, deciduous trees, shrubs and herbaceous plants.

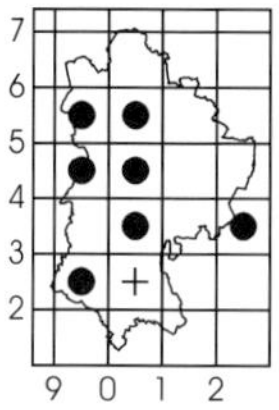

Large Ranunculus ***Polymixis flavicincta*** **([Denis & Schiffermüller]) (2252)**
Pre VCH: J.C.Dale (MS2) recorded receiving this species (as *Flavocincta*) from Abbot's collection from Bedford but not dated.
VCH: "Bedford, Luton, Potton."
Post VCH: Widespread but local and uncommon. Found in gardens, orchards and on waste ground.
Flight: September and October (weeks 36 to 41)*.
Larval Foodplants: Polyphagous on deciduous shrubs and herbaceous plants.

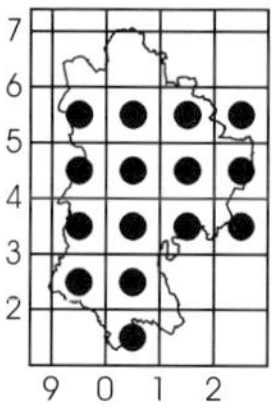

Grey Chi ***Antitype chi*** **(Linnaeus) (2254)**

VCH: "Bedford, usually a northern species."
Post VCH: Recalled by R.M.Craske as "numerous in late July on palings by Salem Thrift between 1918 and 1927". Recorded in S.H.Kershaw's notebooks from Aspley Heath on 14 August 1933. Only one more recent record, from Folly Caravan Park, Clapham, in 1979 by G.Ping.
Flight: Late July, August and September.
Larval Foodplants: Polyphagous on deciduous shrubs and herbaceous plants.

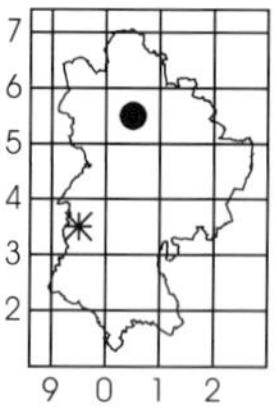

Feathered Ranunculus ***Eumichtis lichenea lichenea*** **(Hübner) (2255)**
Post VCH: A single record from the RIS trap at Cockayne Hatley on 11 October 1991.
Flight: August to October (week 41)*.
Larval Foodplants: Polyphagous on herbaceous plants.

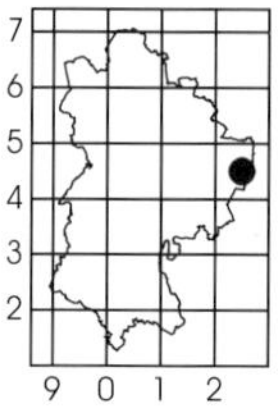

The Satellite ***Eupsilia transversa*** **(Hufnagel) (2256)**
VCH: (as *Scopelosoma satellita* Linn.) "Bedford, Luton."
Post VCH: Widespread and sometimes common in woodlands.
Flight: October to April (weeks 40 to 47 and 1 to 16)*.
Larval Foodplants: Elms*, hawthorns* and other deciduous trees.

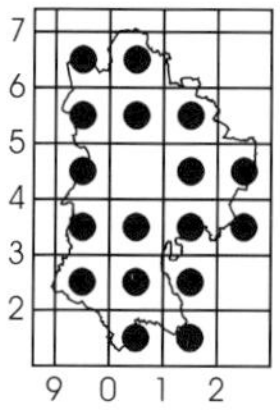

For details of standard weeks see page 6.

Orange Upperwing ***Jodia croceago*** **([Denis & Schiffermüller]) (2257)**
Pre VCH: J.C.Dale (MS2) recorded receiving this species from Abbot's collection from Bedford but not dated. The entry has question marks against both the place and Abbot's name which suggests that Dale thought the origin was doubtful.
Post VCH: Not recorded. "This species is now rarely recorded outside Surrey and South Devon" (Skinner, 1984).

The Chestnut ***Conistra vaccinii*** **(Linnaeus) (2258)**

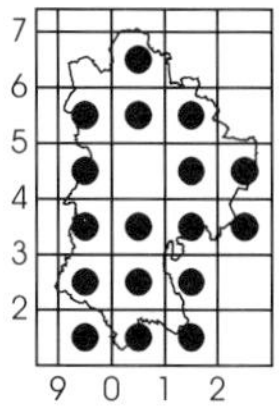

VCH: "Generally common."
Post VCH: Locally common in woodlands throughout the County.
Flight: September to May (weeks 39 to 52 with a peak 41 to 44, and 1 to 18 with a peak 8 to 12)*.
Larval Foodplants: Polyphagous, mainly on deciduous trees and shrubs.

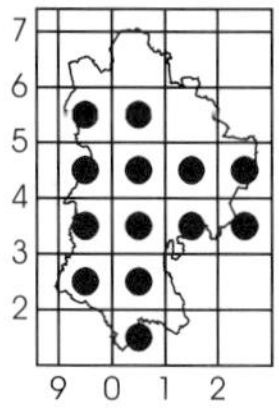

Dark Chestnut ***Conistra ligula*** **(Esper) (2259)**
VCH: "Bedford, Luton, Potton."
Post VCH: Widespread in woodlands but local and uncommon.
Flight: October to February (weeks 40 to 6, peak 42 to 44)*.
Larval Foodplants: Oaks, sallows and hawthorns.

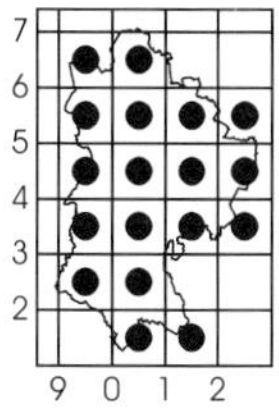

The Brick ***Agrochola circellaris*** **(Hufnagel) (2262)**
VCH: "Generally common."
Post VCH: Widespread and sometimes common in woodlands.
Flight: September to November (weeks 37 to 45, peak 41 to 43)*.
Larval Foodplants: Wych elm, poplars and ash.

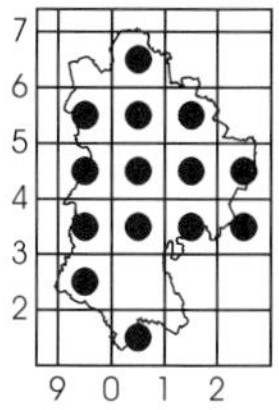

Red-line Quaker ***Agrochola lota*** **(Clerck) (2263)**
Pre VCH: Found near Bedford by C.Abbot (Haworth, 1803).
VCH: "Bedford."
Post VCH: Local but fairly common in woodlands throughout the County.
Flight: September to November (weeks 38 to 45, peak 40 to 43)*.
Larval Foodplants: Sallows and willows.

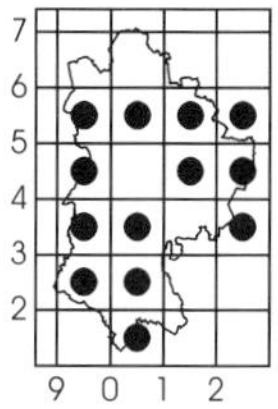

Yellow-line Quaker ***Agrochola macilenta*** **(Hübner) (2264)**
VCH: "Bedford."
Post VCH: A local and uncommon species which is found in woodlands throughout the County.
Flight: September to November (weeks 37 to 47, peak 41 to 45)*.
Larval Foodplants: Polyphagous on deciduous trees and also herbaceous plants.

For key to moth maps see page 3.

Flounced Chestnut ***Agrochola helvola*** **(Linnaeus) (2265)**

Post VCH: A local and uncommon species. R.M.Craske recalled finding it "at light in Bedford but local" between 1918 and 1927. Recorded in S.H.Kershaw's notebooks from Aspley Heath in 1933, 1937 and 1938. More recently it has been recorded from Bedford (1956), Cranfield (1981), Luton (1982), Marston Thrift (1983-1986), Maulden Wood (1975-1977, 1980, 1984-1986) and Studham (1975, 1980). Also from the RIS traps at Old Warden (1978), Whipsnade Wild Animal Park (1973) and The Lodge, Sandy (1969-1971, 1974, 1975 and at MV light there in 1989-1990).
Flight: September to November (weeks 38 to 44, peak 40 and 41)*.
Larval Foodplants: Polyphagous on deciduous trees.

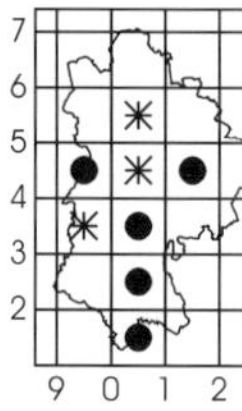

Brown-spot Pinion ***Agrochola litura*** **(Linnaeus) (2266)**

VCH: "Bedford, Potton."
Post VCH: Widespread and common, particularly in wooded areas.
Flight: September and October (weeks 35 to 43, peak 37 to 41)*.
Larval Foodplants: Herbaceous plants and deciduous trees.

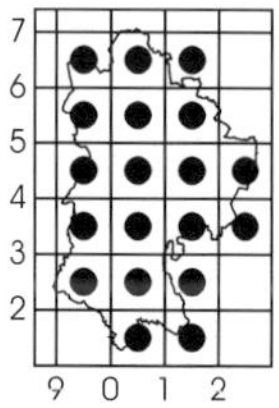

Beaded Chestnut ***Agrochola lychnidis*** **([Denis & Schiffermüller]) (2267)**

Pre VCH: J.C.Dale (MS2) recorded receiving this species, as *Spharulatina*, from Abbot's collection from Bedford but not dated.
VCH: (as *Orthosia pistacina* Schiff.) "Generally common."
Post VCH: Widespread and common.
Flight: September and November (weeks 36 to 47, peak 39 to 42)*.
Larval Foodplants: Herbaceous plants and deciduous trees.

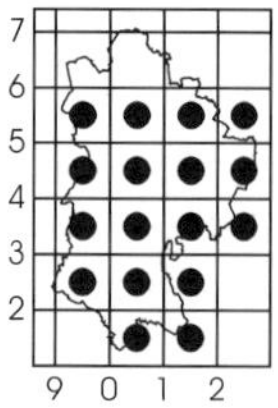

Centre-barred Sallow ***Atethmia centrago*** **(Haworth) (2269)**

Post VCH: Widespread and locally common, particularly near ash trees. Recorded in S.H.Kershaw's notebooks from Aspley Heath in 1947.
Flight: August to October (weeks 34 to 40, peak 35 to 37)*.
Larval Foodplant: Ash*.

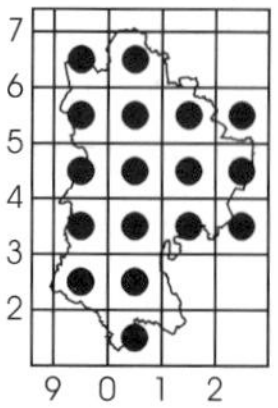

Lunar Underwing ***Omphaloscelis lunosa*** **(Haworth) (2270)**

VCH: "Bedford."
Post VCH: Widespread and locally common.
Flight: August to October (weeks 34 to 42, peak 37 to 41)*.
Larval Foodplants: Grasses.

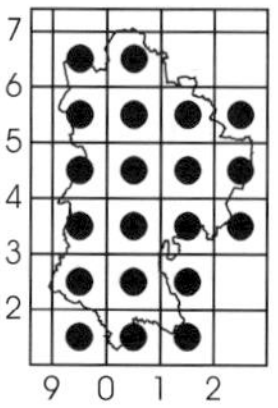

Orange Sallow ***Xanthia citrago*** **(Linnaeus) (2271)**

VCH: "Bedford, among lime."
Post VCH: A local and uncommon species, found in woodlands throughout the County. Aspley Guise is among the sites where it has been found.
Flight: September (weeks 36 to 39)*.
Larval Foodplants: Limes.

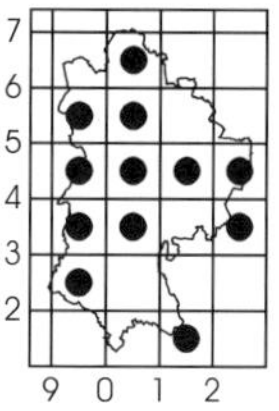

For details of standard weeks see page 6.

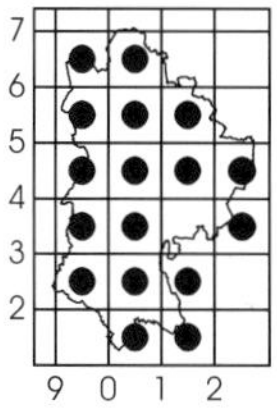

Barred Sallow *Xanthia aurago* ([Denis & Schiffermüller]) (2272)
VCH: "Taken at Potton by Mr. W.Bond-Smith."
Post VCH: Found in woodlands throughout the County but local and uncommon.
Flight: September and October (weeks 35 to 43)*.
Larval Foodplants: Field maple and beech.

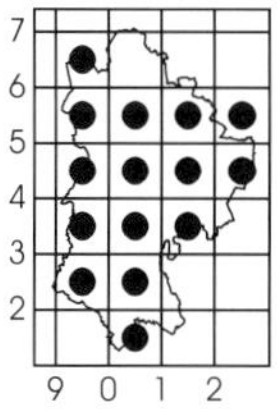

Pink-barred Sallow *Xanthia togata* (Esper) (2273)
Pre VCH: J.C.Dale (MS2) recorded receiving *Flavago* from Abbot's collection. However, this name has been used for both this species and the Frosted Orange so we cannot be sure which species was meant.
VCH: (as *X. silago* Hb.) "Bedford, Luton."
Post VCH: Found throughout the County in damp woodlands. A local and uncommon species.
Flight: September and October (weeks 37 to 42, peak 40)*.
Larval Foodplants: Sallows and low-growing plants.

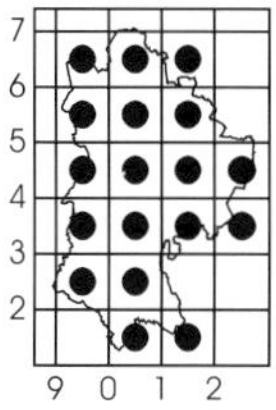

The Sallow *Xanthia icteritia* (Hufnagel) (2274)
VCH: (as *X. cerago* Schiff.) "Bedford, Luton."
Post VCH: Locally common in a variety of habitats throughout the County.
Flight: September and October (weeks 35 to 42, peak 37 to 40)*.
Larval Foodplants: Sallows and low-growing plants.

Dusky-lemon Sallow *Xanthia gilvago* ([Denis & Schiffermüller]) (2275)
VCH: "Bedford, not rare."

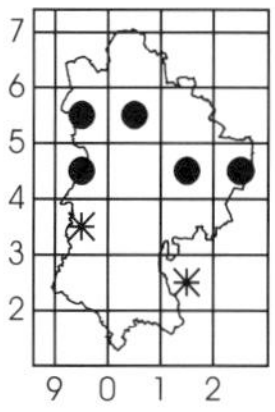

Post VCH: Very local and uncommon. Found in woodlands where its foodplant occurs. S.H.Kershaw noted finding a pupa on wych elm at Pegsdon on 19 May 1933. No records have been received since it was found in Marston Thrift in 1986. The effect of Dutch elm disease has no doubt played a major part in the decline of this species.
Flight: September and October (weeks 37 to 41)*.
Larval Foodplants: Wych elm* and occasionally English elm.

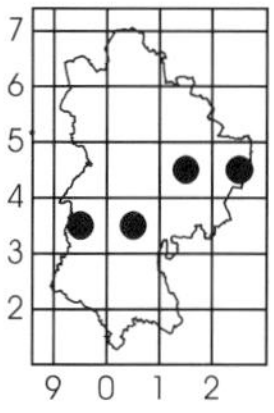

Pale-lemon Sallow *Xanthia ocellaris* (Borkhausen) (2276)
Post VCH: Found at sugar at Brogborough (1982) and in Maulden Wood (1976). Also in the RIS traps at Cockayne Hatley (1986) and Old Warden (1979).
Flight: September and October (weeks 39 and 40)*.
Larval Foodplants: Mainly Black poplar but also herbaceous plants.

Marbled Beauty
(x 1.5)

Subfamily: **Acronictinae**

A subfamily of mostly greyish moths. Wingspan 23-49 mm. The larvae differ from most other noctuid larvae in being brightly coloured with long tufts of hairs. Of the 15 British species, 10 have been found in Bedfordshire, plus two for which the records are doubtful.

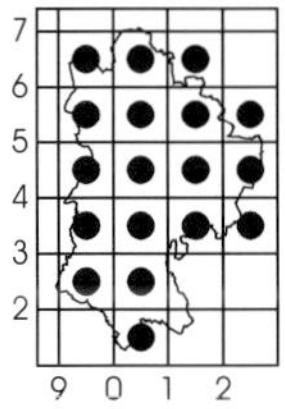

Poplar Grey ***Acronicta megacephala*** **([Denis & Schiffermüller]) (2278)**
VCH: "Bedford, Luton, on poplars."
Post VCH: Widespread and common, particularly in woodlands.
Flight: June to August (weeks 25 to 33)★.
Larval Foodplants: Poplars★ (usually black poplar), aspen and sallows.

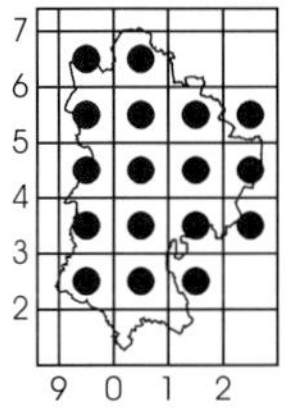

The Sycamore ***Acronicta aceris*** **(Linnaeus) (2279)**
VCH: "Bedford, Potton; about sycamore."
Post VCH: Widespread in woods but local and uncommon.
Flight: June to August (weeks 25 to 31)★.
Larval Foodplants: Horse-chestnut★, sycamore, field maple and oaks.

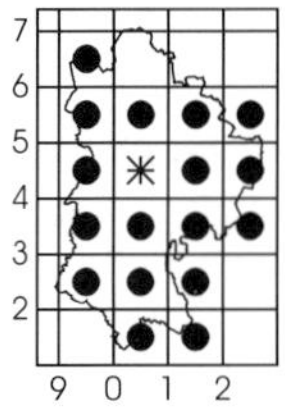

The Miller ***Acronicta leporina*** **(Linnaeus) (2280)**
Post VCH: Widespread but local and uncommon. Usually found in wooded areas.
Flight: June, July (weeks 24 to 30)★ and August.
Larval Foodplants: Alder, birches★, poplars, oaks, aspen and sallows.

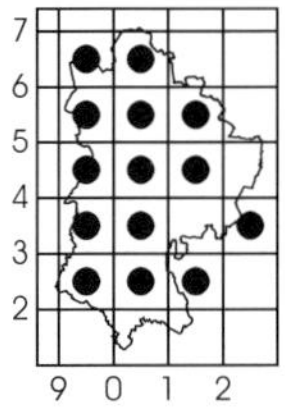

Alder Moth ***Acronicta alni*** **(Linnaeus) (2281)**
Post VCH: Widespread in woods but local and uncommon. There is a specimen in the Kershaw collection from Aspley Heath in 1937.
Flight: May and June (weeks 18 to 26)★.
Larval Foodplants: Polyphagous on deciduous trees, especially alder and birches★. Also brambles★ and roses (wild and cultivated)★.

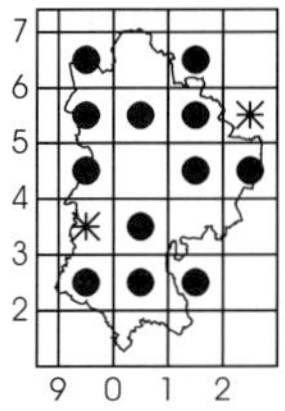

Dark Dagger ***Acronicta tridens*** **([Denis & Schiffermüller]) (2283)**
Pre VCH: J.C.Dale (MS3) recorded finding "*N. psi* ? or *tridens* ?" on 1 June 1820 in Clapham Park Wood.
VCH: "Larvae taken at Potton."
Post VCH: It is impossible to separate the adults of this species from *A. psi* (Grey Dagger) without examination of the genitalia. A number of records for this species are of larvae, which are easily identified. The Dark Dagger

can be found in similar habitats to those of the Grey Dagger but it does not appear to be as common.
Flight: May to July (weeks 22 to 29)★.
Larval Foodplants: Hawthorns★, blackthorn★ and other deciduous trees and shrubs.

Grey Dagger *Acronicta psi* (Linnaeus) (2284) (Plate 39)

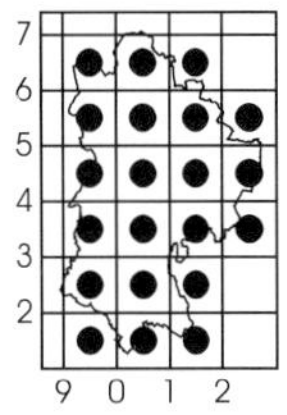

Pre VCH: C.Abbot (MS1) noted "*psi* Dagger Moth *Capta die Maii* 23rd 1798 Corn Close". It is not clear what he meant by "Corn Close". J.C.Dale (MS3) recorded finding "*N. psi* ? or *tridens* ?" on 1 June 1820 in Clapham Park Wood. (See previous species)
VCH: "Generally common."
Post VCH: Common throughout the County. Not all of the records for this species have been checked by genitalia examination.
Flight: May to July (weeks 22 to 31)★.
Larval Foodplants: Blackthorn★, hawthorns★, roses★ and other deciduous trees and shrubs.

Light Knot Grass *Acronicta menyanthidis menyanthidis* (Esper) (2286)
Post VCH: Recorded in S.H.Kershaw's notebook from Aspley Heath on 19-20 July 1937 but no specimens have been seen. Recorded by West (1959) in error. Not otherwise known in Bedfordshire.

Knot Grass *Acronicta rumicis* (Linnaeus) (2289)

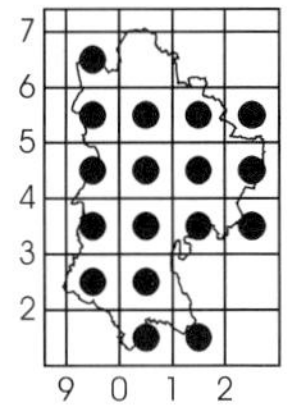

VCH: "Bedford."
Post VCH: Widespread and locally fairly common.
Flight: May to September (weeks 19 to 36)★.
Larval Foodplants: Polyphagous on deciduous trees and herbaceous plants, including teasel★.

Reed Dagger *Simyra albovenosa* (Goeze) (2290)

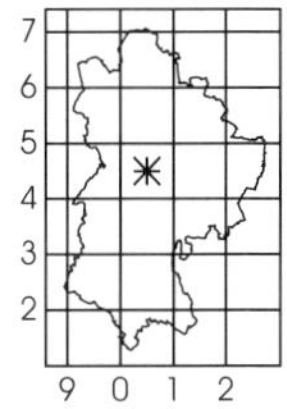

Post VCH: One record only, specimen in B.B.West's collection from Bedford on 8 May 1956 (West, 1957).
Flight: Double-brooded, flying in May (week 19)★ and again in July and August.
Larval Foodplants: Common reed, whorl-grass, tufted sedge, sallow.
Notes: This moth is also referred to as the Powdered Wainscot.

The Coronet *Craniophora ligustri* ([Denis & Schiffermüller]) (2291)

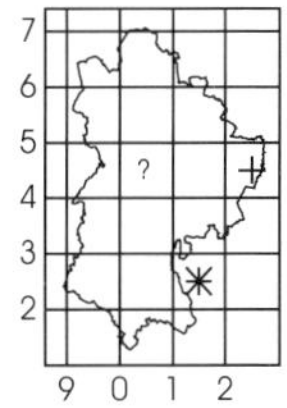

VCH: "Potton."
Post VCH: "Pegsdon Hills, scarce" (Foster, 1917). Also Cardington Road, Bedford, in August 1957 (West, 1958), but West (pers. comm.) felt that this may have been recorded erroneously.
Flight: June and July.
Larval Foodplants: Ash and wild privet.

Marbled Beauty *Cryphia domestica* (Hufnagel) (2293)

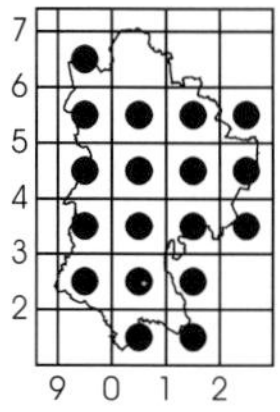

(Drawing on page 348)
VCH: (as *Bryophila perla* Fab.) "Generally common on walls."
Post VCH: Found throughout the County. Often fairly common in gardens.
Flight: June to September (weeks 26 to 35, peak 30 to 32)*.
Larval Foodplants: Lichens growing on walls, roofs, etc.

Marbled Green *Cryphia muralis muralis* (Forster) (2295)
Post VCH: Cardington Road, Bedford (1958) (West, 1959). As no voucher specimen survives, it is possible that this species was confused with the Marbled Beauty (*C. domestica*).
Flight: July and August.
Larval Foodplants: Lichens growing on walls, roofs, etc.

For details of standard weeks see page 6.

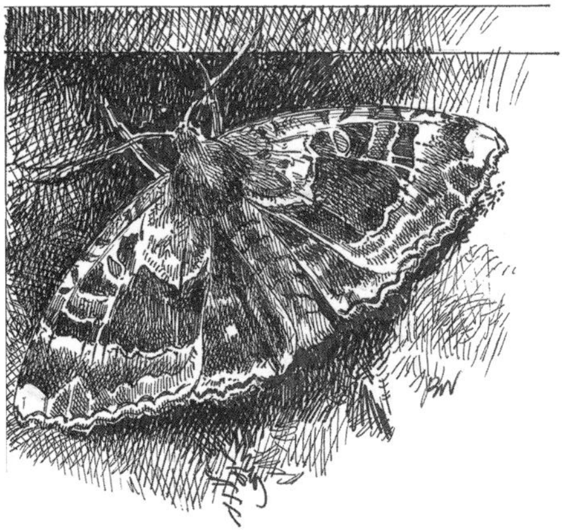

Noctuids - Part 3

(Amphipyrinae to Hypeninae)

V.W.Arnold

Family: **Noctuidae**

Subfamily: **Amphipyrinae**

Old Lady

This is a large and very variable subfamily.
It includes one of the largest noctuid species in Britain, the Old Lady (wingspan 64-74 mm) as well as some relatively small species (wingspan 22-26 mm). A more usual wingspan range would be 35-45 mm. The larvae show a wide range of colour patterns and feeding habits. Many live in the soil, some bore in stems and roots and others feed above ground on leaves. Of the 91 British species, 64 have been found in Bedfordshire, together with three for which the records are doubtful.

Small Yellow Underwing

Copper Underwing ***Amphipyra pyramidea*** **(Linnaeus) (2297)**

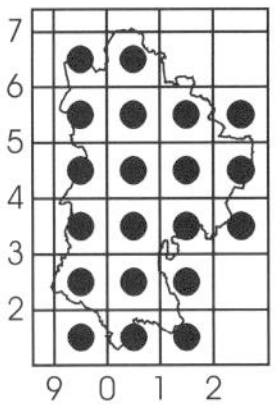

VCH: "Bedford, in woods."
Post VCH: Widespread and common in woodlands. There are specimens in the Kershaw collection from Aspley Heath dated 27 August 1936, 17 September 1936, 12 August 1938, 26 August 1946 and 26 July 1949 (det. A.M.Riley).
Flight: July to October (weeks 28 to 41)★.
Larval Foodplants: Field maple★,oaks★, privet★ and other deciduous trees and shrubs.
Notes: The Copper Underwing was separated from Svensson's Copper Underwing as two distinct species in 1968 but, before 1983, most Bedfordshire records could have been for either species. After 1983, the two species have been recorded separately. Skinner (1984) describes the differences between them. See also Webb (1984b).

Svensson's Copper Underwing ***Amphipyra berbera*** **Rungs ssp.** ***svenssoni*** **Fletcher (2298)**

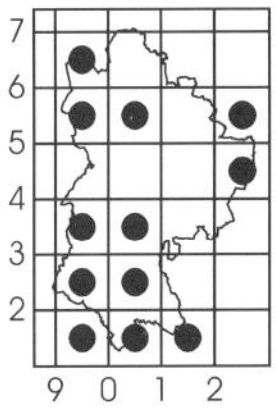

Post VCH: There are specimens in the Kershaw collection from Aspley Heath dated 26 July 1938 and 4 September 1946 (det. A.M.Riley). More recently it was reported from Clapham in 1979 and has been found throughout the County in wooded areas. It is probably more common than current records suggest.
Flight: July to September (weeks 30 to 39)★.
Larval Foodplants: Polyphagous on deciduous trees and shrubs.

For key to moth maps see page 3.

Mouse Moth *Amphipyra tragopoginis* (Clerck) (2299)
VCH: "Generally common, often coming into houses."
Post VCH: Common and widespread. See also Webb (1984b).
Flight: July to September (weeks 27 to 39, peak 31 to 37)*.
Larval Foodplants: Deciduous shrubs and herbaceous plants.

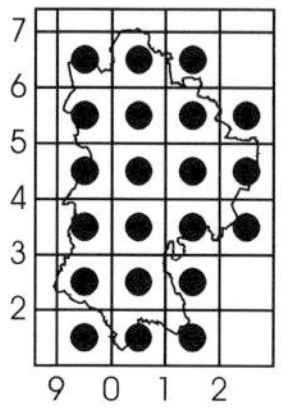

Old Lady *Mormo maura* (Linnaeus) (2300) (Drawing on page 351)
Pre VCH: This species was known as Great Brown Bar by Graham (1878) who reported that "about a dozen were caught in Stoke Mills" (Sharnbrook).
VCH: "Generally distributed."
Post VCH: Widespread but local and uncommon. Roosts by day in houses, sheds, culverts and under bridges.
Flight: July and August (weeks 29 to 33)*.
Larval Foodplants: Polyphagous on herbaceous plants and deciduous trees and shrubs, including sycamore*.

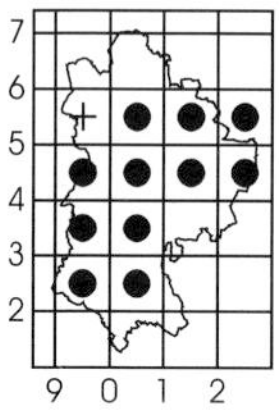

Bird's Wing *Dypterygia scabriuscula* (Linnaeus) (2301)
VCH: "Bedford."
Post VCH: A local and uncommon species, found in woods throughout the County, such as Aspley Heath, Maulden Wood, Stockgrove Country Park and The Lodge, Sandy.
Flight: May to July (weeks 22 to 29)*.
Larval Foodplants: Docks, sorrels and various low-growing plants.

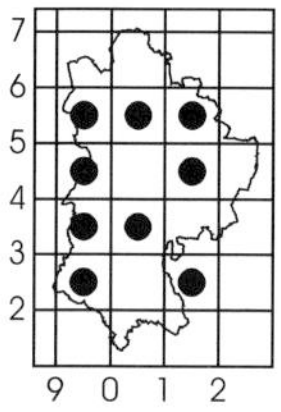

Brown Rustic *Rusina ferruginea* (Esper) (2302)
VCH: (as *R. tenebrosa* Hb.) "Bedford, Luton."
Post VCH: Widespread and common.
Flight: May to October (weeks 21 to 40, peak 23 to 28)*.
Larval Foodplants: Polyphagous on herbaceous plants.

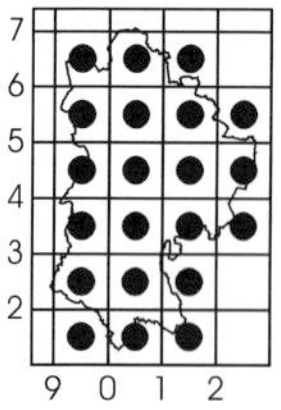

Straw Underwing *Thalpophila matura* (Hufnagel) (2303)
VCH: "Bedford."
Post VCH: Widespread on rough grasslands, where it is locally fairly common.
Flight: June to September (weeks 23 to 36, peak 29 to 33)*.
Larval Foodplants: Grasses.

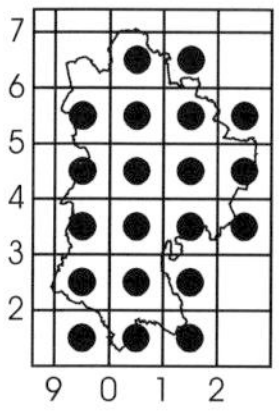

Small Angle Shades *Euplexia lucipara* (Linnaeus) (2305)
Pre VCH: J.C.Dale (MS2) recorded receiving this species from Abbot's collection from Bedford but not dated.
VCH: "Generally common."
Post VCH: Widespread and fairly common in woods and gardens.
Flight: June to August (weeks 23 to 32, peak 28)*.
Larval Foodplants: Bracken and a variety of ferns. Occasionally herbaceous plants and deciduous shrubs.

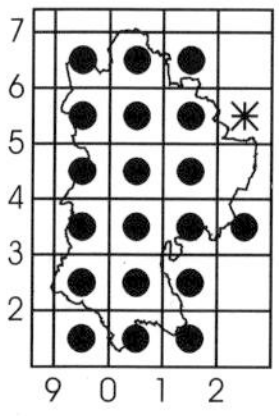

For details of standard weeks see page 6.

Angle Shades ***Phlogophora meticulosa*** **(Linnaeus) (2306)** (Plate 93)

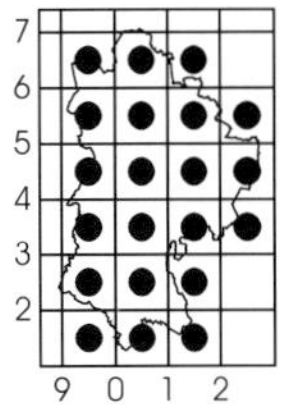

VCH: "Common everywhere."
Post VCH: Widespread and common throughout the County.
Flight: Continuously brooded between April and November (weeks 15 to 49, peak 37 to 42)★.
Larval Foodplants: Polyphagous on herbaceous plants. Sometimes is a pest, damaging greenhouse plants.

The Olive ***Ipimorpha subtusa*** **([Denis & Schiffermüller]) (2312)**

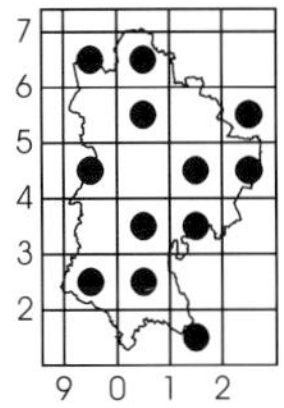

Post VCH: Widespread in damp woodlands but local and uncommon.
Flight: July and August (weeks 28 to 34)★.
Larval Foodplants: Aspen and poplars.

The Suspected ***Parastichtis suspecta*** **Hübner (2268)**

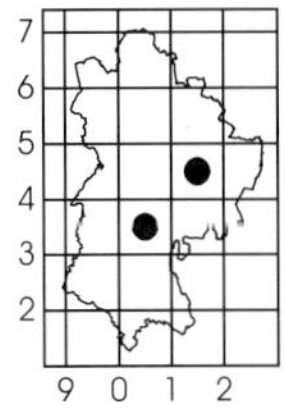

Post VCH: Foster (1934) states "at Flitwick Marsh, by Brocklehurst". More recently at Flitwick Moor (1977, 1980) and in the RIS trap at The Lodge, Sandy (1970, 1975 and at MV light there in 1990).
Flight: July and August (weeks 30 to 32)★.
Larval Foodplants: Birches and sallows.

Dingy Shears ***Parastichtis ypsillon*** **([Denis & Schiffermüller]) (2314)**

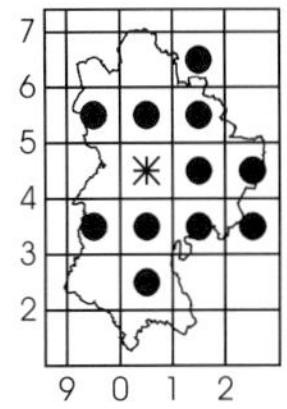

Post VCH: Local and uncommon in damp woodlands.
Flight: June, July (weeks 26 to 29)★ and August.
Larval Foodplants: Willows, sallows and black poplar.

Heart Moth ***Dicycla oo*** **(Linnaeus) (2315)**

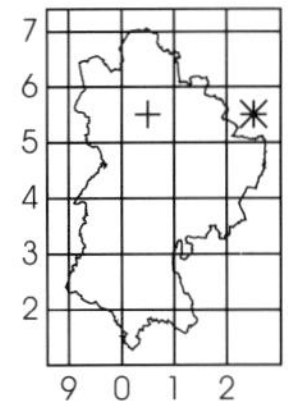

Pre VCH: T. Orlebar Marsh (MS1) noted *Phalaena Oo* from Clapham and Biddenham in 1798. J.C.Dale (MS2) recorded receiving this species (as *Ferruginago*) from Abbot's collection from Bedford but not dated.
Post VCH: Only one record at White Wood on 29-30 June 1957 by B.O.C.Gardiner and J.Renouf. This species prefers mature oak trees in open woodland and the cessation of coppicing may have lead to its decline.
Flight: June and July.
Larval Foodplants: Oaks.

Lesser-spotted Pinion ***Cosmia affinis*** **(Linnaeus) (2316)**

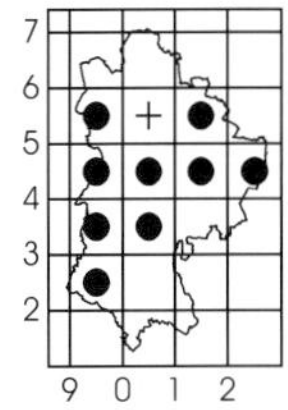

VCH: "Bedford, among elm."
Post VCH: Local and uncommon. Recorded from a number of wooded areas in the County. The destruction of its foodplants by Dutch elm disease may have contributed to the apparent decline of this species.
Flight: July to September (weeks 27 to 37)★.
Larval Foodplants: English elm and wych elm.

For key to moth maps see page 3.

White-spotted Pinion *Cosmia diffinis* (Linnaeus) (2317)

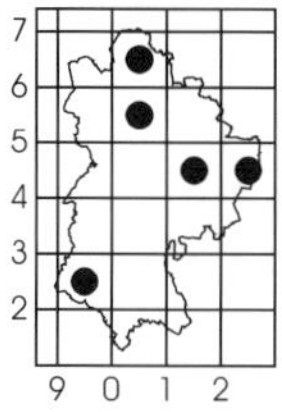

Pre VCH: J.C.Dale (MS2) recorded receiving this species from Abbot's collection from Bedford but not dated.
VCH: "Bedford, among elm."
Post VCH: Recorded from Bedford (1977), Sewell Railway Cutting (1976), Willington (1962) and in the RIS trap at Cockayne Hatley (1977). The effect of Dutch elm disease has no doubt played a major part in the decline of this nationally uncommon species (Skinner, 1984). Last recorded in Bedfordshire in Coppice Wood in 1985.
Flight: August and September (weeks 33 to 37)⋆.
Larval Foodplants: English elm and wych elm.

The Dun-bar *Cosmia trapezina* (Linnaeus) (2318)

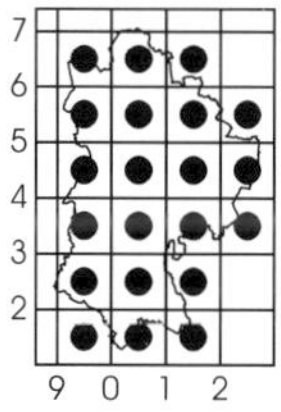

VCH: "Common in woods."
Post VCH: Widespread and common.
Flight: July to September (weeks 27 to 37, peak 30 to 33)⋆.
Larval Foodplants: Field maple⋆, hawthorns⋆, hazel⋆, sallow⋆ and other deciduous trees. Also carnivorous on the larvae of Lepidoptera.

Lunar-spotted Pinion *Cosmia pyralina* ([Denis & Schiffermüller]) (2319)

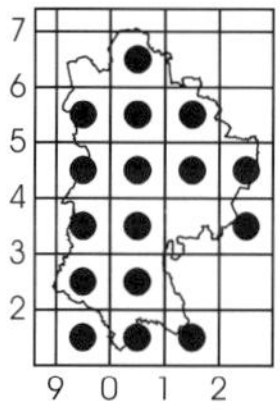

Post VCH: Widespread in woodlands but local and uncommon. Recorded in S.H.Kershaw's notebook from Aspley Heath in 1960.
Flight: July to August (weeks 27 to 33, peak 29)⋆.
Larval Foodplants: Elms⋆ and other deciduous trees.

Dark Arches *Apamea monoglypha* (Hufnagel) (2321)

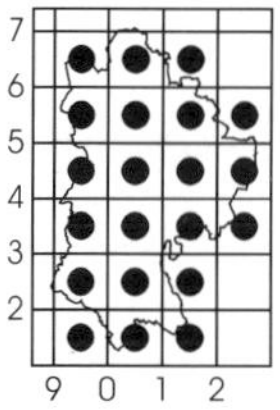

VCH: "Universally abundant."
Post VCH: Widespread and common, sometimes abundant.
Flight: June to September (weeks 23 to 38, peak 27 to 31)⋆.
Larval Foodplants: Grasses, on the roots and stems.

Light Arches *Apamea lithoxylaea* ([Denis & Schiffermüller]) (2322)

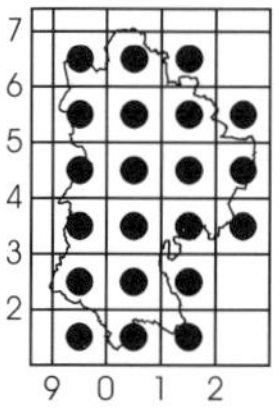

VCH: "Generally common."
Post VCH: Widespread and common.
Flight: June to August (weeks 24 to 35, peak 26 to 30)⋆.
Larval Foodplants: Grasses, on the roots and stems.

Reddish Light Arches *Apamea sublustris* (Esper) (2323)

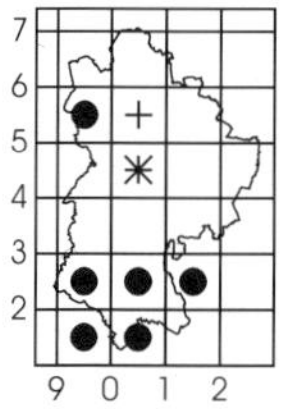

VCH: "Bedford, very local."
Post VCH: A local and uncommon species which is usually found on calcareous soils in the south of the County.
Flight: June and July (weeks 24 to 30, peak 27 to 29)⋆.
Larval Foodplants: Grasses, feeding on the roots.

For details of standard weeks see page 6.

Clouded-bordered Brindle *Apamea crenata* (Hufnagel) (2326)
VCH: (as *Xylophasia rurea* Fab.) "Luton."
Post VCH: Widespread but local and uncommon.
Flight: May to July (weeks 20 to 29)*.
Larval Foodplants: Grasses.

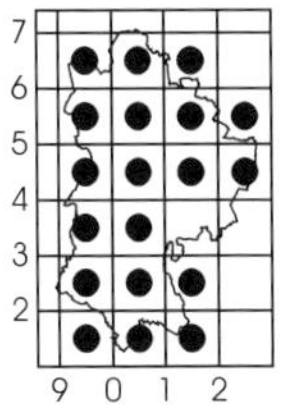

Clouded Brindle *Apamea epomidion* (Haworth) (2327)
VCH: (as *Xylophasia hepatica* Hb.) "Luton."
Post VCH: Widespread in woodlands but local and uncommon.
Flight: June to August (weeks 23 to 31)*.
Larval Foodplants: Grasses.

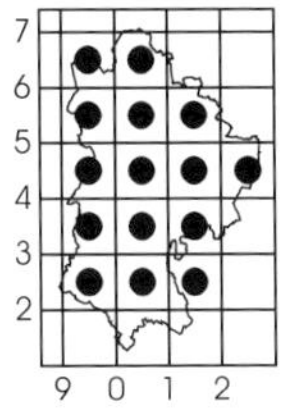

Dusky Brocade *Apamea remissa* (Hübner) (2330)
VCH: (as *A. gemina* Hb.) "Bedford."
Post VCH: Widespread but local and uncommon. Usually found in damp woodlands, downlands and grassy areas.
Flight: June and July (weeks 22 to 29)*.
Larval Foodplants: Grasses.

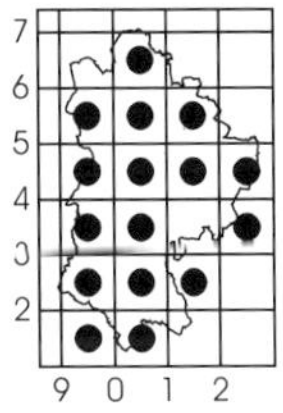

Small Clouded Brindle *Apamea unanimis* (Hübner) (2331)
Post VCH: There is a specimen in the Kershaw collection from Bedford dated 30 May 1933. More recently reported from Carlton (1996), Clapham (1979), Luton (1981, 1983) and Pavenham (1985, 1987).
Flight: May to July (weeks 22, 24, 26)*.
Larval Foodplants: Grasses.

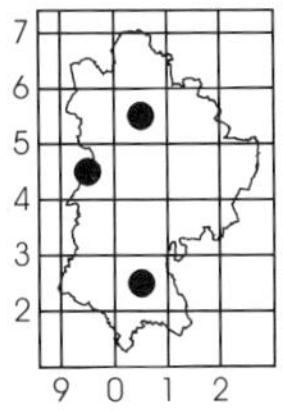

Large Nutmeg *Apamea anceps* ([Denis & Schiffermüller]) (2333)
VCH: "Luton."
Post VCH: Widespread and common, sometimes abundant.
Flight: May to September (weeks 21 to 37, peak 24 to 29)*.
Larval Foodplants: Grasses.

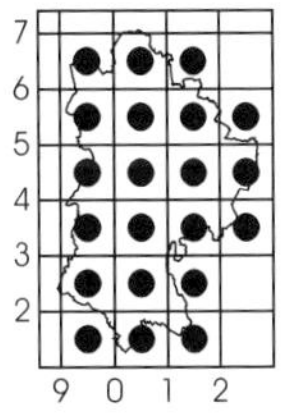

Rustic Shoulder-knot *Apamea sordens* (Hufnagel) (2334)
VCH: (as *A. basilinea* Fab.) "Luton, Bedford."
Post VCH: Widespread and common.
Flight: May to September (weeks 20 to 35, peak 21 to 27)*.
Larval Foodplants: Grasses.

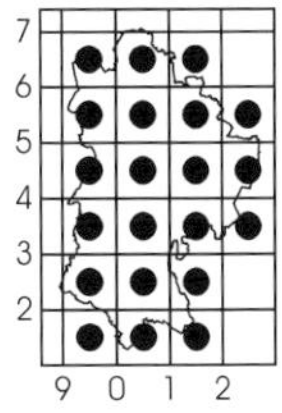

Slender Brindle *Apamea scolopacina* (Esper) (2335)
Post VCH: A woodland species that is local and uncommon. Good sites are Flitwick Moor and Maulden Wood.
Flight: July to September (weeks 28 to 38)*.
Larval Foodplants: Grasses.

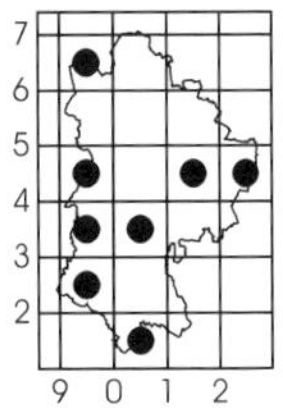

For key to moth maps see page 3.

Double Lobed ***Apamea ophiogramma*** **(Esper) (2336)**

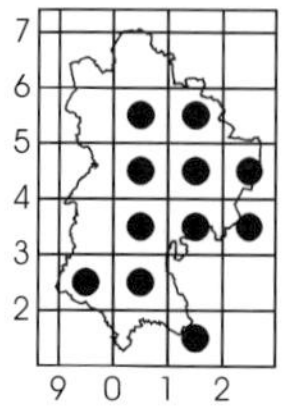

Post VCH: Found in damp woods but local and uncommon.
Flight: June to August (weeks 29 to 35)*.
Larval Foodplant: Reed canary-grass.

Marbled Minor ***Oligia strigilis*** **(Linnaeus) (2337)**

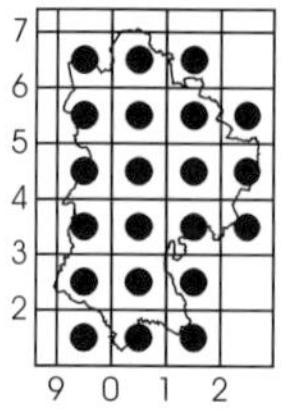

Pre VCH: J.C.Dale (MS2) recorded receiving this species from Abbot's collection from Bedford but not dated.
VCH: "Generally common."
Post VCH: Common throughout the County.
Flight: May to August (weeks 20 to 34, peak 24 to 28)*.
Larval Foodplants: Grasses, on the roots and stems.

Rufous Minor ***Oligia versicolor*** **(Borkhausen) (2338)**

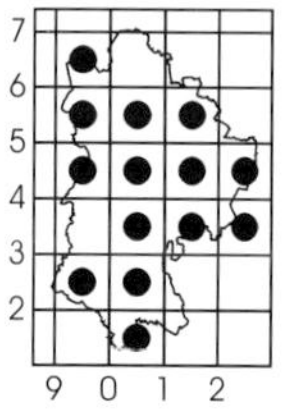

Post VCH: Found throughout the County, but local and uncommon.
Flight: May to August (weeks 22 to 31, peak 24 to 28)*.
Larval Foodplants: Grasses, on the roots and stems.

Tawny Marbled Minor ***Oligia latruncula*** **([Denis & Schiffermüller]) (2339)**

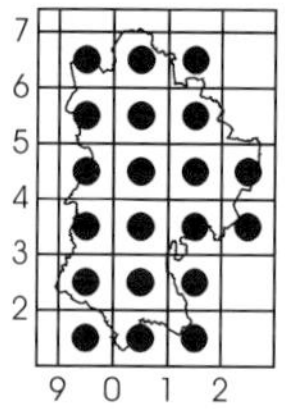

Post VCH: Widespread and common.
Flight: May to August (weeks 21 to 31, peak 26 to 28)*.
Larval Foodplants: Grasses, on the roots and stems.
Notes: These last three species can only be identified confidently by genitalia examination.

Middle-barred Minor ***Oligia fasciuncula*** **(Haworth) (2340)**

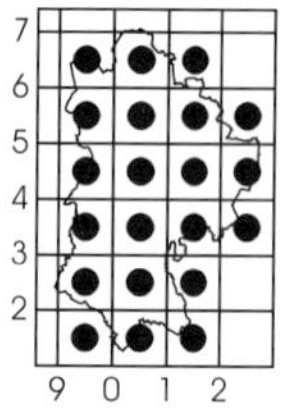

VCH: "Bedford."
Post VCH: Widespread and common in damp localities throughout the County.
Flight: May to September (weeks 21 to 35, peak 24 to 27)*.
Larval Foodplants: Grasses.

Cloaked Minor ***Mesoligia furuncula*** **([Denis & Schiffermüller]) (2341)**

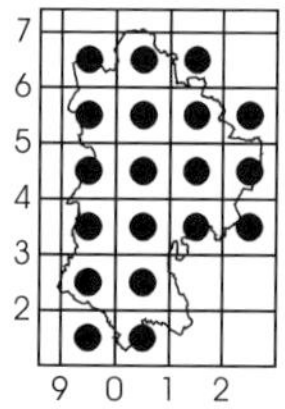

VCH: "Bedford, Luton."
Post VCH: Widespread and locally fairly common.
Flight: June to September (weeks 24 to 37, peak 29 to 33)*.
Larval Foodplants: Grasses.

Rosy Minor ***Mesoligia literosa*** **(Haworth) (2342)**

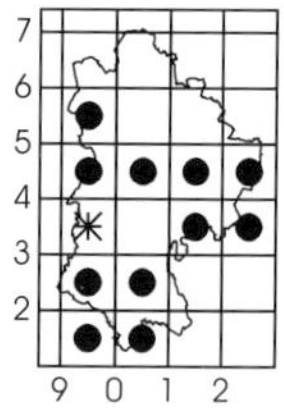

Post VCH: Local and uncommon. Recorded in S.H.Kershaw's notebooks from Aspley Heath in 1935 and 1936.
Flight: July to September (weeks 30 to 36)*.
Larval Foodplants: Grasses.

For details of standard weeks see page 6.

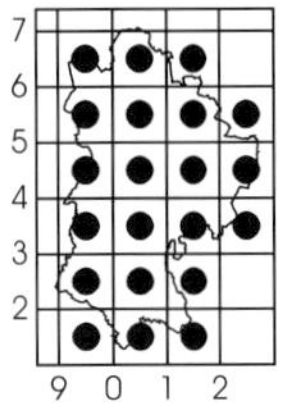

Common Rustic *Mesapamea secalis* (Linnaeus) (2343)
VCH: (as *A. oculea* Gn.) "Abundant everywhere."
Post VCH: Widespread and often abundant.
Flight: June to September (weeks 25 to 39, peak 29 to 34)*.
Larval Foodplants: Grasses.

Lesser Common Rustic *Mesapamea didyma* (Esper) (2343a)
Post VCH: Recorded and confirmed by genitalia examinations from King's Wood, Heath and Reach (1987), Tempsford (1990) and the RIS trap at Cockayne Hatley (1987).
Flight: July and August (weeks 27 and 33)*.
Larval Foodplants: Grasses.
Notes: This species was not separated from the Common Rustic, *M. secalis*, until 1983 (Skinner, 1984). It is only possible to separate these two species by examination of the genitalia. It is assumed that both species are found in similar habitats.

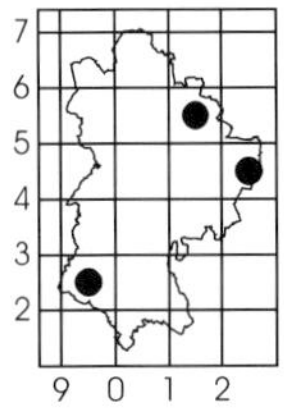

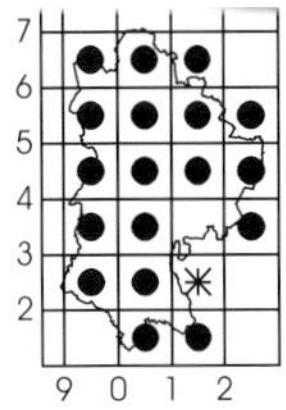

Small Dotted Buff *Photedes minima* (Haworth) (2345)
VCH: (as *Hydrilla arcuosa* Haw.) "Luton, in fields."
Post VCH: Widespread and fairly common in damp woodlands.
Flight: June to September (weeks 22 to 35, peak 26 to 31)*.
Larval Foodplant: Tufted hair-grass.

Mere Wainscot *Photedes fluxa* (Hübner) (2349)
Post VCH: A local and uncommon species, usually found in damp woodlands. Recorded from the RIS traps at Cockayne Hatley (1977-1979, 1981-1984, 1986-1992, 1994-1996), Old Warden (1975-1977, 1979) and The Lodge, Sandy (1970). Also found at Coppice Wood (1985, 1987), King's Wood, Heath and Reach (1981, 1987), Lower Alders (1981), Maulden Wood (1981, 1983), Odell Great Wood (1990), the northern section of Potton Wood (1992) and Sharnbrook (1995, 1996).

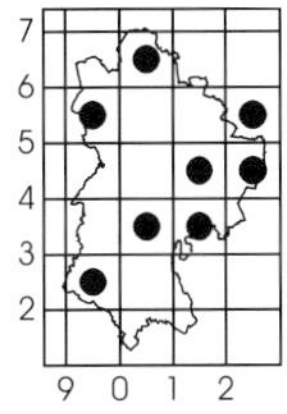

Flight: July to September (weeks 27 to 39, peak 30 to 32)*.
Larval Foodplant: Wood small-reed.

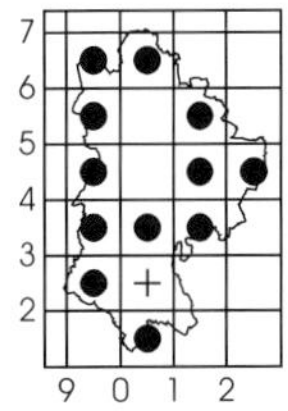

Small Wainscot *Photedes pygmina* (Haworth) (2350)
VCH: (as *Tapinostola fulva* Hb.) "Luton."
Post VCH: Uncommon and local in damp woods.
Flight: July to October (weeks 27 to 41, peak 38)*.
Larval Foodplants: Sedges, rushes and grasses.

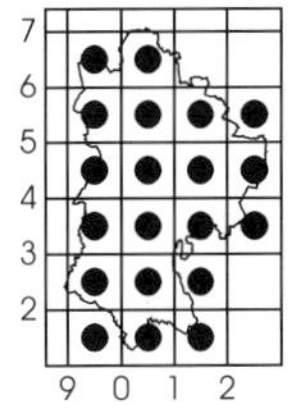

Dusky Sallow *Eremobia ochroleuca* ([Denis & Schiffermüller]) (2352) (Drawing on page 25)
Pre VCH: J.C.Dale (MS2) recorded receiving this species (as *Citrina*)from Abbot's collection from Bedford but not dated. It is also recorded in the Curtis diaries from "Bedfordsh" [*sic*] but with no date.
VCH: "Recorded in Bedfordshire, Westwood and Humphrey ii 228".

For key to moth maps see page 3.

Post VCH: Widespread and fairly common. The Dusky Sallow comes readily to light and can also be found visiting flowers during the day, especially on chalk downland.
Flight: July to September (weeks 27 to 37, peak 28 to 34)*.
Larval Foodplants: Grasses.

Flounced Rustic *Luperina testacea* ([Denis & Schiffermüller]) (2353)
VCH: "Generally abundant."
Post VCH: Widespread and fairly common.
Flight: July to October (weeks 27 to 42, peak 32 to 37)*.
Larval Foodplants: Grasses.

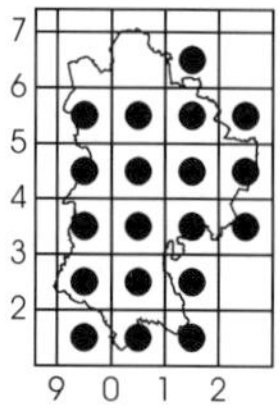

Ear Moth *Amphipoea oculea* (Linnaeus) (2360)
VCH: (as *Hydraecia nictitans* Bkh.) "Bedford."
Post VCH: Local and uncommon in damp woodlands.
Flight: July and August (weeks 30 to 34)*.
Larval Foodplants: Grasses and herbaceous plants.
Notes: Between 1935 and 1955, S.H.Kershaw's notebooks contain several records of *lucens* from Aspley Heath. The Large Ear (*Amphipoea lucens* (Freyer)) does not usually occur in south-eastern England (Skinner, 1984, Riley & Townsend, 1991) and it seems more likely that these were either the Ear Moth or the Saltern Ear (*Amphipoea fucosa paludis* (Tutt)). These species are difficult to identify without examination of the genitalia. Kershaw's entry for 22 August 1955 "a possible dark var of *lucens*, *paludis* etc." suggests that by then he was aware of the identification problem.

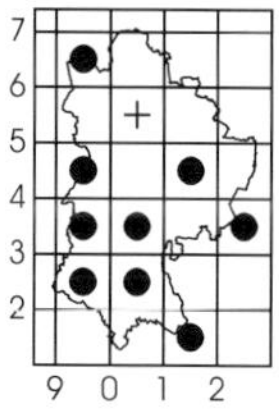

Rosy Rustic *Hydraecia micacea* (Esper) (2361)
VCH: "Bedford, Luton."
Post VCH: Widespread but local and uncommon.
Flight: July to November (weeks 29 to 45, peak 34 to 42)*.
Larval Foodplants: Polyphagous on herbaceous plants.

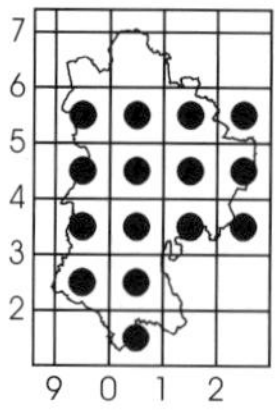

The Butterbur *Hydraecia petasitis* Doubleday (2362)
Post VCH: A single record at light at Flitwick Moor on 11 September 1981. Heath and Emmet (1983) suggest that this species "probably has a distribution similar to that of the foodplant". Butterbur can be found at a number of places in the County (Dony, 1976) so it is possible that this species may be more widespread in Bedfordshire.
Flight: August and September (week 37)*.
Larval Foodplant: Butterbur.

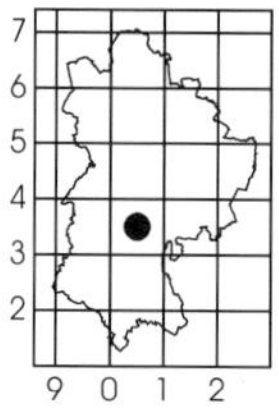

Frosted Orange *Gortyna flavago* ([Denis & Schiffermüller]) (2364)
Pre VCH: J.C.Dale (MS2) recorded receiving *Flavago* from Abbot's collection from Bedford but see also under Pink-Barred Sallow.
VCH: "Bedford, Luton."
Post VCH: Widespread but local and uncommon.
Flight: August to October (weeks 32 to 43, peak 37 to 40)*.

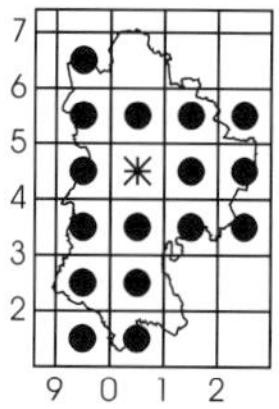

For details of standard weeks see page 6.

Larval Foodplants: Large plants, including thistles*, burdocks* and foxglove, feeding in the stems.

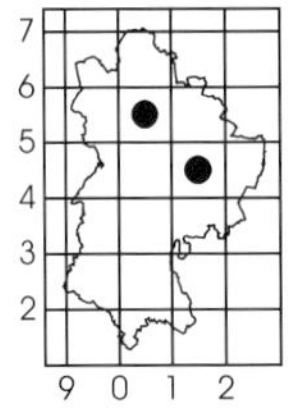

The Crescent *Celaena leucostigma leucostigma* (Hübner) (2368)
Post VCH: Only four records: Bromham (1965, 1966) and the RIS traps at Old Warden (1974) and The Lodge, Sandy (1974).
Flight: July, August (weeks 31 to 33)* and September.
Larval Foodplants: Large fenland plants such as great fen-sedge and yellow iris, feeding in the stems and roots.

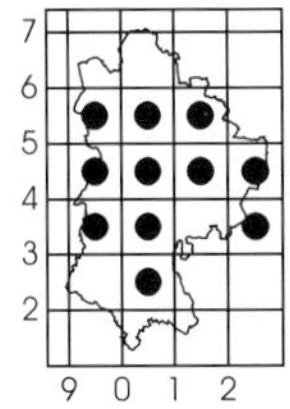

Bulrush Wainscot *Nonagria typhae* (Thunberg) (2369)
Post VCH: Widespread in damp areas of the County, but local and uncommon.
Flight: July to October (weeks 32, 35 and 37)*.
Larval Foodplants: Bulrush and lesser bulrush, feeding in the stems.

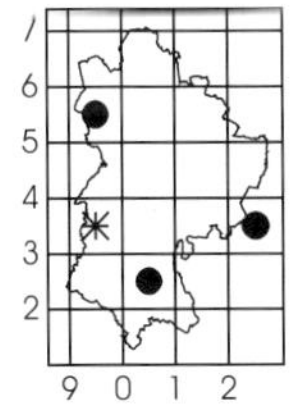

Twin-spotted Wainscot *Archanara geminipuncta* (Haworth) (2370)
Post VCH: There is a specimen in the Kershaw collection from Aspley Heath dated 8 August 1957. Also from Dunstable Downs in 1976, Stotfold in 1982 and Carlton and Sharnbrook on 21 August 1996.
Flight: July, August (weeks 30, 32 and 34)* and September.
Larval Foodplant: Common reed, feeding in the stems.

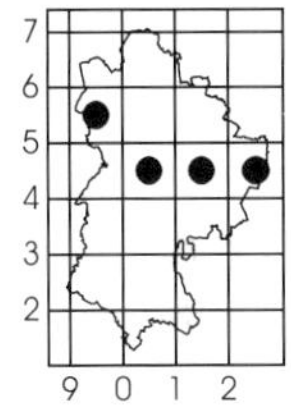

Brown-veined Wainscot *Archanara dissoluta* (Treitschke) (2371)
Post VCH: Recorded from the RIS traps at Cockayne Hatley (1984) and Old Warden (1974-1976, 1978, 1979) and also at light in Priory Country Park on 15 August 1987 and at Carlton on 19 August 1996.
Flight: July and August (weeks 29 to 34)*.
Larval Foodplant: Common reed.

Webb's Wainscot *Archanara sparganii* (Esper) (2373)
Post VCH: Recorded in S.H.Kershaw's notebook from Aspley Heath on 3 August 1960 "by our pond". No specimen has been seen. This is a coastal species but it is possible that this individual may have been brought into Kershaw's garden with pond plants from elsewhere.
Flight: August and September.
Larval Foodplant: Bulrushes, yellow iris, common club-rush and branched bur-reed, feeding in the stems.

Rush Wainscot *Archanara algae* (Esper) (2374)
Post VCH: Recorded from The Lodge, Sandy, by B.B.West (1961) but, as no voucher specimen has survived, it is possible that this species was recorded in error. Not otherwise known from Bedfordshire.

For key to moth maps see page 3.

Large Wainscot *Rhizedra lutosa* (Hübner) (2375)
Post VCH: Local and infrequent: Bedford (1976), Carlton (1995), Clifton (1985), Pavenham (1984), Sharnbrook (1976, 1995), Stotfold (1977) and the RIS traps at Cockayne Hatley (1978) and Eaton Bray (1983).
Flight: August to October (weeks 35 to 45)*.
Larval Foodplant: Common reed, feeding in the stems and roots.

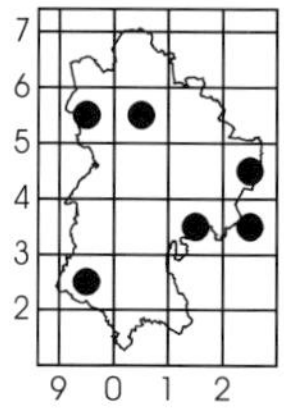

Fen Wainscot *Arenostola phragmitidis* (Hübner) (2377)
Post VCH: Clophill Sand Quarry (1984), Pavenham (1986), The Lodge, Sandy (1990, 1996) and the RIS trap at Cockayne Hatley (1976, 1986).
Flight: July and August (weeks 28 to 34)*.
Larval Foodplant: Common reed, feeding in the stems.

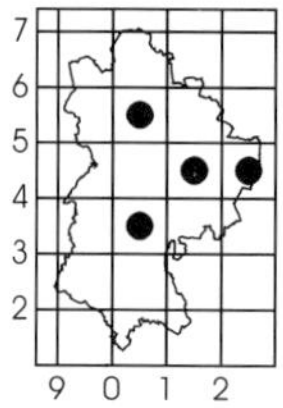

Small Rufous *Coenobia rufa* (Haworth) (2379)
Post VCH: Recorded in S.H.Kershaw's notebook from Aspley Heathon 20 September1947 but no specimen has been seen for this date. More recently found at Flitwick Moor (1977, 1985), Sharnbrook (1976) and Tempsford (1994).
Flight: July and August (weeks 28 to 32)*.
Larval Foodplants: Jointed rush and soft-rush, in the stems.

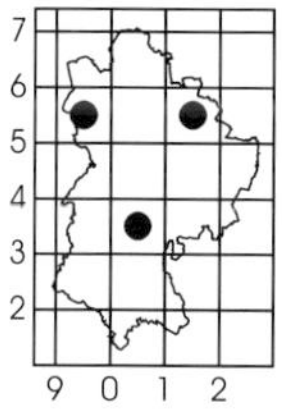

Treble Lines *Charanyca trigrammica* (Hufnagel) (2380)
VCH: "In all woods."
Post VCH: Widespread in woodlands but local and uncommon.
Flight: May to July (weeks 21 to 27, peak 24)*.
Larval Foodplants: Polyphagous on herbaceous plants.

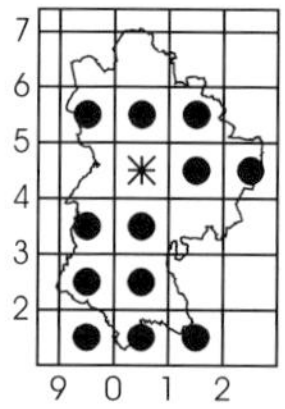

The Uncertain *Hoplodrina alsines* (Brahm) (2381)
VCH: "Bedford, Luton."
Post VCH: Widespread and common.
Flight: May to September (weeks 22 to 35, peak 27 to 32)*.
Larval Foodplants: Polyphagous on herbaceous plants.

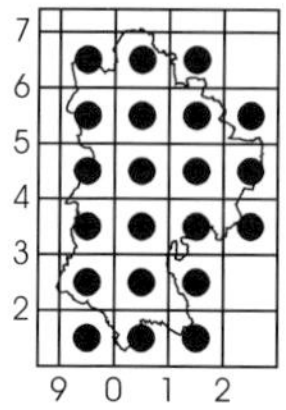

The Rustic *Hoplodrina blanda* ([Denis & Schiffermüller]) (2382)
VCH: "Generally distributed."
Post VCH: Widespread and common.
Flight: June to September (weeks 24 to 36, peak 28 to 30)*.
Larval Foodplants: Polyphagous on herbaceous plants.

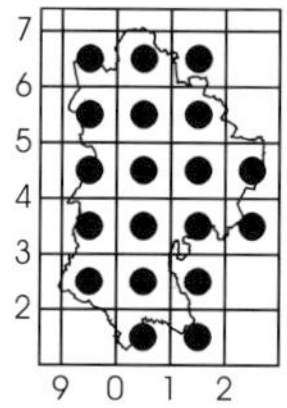

Powdered Rustic *Hoplodrina superstes* (Ochsenheimer) (2383)
Post VCH: Shown in a numerical check list of Bedfordshire moths (West, 1959) as 423 (Heslop's (1947) numbering for the Powdered Rustic) but no confirmation of this record is available. It is suspected that the wrong check list number was printed.

For details of standard weeks see page 6.

Vine's rustic *Hoplodrina ambigua* ([Denis & Schiffermüller]) (2384)

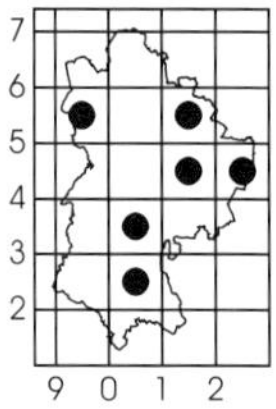

Post VCH: Once thought to be an immigrant but now widely resident in south-east England. Found at Luton (1979, 1983), Maulden Wood (1980), Sharnbrook (1996), Tempsford (1991) and in the RIS traps at Cockayne Hatley (1991, 1995, 1996) and Old Warden (1977).
Flight: May to October (weeks 35 to 41)*.
Larval Foodplants: Polyphagous on herbaceous plants.

Small Mottled Willow *Spodoptera exigua* (Hübner) (2385)
Post VCH: Recorded by Champkin (1970) from Putnoe Wood in 1968 but the specimen was actually the Pale Mottled Willow. One was reported from the RIS trap at Cockayne Hatley on 18-20 August 1996

Mediterranean Brocade *Spodoptera littoralis* (Boisduval) (2386)

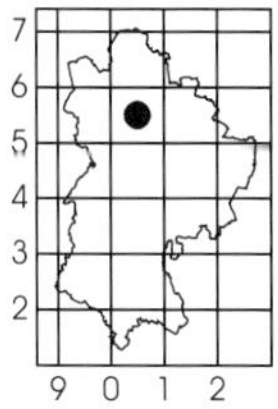

Post VCH: A specimen in G.Ping's collection is labelled "Clapham 1979". No other details are available for this immigrant species which is also occasionally introduced with imported plants and produce.
Flight: September and October.
Larval Foodplants: Abroad this species is a pest on many types of cultivated plant.

Mottled Rustic *Caradrina morpheus* (Hufnagel) (2387)

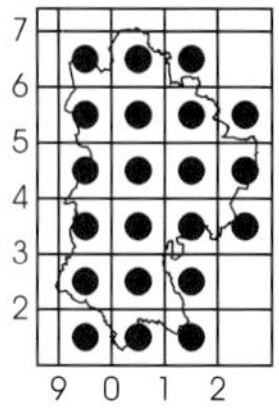

VCH: "Generally common in gardens."
Post VCH: Widespread and common.
Flight: May to October (weeks 22 to 41, peak 25 to 31)*.
Larval Foodplants: Polyphagous on herbaceous plants.

Pale Mottled Willow *Caradrina clavipalpis* (Scopoli) (2389)

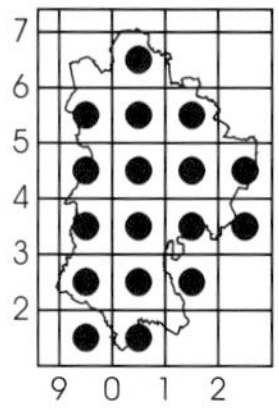

VCH: (as *C. cubicularis* Bkh.) "Abundant everywhere."
Post VCH: Widespread but local.
Flight: May to November (weeks 18 to 44)*.
Larval Foodplants: Polyphagous on grass and cereal seeds.

Silky Wainscot *Chilodes maritimus* (Tauscher) (2391)

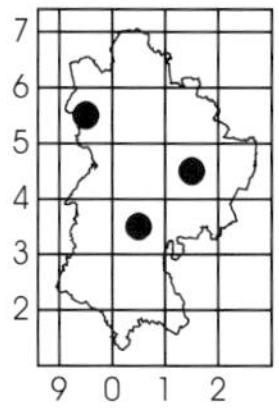

Post VCH: Found at Carlton on 15 July 1996, Flitwick Moor on 29 July 1977 and in the RIS trap at The Lodge, Sandy on 6 June 1970.
Flight: June (week 23)*, July (weeks 28 to 30)* and August.
Larval Food: Animal and vegetable matter in old reed-stems.

The Anomalous *Stilbia anomala* (Haworth) (2394)

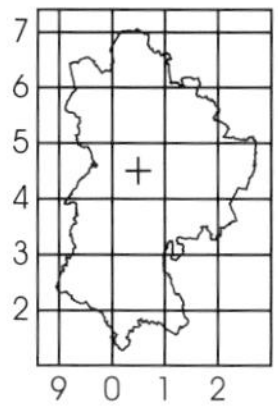

VCH:"Bedford."
Post VCH: Not recorded.
Flight: August and September.
Larval Foodplants: Moorland grasses.

For key to moth maps see page 3.

Small Yellow Underwing *Panemeria tenebrata* (Scopoli) (2397)
(Drawing on page 351)

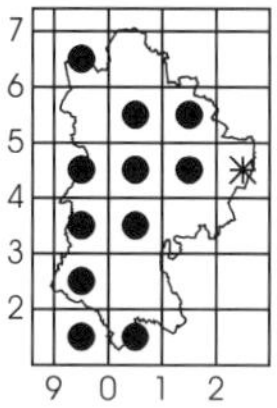

VCH: "Bedford, in meadows."
Post VCH: Widespread in grassy areas, but local and uncommon. Localities where it has been found include Bison Hill, Clophill, Marston Thrift, Maulden Wood and Sharnbrook Summit. It is probably under-recorded.
Flight: Flies by day in May and June (weeks 19 to 25)*.
Larval Foodplant: Common mouse-ear.

Bordered Sallow *Pyrrhia umbra* (Hufnagel) (2399)

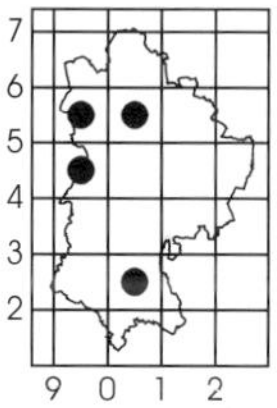

VCH: "Taken near Bedford by Rev. O.W.Harries."
Post VCH: Very local and uncommon: Bedford (1972, 1975), Cranfield (1984), Dunstable (1981), Stevington (1964) and Sundon Quarry (1983).
Flight: May to August (weeks 29 and 30)*.
Larval Foodplants: Restharrows.

Subfamily: **Heliothinae**

The hindwings of moths in this subfamily are bordered with darker scales. Wingspan 32-42 mm. Two of the four British species that are resident or regular immigrants have been found in Bedfordshire.

Scarce Bordered Straw *Heliothis armigera* (Hübner) (2400)

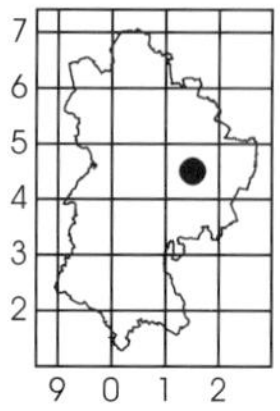

Post VCH: A single record for this immigrant species, at Sandy on 28 August 1974 by I.P.Woiwod.
Flight: August (week 35)* to November.
Larval Foodplants: Has been found on imported plants, such as chrysanthemum and also in imported fruit, especially tomatoes from the Canary Islands.

Bordered Straw *Heliothis peltigera* ([Denis & Schiffermüller]) (2403)

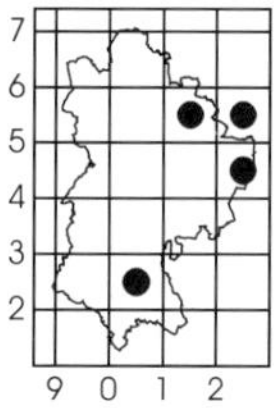

Post VCH: A rare immigrant: Bidwell (1982), Biggleswade (1965, 1980), Luton (1980), Potton Wood (1996), Tempsford (1994) and the RIS trap at Cockayne Hatley (1994, 1996).
Flight: May to September (weeks 21, 31, 34 and 38)*.
Larval Foodplants: Pot marigolds, common restharrow and sticky groundsel, feeding on the flowers.

For details of standard weeks see page 6.

Subfamily: **Acontiinae**

A subfamily in which the moths are small relative to most other noctuids (wingspan 16-32 mm). Two of the four British species have been found in Bedfordshire.

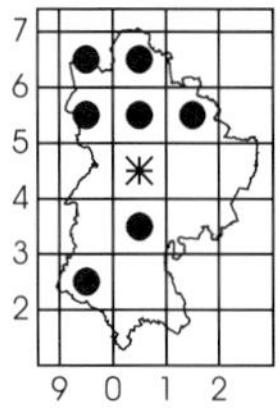

Marbled White Spot *Protodeltote pygarga* (Hufnagel) (2410)
Post VCH: Found at Bedford (1957), Bromham (1983), Clapham Park Wood (1995), Coppice Wood (1989), Maulden Wood (1976), Sharnbrook (1986), Waterloo Thorns (1987), West Wood (1988, 1990, 1996) and in the RIS trap at Eaton Bray (1986).
Flight: May to July (weeks 25 to 29)*.
Larval Foodplants: Purple moor-grass and other grasses.

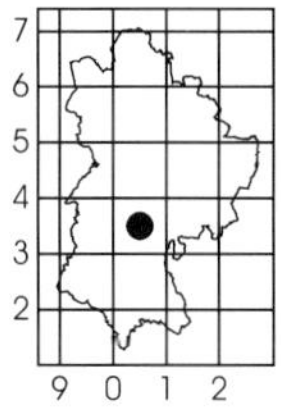

Silver Hook *Deltote uncula* (Clerck) (2412)
Post VCH: Found only at Flitwick Moor on 22 July 1977 and 17 July 1978.
Flight: May to July (week 29)*.
Larval Foodplants: Sedges and coarse grasses.

Subfamily: **Chloephorinae**

All the three British species are found in Bedfordshire. They have green forewings and whitish hindwings. Wingspan 20-48mm.

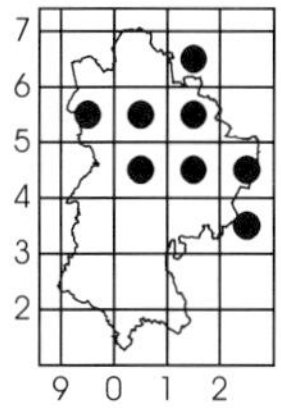

Cream-bordered Green Pea *Earias clorana* (Linnaeus) (2418)
VCH: "Taken in woods around Bedford."
Post VCH: Local and uncommon in damp areas.
Flight: June to September (weeks 26 to 32)*.
Larval Foodplants: Willows*.

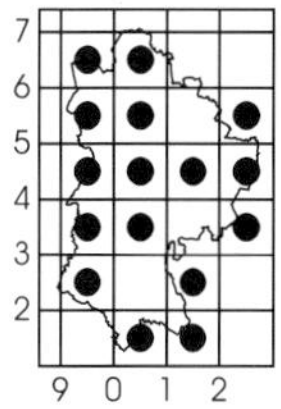

Scarce Silver-lines *Bena bicolorana* (Fuessly) (= *prasinana* auctt.) (2421)
VCH: (as *Halias quercana* Schiff.) "Taken in woods around Bedford."
Post VCH: Widespread in oak woodlands but local and never common.
Flight: Julne to August(weeks 26 and 31 to 34)*.
Larval Foodplants: Oaks*.

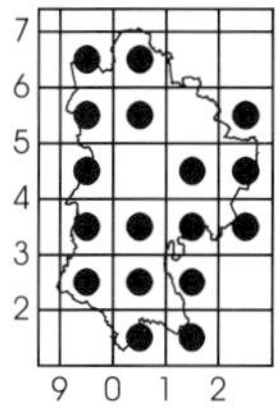

Green Silver-lines *Pseudoips prasinana* (Linnaeus) (= *fagana* (Fabricius) ssp. *britannica* (Warren)) (2422) (Plate 38)
Pre VCH: Abbot (MS1) noted rearing *Fagana* in 1799 but did not record the source.
VCH: (as *Halias prasinana* Linn.) "Taken in woods around Bedford."
Post VCH: Widespread in woodlands but local and uncommon.
Flight: June and July (weeks 23 to 29)*.
Larval Foodplants: Polyphagous on deciduous trees, including birches*.

For key to moth maps see page 3.

Subfamily: **Sarrothripinae**

The only definite British species, the Oak Nycteoline, occurs in Bedfordshire. As its other common name, the Large Marbled Tortrix, suggests, it is a small moth readily mistaken for a tortricid. Wingspan 22-28 mm.

Oak Nycteoline *Nycteola revayana* (Scopoli) (2423)

VCH: "Found by Mr. J. Sharpin near Bedford."

Post VCH: Recorded in S.H.Kershaw's notebooks from Aspley Heath in 1933 and 1937. More recently found at Carlton (1996), Cooper's Hill (1984), Maulden Wood (1976, 1984), the northern part of Potton Wood (1992), Sandy (1961), Studham (1995), West Wood (1990), Willington (1961) and in the RIS trap at Cockayne Hatley (1976, 1991). Although it comes to light, the moth can also be found by beating holly, yew and conifers during the winter. This species has almost certainly been overlooked in the past and is probably more common than current records suggest. Because of its small size, it is sometimes assumed to be a "micro" and discarded as too difficult to identify.

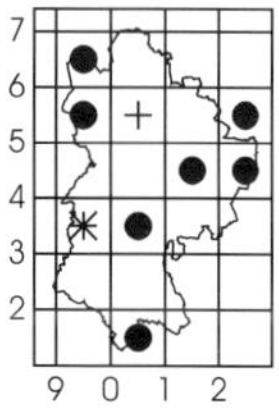

Flight: August to May (weeks 28, 33, 38, 52 and 15, 18)★.

Larval Foodplants: Oaks.

Subfamily: **Pantheinae**

The Nut-tree Tussock is the only recognised British species in this subfamily. It occurs in Bedfordshire. It is a grey and white moth with a wingspan 31-39 mm. Its larva is hairy.

Nut-tree Tussock *Colocasia coryli* (Linnaeus) (2425)

VCH: "Bedford, also taken at Luton at 'light'."

Post VCH: Locally common in woods. The melanic ab. *melanotica* Haverkampf was found at Luton Hoo in 1983.

Flight: Double-brooded, flying in May and June (weeks 20 to 24)★ and again in September (weeks 35 to 36)★.

Larval Foodplants: Polyphagous on deciduous trees, especially beech, hazel, hornbeam★ and birches.

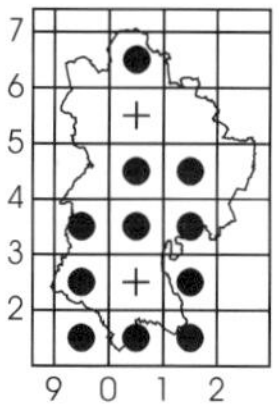

Subfamily: **Plusiinae** **The Y moths**

In Britain this is only a small subfamily. Ten of the 24 British species have been found in Bedfordshire. The moths often have forewings with beautiful metallic markings. Wingspan 28-54 mm. The thorax may be adorned with prominent tufts of scales, most evident in newly-emerged individuals. Many are strong fliers and several species are immigrants. The Silver Y is the best known of these; large numbers of the moths may be seen in some years feeding at flowers in the daytime. The larvae have only two pairs of prolegs in addition to the anal claspers and are often known as 'semi-loopers'.

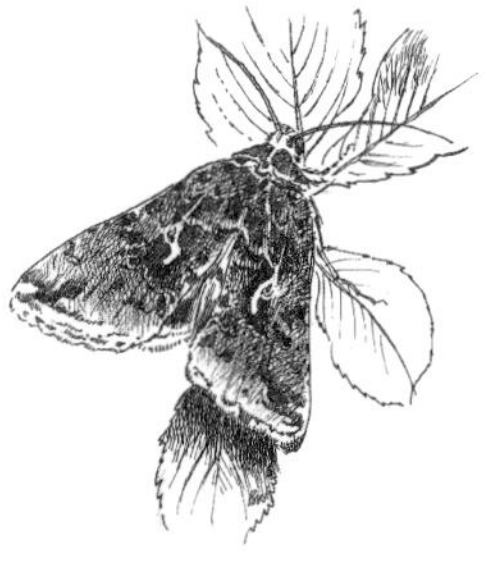

Silver Y

Slender Burnished Brass ***Diachrysia orichalcea*** **(Fabricius) (2433)**

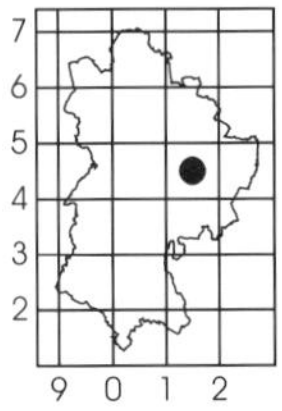

Post VCH: An immigrant species recorded only at Sandy on 19 August 1974 by I.P.Woiwod.
Flight: August (week 33)* to October.
Larval Foodplants: In continental Europe on *Coreopsis* and Solanaceae.

Burnished Brass ***Diachrysia chrysitis*** **(Linnaeus) (2434)** (Plate 91)

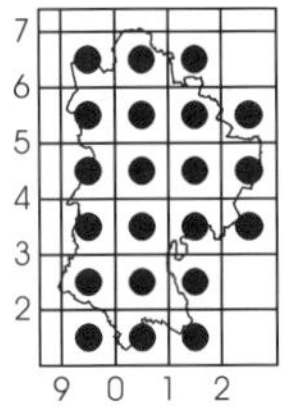

VCH: "Generally distributed."
Post VCH: Widespread and common.
Flight: May to October (weeks 22 to 40, peak 25 to 31)*.
Larval Foodplants: Nettles and other herbaceous plants.

Golden Plusia ***Polychrysia moneta*** **(Fabricius) (2437)**

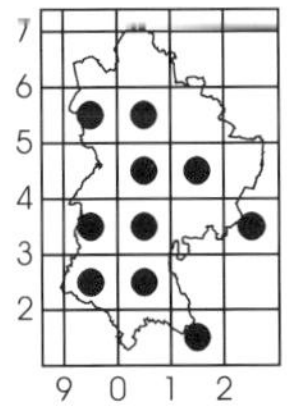

Post VCH: Widely distributed in gardens but local and uncommon. R.M.Craske recalled it in gardens in Bedford, 1918 to 1927. Recorded in S.H.Kershaw's notebooks from Aspley Heath in 1935, 1937, 1952 and 1956. There is also a specimen in his collection from Aspley Heath in 1936.
Flight: June to September (weeks 21 to 31, 36)*.
Larval Foodplants: Monk's-hood and cultivated species of *Delphinium**.

Gold Spot ***Plusia festucae*** **(Linnaeus) (2439)**

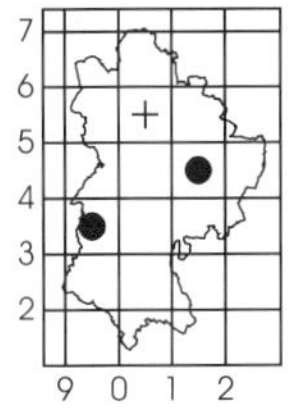

Pre VCH: C. Abbot (MS1) recorded finding *Festucae* Gold Spot Moth in "Clapham Lane Sept 12 1799". J.C.Dale (MS2) noted receiving this species from Abbot's collection from Bedford but not dated.
Post VCH: At light at Aspley Guise (1987), Biggleswade (1989) and Salford (1983).
Flight: June to September, in two broods.
Larval Foodplants: Polyphagous on marshland plants.

Silver Y ***Autographa gamma*** **(Linnaeus) (2441)** (Drawing on page 364)
VCH: "Everywhere abundant, buzzing about flowers."

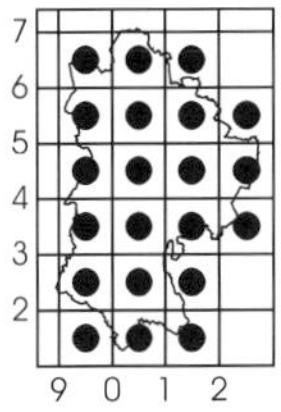

Post VCH: An immigrant species which can be found anywhere. Numbers vary greatly from year to year. D.V.Manning noted "vast numbers" of this species around street lights in Sharnbrook during the early 1970s. It was abundant everywhere in 1994 but many fewer were reported in 1995. Very common again in June and August 1996, when catches reached record levels in the RIS trap at Cockayne Hatley.
Flight: Spring to autumn(weeks 21 to 45)*, flying both in daylight and at night.
Larval Foodplants: Polyphagous on herbaceous plants. A larva was found on small nettle at Stanford Pits, near Clifton, on 15 February 1990 by D.K.Riley (Riley & Riley, 1990).

For key to moth maps see page 3.

Beautiful Golden Y *Autographa pulchrina* (Haworth) (2442)

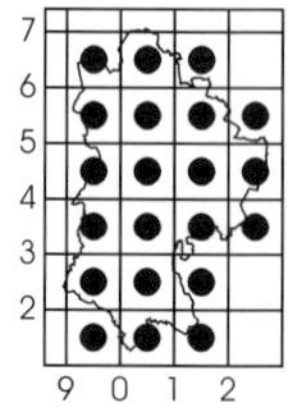

VCH: "Luton."
Post VCH: Widespread but local.
Flight: June to August (weeks 23 to 31)*.
Larval Foodplants: Polyphagous on herbaceous plants.

Plain Golden Y *Autographa jota* (Linnaeus) (2443)

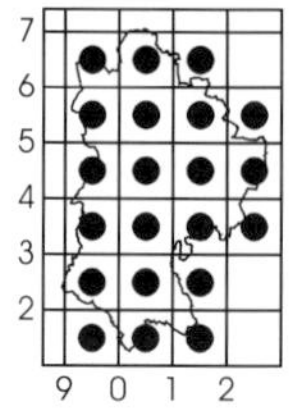

Pre VCH: J.C.Dale (MS2) recorded receiving this species from Abbot's collection from Bedford but not dated.
VCH: "Luton, Bedford, Potton."
Post VCH: Widespread and common.
Flight: June and July (weeks 24 to 30, peak 26 to 27)*.
Larval Foodplants: Polyphagous on herbaceous plants.

Gold Spangle *Autographa bractea* ([Denis & Schiffermüller]) (2444)
Post VCH: Shown in a numerical list of Macrolepidoptera for the County (West, 1959) as 530 (Heslop's (1947) numbering for the Gold Spangle). However, in Heslop's book the numbers 530 and 532 (Plain Golden Y) are in the wrong order, which suggests that the latter was the intended Bedfordshire record. No other record of the Gold Spangle in the County is known.

Scarce Silver Y *Syngrapha interrogationis* (Linnaeus) (2447)

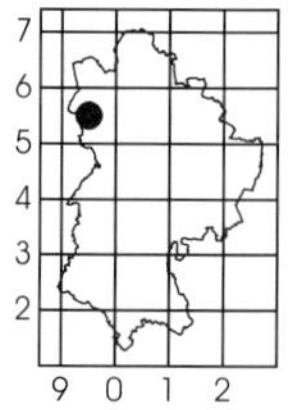

Post VCH: Only one record of this rare immigrant: at Sharnbrook on 8 August 1995 by D.V.Manning.
Flight: June to August (week 32)*.
Larval Foodplants: Heather and bilberry.

Dark Spectacle *Abrostola triplasia* (Linnaeus) (= *trigemina* (Werneburg)) (2449)

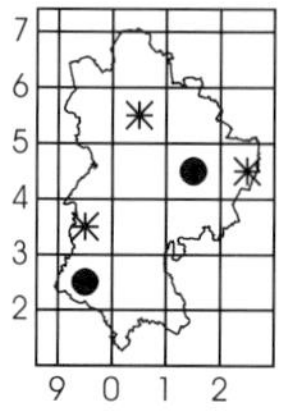

VCH: (as *Habrostola triplasia* Linn.) "Bedford, Potton."
Post VCH: A specimen in the Kershaw collection is labelled "W.G.Nash, June 1919, Bedfordshire". Recorded in S.H.Kershaw's notebooks from Aspley Heath in 1932. West (1959) listed species 538 (Heslop's (1947) numbering for the Dark Spectacle). Also recorded in the RIS traps at Eaton Bray (1986) and The Lodge, Sandy (1969-1972) but some of these records probably refer to the next species.
Flight: June* and July.
Larval Foodplants: Common nettle and hop.

The Spectacle *Abrostola tripartita* (Hufnagel) (= *triplasia* auctt.) (2450)

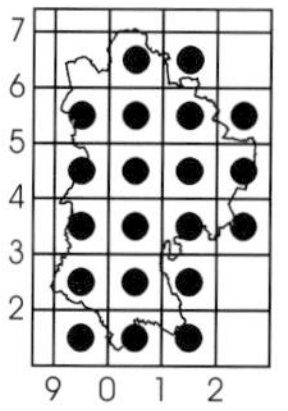

VCH: (as *Habrostola urticae* Hb.) "Potton, Luton, Bedford."
Post VCH: Widespread and locally common.
Flight: May to September (weeks 20 to 36)*.
Larval Foodplant: Common nettle.

For details of standard weeks see page 6.

Subfamily: **Catocalinae The Red Underwings**

This subfamily contains a remarkable mixture of species. The moths, which tend to rest with the wings held horizontally, not pressed close to the body as in most noctuids, vary greatly both in size and colour. The largest, the Clifden Nonpareil, has a wingspan of 84-112 mm while that of the smallest, the Burnet Companion is only 28-32 mm. With their grey camouflaged forewings and pink and black hindwings, the Red Underwings are among the most striking of British moths. There are six British species of which four have been found in Bedfordshire.

Clifden Nonpareil *Catocala fraxini* (Linnaeus) (2451)
Post VCH: One record only: larvae collected from Brogborough in either 1983 or 1984 by K.F.Webb. However, it is possible that this moth was mislabelled.
Flight: August and September.
Larval Foodplants: Aspen and poplars.

Red Underwing *Catocala nupta* (Linnaeus) (2452) (Back Cover)
VCH: "Generally distributed, sitting on trunks of willow."
Post VCH: Widespread in woodlands but local and uncommon.
Flight: August to October (weeks 31 to 43)*.
Larval Foodplants: Aspen, willows* and poplars.

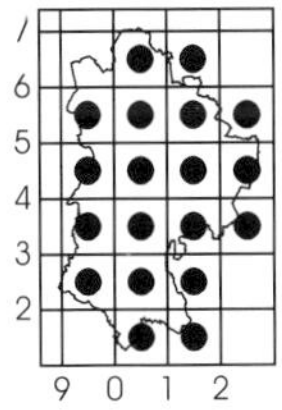

Mother Shipton *Callistege mi* (Clerck) (2462) (Plate 13)
Pre VCH: J.C.Dale (MS3) recorded finding *Phy. mi* on 1 June 1820 in Clapham Park Wood.
VCH: "Bedford, Luton, Woburn."
Post VCH: Widespread and locally fairly common, flying in sunshine in meadows, chalk downlands and other grassy areas.
Flight: May and June (weeks 21 to 25)*.
Larval Foodplants: Clovers.

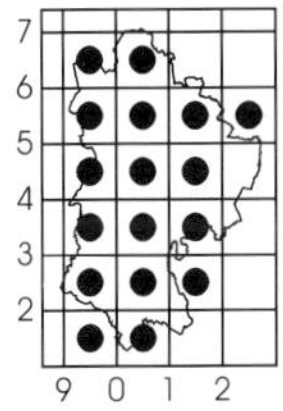

Burnet Companion *Euclidia glyphica* (Linnaeus) (2463) (Plate 12)
Pre VCH: J.C.Dale (MS3) recorded finding *glyphica* with the previous species on 1 June 1820 in Clapham Park Wood.
VCH: "Bedford."
Post VCH: Widespread and locally fairly common, flying in sunshine in meadows, chalk downlands and other grassy areas.
Flight: May and July (weeks 20 to 28)*.
Larval Foodplants: Clovers and trefoils.

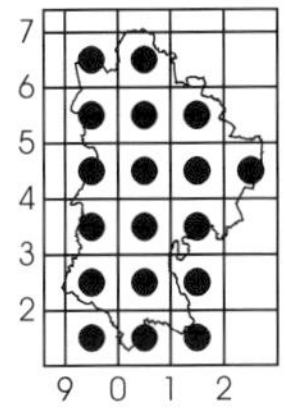

For key to moth maps see page 3.

Subfamily: **Ophiderinae**

Several species in this subfamily, such as the Herald and the Beautiful Hook-tip, have scalloped edges to the forewings. Wingspan 19-52 mm. They also tend to rest with the wings held horizontally, not pressed close to the body as in most noctuids. Six of the nine British species have been found in Bedfordshire.

The Four-spotted *Tyta luctuosa* ([Denis & Schiffermüller]) (2465)
VCH: "Bedford, a very local species."
Post VCH: A specimen from Hanger Wood (8 June 1907) is in the Liverpool Museum, *ex* J.S.Greenhill collection. Recalled by R.M.Craske as occurring in "Twin Wood Lane, Clapham and Sharpenhoe, very local" (1918-1927). More recently found at Bunkers Hill, Sandy, at light (1960), Sharnbrook Summit (1965, 1976-1978, 1984, 1985), Yelnow New Wood (1995) and in the RIS trap at Old Warden (1977). Also found between Souldrop and Sharnbrook by H.A.Smith and D.V.Manning in 1996.
Flight: Between May to July (weeks 21 to 28)★ and August. Flies in sunshine and at night.
Larval Foodplant: Field bindweed.

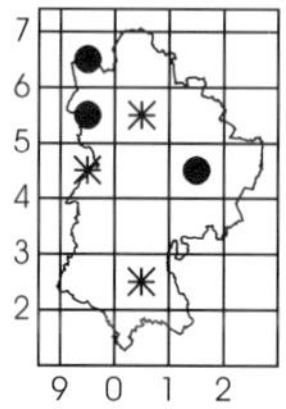

The Blackneck *Lygephila pastinum* (Treitschke) (2466)
Post VCH: Widespread and locally common in damp woodlands and meadows. It has been found commonly at Waterloo Thorns.
Flight: July and August (weeks 27 to 31)★.
Larval Foodplant: Tufted vetch.

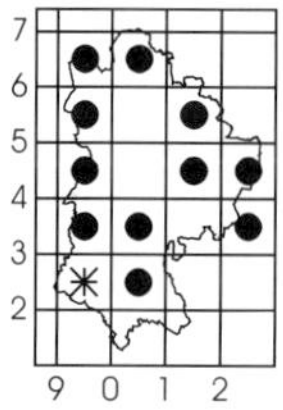

The Herald *Scoliopteryx libatrix* (Linnaeus) (2469) (Plate 76)
Pre VCH: "Two *Phalaena Libatrix* found in the garden in the fly state. September 2nd 1799" (Abbot, MS1).
VCH: "Generally distributed. Fond of hiding in cellars during the winter."
Post VCH: Widespread and common. Comes to light, but most records are obtained by finding hibernating moths in sheds, cellars, ice houses and tree trunks.
Flight: July to October (weeks 27 to 42)★ and, after hibernation, from February to June (weeks 5 to 23)★.
Larval Foodplants: Sallows★, willows, osier and poplars★.

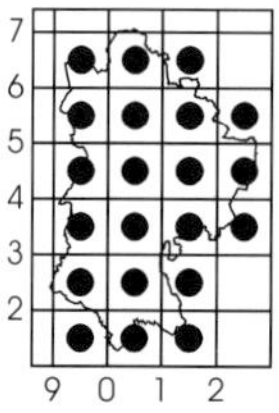

Small Purple-barred *Phytometra viridaria* (Clerck) (2470)
Post VCH: A local, uncommon species which is found on chalk downland in the south of the County. A specimen from Totternhoe in 1947 is in the Kershaw collection.
Flight: May, June (weeks 20 to 24)★ and July, flying both during the day and at night.
Larval Foodplants: Common milkwort and heath milkwort.

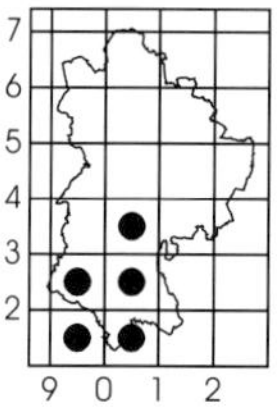

For details of standard weeks see page 6.

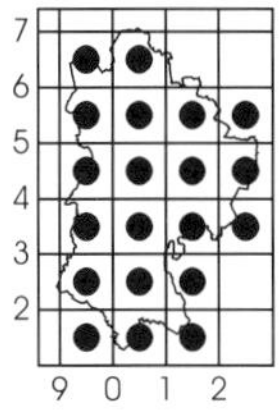

Beautiful Hook-tip *Laspeyria flexula* ([Denis & Schiffermüller]) (2473)
Post VCH: Widely distributed and locally common in woods and parkland.
Flight: June to September (weeks 25 to 38, peak 27 to 29)*. There was a partial second emergence in September 1983.
Larval Foodplants: Lichens growing on trees.

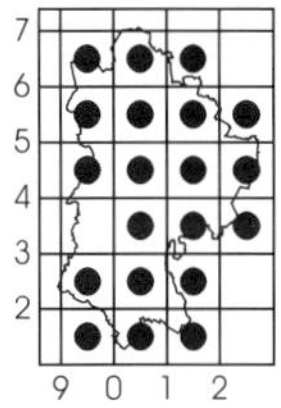

Straw Dot *Rivula sericealis* (Scopoli) (2474)
VCH: "Luton."
Post VCH: Widespread and locally common in damp woodlands and heaths.
Flight: June to September (weeks 23 to 37, peak 28 to 30)*.
Larval Foodplants: Grasses.

Subfamily: **Hypeninae** **The Snouts and Fan-foots.**

The Snout

Several of the moths in this subfamily have elongated palps which project in front of the head; hence the name 'snout'. The snouts are broad-winged, superficially similar to geometers. Wingspan 15-40 mm. There are about 13 British species of which seven have been found in Bedfordshire.

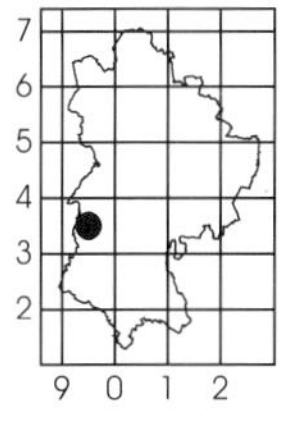

Beautiful Snout *Hypena crassalis* (Fabricius) (2476)
Post VCH: Recorded in S.H.Kershaw's notebooks from Aspley Heath in 1935, 1953 and 1959. There are also specimens in the Kershaw collection from Aspley Heath dated 19 June 1939 and 28 May 1947. More recently at light on Aspley Heath (1984, 1985, 1987) and Aspley Guise (1995). See also Webb (1984e).
Flight: Late May to July (weeks 22 to 29)*.
Larval Foodplant: Bilberry.

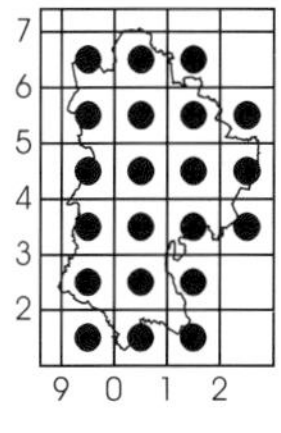

The Snout *Hypena proboscidalis* (Linnaeus) (2477)
Pre VCH: J.C.Dale (MS2) recorded receiving this species (as *Proboscidatus*) from Abbot's collection from Bedford but not dated.
VCH: "Everywhere among nettles."
Post VCH: Common throughout the County.
Flight: June to October (weeks 22 to 41, peaks 25 to 32 and 39)*, in two overlapping broods.
Larval Foodplant: Common nettle.

For key to moth maps see page 3.

Buttoned Snout *Hypena rostralis* (Linnaeus) (2480)
VCH: "Bedford."
Post VCH: Specimens from Bedford (6 September 1909) and Hanger Wood (29 September 1910) are in Liverpool Museum, *ex* A.Robinson collection. A specimen in the Kershaw collection is labelled "Aspley Heath 1937" and there is a record in his notebook for there in 1954. Also recorded in the RIS trap at The Lodge, Sandy (1969). This species has become scarce nationally in recent years.
Flight: August to October (weeks 41 and 42)*, hibernating from November to March and active again April to June.
Larval Foodplant: Hop.

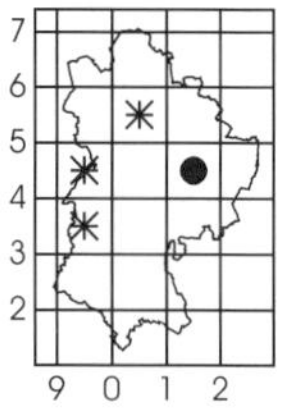

Pinion-streaked Snout *Schrankia costaestrigalis* (Stephens) (2484)
Post VCH: Specimens from Shefford (17 July 1909 and 7 July 1910) are in Liverpool Museum, *ex* A.Robinson collection. The record of "*costigalis* Ribbed Snout" in S.H.Kershaw's notebooks from Aspley Heath on 18 July 1956 may refer to this species but no specimen has been seen. Only one recent record, in the RIS trap at Cockayne Hatley on 19 July 1988.
Flight: June, July (week 29)* and August.
Larval Foodplants: Unknown.

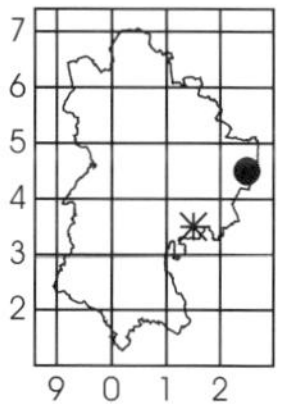

Common Fan-foot *Pechipogo strigilata* (Linnaeus) (2488)
Pre VCH: J.C.Dale (MS2) listed this species as found on 2 June 1820 in Clapham Park Wood. He also noted receiving it from Abbot's collection from Bedford but not dated.
VCH: (as *Herminia barbalis* Linn.) "Luton, among sallow."
Post VCH: Recorded from a number of woodland sites throughout the County before 1983. Recently this species has declined nationally.
Flight: June and July (weeks 26 to 29)*.
Larval Foodplants: Dried withered leaves and birch catkins.

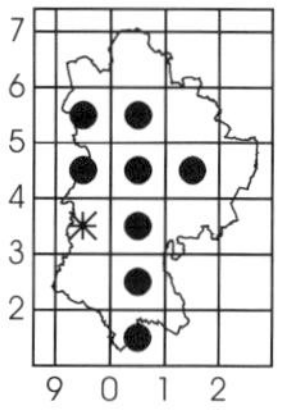

The Fan-foot *Herminia tarsipennalis* (Treitschke) (2489)
VCH: "Luton."
Post VCH: Widespread and fairly common in woodlands throughout the County.
Flight: June to August (weeks 24 to 34, peak 26 to 32)*.
Larval Food: Withered leaves.

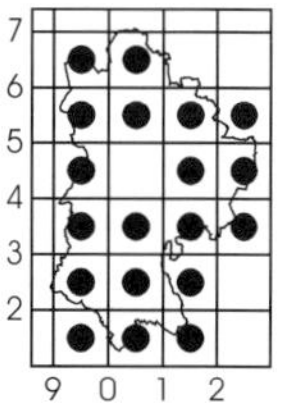

Small Fan-foot *Herminia grisealis* ([Denis & Schiffermüller]) (= *nemoralis* (Fabricius)) (2492)
VCH: "Bedford."
Post VCH: Widespread and common in woodlands throughout the County.
Flight: May to August (weeks 21 to 33, peak 25 to 29)*.
Larval Foodplants: Oaks and alder.

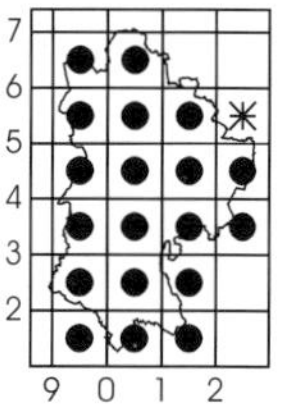

For details of standard weeks see page 6.

Bibliography and References

Abbot, C. (1798) *Flora Bedfordiensis*. Smith, Bedford.

Abbot, C. (1798) Manuscript reports to the Linnean Society 12 August 1798 and 1 November 1798. Linnean Society Archives No. 192a and 192b.

Abbot, C. (1800) XXXI Extracts from the Minute Book of the Linnean Society. November 6th, 1798. *Transactions of the Linnean Society*. **5**, 276.

Abbot, C. (1809) Letter acknowledging receipt of a Convolvulus Hawk-moth. 1 October 1809. Bedfordshire County Record Office. (BS463).

Abbot, C. (MS1) *Lepidoptera Anglica cum Libellulis*. Hope Library, Oxford. (Dale 23).

A.E.C. (1959) J.C.B.Craske. *Entomologist's Record and Journal of Variation*. **71**, 59-60.

Agassiz D.J.L. (1987) Microlepidoptera - a review of the year 1985. *Entomologist's Record and Journal of Variation*. **99**, 169-181.

Agassiz D.J.L. (1988) Microlepidoptera - a review of the year 1986. *Entomologist's Record and Journal of Variation*. **100**, 118-130.

Allan, P.B.M. (1943) *Talking of Moths*. Montgomery Press. Reprinted 1975 E.W.Classey.

Allan, P.B.M. (1964) Colonel Sidney Hardinge Kershaw, D.S.O. *Entomologist's Record and Journal of Variation*. **76**, 265.

Anon, (1872) James Charles Dale M.A., F.L.S. *Entomologist's Monthly Magazine*. **8**, 255-256.

Anon (Ed.) (1891) *Journal of Emily Shore*. London. (Reprinted 1991, University Press of Virginia.)

Anon (1905) Charles Golding Barrett. *The Entomologist*. **38**, 32.

Anon (1907) *Aegeria andreniformis*, bred from Bedfordshire specimens, exhibited at the Entomological Society of London. *Entomologist's Record and Journal of Variation*. **19**, 268.

Anon (1915) Minutes of the Bedford Amateur Natural History Society for 15 July 1896. Bedfordshire County Record Office.

Anon (1935) Mr. W. Gifford Nash. *Bedfordshire Times*. 9 August 1935.

Anon (1929-31) Land Utilisation Survey of Britain. Original 1:10,560 scale maps of Bedfordshire in the Bedfordshire County Record Office.

Anon (1953a) Field Meetings. *Bedfordshire Naturalist*. **7**, 5-7.

Anon (1953b) Mr.W.S.Brocklehurst dies in his eightieth year. *Bedfordshire Times*. 8 May 1953.

Anon (1956) Women's Institute Scrapbook of Pavenham. Bedfordshire County Record Office.

Anon (1966) G.B.Oliver. *Entomologist's Record and Journal of Variation*. **78**, 271.

Anon (1973a) George Graveley-Edwards *Herts Advertiser* 19 October 1973.

Anon (1973b) Hardwick Spinney - 1972. *Bedfordshire Naturalist*. **27**, 40-45.

Anon (1980) *Bedfordshire Landscape and Wildlife*. Bedfordshire County Council.

Arnold, V.W. (1978-85) Moths (Lepidoptera) Report of the Recorder. *Bedfordshire Naturalist*. (1978) **32**, 36-38. (1979a) *Ibid*. **33**, 52-56. (1980a) *Ibid*. **34**, 42-44. (1981a) *Ibid*. **35**, 39-41. (1982) *Ibid*. **36**, 47-49. (1983) *Ibid*. **37**, 46-48. (1984) *Ibid*. **38**, 55-58. (1985a) *Ibid*. **39**, 47-49.

Arnold, V.W. (1979b) A Gynandromorph of *Saturnia pavonia* L.: the Emperor Moth. *Entomologist's Record and Journal of Variation*. **91**, 219.

Arnold, V.W. (1979c) The cloaked pug: *Eupithecia abietaria* Goeze in Bedfordshire. *Entomologist's Record and Journal of Variation*. **91**, 322

Arnold, V.W. (1980b) Moths caught in Rothamsted light traps in Bedfordshire 1969-78. *Bedfordshire Naturalist*. **34**, 47-49.

Arnold, V.W. (1980c) The juniper carpet: *Thera juniperata* L. in Bedfordshire. *Entomologist's Record and Journal of Variation*. **92**, 24

Arnold, V.W. (1981b) Some historical moth records for Bedfordshire. *Bedfordshire Naturalist*. **35**, 41-42.

Arnold, V.W. (1985b) Some historical moth records for Bedfordshire - Part 2. *Bedfordshire Naturalist*. **39**, 50.

Arnold, V.W. (1986-1995) Macro-moths (Lepidoptera) Report of the Recorder. *Bedfordshire Naturalist.* (1986) **40**, 55-57. (1987) *Ibid.* **41**, 71-73. (1988) *Ibid.* **42**, 65-67. (1989) *Ibid.* **43**, 69-71. (1990) *Ibid.* **44**, 62-64. (1991) *Ibid.* **45**, 77-80. (1992) *Ibid.* **46**, 91-93. (1993) *Ibid.* **47**, 87-88. (1994) *Ibid.* **48**, 89-90. (1995a) *Ibid.* **49** (part 1), 63-65.

Arnold, V.W. (1995b) Some historical moth records for Bedfordshire - Part 3. *Bedfordshire Naturalist.* **49** (part 1), 66-70.

Arnold, V.W., Martin, A.J. & Rands, D.G. (1976) Winter moth trapping in Maulden Wood. *Bedfordshire Naturalist.* **30**,55-58. 1977 *Ibid.***31**, 59-62.

Baker, B.R. & Morgan, M. J. (1989) Peter Noel Crow. *British Journal of Entomology and Natural History.* **2**, 83-83.

Baker, C.R.B. (1994-1995) Butterflies (Lepidoptera) Report of the Recorder. *Bedfordshire Naturalist.* **48**, 91-95. (1995) *Ibid.* **49** (part 1), 54-61.

Barrett, C.G. (1893) *The Lepidoptera of the British Islands* Vol. 1. *Rhopalocera*. Reeve, London.

Barrett, C.G. (1904) Lepidoptera. In Doubleday, H.A. & Page, W. (Eds) *The Victoria History of the County of Bedford*. Constable, Westminster.

Birdsall, J. (1988) *The Boys and the Butterflies. A wartime rural childhood.* Pavilion Books, London.

Blackie, J.E.H. (1950a) The range and distribution of *Strymonidea pruni* L. (Lepidoptera Lycaenidae). *The Entomologist.* **83**, 246-248.

Blackie, J.E.H. (1950b) The 1950 season. *The Entomologist.* **83**, 259-260.

Bond-Smith, W. (1892) *Triphaena pronuba*, double brooded. *Entomologist's Record and Journal of Variation*. **3**,15-16.

Bond-Smith, W. (1896) Autumnal emergence of *Acherontia atropos*. *Entomologist's Record and Journal of Variation*. **8**, 244.

Bowden, S.R. (1946) The Speckled Wood Butterfly in the Letchworth District. *Journal of the Letchworth Naturalists' Society* No. 6, 20-21.

Bowden, S.R. (1947) Butterflies in 1947. *Journal of the Letchworth Naturalists' Society*. No. 7, 11-13.

Bowden, S.R. (1948) Butterflies in 1948. *Journal of the Letchworth Naturalists' Society*. No. 8, 8-10.

Bowden, S.R. (1949a) Notes on Butterflies in 1949. *Journal of the Letchworth Naturalists' Society*. No. 9, 7-8.

Bowden, S.R. (1949b) *Lysandra bellargus* and *Thymelicus lineola* in Herts. *The Entomologist.* **82**, 250.

Bowden, S.R. (1954) The Decline of *Lysandra bellargus* Rott. *Entomologist's Record and Journal of Variation*. **66**, 39-40.

Bowden, S.R. (1965) Letter to P.J.Mountford. 14 January 1965.

Bowles, N. (1996) The strange attraction of the Camberwell Beauty. Butterfly Conservation News. No. 62, 34-35.

Braybrooks, F.W. (1949) Appreciation of Mr W.Bond Smith. *Bedford Times*. 16 December 1949.

Bretherton, R.F. (1951) Our lost Butterflies and Moths. *Entomologist's Gazette*. **2**, 211-240.

Bretherton, R.F. & Chalmers-Hunt, J.M. (1982) The immigration of Lepidoptera to the British Isles in 1980: A supplementary note. *Entomologist's Record and Journal of Variation.* **94**, 47.

Bretherton, R.F. & Chalmers-Hunt, J.M. (1984) The immigration of Lepidoptera to the British Isles in 1983. *Entomologist's Record and Journal of Variation.* **96**:147

Brocklehurst, W.S. (1908a) Capture of *Notodonta phoebe* = *tritophus* in Bedford. *The Entomologist*. **41**, 156.

Brocklehurst, W.S. (1908b) Capture of *Notodonta phoebe* Sieb (= *tritophus* F.) in Bedfordshire. *Entomologist's Monthly Magazine*. **44**, 136.

Brown, S.C.S. (1988) A Biographical Account of Some Dorset Entomologists. *Proceedings of the Dorset Natural History and Archaeological Society*. **110**, 3-16.

B.U.T.T. (1986) *The management of chalk grassland for butterflies*. Focus in Nature Conservation. No. 17. Nature Conservancy Council.

Chalmers-Hunt, J.M. (1976) *Nymphalis antiopa* (L.) in 1976. *Entomologist's Record and Journal of Variation.* **88**, 269.

Chalmers-Hunt, J.M. (1977) The 1976 invasion of the Camberwell Beauty (*Nymphalis antiopa* L.). *Entomologist's Record and Journal of Variation.* **89**, 89-105.
Chambers, V.H. (1934) *Polygonia c-album* in Bedfordshire. *Entomologist's Monthly Magazine.* **70**, 277.
Chambers, V.H. (1948) Notes and Observations: Lepidoptera Records. *Journal of the Bedfordshire Natural History Society and Field Club.* **2**, 56.
Champkin, W.J. (1969) Moth evening at Putnoe Wood. *Bedfordshire Naturalist.* **23**, 8-9.
Champkin, W.J. (1970) Moth evening at Flitwick Moor. *Bedfordshire Naturalist.* **24**, 8-9.
Champkin, W.J. (1972-77) Report of the Recorder: Lepidoptera. *Bedfordshire Naturalist.* (1972) **26**, 19-22. (1973b) *Ibid.* **27**, 18-19. (1974) *Ibid.* **28**, 14-15. (1975) *Ibid.* **29**, 18-19. (1976) *Ibid.* **30**, 22. (1977) *Ibid.* **31**, 58-59.
Champkin, W.J. (1973a) Moth evening M.V. Trap at Felmersham Gravel Pit 5th August 1972. *Bedfordshire Naturalist.* **27**, 8-9.
Clarke, C.A., Clarke, F.M.M. & Dawkins, H.C. (1990) *Biston betularia* (the peppered moth) in West Kirby, Wirral, 1959-1989: updating the decline in f. *carbonaria*. *Biological Journal of the Linnean Society.* **39**, 323-326.
Collins, G.A. (1995) *Butterflies of Surrey*. Surrey Wildlife Trust.
Curtis, J. (MS) Notebooks in the Museum of Victoria, Melbourne, Australia.
Dale, C.W. (1890) *The History of our British Butterflies*. London.
Dale, C.W. (1902) Historical notes on *Lycaena acis* in Britain. *Entomologist's Monthly Magazine.* **38**, 76-79.
Dale, J.C. (1830) Art.VII. Notice of the capture of *Vanessa Huntera*, for the first time in Britain with a Catalogue of rare Insects captured. *Louden's Magazine of Natural History.* **3**, 332-334.
Dale, J.C. (1833) Observations on the Influence of Locality, Time of Appearance &c. on Species and Varieties of Butterflies. *Entomological Magazine.* **1**, 355-358.
Dale, J.C. (1837a) *Melitaea dia* & *Argynnis aglaia* var. *Naturalist.* **1**, 145-146.
Dale, J.C. (1837b) *Crambus argyreus* - near Bedford. *Naturalist.* **2**, 491.
Dale, J.C. (MS1) Manuscript Entomological Diary 1835-1865 together with a list of localities entomologised by J.C. Dale 1800-1869. Hope Library, Oxford. (Dale 3).
Dale, J.C. (MS2) Manuscript "*Catalogus Insectorum Mus. Dom. J.C.Dale A.M. F.L.S.*" Hope Library, Oxford. (Dale 44).
Dale, J.C. (MS3) Manuscript "*The Entomological Calendars of the late Revd Charles Abbot, D.D. F.L. & A.S.* [1798-1803] *and of James Charles Dale, M.A. F.L.S.*" [1808-1825] . Hope Library, Oxford. (Dale 5).
Dale, J.C. (MS4) Manuscript list of British Lepidoptera. Hope Library, Oxford. (Dale 18).
Dale, J.C. (MS5) Manuscript collection catalogue and letter book. Hope Library, Oxford. (Dale 56).
Dannreuther, T. (1949) Migration Records 1948. *The Entomologist.* **82**, 106.
Dawson, N. (1995) Letter to C.R.B.Baker on release of Marbled White at Old Warden Tunnel.
Dazley, R.A. & Trodd, P. (1994) *An atlas of the breeding birds of Bedfordshire 1988-92*. Bedfordshire Natural History Society.
Donovan, E. (1797) *Natural History of British Insects*. Vol. 6. Rivington, London.
Dony, J.G. (1948) Bedfordshire Naturalists: II. James Saunders (1839-1925). *Bedfordshire Naturalist.* **2**, 58-61.
Dony, J.G. (1949) Bedfordshire Naturalists: III. Charles Abbot (1761-1817). *Bedfordshire Naturalist.* **3**, 38-42.
Dony, J.G. (1953) *Flora of Bedfordshire*. Corporation of Luton, Museum and Art Gallery.
Dony, J.G. (1972) A new system of recording for Bedfordshire. *Bedfordshire Naturalist.* **26**, 12-15.
Dony, J.G. (1976) *The Bedfordshire Plant Atlas*. Borough of Luton, Museum and Art Gallery.
Dony, J.G., Jury, S.L. & Perring, F.H. (1986) *English Names of Wild Flowers*. The Botanical Society of the British Isles.

Emmet, A.M. (1991) Chart showing the Life History and Habits of the British Lepidoptera. In Emmet & Heath (1991) *q.v.*

Emmet, A.M. (1993) Changes in the nomenclature of certain species of the genus *Coleophora* Hübner, 1822 (Lepidoptera) occurring in Britain. *Entomologist's Gazette*. **44**, 31-35.

Emmet, A.M. (1994) Further changes of nomenclature in the British species of the genus *Coleophora* Hübner, 1822 (Lepidoptera). *Entomologist's Gazette*. **45**, 26.

Emmet, A.M. (1996) *The Moths and Butterflies of Great Britain and Ireland*. Vol 3. Harley Books.

Emmet, A.M. & Heath, J. (1989) *The Moths and Butterflies of Great Britain and Ireland*. Vol 7 Part 1. Harley Books.

Emmet, A.M. & Heath, J. (1991) *The Moths and Butterflies of Great Britain and Ireland*. Vol 7 Part 2. Harley Books.

Foster, A.H. (1916) Manuscript butterfly report to the Letchworth Naturalists' Society. North Herts Museum Services, Hitchin.

Foster, A.H. (1917) A list of macro-lepidoptera occurring in north Hertfordshire, with notes on each species. *Transactions of the Hertfordshire Natural History and Field Club*. **16**, 237-258.

Foster, A.H. (1934) Butterflies and Moths. In Hine, R.L.(Ed.) *The Natural History of the Hitchin Region*. The Hitchin and District Regional Survey Association, Hitchin.

Foster, A.H. (1937) A list of the Lepidoptera of Hertfordshire. *Transactions of the Hertfordshire Natural History and Field Club*. **20**, 157-279.

Foster, A.H. (1943) Reappearance of *Euphydryas aurinia* and *Lysandra bellargus* in Herts. *The Entomologist*. **76**, 209-210.

French, R.A. (1973) Migration Records 1968. *Entomologist's Record and Journal of Variation*. **106**: 260.

Frohawk, F.W. (1924) *Natural History of British Butterflies*. Vols I & II. Hutchinson, London.

Frohawk, F.W. (1938) *Varieties of British Butterflies*. Ward Lock.

Fry, R. & Lonsdale, D. (Eds.) (1991) *Habitat conservation for insects - a neglected green issue*. Amateur Entomologists' Society.

Fryer, J.C.F. (1938) Lepidoptera. In *The Victoria History of the County of Cambridgeshire and the Isle of Ely*. Ed. Salzman L.F.

Fuller, R.J. & Warren, M.S. (1993) *Coppiced woodlands: their management for wildlife*. Joint Nature Conservation Committee.

F.W.F. (1895) *Diopeia pulchella*. Taken at Bedford. *The Entomologist*. **28**, 308.

Gibeaux, C.A. & Nel, J. (1991) Revision of the French species of the *bipunctidactyla* (Scopoli, 1763) complex in the genus *Stenoptilia* Hübner, 1825 (Lepidoptera: Pterophoridae). *Alexanor*. **17** (2), 103-119.

Gielis, C. (1993) A Generic Revision of the Superfamily Pterophoroidea (Lepidoptera). *Zoologische Verhandelingen*, Leiden **290**, 1-139, figs 1- 241.

Goodson, A.L. (1966) Aberrations of British Macrolepidoptera. *Entomologist's Record and Journal of Variation*. **78**, 151-153.

Graham, W.B. (1878) A few notes on the Entomology of Bedfordshire. *Transactions of the Bedfordshire Natural History Society*. 1876-1877, 126-133.

Greenwell-Lax, W. (1878) *Acherontia atropos* and *Thecla quercus* near Bedford. *Entomologist's Monthly Magazine*. **15**, 107.

Guppy, A.W. (MS, undated but latest record included is 1971) Bedfordshire Butterflies.

Hall, M.L. (1981) *Butterfly Monitoring Scheme: instructions for independent recorders*. Institute of Terrestrial Ecology, Cambridge.

Harman, A. & Boyd, R. (1990) *More than Seventy Summers*. Whittet Books, London.

Harrington, R. & Woiwod, I.P. (1995) Insect crop pests and the changing climate. *Weather*. **50**, 200-208.

Harris, M. (1775) *The Aurelian or a natural history of insects and plants etc*. London.

Hasted, A. (1890) Notes on natural history. MS in Bedford Museum.

Hatton, E.A.S. (1898) *Hesperia lineola* (and *H. thaumas*) near Bedford. *The Entomologist*. **31**, 221.

Haworth, A.H. (1803) *Lepidoptera Britannica*. Murray, London.
Heath, J. (1976) *The Moths and Butterflies of Great Britain and Ireland*. Vol 1. Blackwell Scientific Publications and Curwen Press.
Heath, J. & Emmet, A.M. (1979) *The Moths and Butterflies of Great Britain and Ireland*. Vol 9. Curwen Press (Harley Books after 1983).
Heath, J. & Emmet, A.M. (1983) *The Moths and Butterflies of Great Britain and Ireland*. Vol 10. Harley Books.
Heath, J. & Emmet, A.M. (1985) *The Moths and Butterflies of Great Britain and Ireland*. Vol 2. Harley Books.
Hedges, A.V. (1932) *Vanessa antiopa* in Bedfordshire. *The Entomologist*. **65**, 159.
Hepple L.W. & Doggett A.M. (1992) *The Chilterns*. Phillimore.
Herbert, G. (1995) South Bedfordshire Butterfly Transects : Annual Report 1995. Bedfordshire & Northamptonshire Branch of the Butterfly Conservation .
Heslop, I.R.P. (1947) *Indexed Checklist of the British Lepidoptera*. 2nd edition. Watkins & Doncester, London.
Higgins, L.G. (1911) *Sphinx convolvuli* in Bedfordshire. *The Entomologist*. **44**, 406.
Hill, H.A. (1889) Diminutive *Polyommatus*. *The Entomologist*. **22**, 46.
Hollingsworth, T.S. (1984) Some notes on microlepidoptera in Bedfordshire. *Bedfordshire Naturalist*. **38**, 59-61.
Houghton, J.T., Meira Filho, L.G., Callander, B.A., Harris, N., Kattenberg, A. & Maskell, K. (1996) *Climate Change 1995: The Science of Climate Change*. Cambridge University Press.
Jeffreys, T. (1765) Map of Bedfordshire. Reproduced by the Bedfordshire Historical Record Society 1983. Eight sheets, 2 in to 1 mile.
Jennings, P.H. (1865) *Acherontia atropos* near Luton. *The Entomologist*. **2**, 235.
Kershaw, S.H. (MS) Notebooks 1932-61, in the Booth Museum, Brighton.
Kershaw, S.H. (1936) *Acherontia atropos* in Bedfordshire. *The Entomologist*. **69**,19. (at Bow Brickhill, Bucks)
Kershaw, S.H. (1953) Incidence of *Argynnis euphrosyne* L. in 1953. *Entomologist's Record and Journal of Variation*. **65**, 220.
Kershaw, S.H. (1954) Unpublished report to the Nature Conservancy on King's Wood, Heath and Reach.
Kershaw, S.H. (1955) Unpublished report to the Nature Conservancy on King's Wood, Heath and Reach.
Kershaw, S.H. (1956) Luck and Coincidence. *Entomologist's Record and Journal of Variation*. **68**, 21-23.
Kershaw, S.H. (1958) Scottish varieties in Bucks. *Entomologist's Record and Journal of Variation*. **70**, 167.
King, J. (1875) *Diopeia pulchella* at Biggleswade. *The Entomologist*. **8**, 226.
Kirby, P. (1992) *Habitat Management for Invertebrates: a practical handbook*. Joint Nature Conservation Committee.
Kitchener, P.G. (1964) Bedford School Natural History Society Moth Report. *Bedfordshire Naturalist*. **18**, 29.
Knight, T.F. (1967) *Acherontia atropos* L. in Bedford. *Entomologist's Record and Journal of Variation*. **79**, 234.
Laurence, B.R. (1945) Early appearance of butterflies in Bedfordshire. *Entomologist's Monthly Magazine*. **81**, 117.
Laurence, B.R. (1949) Courtship of the Wall butterfly. *Bedfordshire Naturalist*. **3**, 44.
Laurence, B.R. (1953) Minor evils of a garden in Luton. *Bedfordshire Naturalist*. **7**, 32.
Lewin, W. (1795) *The Papilios of Great Britain*. London.
Lucas, A. (1855) The diurnal lepidoptera found in the neighbourhood of Luton Bedfordshire. *Naturalist*. (B.R.Morris). **5**, 276-277.

Manley, G. (1974) Central England temperatures: monthly means 1659 to 1973. *Quarterly Journal of the Royal Meteorological Society*. **100**, 389-405.
Manning, D.V. (1979) *Blastobasis decolorella* Wollaston (Lep.: Blastobasidae) at Sharnbrook, Bedford. *Entomologist's Record and Journal of Variation*. **91**, 77.
Manning, D.V. (1986-1995) Micro-moths (Lepidoptera) Report of the Recorder. *Bedfordshire Naturalist*. **40**, 53-55. (1987) *Ibid.* **41**, 69-70. (1988) *Ibid.* **42**, 67-68. (1989) *Ibid.* **43**, 71-72. (1990) *Ibid.* **44**, 61. (1991) *Ibid.* **45**, 76. (1992) *Ibid.* **46**, 90. (1993) *Ibid.* **47**, 89-90. (1994) *Ibid.* **48**, 95. (1995) *Ibid.* **49** (part 1), 62.
Manning, D.V. (1993) *Coleophora vestianella* (Linn.) (Lep.: Coleophoridae) in Bedfordshire. *Entomologist's Record and Journal of Variation*. **105**, 181.
Marsh, T. Orlebar. (MS1) Natural History Notebooks. Vol. 1. Bedfordshire County Record Office.
Marsh, T. Orlebar. (MS2) Collections for a biography of remarkable persons connected with the county of Bedfordshire. British Library. BM Add. MS 21,067.
Martin, A.J. (1978-92) Butterflies (Lepidoptera) Report of the Recorder. *Bedfordshire Naturalist*. (1978a) **32**, 33. (1979) *Ibid.* **33**, 51-52. (1980a) *Ibid.* **34**, 40-41. (1981a) *Ibid.* **35**, 35-37. (1982) *Ibid.* **36**, 44-46. (1983) *Ibid.* **37**, 48-49. (1984) *Ibid.* **38**, 52-54. (1985a) *Ibid.* **39**, 51-52. (1986) *Ibid.* **40**, 58-59. (1987) *Ibid.* **41**, 68-69. (1988) *Ibid.* **42**, 62-63. (1989) *Ibid.* **43**, 68-69. (1990) *Ibid.* **44**, 59-61. (1991) *Ibid.* **45**, 81-82. (1992) *Ibid.* **46**, 94-95.
Martin, A.J. (1978b) Checklist of Lepidoptera - Rhopalocera (Butterflies) for Bedfordshire. *Bedfordshire Naturalist*. **32**, 34-35.
Martin, A.J. (1980b) An experiment on the assembling of the Emperor moth (*Saturnia pavonia*). *Bedfordshire Naturalist*. **34**, 45-46.
Martin, A.J. (1981b) A further experiment on the assembling of the Emperor moth (*Saturnia pavonia*). *Bedfordshire Naturalist*. **35**, 38.
Meynell, L. (1950) *Bedfordshire*. Hale, London.
Meyrick, E. ([1928], reprint 1970) *A Revised Handbook of British Lepidoptera*. Watkins and Doncaster. Reprint E.W.Classey.
Mitchell, B.R. (1990) Letter to Bedford Museum detailing marginal annotations by E.R. Williams in a copy of Morris (1895).
Morris, F.O. (1895) *A History of British Butterflies*. 8th edition. Nimmo, London.
Nash, W.G. (1902) *Sphinx convolvuli* in 1901. *The Entomologist*. **35**, 172.
Nash, W.G. (1916) Abundance of *Celastrina argiolus*. *The Entomologist*. **49**, 140.
Nash, W.G. (1918) *Adopaea lineola* in the Bedford district. *The Entomologist*. **51**, 234.
Nash, W.G. (1922) *Herse convolvuli* at Bedford. *The Entomologist*. **55**, 278.
Nash, W.G. (1924) *Diopeia pulchella* at Bedford. *The Entomologist*. **57**, 164.
Nash, W.G. (1925) *Polygonia c-album* in Beds. and Herts. *The Entomologist*. **58**, 62.
Nash, W.G. (1931) *Colias croceus*. *The Entomologist*. **64**, 223.
Nash, W.G. (1934) *Colias hyale* in Bedfordshire. *The Entomologist*. **67**, 257.
Nau, B.S., Boon, C.R. & Knowles, J.P. (1987) *Bedfordshire Wildlife*. Castlemead, Ware.
Newman, E. (1869) *The natural history of British moths*. London.
Newman, E. (1870-71) *The illustrated natural history of British butterflies*. London.
Newman, L.H. (1952) *British Moths and their Haunts*. Country Book Club, London.
Newman, L.H. (1954) *Butterfly Farmer*. London.
Oliver, G.B. (1949) *Lysandra bellargus* in Herts. and Bucks. *Entomologist*. **82**, 277.
Outen, A.R. [1995] *The Possible Ecological Implications of Artificial Lighting*. Hertfordshire Environmental Records Centre.
Palmer, R. (1942) A note on the Comma butterfly. *Journal of the Letchworth and District Natural History and Antiquarian Society*. No. 2, 14-15.
Palmer, R. (1949) A rare hawkmoth in Bedfordshire. *Bedfordshire Naturalist*. **3**, 44.
Palmer, R. (MS1) Nature Diary, 1923-1933. Bedford Museum.

Palmer, R. (MS2) Nature Diary, 1934-1969. Bedford Museum.
Parsons M.S. (1995) *A review of the scarce and threatened ethmiine, stathmopodine and gelechiid moths of Great Britain*. U.K. Nature Conservation publication No. 16.
Pittman, S. (1990) *The Butterflies of Bedfordshire*. 1815-1990. Duplicated.
Pollard, E. (1988) Temperature, rainfall and butterfly numbers. *Journal of Applied Ecology*. **25**, 819-828.
Pollard, E. (1991) Changes in the flight period of the hedge brown butterfly *Pyronia tithonus* during range expansion. *Journal of Animal Ecology*. **60**, 737-748.
Pollard, E., Elias, D.O., Skelton, M.J. & Thomas, J.A. (1975) A method of assessing the abundance of butterflies in Monks Wood Nature Reserve in 1973. *Entomologist's Gazette*. **26**, 79-88.
Pollard, E. & Greatorex-Davies, J.N. (1996) The butterfly monitoring scheme report to recorders 1995. ITE, Monks Wood.
Pollard, E., Hall, M.L. & Bibby, T.J. (1984) The clouded yellow butterfly migration of 1983. *Entomologist's Gazette*. **35**, 227-234.
Pollard, E., Hall, M.L. & Bibby, T.J. (1986) *Monitoring the abundance of butterflies 1976-1985*. Nature Conservation Council, Peterborough.
Pollard, E. & Yates, T.J. (1993) *Monitoring Butterflies for Ecology and Conservation - The British Butterfly Monitoring Scheme*. Chapman & Hall, London.
Pullin. A.S. (Ed.) (1995) *Ecology and Conservation of Butterflies*. Chapman & Hall, London.
Ravenscroft, N.O.M. (1995) The conservation of *Carterocephalus palaemon* in Scotland. In *Ecology and Conservation of Butterflies*. A.S.Pullin (Ed.) 165-179. Chapman & Hall, London.
Reay, P.J. (1961) Dominant moth species during the summer. *Bedfordshire Naturalist.* **15**, 38-39.
Reay, P.J. (1962) Bedford School Natural History Society. Report for 1961. Lepidoptera. *Bedfordshire Naturalist.* **6**, 31-38.
Rennie, J 1832 *A Conspectus of Butterflies and Moths found in Britain*. Orr, London.
Revels, R.C. (1965) *Herse convolvuli* L. in Bedfordshire. *Entomologist's Record and Journal of Variation*. **77**, 238.
Revels, R.C. (1971) A new food plant for the Privet Hawk moth larva? *Entomologist's Record and Journal of Variation*. **83**, 394.
Revels, R.C. (1994) The rise and fall of the Holly Blue butterfly. *British Wildlife*. **5**, 236-239.
Riley, A.M. (1986) *Cochylis flaviciliana* (Westwood) (Lep.: Tortricidae) and *Phycitodes saxicola* (Vaughan) (Lep.: Pyralidae) in Bedfordshire. *Entomologist's Record and Journal of Variation.* **98**, 230.
Riley, A.M.(1991a) *Plodia interpunctella* Hübner, the Indian meal moth (Lep.: Pyralidae) in Bedfordshire. *Entomologist's Record and Journal of Variation.* **103**, 72.
Riley, A.M. (1991b) *A Natural History of the Butterflies and Moths of Shropshire*. Swann Hill, Shrewsbury.
Riley, A.M. & Riley, D.K. (1990) Possible overwintering in Britain of *Autographa gamma* Linn. (Lep: Noctuidae), the Silver Y. *Entomologist's Record and Journal of Variation.* **102**, 299-300.
Riley, A.M. & Townsend, M.C. (1991) *Amphipoea lucens* Freyer, the Large Ear, and *A. fucosa* Freyer, the Saltern Ear (Lep: Noctuidae) in Hertfordshire *Entomologist's Record and Journal of Variation.* **103**, 72
Rowland-Brown, H. (1917) Arthur Ernest Gibbs, F.L.S., F.Z.S., F.E.S. 1859-1917. *The Entomologist*. **50**, 95.
Saunders, J. (1911) *The field flowers of Bedfordshire*. London.
Sawford, B. (1987) *The Butterflies of Hertfordshire*. Castlemead, Ware.
Seymour, P.R. (1989) *Invertebrates of economic importance in Britain. Common and scientific names.* HMSO London.
Skinner, B. (1984) *Colour Identification guide to Moths of the British Isles*. Viking, London.
South, R. (1906 and subsequent editions) *The Butterflies of the British Isles*. Warne, London.
South, R. (1907-8 and subsequent editions) *The Moths of the British Isles*. Series 1 & 2, Warne, London.

Spooner, G.M. (1963) On causes of the decline of *Maculinea arion* L. (Lep. Lycaenidae) in Britain. *The Entomologist*. **96**, 199-210.
Stace, C.A. (1991) *New flora of the British Isles*. C.U.P.
Stainton, H.T. (1857) *A manual of British butterflies and moths*. I, London.
Stephens, J.F. (1828) *Illustrations of British Entomology. Haustellata* Vol. 1. Baldwin & Cradock, London.
Steuart, D.H.S. (1891a) Varieties of *Smerinthus tiliae, Pararge megera* and *Hepialus humuli*. *Entomologist's Record and Journal of Variation*. **2**, 199.
Steuart, D.H.S. (1891b) Bedford (In 'Notes on Collecting etc.'). *Entomologist's Record and Journal of Variation*. **2**, 206-207.
Stoneham, H.F. (1917) *Macroglossum stellatarum* in Bedfordshire. *The Entomologist*. **50**, 279.
Taylor, L.R. & Carter, C.I. (1961) The analysis of numbers and distribution in an aerial population of Macrolepidoptera. *Transactions of the Royal Entomological Society of London*. **113**, 369-386.
Taylor,L.R., Kempton, R.A. & Woiwod, I.P. (1976) Diversity statistics and the log-series model. *Journal of Animal Ecology*. **45**, 255-172.
Tebbs, H.A.N. (1923) *Polygonia c-album* in Bedfordshire. *The Entomologist*. **56**, 235.
Thomas, J.A. (1975) *The black hairstreak: conservation report*. NERC. Cambridge.
Tomlinson, H.W. (1892) *Colias edusa* (and var. *helice*) in Bedfordshire. *The Entomologist*. **25**, 275.
Tutt, J.W. 1905-09. *A natural history of the British Lepidoptera*. 8-10. London.
Verdcourt, B. (1945) Butterflies in Bedfordshire. *Entomologist's Monthly Magazine*. **81**, 75.
Verdcourt, B. (1946) Two scarce moths in Bedfordshire. *Entomologist's Record and Journal of Variation*. **58**, 155.
Walker, J.J. (1907) Some notes on the Lepidoptera of the "Dale Collection" of British insects, now in the Oxford University Museum. I: Rhopalocera. *Entomologist's Monthly Magazine*. **43**, 93-101, 130-134.
Waring, P. & Haggett, G. (1991) Coppiced Woodland Habitats. In Fry and Lonsdale *q.v.*
Warren, M.S. (1995) The Chequered Skipper returns to England. *Butterfly Conservation News*. No. 60, 4-5.
Warren, M.S. & Fuller, R.J. (1993) *Woodland rides and glades: their management for wildlife*. Joint Nature Conservation Committee.
Webb, K.F. (1983) Noctuid larva at sugar. *Entomologist's Record and Journal of Variation*. **95**, 204.
Webb, K.F. (1983) *Commophila aeneana* Hbn. (Lep.: Cochylidae). *Entomologist's Record and Journal of Variation*. **95**, 215.
Webb, K.F. (1984a) The status of the pine hawk: *Hyloicus pinastri* L., in Bedfordshire. *Entomologist's Record and Journal of Variation*. **96**, 53.
Webb, K.F. (1984b) Copper underwings *Amphipyra pyramidea* L. and *A. berbera svenssoni* Fletcher in Bedfordshire. *Entomologist's Record and Journal of Variation*. **96**, 91.
Webb, K.F. (1984c) *Sesia bembeciformis* Hbn.: Lunar hornet moth in Bedfordshire. *Entomologist's Record and Journal of Variation*. **96**, 91.
Webb, K.F. (1984d) *Daraba laisalis* in Bedfordshire. *Entomologist's Record and Journal of Variation*. **96**, 123.
Webb, K.F. (1984e) *Hypena crassalis* F.; Beautiful snout in Bedfordshire. *Entomologist's Record and Journal of Variation*. **96**, 263.
Webb, K.F. (1985a) *Synanthedon anthraciniformis* Esp.: Orange-tailed clearwing in Bedfordshire. *Entomologist's Record and Journal of Variation*. **97**, 6.
Webb, K.F. (1985b) The sloe pug; *Chloroclystis chloerata* (Mabille), and the marsh pug: *Eupithecia pygmaeata* (Huebner) in Bedfordshire. *Entomologist's Record and Journal of Variation*. **97**, 69.
West, B.B. (1948) Butterflies of the Bedfordshire Woodland. *Bedfordshire Magazine*. **1**, 193-196.
West, B.B. (1949) Bedfordshire Butterflies. *Bedfordshire Naturalist*. **3**, 16-21.
West, B.B. (1950) Butterflies of the Bedfordshire Chalk Hills. *Bedfordshire Magazine*. **2**, 196-198.

West, B.B. (1950-63) Reports of Recorders: Lepidoptera. *Bedfordshire Naturalist.* (1950) *Ibid.* **4**, 45. (1953) *Ibid.* **7**, 24. (1954b) *Ibid.* **8**, 32. (1957a) *Ibid.* **11**, 26-28. (1958) *Ibid.* **12**, 27-30. (1959) *Ibid.* **13**, 24-33. (1960) *Ibid.* **14**, 39-43. (1961) *Ibid.* **15**, 14-17. (1962) *Ibid.* **16**, 17-19. (1963) *Ibid.* **17**, 13-15.

West, B.B. (1954a) Ecological Survey of Hardwick Spinney: Lepidoptera. *Bedfordshire Naturalist.* **8**, 31.

West, B.B. (1957b) Collecting Notes on the 1956 Season. *Entomologist's Record and Journal of Variation.* **69**, 158-161.

West, B.B. & West, K.E. (1954) Decline of *Lysandra bellargus* Rott. *Entomologist's Record and Journal of Variation.* **66**, 117-118.

Westwood, J.O. (1855) *The Butterflies of Great Britain.* Orr, London.

Wilkinson, R.S. (1982) The Scarce Swallow-tail: *Iphiclides podalirius* (L.) in Britain. *Entomologist's Record and Journal of Variation.* **94**, 168-172.

Wilson, D.E. (1989) *British Journal of Entomology and Natural History.* **2**(1), Plate II, figures 2 and 5.

Wilson, E.O. (1988) The current state of biological diversity. In E.O.Wilson & F.M. Peters (eds.) *Biodiversity* pp 3-18. National Academy Press, Washington, DC.

Woiwod, I.P. (1991) The ecological importance of long-term synoptic monitoring. In L.G.Firbank, N.Carter, J.F.Darbyshire & G.R.Potts (eds) *The Ecology of Temperate Cereal Fields.* 275-304. Blackwell Scientific Publications, Oxford.

Woiwod, I.P. & Harrington, R. (1994) Flying in the face of change: The Rothamsted Insect Survey. In R.A. Leigh and A.E. Johnston (eds) *Long-term Experiments in Agricultural and Ecological Sciences.* 321-342. CAB International, Wallingford.

Woiwod, I.P. & Manning, D.V. (1996) Two new migrant species for Bedfordshire. *Entomologist's Record and Journal of Variation.* **108**, 92.

Woiwod, I.P. & Thomas, J.A. (1993) The ecology of butterflies and moths at the landscape scale. In R.Haines-Young (ed.) *Landscape Ecology in Britain.* pp. 76-92. University of Nottingham: IALE(UK)/Department of Geography.

Worms, C.G.M. de (1959) John Christopher Beadnell Craske. *The Entomologist.* **92**, 88.

Appendix

The following tables show the annual indices of abundance of butterflies seen on transect walks. The indices are the total numbers of individuals seen on the 26 weekly walks between 1 April and 30 September. When the transect was not walked in any one week a count is interpolated, as an average of the two adjacent weeks, and the figure included in the annual index.

Year	**1987**	**1988**	**1989**	**1990**	**1991**	**1992**	**1993**	**1994**	**1995**	**1996**
Small & Essex Skipper	10	4		74	40	34	40	33	31	36
Large Skipper	3	6		2	1	23	12	9	88	32
Dingy Skipper	14	23		17	10	6	9	2	10	6
Grizzled Skipper		2								
Brimstone	12	33	N	43	45	75	44	44	66	117
Large White	29	92	o	46	170	383	74	59	69	26
Small White	33	45		137	114	211	48	167	303	180
Green-veined White	34	120	D	24	39	9	9	2	3	16
Orange Tip	9	7	a	5	10	21	9	2	13	9
Green Hairstreak			t	6	1	7	5	16	2	2
White-letter Hairstreak										1
Small Copper	1	17	a	4	1	5		3	2	16
Brown Argus	19	39		65	257	231	39	26	213	670
Common Blue	49	114		92	178	144	70	61	94	96
Chalkhill Blue	67	28		41	58	100	259	338	536	911
Holly Blue					102	12				64
Red Admiral	5	8		6	4	42	11	11	17	11
Painted Lady	1	1		1		1			2	78
Small Tortoiseshell	42	11		4	58	56	12	5	17	35
Peacock	5	19		35	47	78	50	35	29	72
Comma	3	3		5	24	42	5	11	27	11
Dark Green Fritillary								1		
Speckled Wood		1		23	120	142	131	131	45	34
Wall Brown	18	30		76	51	11	3	4	5	2
Marbled White						3		2	9	40
Gatekeeper	22	17		196	441	312	405	263	309	377
Meadow Brown	131	79		153	169	491	286	227	283	265
Ringlet	29	27		24	67	175	123	161	203	105
Small Heath	354	332		380	205	258	181	273	326	362
ANNUAL TOTALS	890	1058		1459	2212	2872	1825	1886	2702	3574

Table 1 Barton Hills National Nature Reserve butterfly transect totals 1987-96 (no data for 1989) **(Blank = 0)**
Recorders – Graham Bellamy, Geof Wolstencroft, Den Whitfield, Amanda Proud.

Year	1987	1988	1989	1990	1991	1992	1993	1994	1995	1996
Small & Essex Skipper	15	19	181	168	252	382	224	332	259	514
Large Skipper	3	7	34	48	10	50	47	62	116	51
Dingy Skipper		1	2		1				1	
Grizzled Skipper			2	4	3	6	11		2	23
Clouded Yellow										2
Brimstone	16	12	28	41	81	137	135	98	77	135
Large White	13	100	168	115	136	681	129	293	106	55
Small White	49	191	531	237	107	229	91	763	491	128
Green-veined White	9	20	48	36	40	155	68	89	62	67
Orange Tip	8	6	5	18	27	6	18	24	21	10
Green Hairstreak	12	3	12	34	41	22	89	89	67	12
Small Copper	1	4	14	20	5	10	1	11	15	11
Small Blue	2		11	6	2	1	2			
Brown Argus	5	20	90	85	114	72	48	143	122	419
Common Blue	18	31	109	153	177	172	140	259	108	304
Chalkhill Blue	32	42	46	63	96	194	234	311	288	569
Holly Blue			1	17	15		7			33
Duke of Burgundy	6		6	2	7	16		16	15	25
Red Admiral	1	8	4	5	17	19	12	5	26	22
Painted Lady		22	3	5	3	11		4	6	463
Small Tortoiseshell	131	76	136	76	54	328	22	28	239	334
Peacock	26	20	17	31	33	156	99	24	54	163
Comma	4		8	6	12	8	1	7	31	22
Speckled Wood	1	7	36	59	113	302	214	197	122	25
Wall Brown	8	18	28	77	42	65	65	48	10	2
Marbled White	32	17	81	154	341	414	170	218	220	625
Gatekeeper	11	18	99	136	340	345	238	172	284	999
Meadow Brown	109	205	537	343	1042	1071	698	1334	872	2529
Ringlet	271	106	251	164	252	317	211	468	470	240
Small Heath	122	186	857	481	152	116	75	133	136	245
ANNUAL TOTALS	905	1145	3345	2584	3515	5286	3049	5128	4220	8023

Table 2 Whipsnade Downs butterfly transect totals 1987-96.
Recorders – Greg & Margaret Herbert, Dave & Sue Draper, Charles Baker.
Table adapted from Herbert (1995) with 1996 totals added. (**Blank = 0**)

	Year	1974	1976	1977	1978	1979	1980	1981	1982	1983	1984	1985
Small & Essex Skipper		1	9	30	25	28	20	7	12	55	13	39
Large Skipper		42	28	25	21	47	52	19	154	53	149	140
Brimstone	1	7	73	8	36	9	49	13	44	60	84	27
	2	16	24	41	48	28	28	68	107	64	87	54
Large White	1	43	39	2	43	108	86	43	60	38	16	26
	2	30	22	2	42	373	33	68	135	31	25	43
Small White	1	19	11	14	24	36	4	9			2	4
	2	49	154	37	522	218	10	22	255	43	204	42
Green-veined White	1	161	161	39	160	298	214	154	72	74	100	101
	2	290	197	258	679	572	240	123	371	183	340	360
Orange Tip		35	69	34	43	30	51	19	20	15	24	49
Purple Hairstreak									1			
White-letter Hairstreak						1				1		
Small Copper	1	2										
	2	4	10			2				3	1	
Brown Argus												
Common Blue	1	1	5							2		
	2	1	13			4	1		2	2	3	4
Holly Blue	1	1				1	10					2
	2		1			2					2	
Red Admiral			8	2	1	5	7	4	46	6	13	28
Painted Lady		1	6	2		1	5	1	21	1		8
Small Tortoiseshell		14	13	2	36	24	33	9	114	5	108	20
Peacock	1	68	72	2	13	26	68	18	50	52	152	25
	2	43	23	53	173	313	27	298	327	199	545	318
Comma		4		3	7	2	46	22	65	36	23	18
Speckled Wood		1	1									1
Wall Brown	1	53	75							2	2	1
	2	153	92			8	3	11	32	86	47	3
Gatekeeper		246	644	639	344	668	288	277	382	299	578	276
Meadow Brown		84	673	784	445	501	214	357	471	522	984	450
Ringlet		249	117	84	138	276	458	129	656	494	1029	1053
Small Heath		15	56	10	30	15	6		1			1
ANNUAL TOTALS		1633	2596	2079	2071	3596	1953	1667	3398	2326	4532	3092

Table 3 Potton Wood butterfly transect totals part 1) 1974-85 (no data for 1975).
In 1974 section 9 was not included.
See Table 3 for additional species which include Wood White, Clouded Yellow, Chalkhill Blue, White Admiral and Silver-washed Fritillary.
Where a species has two distinct generations, totals for these are given separately.
Blank = 0. Recorder – Ian Woiwod

Erratum
The Table 3 referred to in the captions on this and the next page is on page 65.

Year		1986	1987	1988	1989	1990	1991	1992	1993	1994	1995	1996
Small & Essex Skipper		36	9	3	25	67	76	37	23	51	52	110
Large Skipper		163	40	35	37	42	90	123	58	90	80	80
Brimstone	1	15	38	13	24	47	19	41	38	27	24	38
	2	47	7	10	27	25	31	78	75	57	38	53
Large White	1	34	52	47	89	33	53	70	54	37	10	4
	2	225	23	203	363	112	192	716	210	105	41	31
Small White	1	13	4	5	3	6	1	5	3	2	3	3
	2	1069	30	180	1132	298	318	567	121	580	807	181
Green-veined White	1	108	116	120	110	94	72	71	81	68	94	43
	2	594	191	376	1032	266	360	716	590	588	591	219
Orange Tip		39	38	18	22	82	55	18	26	29	24	32
Purple Hairstreak					2		2				1	
White-letter Hairstreak									1			
Small Copper	1			1		4		1			2	
	2				16	23	6	3	4	2	7	1
Brown Argus											210	117
Common Blue	1					39	2	5	1	1		1
	2	5		1	52	192	7	107	15	129	33	15
Holly Blue	1	9			1	6	42	14				1
	2					31	31					23
Red Admiral		52	17	20	21	38	6	41	26	21	22	43
Painted Lady		6	1	16	6	14	24	24		17	7	332
Small Tortoiseshell		32	75	13	87	36	55	154	7	24	72	50
Peacock	1	31	30	56	61	128	30	86	175	89	10	91
	2	560	116	326	243	182	590	435	918	366	41	1106
Comma		70	43	5	18	42	29	35	27	9	53	30
Speckled Wood		1	3	4	20	64	297	399	198	328	235	132
Wall Brown	1					38	9		3			1
	2	2	2	2	120	131	43	14	13	15	14	
Gatekeeper		109	17	4	83	299	289	166	69	58	109	240
Meadow Brown		231	146	67	460	1095	936	904	486	715	752	774
Ringlet		1213	835	195	214	284	1154	1057	548	457	282	487
Small Heath				2		20	2	5			11	1
ANNUAL TOTALS		4664	1833	1722	4268	3738	4821	5892	3770	3865	3625	4239

Table 4 Potton Wood butterfly transect totals (part 2) 1986-96. See Table 3 for a complete list of butterfly species. Where a species has two distinct generations, totals for these are given separately. **Blank = 0**. Recorders – Ian Woiwod and Brian Fensome.

Scientific Names Index

Figures in normal type are page numbers and those in *italics* are pages on which black-and-white illustrations occur. Those in **bold** are colour plate numbers. ★ = synonym or old usage.
Where an English name is used without an accompanying scientific name, the page will not appear in this index. Check the index of common names as well.

Common Names Index

Figures in normal type are page numbers and those in *italics* are pages on which black-and-white illustrations occur. Those in **bold** are colour plate numbers.

Larval Foodplant Index

Figures are page numbers. Where foodplants have not been identified to species they have been cited throughout the book under a collective name, *e.g.* "oaks", but this does not necessarily mean that every species in the group is known to be a satisfactory foodplant.

Places Index

Figures in normal type are page numbers and those in *italics* are pages on which black-and white illustrations occur. Those in **bold** are colour plate numbers.
Not all localities are cited in the text for each species so the listings below cannot be used to produce a complete species list for each site.